SOUTH ASIAN PREHISTORY
A Multidisciplinary Study

ARCHAEOLOGY OF SOUTH ASIA – I

SOUTH ASIAN PREHISTORY
A Multidisciplinary Study

D.P. AGRAWAL and J.S. KHARAKWAL

ARYAN BOOKS INTERNATIONAL
NEW DELHI

SOUTH ASIAN PREHISTORY: A MULTIDISCIPLINARY STUDY

ISBN-81-7305-236-0

First published in **2002** by
ARYAN BOOKS INTERNATIONAL
Pooja Apts., 4B, Ansari Road, Darya Ganj, New Delhi-110 002 (India)
Tel. : 3287589, 3255799; Fax : 91-11-3270385; E-mail : aryanbooks@vsnl.com

Computer Typeset at ABI Prints & Publishing Co., New Delhi
Printed in India at B.B.N. Printers, New Delhi

Dedicated to
Professors D. Lal and V.N. Misra

PREFACE

It has been felt that a book on South Asian prehistory using a multidisciplinary perspective was very much required. We have worked on Quaternary sediments in Kashmir and Rajasthan, with large multidisciplinary teams, both with Palaeoclimatic and archaeological objectives. As we have also employed various physical techniques of dating, related to archaeology, we realised that a chronological framework based on physical dating was also required. We found that an updated summary of Palaeolithic was also not available. We therefore decided that a book covering both Palaeoenvironmental and chronological aspects of South Asian Palaeolithic cultures should be done in a holistic manner.

The beginnings of agriculture throw up many challenges about their origins, especially of rice technology. We have included a chapter on the beginning of domestication of plants and animals. Thus the story of South Asian prehistory unfolds in the backdrop of changing environment with time. We have thus tried to synthesise the multidisciplinary data in an archaeological narrative.

In writing such a book, one has to collect a lot of published and unpublished data, as there is still a big gap between research and publications. We have been lucky that scholars from India, Pakistan, and other countries have been very liberal in supplying us both published and unpublished data, as also illustrations.

We have aimed this book on interested layman, although we have provided adequate material for both teachers and students. We have taken special care to give a summary of recent hominid finds as well and we hope that this book will provoke the younger workers to look for early hominids in South Asia.

In this venture we have received help from so many colleagues and friends that space does not permit us to name them all individually. We are grateful to them all. A few friends have given us a lot of their time. To R.S. Bisht, R. Meadow, V.N. Misra, Sheila Mishra, K. Paddayya, G.L. Possehl, V.S. Shinde, R.K. Mohanty, Gajul, I. Chattopdhyaya, U. Chattopdhyaya, Sheela Kusumgar, V. D. Misra, J.N. Pal, R. Ramesh, A. Singhvi, K. Thomas, M. Yadava, Murari Lal Sharma, Rakesh Tewari, Rima Hooja, S. Aruni, Y. Yasuda, Takeshi Nakagawa, Miroslaw Makohonienko, Yano, Azusa, Junko Kitagawa, Nicole Boivin, Tripta Jain, B.P. Bhatnagar, L. Pandey, V.K. Uppal, and M.S. Rawat we owe deep gratitude. Shanti Pappu took a lot of trouble in going through the texts and references for which words are not enough to express our gratitude.

We also thank the authorities of the Archaeological Survey of India, Deccan College, Pune, and International Research Centre, Kyoto, both for providing us with institutional facilities and illustrations. Without the dedicated help from Neha it would have been impossible to complete the work on time. We have also to convey our thanks to our respective wives, Shanti Lata (DPA) and Niru (JSK). JSK also thanks his family for constant support. Finally, the help and co-operation of our young publisher Vikas Arya have enabled us to bring the book out not only on time but also in maintaining its quality.

D.P. Agrawal
J.S. Kharakwal

CONTENTS

LIST OF ILLUSTRATIONS

MAPS

FIGURES

PLATES

TABLES

ABBREVIATIONS

AA	:	Astro-Asiatic
AMS	:	Accelerator Mass Spectroscopy
AMSL	:	above from mean sea-level
ANU	:	Australian National University
BC	:	Before Christian era
BP	:	Before Present
c.	:	circa
C/N	:	carbon/nitrogen ratio
cm	:	centimetre
GSI	:	Geological Survey of India
IAR	:	Indian Archaeology: A Review
Ka/Kyr	:	thousand years
KGM	:	Kili Ghul Mohammad
LGM	:	Last Glacial Maximum
LRW	:	Lustrous Red Ware
m	:	metre
mm	:	millimetre
Myr	:	million years
NBPW	:	Northern Black Polished Ware
OCP	:	Ochre Coloured Pottery
PGW	:	Painted Grey Ware
PPNB	:	Pre-Pottery Neolithic B
sq.	:	square
Th	:	thorium
TL	:	thermoluminescence
U	:	uranium
Yr	:	year
YRCP	:	Yangtze River Valley Civilisation Project

Chapter 1

INTRODUCTION

Archaeology of India (Agrawal 1982) proved quite popular among scholars, students and laymen alike. Its main plus points were that it was profusely illustrated, brief, and interdisciplinary yet holistic in approach. We have been flooded with requests from students, teachers and even laymen that a new version should be brought out as in two decades a vast amount of new data have accumulated. To cover the whole gamut from Palaeolithic to Neolithic cultures for South Asia (Map 1-1), that too in an interdisciplinary perspective, was a daunting task and we kept postponing the decision. Finally the persuasion of the publisher and friends prevailed and we took up the gauntlet, and here is the product.

In this introduction, we have highlighted only the exciting new problems that we have discussed in the book. The bulk of the chapters do describe in detail the latest account of archaeological discoveries in different periods of South Asian prehistory. As the book is aimed both at the layman and the specialist, we had to balance the descriptive archaeology against the new excitement of research.

For the Palaeolithic period major strides were made mainly in Pakistan and Sri Lanka, though Misra, Paddayya, and Shanti Pappu, and others broke some remarkably fresh ground in India too. But on the whole, it appears that Palaeolithic archaeology does not attract too many scholars and students any more, though globally this is the most exciting field. In any international conference, the scholars working on early hominids hog all the limelight. Except for Sonakia's exciting discovery of a hominid skull from the Narmada Valley, there are no hominid remains to talk about despite more than a hundred years of prehistoric studies in South Asia, which obviously points to faulty strategies of research. We have millions of stone tools but no trace of their makers! Part of the explanation perhaps lies in our lack of interdisciplinary approach and the still continuing - if not widening - gulf between the two cultures. We must admit here that despite 30 years of close interaction between archaeologists and the Radiocarbon Dating Lab (at TIFR, Bombay and later at PRL, Ahmedabad), the gulf continues. The early periods of human history require more of modern scientific techniques than perhaps the later periods. Very few primary Palaeolithic sites have been studied so far. The Bhimbetka rock-shelter sites in Madhya Pradesh and Hunsgi in Karnataka are perhaps the exceptions.

As far as dating of the Palaeolithic cultures is concerned, the British team has dated the Pakistan Palaeolithic cultures beyond 2 Myr. In Kashmir we have dated the Karewa sequence using Palaeomagnetic, fission track, TL and ^{14}C dating techniques. We have been able to show that the Villafranchian fauna there is younger than 2.4 Myr. But this absolute chronology could not be applied to Palaeolithic cultures, as except for an Upper Palaeolithic blade-and-burin industry, which is about 18 Kyr old, there are no reliable discoveries of Palaeoliths there. Recent applications of TL and Th/U dating have also provided some clues to the dates of Palaeolithic cultures. All this exciting new work is discussed in Chapter 3.

We have presented the South Asian Palaeolithic cultures (Chapter 3) in a global perspective, with emphasis on the story of early hominids. We have tried to bring in some of the excitement of these discoveries and their far-reaching implications. We do feel that our treatment of the Palaeolithic cultures would attract at least some younger scholars to these exciting areas. In the Palaeolithic chapter we have surveyed the recent hominid finds and their exciting implications. We have also thrown some light on Out-of-Africa theories and their relevance to new discoveries being made in Indonesia and Australia. We have tried to impart the feeling of the common ancestry of all humans—black, brown, white and yellow - as so powerfully conveyed by the authors of *African Exodus* (Stringers and McKie 1996) and the role of the Kibish Man.

We must admit that Jared Diamond, a psychologist by profession and an ornithologist by choice, has opened new vistas for looking at our past. Diamond carries out very interesting and profound discussions with Yali, an aborigine of New Guinea, about why some countries today are dominating the world and why some others are languishing behind. The result of these discussions was his *Guns, Germs and Steel* (Diamond 1997). Basically he discusses the role of environment in influencing the human destinies. In the past there have been a lot of controversies about environmental determinism and there were many scholars who thought that humans could master any type of environment. Diamond says:

> But mention of these environmental differences invites among historians the label geographic determinism, which raises hackles. The label seems to have unpleasant connotations, such as that human creativity counts for nothing, or that we humans are passive robots helplessly programmed by climate, fauna, and flora. Of course these fears are misplaced. Without human inventiveness, all of us today would still be cutting our meat with stone tools and eating it raw, like our ancestors of a million years ago. All human societies contain inventive people. It is just that some environments provide more starting materials, and more favourable conditions for utilising inventions, than do other environments (Diamond 1997: 410-24).

We have therefore provided an ecological backdrop (Chapter 2) to our chapters on archaeology.

Remarkable progress has been made in the last few decades in the multidisciplinary studies towards reconstruction of past environment and climate. We have ourselves (D.P. Agrawal) carried out extensive projects in Kashmir, Rajasthan and Kumaun towards environmental reconstruction. Following Paddayya, we have also explained how the different types of Palaeolithic sites are basically controlled by seasonal changes. In the marginal areas like Kashmir and Rajasthan, a little change in temperature or precipitation can result in flourishing of cultures or being forced out to look for greener pastures. We have also explained the complex situations where several ecological factors superimpose on each other. For example, in Rajasthan, besides the Holocene climatic changes, neo-tectonics has resulted in changing the loyalties of the rivers like the Satluj and the Yamuna; also, semi-arid ecologies are not suited for large sedentary populations for long periods of time. We have discussed such issues under Chapter 2, Environmental Changes.

Chapter 4 deals with the Transitional Cultures as basically the Upper Palaeolithic and Mesolithic cultures are in a way transitional in nature. The Upper Palaeolithic represents the refining of Palaeolithic technologies, rock art, awareness of finer things about life and death, and a sudden growth in human populations all over the world. Perhaps reduction in size of tools led to the innovations of spear thrower, traps, arrows and bows which did not require the strength and size of the Early Stone Age tools. In fact, there are several theories about what caused it. Was it the advent of symbolic language, appearance of nuclear family, or some fundamental change in structure of the brain? "It transformed us from minor bit players in a zoological soap opera into evolutionary superstars" (Stringer and McKie 1996).

Similarly, the Mesolithic phase leads to the biggest transformation in human history—the

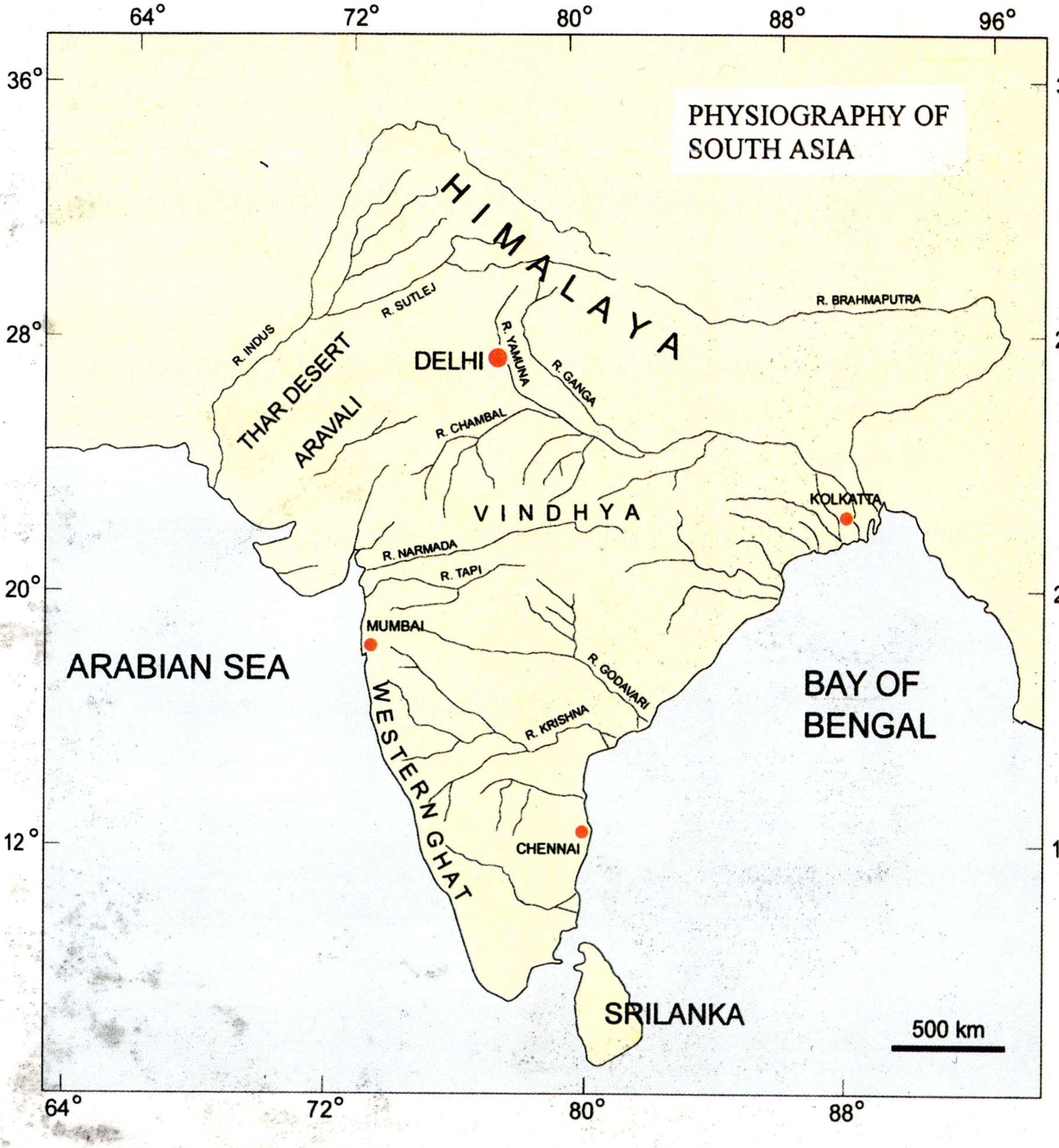

Map 1-1. Physiography of South Asia

agricultural revolution. In fact, we feel that the non-agricultural Mesolithic should be merged with the Upper Palaeolithic and the Microlithic using cultures, which show signs of domestication of plants and animals, should belong to the Neolithic stage.

India and Sri Lanka appear to be quite rich in rock art. In fact, in Central India, the Bhimbetka group of painted rock shelters is one of the richest sites in the world. Northern sites like in the Central Himalayas, Mirzapur in UP, Central India and many other areas have yielded examples of rock art. Their dates and significance are very controversial, as in other places in the world. It is however recognised that basically rock art is an Upper Palaeolithic phenomenon. But whether South Asian rock art can be assigned such an antiquity is still not agreed upon. Though we now have AMS dates for European rock art, we have not yet been able to date the Indian rock art so far. With the AMS facility at the Institute of Physics at Bhubaneswar now in place, soon we should be able to date the rock art sites too.

There are so many theories about the meaning and origin of rock art. We have tried to give a brief survey of the major theories in the field today, to facilitate interpretation of our rock art sites. All these interesting developments in rock art are dealt with in Chapter 5.

Agriculture has not been an unmitigated bliss as has been quite often made out. We have opened Chapter 6 on Early Farming with the following words, "Let us have a look at the early agricultural revolution from the evolutionary point of view. Agriculture allowed us to sustain very large populations. About 100 Kyr ago the population was only about 10,000 and now very soon we will be crossing the 10 billion mark - a million-fold increase in just a few millennia! Though we generally regard the hunting-gathering as a primitive stage and attribute civilisation to agricultural surplus, agriculture brought several problems with it. The easily digestible food of the *Homo sapiens* gradually led to shrinking of the jaw. Our jaw now can accommodate only 28 teeth. The wisdom teeth create a variety of problems when they come out. About 15% Europeans and 30% East Asians do not grow more than 30 teeth. During the last 10 Kyr *H. sapiens* is shrinking. From Cro-Magnon man's 6' height, today it has come down to 5'8". Even our brains are shrinking. Molleson, who studied skeletons from Abu Hureyra (Syria) dating back to 11.5 -7.5 Kyr, found that daily grinding of grain for several hours resulted in damaged discs and crushed vertebrae. Maize cultivation, which started 8,000 years back by the American Indians, resulted in severalfold increase in tooth cavities, anaemia, TB, yaws, arthritis and syphilis. Almost 1/5th population died in infancy. Dense populations led to a variety of epidemics". If it is so bad why did the humanity opt for it at all?

The answer is simple. For a given area of land, where hunting-gathering style of sustenance can support a given population, agriculture can sustain 10 times more. We also discuss the possibility of rice technology travelling from China to South-east Asia, Brahmaputra Valley and on through the corridors of Central Himalayas. From Central Himalayas to the Ganga Valley, it was easier to disseminate this technology. We also discuss the possibility of an early beginning of agriculture in Rajasthan as indicated by pollen and charcoal evidence. We point out the need of a multidisciplinary project to resolve these problems. All these new data and ideas are part of Chapter 6 on Early Farming.

We have inserted a small Chapter 7 on the role of the Central Himalayas in the archaeology of Northern India, though the Central Himalayas have been traditionally taken as cul-de-sacs as far as the dynamics of North Indian cultural evolution is considered. We however find that, on the basis of our own research in that area, the Central Himalayas have played a seminal role in socio-economic development of the Ganga Valley. We have discussed the circumstantial evidence of rice technology travelling from China with the Mon-Khmer speaking people to the Central Himalayas and from there to the Ganga Valley.

Even in the spread of copper and iron technology and supply of ores and ingots, the Central

Himalayas seem to have played a significant role. We feel that taking into account the role of Central Himalayas in the archaeology of North India and the possibility of rice and copper technology travelling from China, through the Himalayan corridors, brings about a paradigm shift in South Asian archaeology. These new developments required that we insert a separate chapter discussing these issues (Chapter 7).

We would like to mention here that we have tried to retain the British spellings, though in view of large quotations, within inverted commas and without, it has not been always possible.

In the last and concluding chapter we summarise the evidence and point towards the lacunae to be filled and the new directions of research.

We may point out here that we have tried to give an adequate number of references, within the limits of space. But where we have quoted opinions/statements from reports published in *Time* or *National Geographic*, original references could not be given. Where a quotation contains a large number of references, we have referred to the author quoted.

CHAPTER 2

ENVIRONMENTAL CHANGES

Contents :

INTRODUCTION

Effect of environment on humans is a hotly debated subject. But in sensitive zones, it assumes special importance. When, for example, it became too cold in Kashmir, or too arid in Rajasthan, humans had to migrate elsewhere. To explain the effect of environment on humans, we would like to quote a longish but very telling extract from Diamond, as it is very germane to our discussion of environment.

Jared Diamond (1997: 400-424) in his famous book *Guns, Germs & Steel* tries to reply to Yali, an aborigine of New Guinea, that

> The striking differences between the long-term histories of peoples of the different continents have been due not to innate differences in the peoples themselves but to differences in their environments. I expect that if the populations of Aboriginal Australia and Eurasia could have been interchanged during the Late Pleistocene, the original Aboriginal Australians would now be the ones occupying most of the Americas and Australia, as well as Eurasia, while the original Aboriginal Eurasians would be the ones now reduced to downtrodden population fragments in Australia. One might at first be inclined to dismiss this assertion as meaningless, because the experiment is imaginary and my claim about its outcome cannot be verified. But historians are nevertheless able to evaluate related hypotheses by retrospective tests. For instance, one can examine what did happen when European farmers were transplanted to Greenland or the U.S. Great Plains, and when farmers stemming ultimately from China emigrated to the Chatham Islands, the rain forests of Borneo, or the volcanic soils of Java or Hawaii. These tests confirm that the same ancestral peoples either ended up extinct, or returned to living as hunter-gatherers, or went on to build complex states, depending on their environments. Similarly, Aboriginal Australian hunter-gatherers, variously transplanted to Flinders Island, Tasmania, or south-eastern Australia, ended up extinct, or as hunter-gatherers with the modern world's simplest technology, or as canal builders intensively managing a productive fishery, depending on their environments....Of course, the continents differ in innumerable environmental features affecting trajectories of human societies. But a mere laundry list of every possible difference does not constitute an answer to Yali's question. Just four sets of differences appear to me to be the most important ones.... The first set consists of continental differences in the wild plant and animal species available as starting materials for domestication. That's because food production was critical for the accumulation of food surpluses that could feed non-food-producing specialists, and for the build-up of large populations enjoying a military advantage through mere numbers even before they

had developed any technological or political advantage....For both of those reasons, all developments of economically complex, socially stratified, politically centralised societies beyond the level of small nascent chiefdoms were based on food production....But most wild animal and plant species have proved unsuitable for domestication: food production has been based on relatively few species of livestock and crops. It turns out that the number of wild candidate species for domestication varied greatly among the continents, because of differences in continental areas and also (in the case of big mammals) in Late Pleistocene extinction. These extinctions were much more severe in Australia and the Americas than in Eurasia or Africa. As a result, Africa ended up biologically somewhat less well endowed than the much larger Eurasia, the Americas still less so, and Australia even less so, as did Yali's New Guinea (with one-seventieth of Eurasia's area and with all of its original big mammals extinct in the Late Pleistocene).... On each continent, animal and plant domestication was concentrated in a few especially favourable homelands accounting for only a small fraction of the continent's total area. In the case of technological innovations and political institutions as well, most societies acquire much more from other societies than they invent themselves. Thus, diffusion and migration within a continent contribute importantly to the development of its societies, which tend in the long run to share each other's developments (insofar as environments permit) because of the processes illustrated in such simple form by Maori New Zealand's Musket Wars. That is, societies initially lacking an advantage either acquire it from societies possessing it or (if they fail to do so) are replaced by those other societies....Hence a second set of factors consists of those affecting rates of diffusion and migration, which differed greatly among continents. They were most rapid in Eurasia, because of its east-west major axis and its relatively modest ecological and geographical barriers. The reasoning is straightforward for movements of crops and livestock, which depend strongly on climate and hence on latitude. But similar reasoning also applies to the diffusion of technological innovations, insofar as they are best suited without modification to specific environments. Diffusion was slower in Africa and especially in the Americas, because of those continents' north-south major axes and geographic and ecological barriers. It was also difficult in traditional New Guinea, where rugged terrain and the long backbone of high mountains prevented any significant progress toward political and linguistic unification.... Related to these factors affecting diffusion within continents is a third set of factors influencing diffusion between continents, which may also help build up a local pool of domesticates and technology. Ease of intercontinental diffusion has varied, because some continents are more isolated than others. Within the last 6,000 years it has been easiest from Eurasia to sub-Saharan Africa, supplying most of Africa's species of live-stock. But inter-hemispheric diffusion made no contribution to Native America's complex societies, isolated from Eurasia at low latitudes by broad oceans, and at high latitudes by geography and by a climate suitable just for hunting-gathering. To Aboriginal Australia, isolated from Eurasia by the water barriers of the Indonesian Archipelago, Eurasia's sole proven contribution was the dingo....The fourth and last set of factors consists of continental differences in area or total population size. A larger area or population means more potential inventors, more competing societies, more innovations available to adopt and more pressure to adopt and retain innovations, because societies failing to do so will tend to be eliminated by competing societies.

Those four sets of factors constitute big environmental differences that can be quantified objectively and that are not subject to dispute. While one can contest my subjective impression that New Guineans are on the average smarter than Eurasians, one cannot deny that New Guinea has a much smaller area and far fewer big animal species than Eurasia. But mention of these environmental differences invites among historians the label "geographic determinism", which raises hackles. The label seems to have unpleasant connotations, such as that human creativity counts for nothing, or that we humans are passive robots helplessly programmed by climate, fauna, and flora. Of course these fears are misplaced. Without human inventiveness, all of us today would still be cutting our meat with stone tools and eating it raw, like our ancestors of a million years ago. All human societies contain inventive people. It is just that some environments provide more starting materials, and more favourable conditions for utilising inventions, than do other environments (Diamond 1997: 410-24).

We think that Diamond's profound observations provide a fitting prelude to our discussion of climatic and environmental changes in South Asia.

We have to enter a caveat here. Diamond seems to take climate and environment as constants, though they are subject to short and long-term fluctuations. We have taken a dynamic view of these parametres.

Recent evidence shows that during the last 2 million years climate has been changing with 100 Kyr long cold periods alternating with 10-12 Kyr long warm ones. The earth has already enjoyed this sunshine period. So if this trend is right, the planet should be slipping into another glacial period. But the global warming due to higher emissions of Greenhouse gases (CO_2, CH_4, CFCs) may have reached a point where it could reverse the natural trends. It has therefore become all the more important to know accurately the past trends and periodicities of climatic change so that we have a better understanding of the climate machine. It may alone enable us to predict the effects of anthropogenic factors on global climatic change.

The past global changes have been recorded in a variety of natural archives like ocean sediments (Fig. 2-1), lake deposits, wind-borne loess, ice sheets and glaciers, tree-rings, etc.

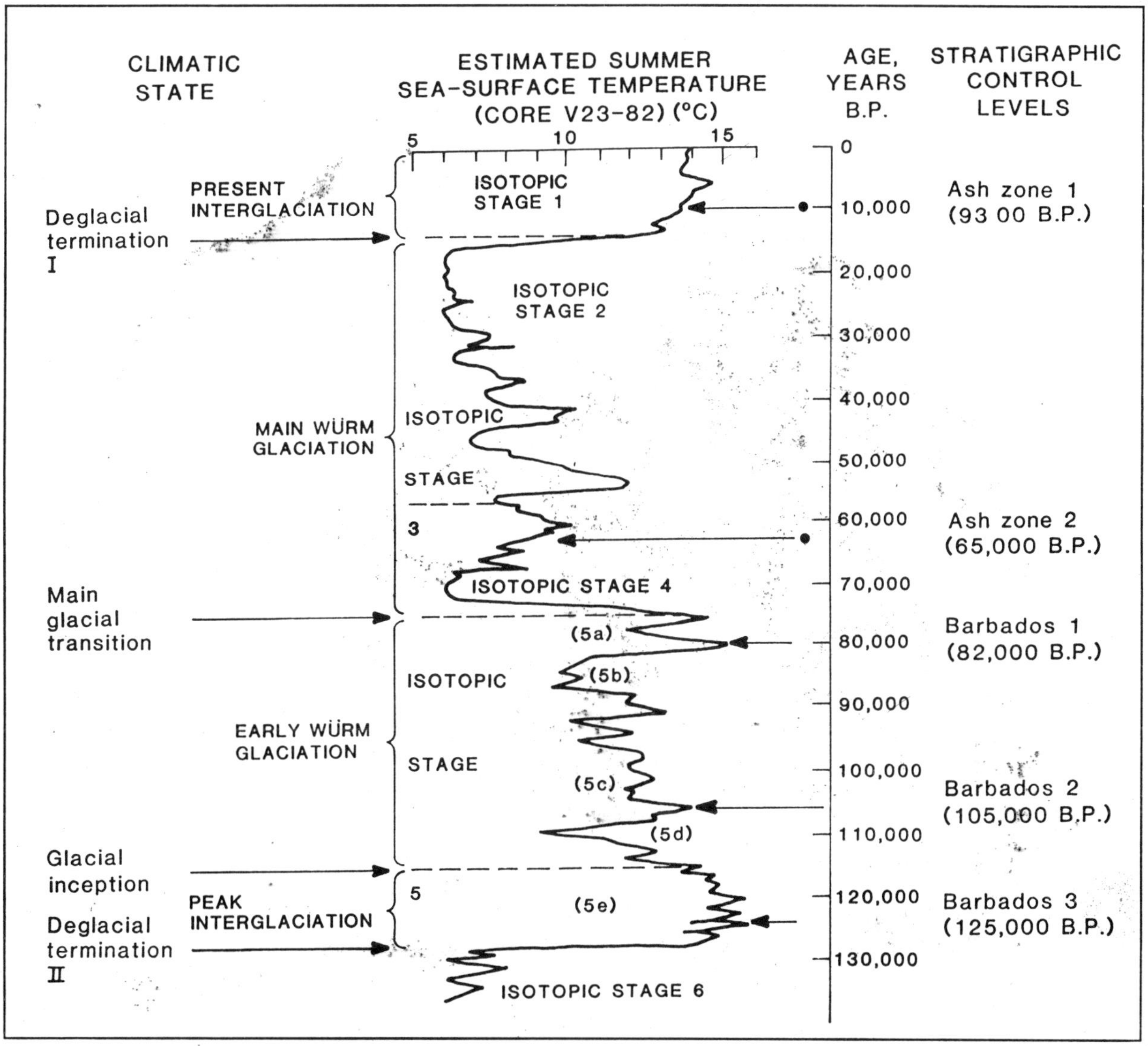

Fig. 2-1. Isotopic stages based on $\delta^{18}O$ measurements from sea cores (V23-82) and the glacial sequence

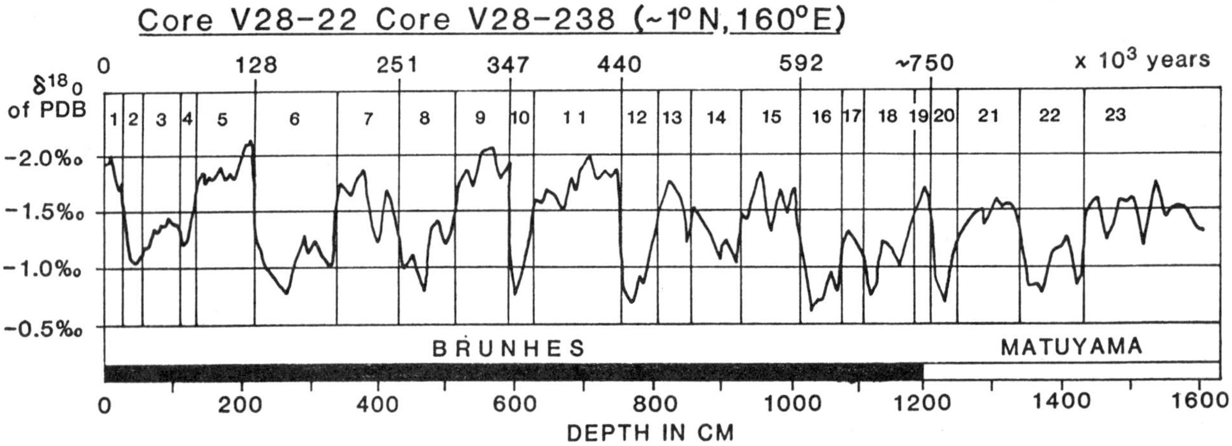

Fig. 2-2. Chronology based on magnetic reversals and marine isotope stages based V28-238 core

Unlike the sea and ice cores, which generally provide uninterrupted sequences (Fig. 2-2), on the land there are often disturbances and gaps due to various geomorphic processes. The continental records, however, provide higher spatial and temporal resolution. For example, the marine oxygen isotope record from 1.2 to 2.4 Myr shows a relatively monotonous 40 Kyr oscillation with an even amplitude, while on land at least 4, and possibly 6, exceptionally intense and/or prolonged glacial climate episodes spaced some 200-300 Kyr apart took place during the same time (Kukla 1989). Here lies the importance of the land archives, and hence of the Kashmir Karewas. Research on climatic and environmental changes in the past is being carried out in different parts of the Indian subcontinent by different institutions using a variety of techniques. The more definitive type of proxy climatic data, however, are available only from the transact, which runs from south-west to north-east, from the Arabian Sea to the Kashmir Himalayas. We have been associated with major interdisciplinary Palaeoclimatic research projects in Rajasthan (Agrawal 1992; Singh *et al.* 1990) and Kashmir, besides our initial work on the sea-level changes on the western coasts (Agrawal and Guzder 1972). Here we are highlighting our work on the Kashmir Himalayas, which was carried out under an interdisciplinary project for about a decade in the background of the other work done in India but in a global perspective. We are trying to present a review of the work done so far, as also a summary of more recent findings so that this body of recent proxy climatic data, based on the natural archives located in continental South Asia, are available for regional and global correlation. The work on Kashmir has now been published in the form of two monographs (Agrawal *et al.* 1985, 1988) and a number of papers. The present review, however, gives the latest position regarding the palaeoclimatic evidence obtained from Kashmir along with its comparison with other parts of South Asia including the role of the Tibetan plateau in forcing climatic change.

With this backdrop, we would now take a brief look at the palaeoenvironment of the subcontinent.

ENVIRONMENTAL CHANGES AND CIVILISATIONAL PROCESSES

In marginal areas the environmental changes have played almost a deterministic role in affecting human settlements. As two case studies, one in Kashmir and the other in Rajasthan, we will examine the evidence in retrospect.

The earliest evidence of man in Kashmir seemed to be the discovery of some pebble tools.

Later on their association with the earlier Neolithic levels of the valley ruled out their Palaeolithic association. The next culture is marked by the presence of stone blades and burins of the Upper Palaeolithic vintage. Though stratigraphic evidence is not conclusive, they appear to be associated with the second palaeosol dateable to c. 18,000 BP in the valley. Thus we see that there is evidence of climatic amelioration as manifested by soil development, $\delta\ ^{13}C$ values of the humus, dominance of thermophilous plants over conifers, etc. at this time. The next climatic amelioration is of mid-Holocene date as evidenced by both pollen spectra and the development of the topmost palaeosol in the valley. This warm temperate climate is associated with largescale Neolithic settlements all over the valley. Again we have evidence of climatic amelioration at about 1,800 BP and 1000 BP. The warm climate of c. 1800 BP is marked by a large number of Kushana sites in the valley. The medieval warming was a global phenomenon. Even Iceland was colonised by the Vikings during this period. In Kashmir this period is marked by the famous Hindu dynasty represented by such illustrious kings as Lalitaditya, Avantivarman and others. The Kashmir valley is literally strewn with the monumental remains of this period both secular and religious. The famous temples of Martanda near Pahalgam and near Srinagar belong to this period.

On the one hand, the periods of climatic amelioration are marked by significant palaeodemographic increases; on the other, the intervening cold, arid periods do not seem to show any significant human activity. In such marginal areas a drop of few degrees in the average annual temperature would result in large ice sheets covering not only the cultivable area but also the lakes. During cold periods, therefore, the possibilities of economically surviving in the valley will be bleak indeed and man must have migrated to greener and warmer pastures during such periods. The other thing one notices is that for the first time the alluvial plains were colonised only during the Kushana period. The earlier settlements were on the top of the Karewa plateaus. This only means that during this period the alluvial plains were drained out of the remaining water bodies or swamps.

A similar picture emerges from Rajasthan. In this area also large settlements appear only during periods of higher rainfall. The Upper Palaeolithic, the Mesolithic and the Harappa cultures are associated with relatively wetter periods. During the Harappan period the rainfall was much more than even today.

Superimposed on a trend towards aridity were other factors, which made life difficult for early man. Neotectonic movements led to changes in the loyalties of older tributaries of the Saraswati.

The palaeo-Satluj joined the Indus and the palaeo-Yamuna, the Ganga. The Saraswati river became an ephemeral river. In fact, one can trace the movement of cultures as palaeo-Yamuna was shifting towards the Ganga. Besides the environmental causes, there was the intrinsic constraint of the semi-arid ecology, which could not sustain very large sedentary populations of towns and urban centres. Besides these there may have been invasions from the west. Though the case of Rajasthan appears to be a bit more complex, it is obvious that here too environmental changes were playing a deterministic role.

We also note that due to aridity at the turn of the second millennium BC, the Harappans started migrating towards the monsoonal ecology of the Gangetic doab. But they were not equipped to cope up with a high rainfall environment, which was covered with dense forest and big swamps. The doab could be colonised only with the advent of iron technology, which could provide an abundance of cheap iron tools.

Early man too had to face environmental crisis, as human kind is facing today, during different periods of the past. When in the Indus region water tables rose up, or salinity of the lakes increased, or the rivers became dry, early man had to move towards more congenial environments. Iron technology, as explained above, allowed him to colonise even monsoonal forest. Early man had faced other environmental crises even in the early Stone Age for which he had found a technological solution. In the early Stone Age he could match neither the strength nor the speed of the animals and had to resort to wasteful mass killing of large herds of animals by stampeding them across cliffs and precipices. This resulted in large scale extinction of mammals. The Middle Palaeolithic man, therefore, invented the first missiles in the form of spearheads and arrow-heads. With this new technology he could not only pick and choose the animal he wanted to kill but it was ecologically less wasteful too.

With our concern for the future of this planet we may perhaps draw some lessons from the past. Early man resolved his economic crisis either by moving into more congenial environments or by developing new technologies to face new environmental challenges. Today the American prosperity is based on the exploitation of 45% mineral wealth of the world. If the whole world, including the largely populated developing countries, want to attain that sort of prosperity, there are no more worlds left to exploit. With our better understanding of the globe now we also know that largescale denudation of the tropical forests or melting of snow-covered polar areas in the north and south will lead to devastating damage to the overall ecology of the planet. By developing new technologies man could live under the sea or colonise other planets. But is this the answer to the environmental crisis that we are facing today mainly because of the exorbitantly rich standard of living and impossible levels of consumption of the people of the North? The North now wants to put a moratorium on the developmental activities of the South on the plea that the South would further pollute the earth by burning its coal, by growing paddy and with its large cattle population. Today the North seems to have forgotten that they have polluted the earth so much during the last 200 years to raise their levels of consumption to impossible heights. If we want to maintain ecological balance today and leave a healthy environment for posterity, the only way to do it is by reducing our wants by following Gandhian ideals of modest living and symbiosis with nature.

Let us now discuss the palaeoenvironmental evidence of different regions of the subcontinent.

North-western Region

The Sohanian culture is known only from the Siwalik hills in north-west India and Pakistan. Half-a-century ago de Terra and Paterson (1939) reported Early Sohan tools from Terrace I (T1) of the Sohan river, a tributary of the Indus river. They also found Acheulian tools in the same deposit, though at discrete localities. They dated T1 to the Second Interglacial age in the fourfold scheme of Pleistocene glaciation that they had proposed for the Himalayas. The faunal remains from this deposit included the horse, buffalo, straight-tusked elephant and hippopotamus, suggesting an environment characterised by perennial water sources, tree vegetation and grass steppes. Younger deposits showed the Sohan industry to have evolved over time. T2, with gravel at the base and loess on top, yielded Acheulian and Late Sohan A industries from the basal gravels. Late Sohan A comprised refined pebble choppers and Levallois flakes. The overlying loess of the same terrace produced the Late Sohan B industry, characterised by Levallois flakes and blades and by the complete absence of Acheulian elements. The fauna of this horizon included horse, bovids, camel and wolf (Misra 1989: 17-27). No detailed palaeoclimatic research has been carried out in this region, except for the geological and archaeological work carried out by the British team (Rendell *et al.* 1989) which has been discussed in detail in Chapter 3.

A multidisciplinary and multi-agency research project was carried out, spanning a decade, in Kashmir in the 1980s under the leadership of the senior author (Agrawal *et al.* 1989; Agrawal 1992). This is the only region of South Asia where such detailed work is available and therefore we would like to give a detailed summary of this work.

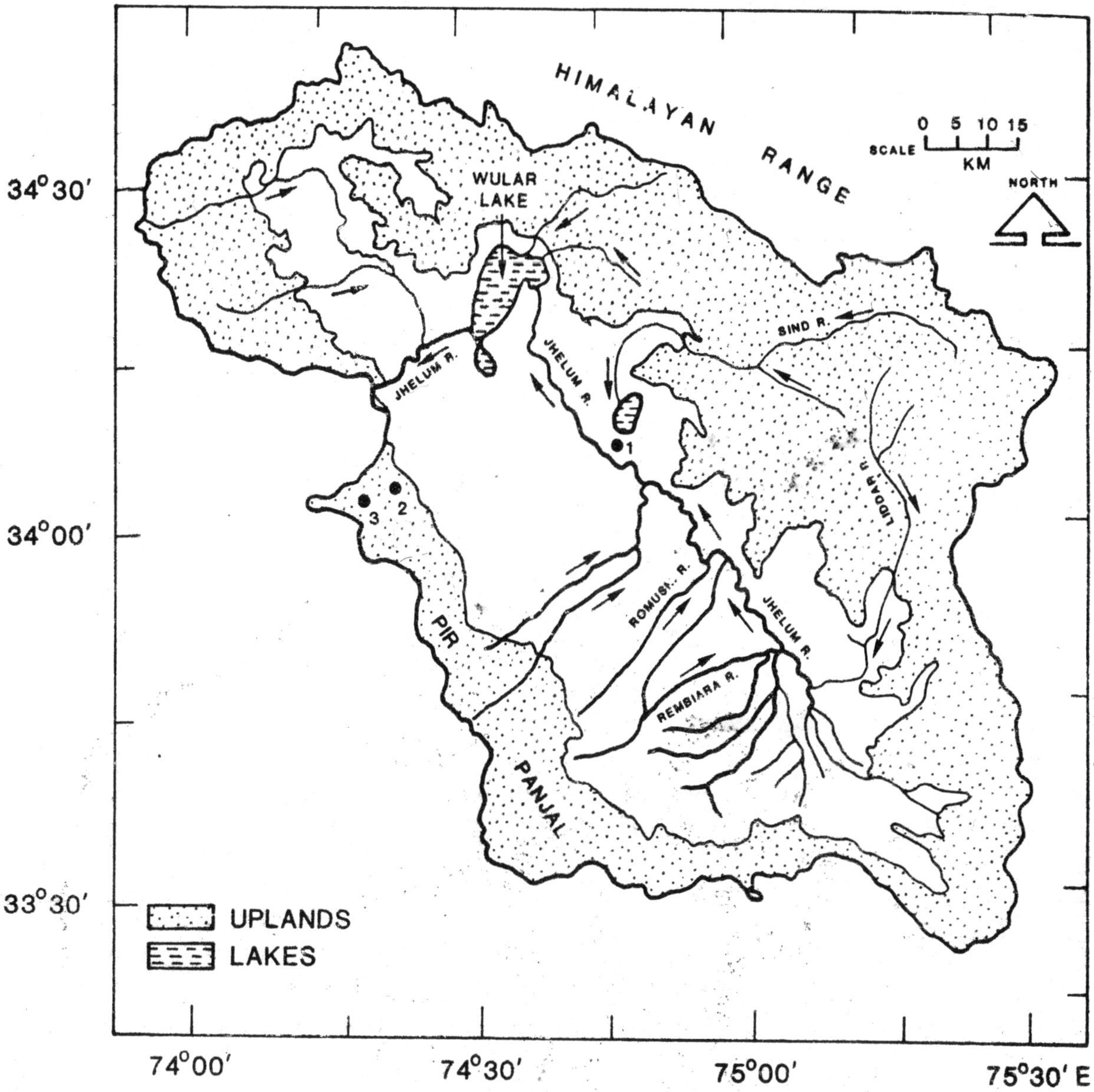

Fig. 2-3. Map of Kashmir showing the main rivers (Jhelum, Rembiara, and Romushi) cutting though the Neogene lake sediments (marked with dots) called Karewas

Kashmir

The Kashmir valley (Fig. 2-3) is one of the intermontane basin-fills in the midst of the Himalayan ranges, like the Kathmandu and other valley-fills in Nepal. The Kashmir valley is situated between 33°-34°33' north latitude and 74°10'-75°30' east longitude. Today, the Jhelum river drains the valley and joins the Indus system in Pakistan. Kashmir provides almost a 1.2 km thick fluvio-lacustrine deposit covering the last 4 Myr. The orogenic processes associated with the Himalayan uplift, basically the upthrusting of the Pir Panjal ranges, have been discussed by various authors (Agrawal *et al.* 1989; Burbank and Reynolds 1984). Thus from the northern-most part of South

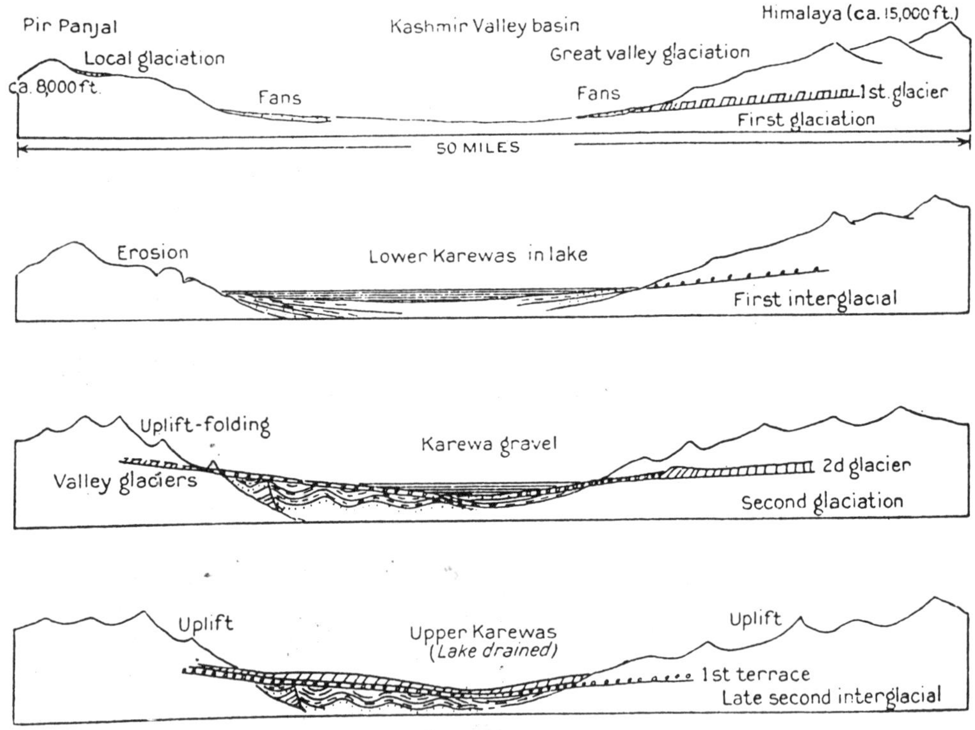

Fig. 2-4. The Glacial-Interglacial sequence in the Kashmir valley as perceived by de Terra and Paterson (1939)

Asia, we have almost an uninterrupted fluvio-lacustrine archive preserving the signatures of climatic change (Fig. 2-4).

In brief, the previous Himalayan drainage debouched directly into the Panjab, i.e., north-east to south-west before 4 Myr ago. About that time, the upthrusting of the Pir Panjals created a boat-shaped valley, impounding the Himalayan drainage, thus giving rise to a large lake of about 5,000 sq. km. As the Pir Panjals continued to rise, the lake was shifted to the Himalayan side, thus exposing the lower lacustrine sediments for aeolian deposition on the south-western flank of the valley. Eventually the Jhelum emerged c. 85,000 years BP and drained out the remaining primeval lake and provided a surface for aeolian deposition of loess on the Himalayan flank also. Subsequent upheavals and erosion by the Jhelum and its tributaries have exposed several geological sections, which made sampling of the total fluviolacustrine deposits easier. We could manage without recourse to expensive drilling operations. About 50% of the valley is still covered by these fluvio-lacustrine sediments, topped by a mantle of loess giving rise to a flat plateau-like surface which is called 'Karewa' in the local language, a term now used by geologists to represent these fluviolacustrine deposits of Kashmir of Plio-Pleistocene age.

Despite the earlier claims, and our initial suspicions, there are no Early Palaeolithic artefacts found in the Kashmir valley. But the later story of climatic and environmental amelioration coincides with the flourishing of the human habitations. Climate begins to improve from around 20 Kyr itself, though in the northern latitudes it was still the LGM.

Around c. 18 Kyr, thermophilous plants like *Corylus, Juglans,* etc. start thriving at the expense of the conifers. A palaeosol develops. In the valley an Upper Palaeolithic culture appears at this time. Again by the mid-Holocene climatic amelioration (Fig. 2-5), there is a proliferation of Neolithic sites. Kushan period (c. 1800BP) is also a period of warming up accompanied by

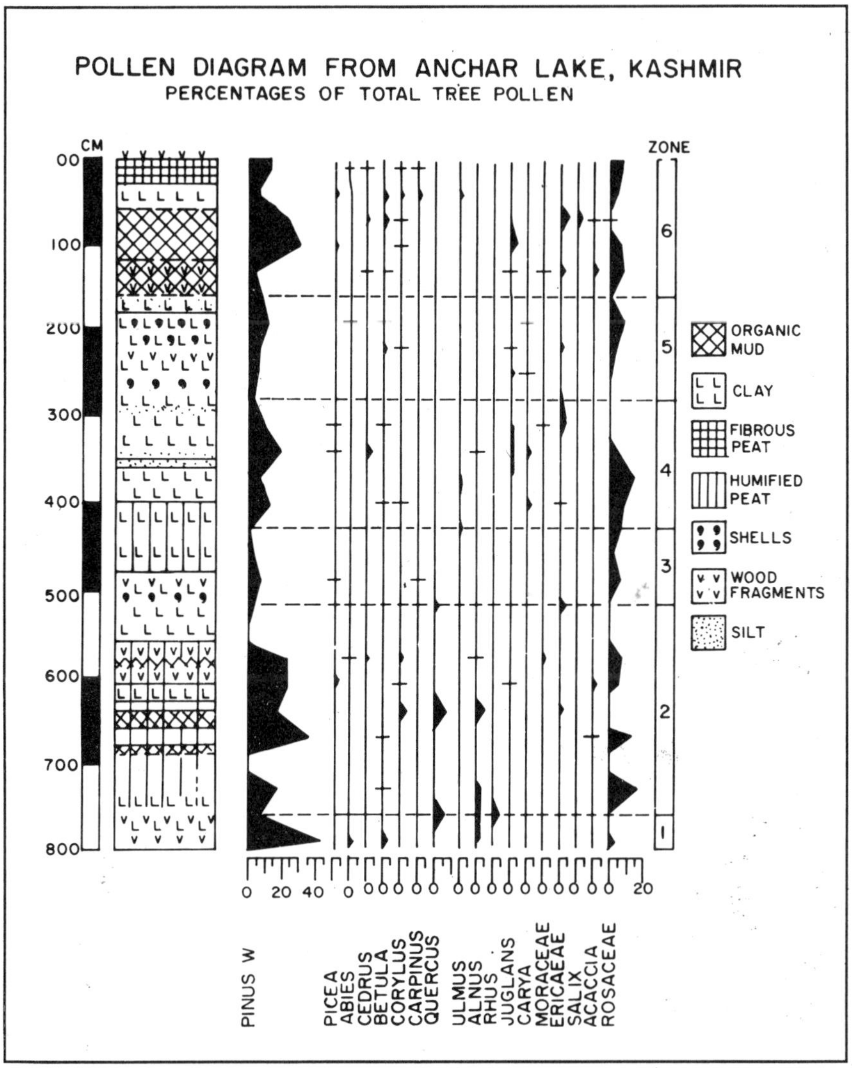

Fig. 2-5. Tree pollen diagram from the Anchar lake, Kashmir, covering the last 5000 years, indicated mid-Holocene warming in Zone 3

increase in population. The mediaeval warming, a global phenomenon, is also marked in the valley by the historical towns of Lalitaditya and others of his dynasty.

The two major sections in Kashmir studied by us have been exposed by the rivers Rembiara and Romushi, both tributaries of the Jhelum, originating from the Pir Panjal flank. The two sections have been sampled in detail at 50-100cm intervals and all the multiple analyses of various samples have been carried out within a common chronostratigraphic framework, which enables us to interdigitate the multiple data. The two sections have been divided into lithostratigraphic zones: Remzones (exposed by the Rembiara) and Romzones (exposed by the Romushi). Due to the limitations of inter-river exposures, the two sections have not been physically interconnected. The correlations between the two sections are based on palaeomagnetic stratigraphy and the dated volcanic ash fall. The Pir Panjal flank Karewas became available for aeolian sedimentation around 200,000 years BP due to the rise of the Pir Panjal and the shifting of the primeval lake towards the Himalayan side. The Himalayan flank of the Karewa deposits, however, became available for aeolian deposition of loess, only after about 85,000 years BP, when the Jhelum emerged. As a result, the south-western (Pir Panjal) flank loess deposits are about 20m thick with 10 palaeosols and the Himalayan side loess deposits only 10m thick with five palaeosols.

Besides geological techniques, a number of physical methods have been used to provide an absolute chronological framework to these inter-montane valley-fill deposits. Palaeomagnetic measurements have been made at a minimum interval of 1m from all these exposed sections. According to our estimates, the Karewa deposits date back to 3.8 Myr (Cochiti sub-chron) and continue up to the Brunhes chron. On the basis of the volcanic ash occurring towards the top of Remzone-5 and in Romzone-1, the two major sections have been interconnected. The volcanic ash dates to 2.3 Myr (Kusumgar *et al.* 1985). The uppermost part of the sequence is covered by the normal polarity of the Brunhes chron.

The loess deposits have been dated using TL and radiocarbon techniques. There are two estimates of TL dating of the loess. Rendell *et al.* (1989) date the beginning of the loess as younger than 140,000 years BP whereas Bronger *et al.* (1987) pushed the beginning of the loess deposition to 350,000 years BP, making them cover the last three major interglacials. Elsewhere we have explained why the loess deposits of Kashmir cannot be older than 200,000 years BP (Agrawal *et al.* 1989). For more recent sediments, coring from the living lakes and peat bogs was carried out; the chronologies are based only on ^{14}C dates.

Climatic change is a complex process and has multiple manifestations on land and consequently in the continental deposits. Some markers are quite well established like pollen while others have to be developed and calibrated to yield at least qualitative evidence of climatic change. In this process we had to develop and adapt new techniques also to delineate climatic oscillations.

The detailed pollen evidence is described in various papers included in the two monographs (Agrawal *et al.* 1985, 1988) and in a summary (Agrawal *et al.* 1989; Agrawal 1992). C/N ratios and $\delta^{13}C$ measurements on lignitic material in the Karewa profile showed a negative correlation between them and indicated low lake levels during cold and glacial periods. It is interesting to note that major climatic fluctuations in this long profile coincide with geomagnetic reversals. This perhaps is the first definitive proof of a correlation between geomagnetic changes and climatic oscillations. This inference is based on the fact that there is a significant difference between the $\delta^{13}C$ values of land plants versus aquatic plants, e.g., $\delta^{13}C$ values of C-3 type of plants are about -27‰ and of C-4 type plants, -14‰. The aquatic plants in comparison are much richer. Similarly, the land plants have higher C/N ratios compared to the aquatic plants which are richer in proteins (N) (Krishnamurthy *et al.* 1986). An attempt was also made to identify the source of pedogenic carbon to determine whether it is derived from C3 or C4 plants, e.g., in the palaeosol dated to c. 18,000 years BP the $\delta^{13}C$ values were -25‰ indicating a significant contribution of C3 plants and, therefore, climatic amelioration.

We did try to achieve, wherever possible, concordance between different parametres to verify the definite occurrence of a specific climatic event, e.g., the loess profile showed a well developed palaeosol at c. 18,000 years BP which itself is an indication of climatic amelioration; the humus from the palaeosol gave $\delta^{13}C$ value of -25‰ (indicating C-3 type of plants), hence climatic amelioration as explained above. Around this time, a significant presence of the Upper Palaeolithic man in the valley is evident, a sure sign of better climate. On the other hand, the Butapathri pollen profile shows a clear dominance of thermophilous plants like *Alnus, Juglans, Carpinus,* etc. at about the same time, at the cost of the conifers. Thus we find that there is convergence among four different parametres showing climatic amelioration at c. 18,000 years BP, a time when in the northern latitudes, it was still the last glacial maximum (LGM).

Pollen analyses were carried out on the whole of the Karewa sequence except where deposits proved sterile either because they were permeable like sand or gravel or alkaline like loess. We will not go into the details of pollen spectra which have been discussed above and elsewhere (Agrawal *et al.* 1989), except to point out that climatic succession (given in Agrawal 1992, Tables 5.2, 5.3) is mainly based on pollen evidence. The Baltal pollen sequence, however, is important to mention as it indicates five glacial stages alternating with a temperate climate, approximately between c. 0.6-0.3 Myr, out of which three are longer cold stages (Dodia 1988). The climatic inferences are mainly based upon B/C ratio (B represents broad leaved elements and C, conifers) fluctuations, which range between 0.1 and 0.5. At present the B/C ratio value is 0.5-0.6 representing a temperate interglacial type of climate. The values below this indicate a colder climate and those above it, warm temperate conditions. The Butapathri pollen profile, which covers the last 17,000-18,000 years BP has been briefly discussed above and shows a distinct climatic amelioration at the beginning of the profile. At about 10,000 years BP, these bogs show cool temperate conditions changing to warmer conditions of the Hypsithermal period around 7000-4000 years BP. At the top of the profile, a cooler climate sets in again. The Anchar pollen profile again shows (Agrawal 1992, Figs. 5.4, 5.5) a mid-Holocene warming. The Hokarsar profile records a warming at c. 1000 years BP.

The Kashmir valley provides a long sequence of unconsolidated fluvio-lacustrine sediments which are easily accessible because of the tectonic uplifts and subsequent erosion. Most of the exposures of the Karewas in the valley were fully mapped and their mutual correlations studied. A combination of radiocarbon, fission track, palaeomagnetic, and TL dating has allowed us to date the sequence back to about 4 Myr. Though a very high resolution is neither feasible nor expected for such a long sequence, a reasonable chronological framework is now available to interdigitate the multiple proxy climatic data. Though other parametres were also studied, the main climatic inferences were based on pollen, stable isotopic and faunal data. The convergence between the different climatic parametres, within the limitations of the dating resolution, is quite satisfactory, as briefly indicated.

Up to 3.8 Myr the climate seems to be warm temperate, becoming cooler towards the top of the Remzone I profile. From 3.7 to 2.6 Myr, there is a transition from a sub-tropical type of climate to a cool temperate type, with some variation in precipitation, cool temperate until c. 2 Myr. Between 0.6 and 0.3 Myr there are three relatively long cold periods. This evidence is mainly based on pollen but is supported by stable isotopic and faunal data. The loess deposit covers the last 200 Kyr. Field characters of pedogenic development, geochemical and magnetic susceptibility variations indicate 10 palaeosols during this period, out of which three palaeosols show greater weathering and may therefore reflect warmer/humid conditions compared to the others. For the last 18 Kyr there are a few pollen profiles available now. Between 10,000 yr BP and present, the pollen profiles show a cool temperate-warm temperate-cool temperate cycle. What is remarkable, however, is that the warming of the valley is indicated by the thermophilous elements around 18 Kyr (Fig. 2-6) and is confirmed by the soil debris of the palaeosol from Burzahom, derived from C3 type of plants and dated to c. 18 Kyr, as already discussed above. By mid-Holocene, a warming up is evident accompanied by culture pollen which indicates Neolithic occupation of the valley, as shown by Burzahom excavations (Pande 1970). It needs to be emphasised that in the valley human settlements thrived only during periods of climatic ameliorations. At c. 18000 BP, there was an Upper Palaeolithic culture; at c. 5000 yr BP, Neolithic cultures; at c. 18,00 BP, Kushana culture; and at c. 1000 BP, historical dynasties (Agrawal *et al.* 1988).

We can also infer palaeogeographic changes witnessed by the Kashmir valley. Around 4 Myr, the Pir Panjal range was further upthrusted to impound the Himalayan drainage, thus forming a vast lake the exposed sediments of which are called Karewas. At around 3 Myr, the Pir Panjal range rose to a height where it could block the south-west monsoon from entering the valley and thus converting it from a region of sub-tropical climate to a temperate one. Since then it has followed a Mediterranean pattern of climate with winter rains. Some time before c. 200 Kyr, the primeval lake shrank and shifted to the Himalayan side, exposing the Karewa sediments on the SSW. Once these Karewas were exposed, they provided a stable land surface for the aeolian deposition of loess. The Jhelum river emerged around 85 Kyr and drained the remaining lake also. These newly exposed lake deposits provided land surfaces for the aeolian deposition on the Himalayan flank as well.

From the data discussed above, it is obvious that Indian continental records provide almost an uninterrupted climatic sequence for the last 4 million years. As our glaciers were confined to the northern belt and did not come down below about 2,000 metres, our natural archives are

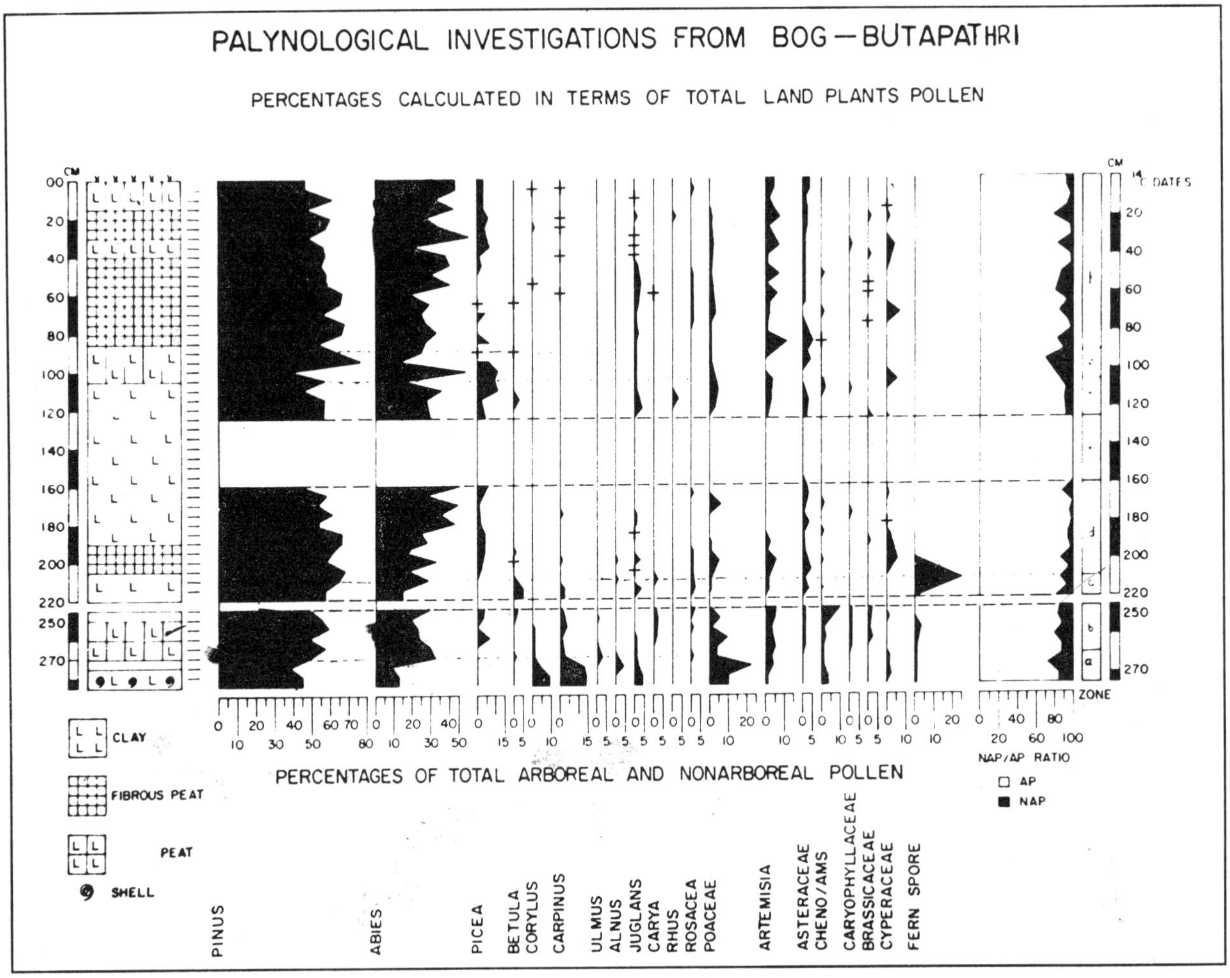

Fig. 2-6. Pollen diagram from Butapathri Bog, Kashmir showing advent of thermophilous plants from the beginning of the sequence datable c. 18 Kyr

better preserved. Admittedly, the time resolution for the earlier part of the sequence is poor, though acceptable, as we have used all the physical dating techniques available today. For the earlier part, the climatic sequence between Rajasthan and Kashmir appeared to be following the same trend. However, after the rise of Pir Panjal around 3 Myr, the heat and moisture of the SW monsoon did not affect any more the climate of the Kashmir valley. The cooling of the climate during Plio-Pleistocene transition in Kashmir does not appear to follow a flip-flop mechanism but appears to be a more gradual process. The first significant cooling trend appears around 2.6 Myr in the valley. Though the record is fairly complete, fast depositing sediments like sands and gravels do not preserve much evidence to infer climatic changes. Between 0.7 and 0.2 Myr, five distinct glacial periods are documented, out of which two appear milder. At this stage it is difficult to document all the glacial stages witnessed by the valley.

Kashmir Loess: According to our chronology the loess deposits should be around 200,000 years and not 350,000 years BP as claimed by Bronger *et al.* (1987). We have discussed various aspects and chronology of loess in other publications (Agrawal *et al.* 1989; Agrawal 1992). The Kashmir loess sequences have about 20m thick deposit on the Pir Panjal flank with 10 palaeosols spanning the last 200,000 years BP. On the Himalayan side, however, the loess deposit is only 10m thick with five palaeosols covering the last 85,000 years. There is no way one can justify the recording of the last three interglacials in this short loess profile as claimed by Bronger *et al.* (1987). On the other hand, we have also carried out extensive radiocarbon and TL dating of these loess profiles, besides the geochemical and mineral magnetic measurements. We have already mentioned above the inferences based on $\delta\ ^{13}C$ measurements. The geochemical variations reflect the source as there is a distinct enrichment in iron and titanium in the Pir Panjal loess compared to the Himalayan side. Besides, iron and some other elements show enrichment in the palaeosols due to plant activity. The low susceptibility anti-ferromagnetic haematite of the parent rock in the loess gets converted into high susceptibility ferrimagnetic meghamite and magnetite during the process of weathering caused by climatic change. During pedogenesis fining of magnetic grains also takes place, which is reflected in the variations in the frequency dependent component of magnetic susceptibility. The variations in various mineral magnetic parametres and elemental iron with the marine $\delta\ ^{18}O$ profiles in the loess deposits have been compared (Gupta *et al.* 1991). The data from different loess profiles of Wagahoma, Pehru, Khanchikhol-l and Dilpur show excellent correlation.

There are 10 soils developed in the loess profile indicating warmer and more humid conditions. Out of these 10 soils, only three appear to be fairly well developed. The valley starts warming up, indicating the onset of deglaciation around 18,000 BP which was the time of the last glacial maximum elsewhere. During this time, Arabian Sea shows glacial conditions and Rajasthan an arid climate. There seems to be an anti-correlation between Kashmir and Rajasthan. In Kashmir, the NW monsoon probably became stronger at about c. 18,000 yr when the SW monsoon was very weak. This is now confirmed by Sarkar *et al.*'s (1990) work on the Arabian Sea cores. During the last 10,000 yr, Kashmir shows a distinct cool-warm-cool oscillation which is confirmed by the Nepalese pollen diagrams. In Rajasthan between 13,000 and 6,000 BP, the lakes record violent fluctuations between hypersalinity and sweet water. During mid-Holocene both Kashmir and Rajasthan were warmer and wetter (Wasson *et al.* 1984). Minor and high resolution changes in climate were monitored through a study of modern lake sediments from Kashmir, e.g., the Manasbal lake seems to fluctuate between oligotrophic and eutrophic conditions with distinct cooler periods during which pigments were better preserved. About 1000 BP, the pollen diagrams, magnetic susceptibility data, etc. show a warmer and more humid climate, in tune with the global mediaeval warming.

Spectral analysis of the values of magnetic susceptibility time series for all the major loess profiles indicates significant variance in the frequency band corresponding to 17,000-25,000 and 35,000-45,000 years periodicities. There is a high degree of coherency corresponding to global climatic records controlled by Milankovitch parametres.

It is important to note that in such marginal areas as Kashmir, climatic amelioration at c. 18,000, 6000-5000, 1800 and 1000 years BP is accompanied by an increase in human population, as indicated by larger settlements. In fact, during colder periods early man seems to have migrated out of the valley (Agrawal 1992).

The Role of Tibetan Plateau

Though the role of Laurentide ice mass as a forcing mechanism for causing climatic fluctuations was known, the role of Tibetan plateau was ignored for a long time. Then we found evidence of warming up around 18,000 BP, when in the north it was the LGM; we had to look for causes for such anomaly. The evidence of warming up seemed quite compelling as there were several indicators showing the same trend. At this time, we found the growth of thermophilous plants like *Juglans, Carpinus, Alnus*, etc. at the cost of the conifers. The loess profile showed the development of the palaeosol datable to c. 18,000 BP and presence of an Upper Palaeolithic culture in the valley about the same time. Even the humus of this palaeosol showed that it mainly derived from C3 type of plants as the $\delta\ ^{13}C$ value was -25‰. We suspected the role of Tibet in forcing a faster climatic warming around this time.

The Tibetan plateau is about 2.4 million sq. km in area and more than 5 km ASL. During cold periods the ice could cover this large area by the lowering of ELA (equilibrium line altitude). Similarly, when the ice started melting, it would melt over a large area in a short time, thus considerably changing the insolation received. Further studies have demonstrated the validity of earlier guesses. When the ice started melting at c. 18,000 BP, from the Tibetan plateau, fresh water which was depleted in $\delta^{18}O$ and had low salinity was introduced into the Bay of Bengal and the Indian Ocean through Brahmaputra and other rivers draining the southern flanks of the Tibetan Plateau.

In other parts of the subcontinent, we have to admit, the climatic and environmental data are of qualitative nature.

The cultural remains of the Acheulian hunter-gatherer have been found in a variety of ecologies: from semi-arid western Rajasthan; from the Gujarat alluvial plains; from the sub-humid dry as well as the moist deciduous woodland zones of Central India, from the Deccan plateau; from the Chota Nagpur plateau; from the Eastern Ghats; and the south-east coast.

Western India: Rajasthan and Gujarat

Misra also admits that direct evidence for ecological conditions during the Acheulian period is limited. The regions immediately to the south of the Himalayas did experience the impact of Quaternary climatic changes. Our best evidence of climatic changes and human responses to them during the Quaternary period comes from the semi-arid zone of Rajasthan (Agrawal 1992; Misra 1987a; Misra and Rajaguru 1986). In the drainage-less sandy plains of western Rajasthan mighty streams which must have had their origin in the Himalayas existed during the Early Pleistocene. These streams laid down extensive and thick boulder beds in the Nagaur and Jodhpur districts. There is no evidence that man was present in the area during this period. Subsequently the gravel beds were tectonically uplifted and the landscape rejuvenated. The new streams that came into existence were of shallow, anatomising type, flowing in wide flood plains marked with numerous pools and lakes. They deposited marls and calcareous clays in pans or shallow depressions. Acheulian artefacts in mint condition are found buried in these marl deposits as in the Didwana region (Misra and Rajaguru 1986) suggesting that their makers camped along the pools and lakes in the flood plains. They also camped on widely exposed gravel beds where an unlimited supply of fine-grained quartzite for making tools must have been a strong attraction. The climate during this period was essentially semi-arid but it fluctuated several times between cool and dry on the one hand and warm and wet on the other. During cool and dry phases extensive and thick deposition of sand sheets and sand-dunes took place, while during wet and humid phases the dunes were stabilised. Acheulian groups occupied stable dune surfaces. While no faunal or plant remains have survived in fluvial and aeolian sediments, the density of Acheulian sites around Didwana strongly implies that plant and animal life must have flourished in abundance (Misra 1989).

The Acheulian people occupied a variety of microhabitats. In western Rajasthan the discovery of sites buried in fine-grained alluvium around Didwana in Nagaur district suggests that the Acheulian hunter-gatherers camped along lakes and pools in wide flood plains of shallow meandering stream. In addition they also camped on stable dune surfaces and on extensively exposed gravel beds. In the Vindhya hills region of Central India, where natural rock shelters abound, some of them were occupied by Acheulian groups.

There have been various theories about the origin of the Thar desert. Now we have worked out an outline of the Quaternary climatic history of Rajasthan and we know that the Thar desert came into existence about 200 Kyr. The loessic deposit of Kashmir also dates to the same period.

Here we will confine our discussion to the Holocene period.

We think that man-environment relationship in Rajasthan is determined by three main factors:

1. Change in rainfall.
2. Change in palaeochannels caused by neo-tectonics (Fig. 2-7).
3. Limited capacity of semi arid ecology to sustain large sedentary populations. Singh *et al.* (1973, 1990) had carried out pollen studies on the cores raised from the saline lakes of Didwana, Lunkaransar and Sambhar in Rajasthan (Fig. 2-8). There have been mainly four theories about the origin of their salinity, as summarised by Possehl (1999c: 263-65): (a) It is marine and results from the regression of the Tethys Sea; (b) the salt derives from brine springs in the region; (c) it is wind-borne, from the Arabian Sea and the Ranns of Katchchha; and (d) G. Singh's hypothesis that it results from the concentration of salt through the evaporation of lake water with dissolved salt in it.

For periods younger than 20,000 BP, the palaeoecological data derived from pollen and the physical and geochemical evidence of Wasson *et al.* (1984) from the Didwana lake (Rajasthan) profile show independent, but converging, trends that clearly reflect the history of past changes in climate and the vegetation response in the semi-arid region of the Thar Desert (Fig. 2-9).

The evidence for tree-less steppe environments, the extremely low values of wetland taxa, and the simultaneous deposition of halites together with low sedimentation of clastics in the lake basin, from about the time of the Last Glacial Maximum to c. 13,000 BP, indicate hyper-arid conditions. As *Artemisia* (a winter rain taxon) values are much higher in pollen zone Dl than those at present, it appears that hyperaridity was probably caused by a decline in summer monsoon precipitation and that winter precipitation was probably higher than that at present. For this rainfall pattern to exist, the westerly circulation must be farther south and the summer monsoon circulation must be weaker. The evidence of increased aridity during the Last Glacial Maximum and the late Pleistocene, in the Thar desert, has many parallels in other parts of the world (Sarnthein 1978; Singh 1988). That the monsoon circulation had weakened during the Last Glacial Maximum is also amply supported by pollen, oxygen isotope and faunal analyses of deep sea cores from the Arabian Sea (Van Campo *et al.* 1982).

The change in a shrub savanna grassland, about 13,000 yr BP, corresponds closely with the transformation of the lake basin to a fluctuating, saline to deep freshwater regime, in Zone D2. Both these developments, together with the rise in the values of freshwater wetland taxa in the later part of the zone, are indicative of a rise in precipitation, presumably through reinvigoration of summer monsoon circulation, about 13,000 yr BP (cf. Van Campo 1986). That the winter precipitation was not adversely affected was shown by the fact that *Artemisia* values remained high, increasing towards the top of the zone, dating about 9400 yr BP. It is possible that with the rise in sea-level, and increasing sea surface temperatures, during the terminal Pleistocene and early Holocene, both summer and winter atmospheric circulation carried greater moisture than before.

In Zone D3 (c. 9300-7500 yr BP) and Zone D4 (c. 7500-6000 yr BP), the trend continued towards increasing precipitation (cf. Singh *et al.* 1990, Swain *et al.* 1983). The establishment of a tree savanna in Zone D4 correlates with a sustained deep, fresh-water lake condition around 6000 yr BP. Precipitation levels were considerably higher than at present. As taxa from the sub-humid and humid zones (with almost twice the present rainfall at Didwana), comprising both summer (*Oldenlandia*) and winter (*Artemisia*) precipitation, reached their highest values in Zone D4, it would appear that the total mean annual precipitation during the mid-Holocene between c. 7500 and 6000 yr BP was about twice the modern value. It seems likely that the doubling was

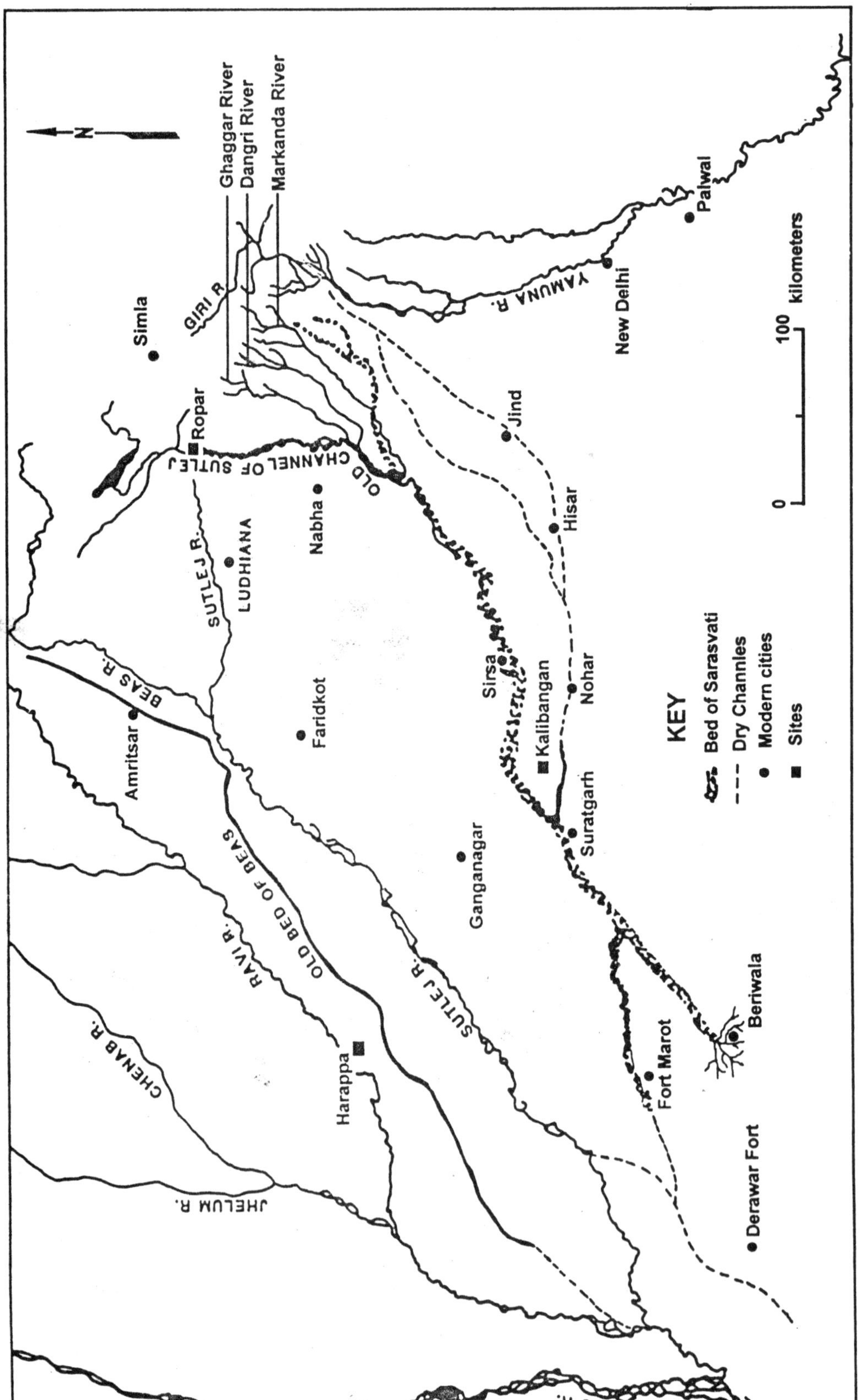

Fig. 2-7. Palaeochannels of the Ghaggar river, Rajasthan

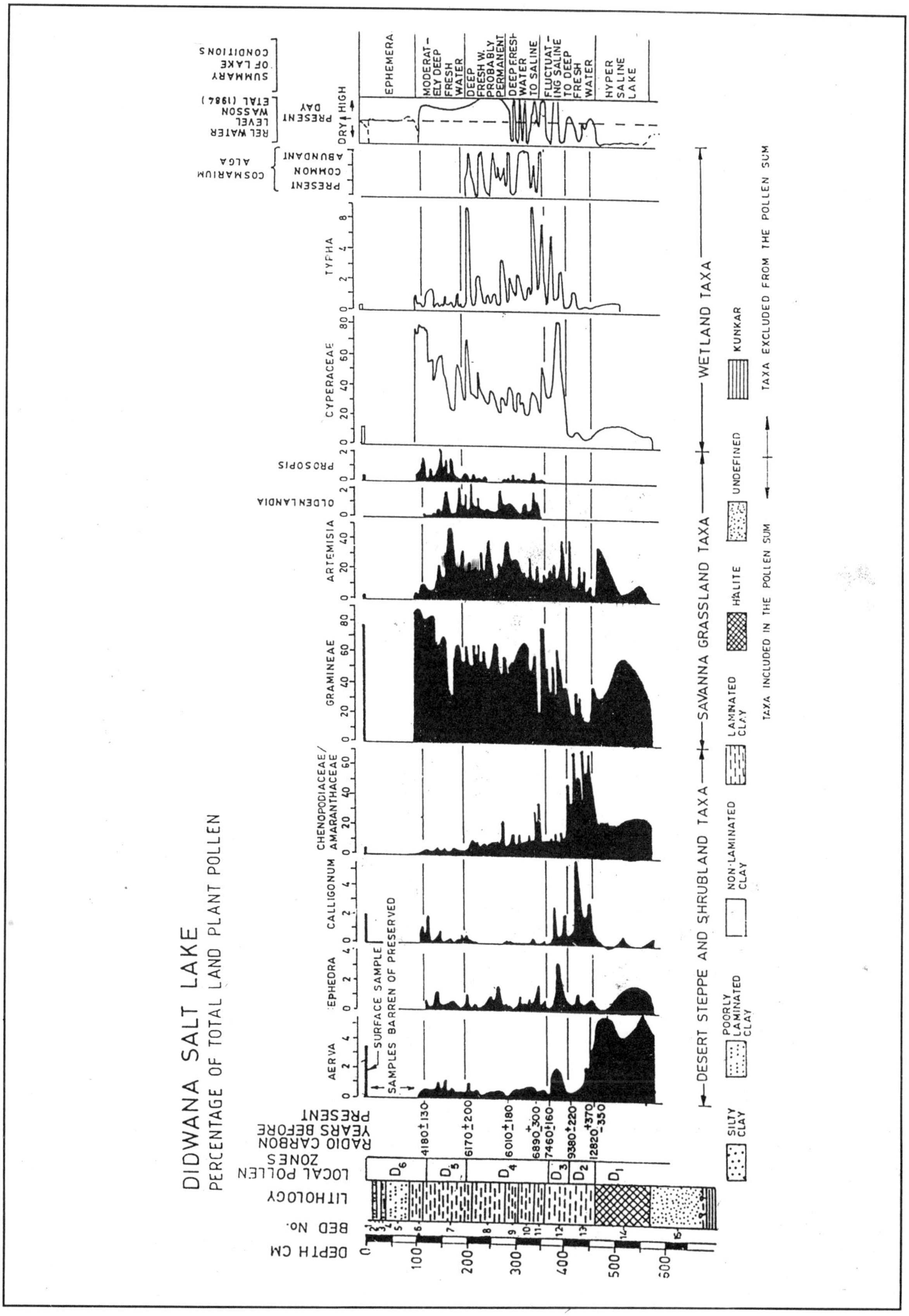

Fig. 2-8. Percentages of total land plant pollen from the Didwana lake and their climatic interpretation (Singh *et al.*, 1990)

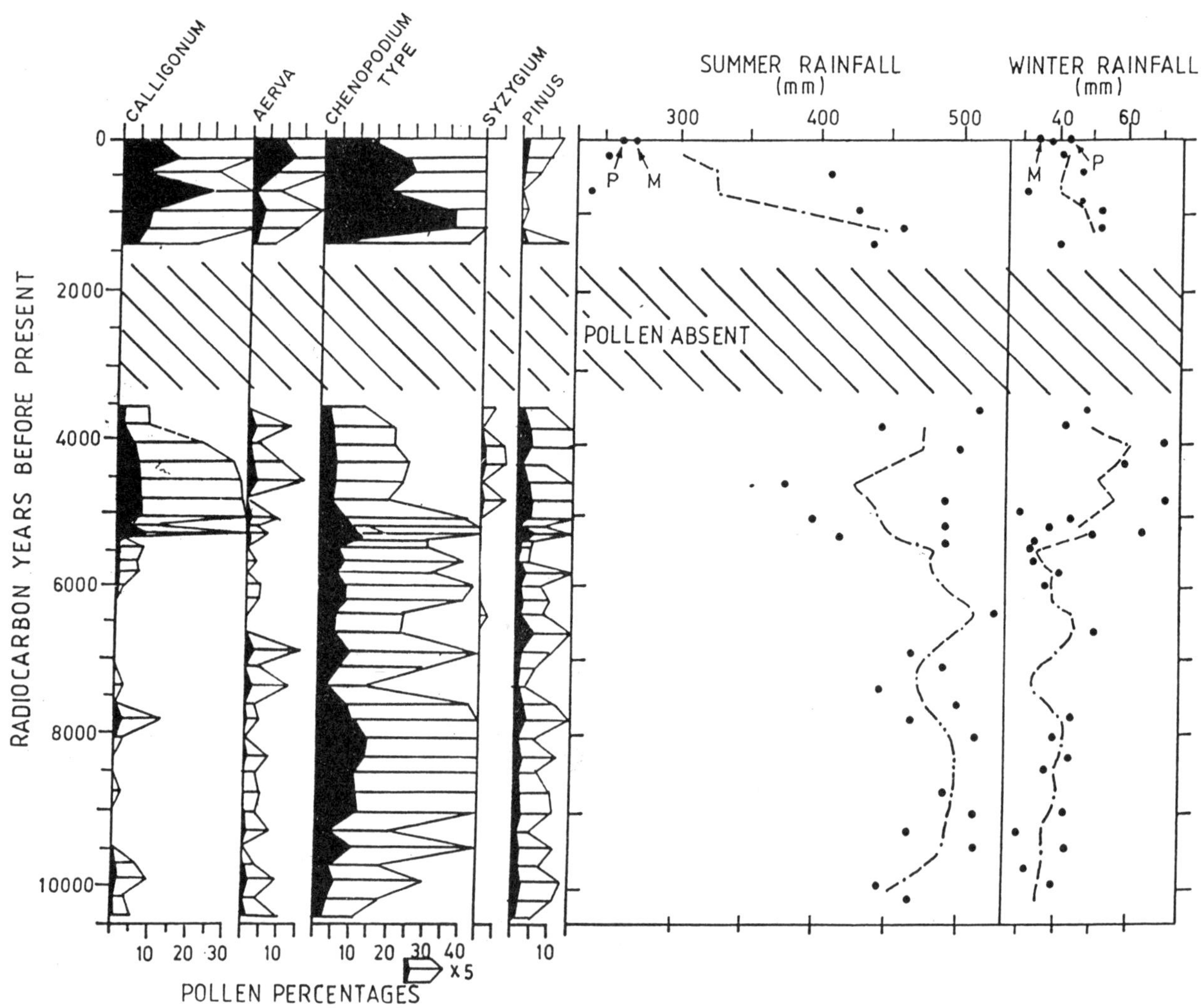

Fig. 2-9. Summer and winter rainfall inferred from the precipitation-sensitive plants from the Rajasthan lakes. Around 2000 BP there was intense aridity which developed halites in the lakes and no pollen survived (after Swain *et al.* 1983)

largely due to an increase in summer precipitation and that winter precipitation had remained as during the early Holocene (Fig. 2-10).

After c. 6000 yr BP, the change to moderately deep freshwater conditions, in Zone D5 (c. 6000-4200 BP), corresponds with the return of *Calligonum* shrubs on dunes in the region. By about 5000 yr BP, both *Oldenlandia* and *Artemisia* show decline indicating that both summer and winter precipitation had started to decline, a trend which appears to have intensified further from c. 4000 yr BP to the present day. The evidence for intensification comes from the change in the lake to an ephemeral regime, from c. 4200 yr BP, and from the quality of the surface pollen spectrum in which *Aerva, Calligonum* and *Gramineae* pollen is shown to dominate the present day sedimentary record. As *Artemisia* values are at their lowest level and *Oldenlandia* practically non-existent at either end of Zone D6, it is likely that both summer and winter precipitation fell to present levels at or soon after c. 4200 yr. BP.

The Singh *et al.* (1973) hypothesis has been recently questioned, most seriously from the following observations. The salt lakes are all grouped together within a very small region of an Indian State. They are under one climatic regime. On the other hand there are freshwater lakes

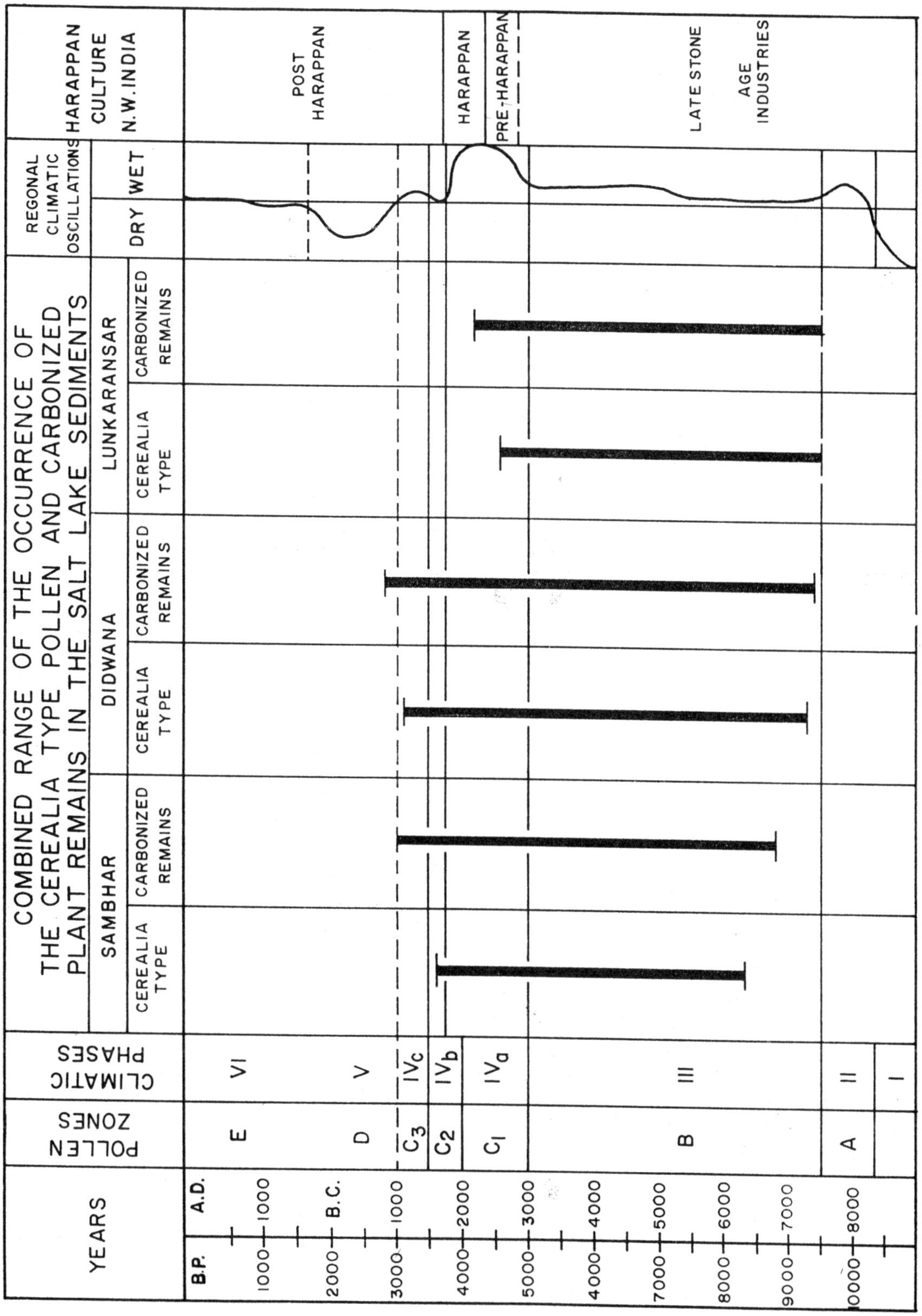

Fig. 2-10. Diagram showing the occurrence of charcoal pieces, Cerelia type pollen and climatic changes in the main lakes of Rajasthan, indicating forest clearance and beginning of agriculture (after Singh *et al.* 1971)

in this same region, flourishing under the same climatic conditions that produced the hypersalinity in the lakes that have been studied by the geoclimatologists. The freshwater bodies are Pushkar lake at Ajmer, and the lesser-known lake Gajner 30 kilometres south of Bikaner city.

The salinity of the lake water is a function of the balance between rainfall and surface drainage on the one hand, and sub-surface conditions on the other. A change in total average annual rainfall, surface drainage or sub-surface drainage will change the halite content of these bodies of water. As indicated by the changing palaeochannels of the Satluj, Yamuna, Drishadvati, etc., the area is riddled with lineaments and fault lines caused by neotectonics. These changing lineaments could change both surface run-off and also sub-surface drainage, affecting the salinity of the lakes. There is no doubt that Pushkar and some other lakes have access to sub-surface water which more than neutralises evaporation. But that does not mean that the lakes of Sambhar, Lunkaransar and Didwana, separated from each other by a few hundred km, could have remained unaffected by severe changes in precipitation. Swain *et al.* (1983: 1-17) used precipitation sensitive species to calculate quantitative changes in precipitation in Rajasthan. They estimated greatly increased summer precipitation of about 480 mm/yr, from 10.5 to 3.5 Kyr. The interval from 5–3.5 Kyr had the highest winter rainfall. Bryson (1988: 233) also remarks, "In northern India, summers during the mid-Holocene were much wetter. Now the summer monsoon is essentially the only rain in northern India, but in mid-Holocene time there was also considerable winter rainfall". One has therefore to note that not only the summer monsoon but also the winter rainfall was significantly higher during the mid-Holocene, which brought down the salinity of the lakes in question. These climatic inferences were based on rain-sensitive pollen spectra. Wasson *et al.* (1984) carried out extensive geochemical and sedimentological studies at Didwana. They inferred that the deepest water conditions in the entire sequence were indicated soon after 6 Kyr, thus confirming the climatic pattern indicated by pollen studies. Recently, a Japanese team in collaboration with the Deccan College, Poona, has again raised cores from Didwana for high-resolution work. Their results are still awaited.

Bryson (1988: 233) emphasises the importance of the fact that there was "the long dry period from 3500 to 2000BP". Recent work on the cores taken from the "oxygen minimum zone off Karachi at water depth of 700m contains continuously laminated sediments with a sedimentation rate of 1.2 mm/yr and a unique record of monsoon climatic variability covering the last 5,000 years" (Rad *et al.* 1999: 39-53). They further notice that the period from 3900BP is marked by varve thickness minima and low turbite activity, which they interpret as indicators of low precipitation and decreased river run-off.

Prasad *et al.* (1997) carried out multidisciplinary studies in the Nal Sarovar in Gujarat involving sedimentological, faunal, $\delta\ ^{13}C$, C/N in organic matter, magnetic susceptibility, and measurements of crystalline index of clay minerals. Their study concludes that this period (6-4.8 Kyr) "showed the highest value of C/N indicative of higher proportion of terrestrial plants in association with enriched $\delta\ ^{13}C$, shallow water loving *Bittium* and land snails". The overall climate was dry but evenly spaced with wet spells. During 4.8–3 Kyr the climate was wet. Thus we see that the Rajasthan climatic data, though admittedly not of high-resolution quality, do show convergence not only between different indicators but also agree with the multidisciplinary studies carried out by Gupta and Prasad in nearby Gujarat. We have also to note that the whole of Northern Hemisphere shows mid-Holocene warming and wetter conditions (Bryson 1988, Figs. 10 & 11).

A recent study by Thomas *et al.* (1999: 192) supports the findings of Singh *et al.* This study concludes: "(1) The present study provides evidence that during the Holocene the Thar desert experienced multiple episodes of aeolian accumulation of short duration. These are spaced by periods of 1.5—2.0 ka of low accumulation/quiescence. These results also pose new questions that would require further work to consider: i) the role of winter precipitation changes in regulating aeolian dynamism; and ii) the implication of monsoonal teleconnections and phase lag in dune accretion. (2) The study also indicates that the earlier phase of desertification in the Thar ended at -0.6-0.8 ka ago. This may be an important input for land use planning of the region. (3) Evidence of increased sand mobilisation/accretion is seen during the past 0.3 ka, suggesting anthropogenic effects".

Bryson (1988: 234-35), Singh (1971: 177-89), Singh *et al.* (1990: 351-58) and Agrawal (1992) all have emphasised the role of climate and environment in affecting habitations, especially the Harappa culture. But one has to admit that in Rajasthan the situation is more complex.

The changing river channels, mainly in response to neotectonic movement of lineaments in Rajasthan, have resulted in changes in the courses of Satluj, Ghaggar and Drishadvati as indicated by both the distribution of archaeological sites and satellite imageries (Agrawal & Sood 1982; for a detailed historical summary of such studies see Possehl 1999c). As a result of these tectonic changes, the Satluj joined the Indus system and the Drishadvati, the Yamuna drainage. The ancient Harappan settlements of Kalibangan and other smaller sites were on the banks of the Ghaggar, which eventually dried as its main tributary joined the Indus system.

The third factor one has to take into account is the limited sustainability of semi-arid ecology for large sedentary populations. Despite the mid-Holocene climatic amelioration, Rajasthan remained a semi-arid ecology. It could not sustain large towns for any length of time. The ecology had to give way once a threshold was crossed, till it regenerated again. We see this phenomenon in Rajasthan. The Harappans appear around 2500 BC and wither away around 1800 BC. The painted grey ware culture again appears around 800BC and disappears a few centuries later. So also the Rangmahal culture, which appears around 2-3 centuries AD and withers away in a couple of centuries.

We thus see that in Rajasthan, it is not only the changing precipitation that affects habitation but also the changing loyalties of the rivers and the sustainability thresholds of semi-arid ecology to allow large sedentary populations for long periods of time. All these trends are superimposed on each other in Rajasthan.

More recent work of Singhvi *et al.* (1998) has shown that the main dune building activity is dateable to c. 14 Kyr, just before the onset of the strengthening of the monsoon. Our studies also have brought out the vital role of the Tibetan Plateau in forcing climatic change (Agrawal and Yadava 1998).

Other Areas

Misra thinks that heavy rainfall and dense vegetation probably inhibited early man from colonising the Western Ghats region and north-east India. Elsewhere in the Old World too early hominids avoided dense tropical forests. In the case of the Ganga valley, the non-availability of stone, the basic raw material for making tools, may have been responsible for man avoiding this region.

Acheulian sites are particularly densely concentrated and are richer in Central India and the southern Eastern Ghats. Both these regions today receive adequate rainfall, have a thick vegetation cover, and are rich in wild plant and animal food resources.

Further east, recently some studies have been carried out on the lagoons of the Pulicat lake in Orissa. The evidence is relevant to the climatic changes during mid-Holocene as it reflects the sea-level changes in this area (Farooqui and Vaz 2000). They report, "Monsoon appears to have increased in strength abruptly since the last deglaciation, firstly, between 13 to 12.5 ka and 10 to 9.5 ka and secondly, between 9.5 and 5.5 ka (ref. 21). The latter may have been punctuated by centuries-long periods of weaker monsoon circulation. Records of maximum monsoon from the Arabian Sea and terrestrial sites in the adjacent areas of Africa and Asia and North Atlantic warmth were thus coincident with each other between 9.5 and 5.5 ka, and after 5.5 ka, the monsoon weakened more gradually in concert with slowly decreasing summer insolation in the Northern Hemisphere. However, the records of maximum winter precipitation in north-western India during the Indus culture period of 5000 to 3500 yrs BP have also been reported....It was during this period that the Northern Hemisphere summer monsoon strengthened over the African-Eurasian land. Reduction of monsoonal rainfall indicated by the decay of mangroves after 11,000 yrs BP and a drier period in Central India, from 4500 to 3000 yrs BP and in Rajasthan from 4000 to 2000 yrs BP have also been reported. The dynamics of the south-west Indian monsoon and related sea-level over the last 18,000 years conforms with the changes recorded in the present study. The above records indicate that the transgression and strong monsoon should also have favoured the establishment of mangrove vegetation along this part of the Indian coast during early Holocene. But the drier period coupled with intermittent sea regression during late Holocene rendered the ecosystem not favourable for mangroves".

Farooqui & Vaz further say, "The post-LGM sea-level rise reached its maximum around 6650 yrs BP at Sulurpet and after this the area experienced regression and desiccation with the decelerating mangrove line too".

Central India

Today there are perennial water springs at Bhimbetka which are the only source of water for human as well as animal populations, both domestic and wild. If these springs were also active during the Pleistocene, occupation of the shelters would have been possible throughout the year. However, stone tool industries found in the rock shelters and nearby open-air sites, as at Barkhera near Bhimbetka and Putli Karar area, both in the Raisen district, are so similar as to be the work of one and the same people. It would appear that these two locations represent seasonal camping places of the same populations, the rock shelters being used during the rainy season and the open-air sites during the winter months. Misra however thinks that over most of the country the hunter-gatherers lived in the open, along perennial as well as seasonal streams. In the latter context the occupation probably took place only during the rainy season and early winter months when water would have been available in the streams and local pools. During the summer months, when water in seasonal streams and pools dried up, all human groups must have been forced to congregate along perennial rivers.

Chemical analysis of sediments from Bhimbetka shelters in Central India suggests that conditions in the past were as humid, if not more humid, than they are today. Both plant and animal life must therefore have been abundant. Fossil faunal evidence from the alluvium of the Narmada, Godavari and their tributaries supports this inference. On the northern Deccan plateau sites are comparatively sparse. A plausible explanation for this phenomenon is that basalt, which was the only rock used for tool-making in this region, is highly susceptible to disintegration by weathering. Thus many or most of the Acheulian sites may have been totally destroyed by weathering.

Ganga valley

The Ganga valley has hardly much scientific palaeoclimatic data. H.P. Gupta collected a pollen sequence from an oxbow lake in Pratapgarh district of Uttar Pradesh in Ganga valley. He has concluded, "The climatic sequence, as determined from the biostratigraphy of the lake-basin has been grouped into four phases (I-IV). The general vegetation pattern is rather uniform and is tipped more towards open savannah forest with vast stretches of grasslands and a few scattered stands of arboreal vegetation" (Gupta 1976: 115). Gupta's chronology has poor controls and is not of much use in the present context. But in the Ganga valley, which is a monsoonal area with 100-150 cm/per year rainfall even today, finding savannah grasslands in mid-Holocene ameliorated climatic condition looks highly improbable. The University of Allahabad is now making fresh attempts at raising cores and getting them analysed in collaboration with the Japanese team.

Development of morphology and soils of the study area in the Ganga plains, according to a more recent study by Kumar *et al.* (1996) can be considered to have taken place in the following stages.

> *Stage I* : (10000-8000 BP)—Large areas of the Indo-Gangetic plains experienced a long spell of dry and cold climate during the last glaciation, effects of which were felt till about 6000 yrs (Fig. 11a). The study area, however, has surficial soil deposits that are no older than ca. 10,000 yrs. During the period starting from the Early Holocene vegetation was scant, rivers had braided nature over vast stretches due to low and variable discharge and high sediment load. Soils developed with concentration of salts near the surface and precipitation of pedogenic calcite in the sub-surface over only small upland areas in the east and north-east.
>
> *Stage II* : (8000-5000 BP)—This stage started with uplift of the Lower Ganga-Yamuna Block and corresponding activity along Ganga, Yamuna and Meerut Faults. Till about 6000 BP climate continued to be cold and dry and later climate was warmer and wetter. This led to higher vegetation in the area and higher discharge and low sediment load of the streams.
>
> *Stage III* : (5000-2500 BP)—At the start of this stage, the Upper Ganga-Yamuna Block subsided and became a site of deposition. Also, the Yamuna river, which was flowing in Haryana (west of the present area) and was a part of the Indus system, shifted to south and became a tributary of the Ganga river. Both the Yamuna and Ganga rivers deposited sediments in the Gn-YP. Lateral erosion by the two rivers modified the northern boundary of the Lower Ganga-Yamuna Block (Fig. 8): and changed it to V'-shaped with end pointing to the north. These plains were also the hub of activity of the Ochre Coloured Pottery (OCP) (3900-3000 BP) and painted grey ware (PGW) (3000-2600 BP) cultures.
>
> An increase in rainfall and improved drainage led to some regressive pedogenesis in Gn-YI (NSA) adjoining to the Ganga and Yamuna rivers and the Gn-Rgl. Salts and pedogenic calcrete were washed down partially to completely to the deeper levels (Kumar *et al.* 1996: 307-309).

This study by Kumar *et al.* also is in conformity with the general pattern of climatic amelioration during mid-Holocene in all the three regions of Kashmir, Rajasthan and the Ganga valley.

But it is obvious that in the Ganga valley the urbanisation processes had to wait till the middle of the first millennium BC. The monsoonal forests, mentioned in the epics as *mahavana*, which were dark even in the day, could be cleared only after the mass-production of iron artefacts which alone made it possible to drain the swamps and clear the dense forests to produce the requisite agricultural surplus which could sustain towns and cities. The Harappans, who were only equipped to deal with the semi-arid ecology of Rajasthan and Sindh, simply withered away on the fringes of the Ganga valley.

Peninsular India

Misra (1989) derives the Acheulian man's environment from the fluvial deposits. Acheulian artefacts here are usually found buried in bouldery and pebbly gravels of the Son, Chambal, Narmada, Godavari and other rivers and their tributaries. These gravels are believed to have been deposited in a semi-arid climate with intermittent, erratic rainfall and sparse to absent plant cover. These gravels are invariably covered by fine silts and silty clays, which are usually devoid of archaeological material. But this situation is almost certainly due to the fact that such sediments were deposited by low energy streams, which were unable to carry coarser material including stone artefacts. Acheulian occupations contemporary with the deposition of fine sediments have to be searched for outside fluvial deposits. Numerous surface sites of Acheulian found in Central India and the Eastern Ghats, are probably such occurrences. Faunal remains have been preserved in Acheulian-bearing gravels in some of the peninsular rivers. The Lower Group of the Narmada stratigraphy which has yielded Acheulian tools contains fossils of *Sus namadicus, Bos namadicus, Elephas hysudricus, Equus namadicus, Hexaprotodon namadicus, Stegodon insignis*-ganesa, which are all believed to be of Middle Pleistocene age. The coarse gravel unit of the Pravara river, a tributary of the Godavari, has yielded fossils of *Bos namadicus, Equus namadicus* and *Elephas namadicus* as well as pieces of fossilised tree trunks and branches in association with Acheulian assemblages (Corvinus 1983). These animals indicate the existence of both forest and open grassland environments and the availability of plentiful water round the year. There is little doubt that all these animals formed a source of food for Acheulian populations but whether they were hunted or scavenged or exploited in both these ways can be ascertained only when faunal remains are found in association with undisturbed occupation sites. At the moment such occurrences are conspicuous by their absence. Heavy rainfall and dense vegetation probably inhibited early man from colonising the Western Ghats and north-east India. Elsewhere in the Old World too early hominids avoided dense tropical forests. In the case of the Ganga valley, the non-availability of stone, the basic raw material for making tools, may have been responsible for man avoiding this region (Misra 1989).

Terminal Pleistocene

During this period, in western Rajasthan, the Himalayan drainage, which had been steadily declining in importance and shifting westward from the Early Pleistocene, now became defunct over the greater part of the desert. But in the extreme North-west corner of the state, the rivers continued to flow even during the terminal Pleistocene and probably during the early Holocene as well as is indicated by the presence of several wide palaeochannels with Upper Palaeolithic sites along their banks between Jaisalmer and Ramgarh. Everywhere aeolian activity was intense, depositing extensive sand sheets and sand-dunes in Rajasthan, Punjab, Haryana and Gujarat (Wasson *et al.* 1984). Several TL (thermoluminescence) dates obtained on sand quartz from Rajasthan and Gujarat have helped in accurately dating this phase of aridity (Singhvi *et al.* 1983). Well-dated geomorphic data suggest that the vegetation cover over most of the country thinned out during the terminal Pleistocene. As a result of the decreased rainfall and the reduction in vegetation cover on the valley slopes, considerable colluvial sediments were contributed to upland rivers like the Krishna, Bhima and Godavari in Maharashtra and to the Imphal river in Manipur. Owing to decreased discharge and increased sediment loads, most of the streams in these regions aggraded and developed an anatomising drainage pattern at this time (Misra 1989 and references therein).

Misra reports that at around 20,000 BP, the Lokthak lake in the Manipur valley shrank and thick colluvial cones developed on its periphery due to increased frost activity, and reduction in rainfall and possibly also in vegetation density. In coastal areas in the interior pans of south-western Tamil Nadu, Saurashtra and Kutch quartz and carbonate dunes developed as a result of lowered sea-level also occurring at approximately 20,000 BP. Extensive formation of an oolitic carbonate reef on the continental shelf of western India around 12,000-10,000 BP suggests reduction in discharge in the westerly-flowing streams of Maharashtra and Karnataka. During the terminal Pleistocene south-westerly monsoons were weak and the sea-level was lower by several metres. Thus the palaeoclimatic evidence suggests that much of the Indian subcontinent was a part of the global circulation pattern during the peak of the last glaciation c. 20,000 BP, though as we have noticed in Kashmir and Ladakh the onset of deglaciation was much earlier, perhaps around 20,000 BP (Agrawal 1992).

Faunal remains do provide some evidence of the extant environment. Fossil finds from the Belan valley, a sub-tributary of the Ganga, the Mahanadi and Manjra valleys in Central India, and the Godavari, Ghod and Krishna valleys in the Deccan have yielded *Canis* sp., *Bubalus* sp., *Cervus* sp., *Bos namadicus* and *Hexaprotodon palaeindicus*. Misra thinks that the fauna suggests the existence of a grassland environment with pockets of forests and swamps. The discovery of ostrich eggshells at over 40 sites in Rajasthan, Madhya Pradesh and Maharashtra, several of them ^{14}C dated, shows that the ostrich, a bird adapted to arid climate, was widely distributed in western India during the later part of the Upper Pleistocene.

The arid climate, poor vegetation and animal life led to a reduction in human population. This is suggested by the sparse human settlements found during this period. In Pakistan and in Rajasthan and Gujarat only isolated sites of this phase have been found. These Upper Palaeolithic people camped on sand-dunes as at Budha Pushkar and Didwana (Misra and Rajaguru 1986) in Rajasthan. In Central India too only a limited number of sites are known from the Son valley. Only in the relatively humid region of the Eastern Ghats, the Upper Palaeolithic sites are plentiful.

The Upper Palaeolithic tool assemblages are dispersed in desert grassland, woodland, woodland savanna, scrub woodland and thorny thicket zones. Several species of game inhabit these regions, the most important of them being nilgai (*Boselaphus tragocamelus*), chinkara (*Gazella gazella*), four-horned antelope (*Tetracerus quadricornis*), sambar (*Cervus unicolor*), chital (*Axis axis*), barking deer (*Muntiacus muntjac*), mouse deer (*Tragulus cf. meminna*), wild boar (*Sus scrofa cristatus*), jungle cat (*Felis chaus*), porcupine (*Hystrix indica*), hare (*Lepus nigricollis*), giant squirrel (*Ratufa indica*), monitor lizard (*Varanus dracaena*), and langur (*Presbytis entellus*). While remains of most of these species occur in late Pleistocene riverine deposits, and are also closely associated with Upper Palaeolithic occupations in Kurnool caves (Murty 1975; Murty & Reddy 1976: 214), there is fossil evidence showing the distribution of other species like ox (*Bos sp.*), buffalo (*Bubalus sp.*), horse (*Equus sp.*), hippopotamus (*Hippopotamus sp.*), rhinoceros (*Rhinoceros sp.*), and elephant (*Elephas sp.*). Besides, these ecosystems are also rich in avifauna and a wide variety of plant foods like yams, fruits, flowers, nuts, bamboo shoots, bamboo grain, leafy vegetables and mushrooms (Misra 1989).

For pre-Iron Age settlements, Murty (1981: 65-81) has given a detailed account of the South Indian ecology. This is one of the few papers dealing with the South Indian evidence.

This summary indicates that a lot remains to be done in the area of palaeoclimatic and palaeoenvironmental reconstruction in South Asia. Except for Kashmir and Rajasthan where multidisciplinary research has been carried out, in other regions there is hardly any work worth the name. Now the Japanese team under the leadership of Prof. Y. Yasuda is taking keen interest in some areas of India in collaboration with Indian universities.

Having discussed the environmental backdrop of the South Asian cultures from the Palaeolithic to historical periods, we now will examine the evidence of the cultures themselves, beginning in the next chapter with the Palaeolithic cultures.

Chapter 3

PALAEOLITHIC CULTURES

Contents :

OUR ANCESTORS : A GLOBAL VIEW

We find humans all over the world today. Even the early humans went out and colonised the world. The enigma has been what drove the early hominids to explore the globe. Gamble does not believe that it was only the agricultural technology that helped people to colonise the world. In his famous book *Timewalkers*, Gamble says:

> Humans went everywhere in prehistory because humans have purpose. The timewalker has brought this out time and time again. We no longer have to accent a world prehistory, which denies the significance or denigrates the process of prehistoric global colonisation. Instead we can see it for what it was—another example of humanity unfolding—variable and different but always recognisable. No longer is it sufficient to explain the past away by human drift or the diffusion of ideas or people from one centre to the rest of the world in a rerun of recent imperial history. We can see clearly, as did the Neapolitan philosopher Giambattista Vico as long ago as 1725, that common ideas are the independent discovery by every society of what it needs at any given stage in its own development. To admit a purpose in the process of prehistoric global colonisation is to regain this historical track where, as R.G. Collingwood maintained, 'the plan of history is a wholly human plan' (1994:241-42).
>
> I have argued that the reason people were everywhere was the result of purpose, the process of deliberate action. This operated in ecological time as behaviour was expected to meet changing circumstances. There was no direction or goal to such behaviour other than survival and the reproduction of existing social life, where purpose is provided by negotiation. The effect in evolutionary time was the extension of human range. This was accompanied by changes to the time-walkers. Many of these were adaptive, for example skin colour, stature, and head size. They also acquired the many facets of their humanity in this process since they excessively constructed social worlds to engage and transform new natural worlds. Human nature, as Vico pointed out almost three hundred years ago is not fixed. Instead it is a social creation in continuous evolution determined in respect to human needs and utilities. With the novelist's perspective, Carlos Fuentes has remarked on how the possibilities of our unfinished humanity still remain to be explored. The process continues and remains infinite even in a world with no new lands to unveil, only whole continents of social geography, because in Kant's phrase, 'Man is unsocially social'. One rich avenue for exploration lies in the themes of the past. The substance of a world prehistory, to quote Grahame Clark, 'is no less than the emergence and self-realisation of humanity itself' (Gamble 1994:245-46).

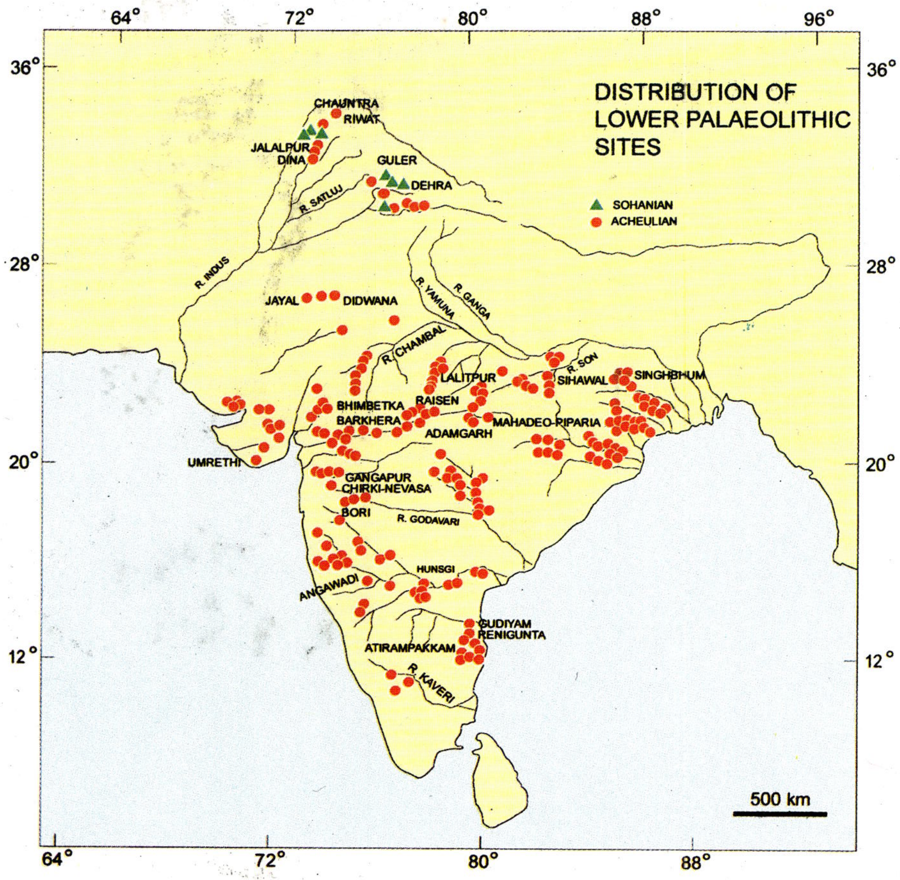

Map 3-1. Main Early Palaeolithic sites in South Asia (after Misra 1989)

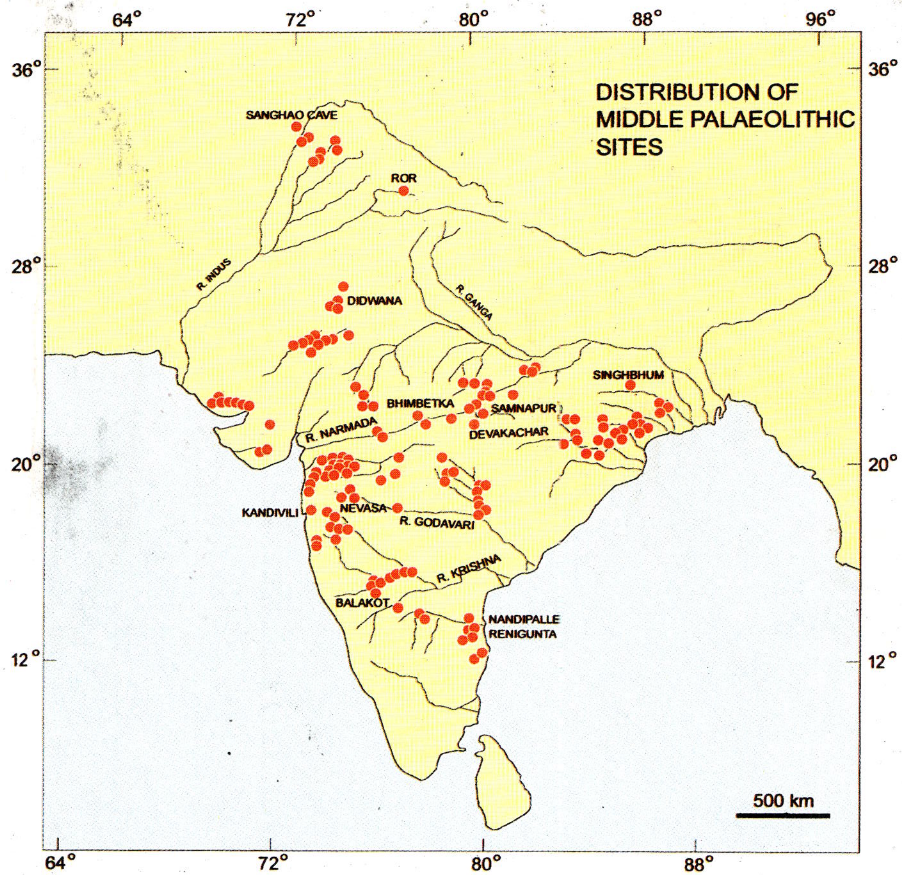

Map 3-2. Distribution of Middle Palaeolithic sites in India (after Misra 1989)

Gamble further explains:

> For those archaeologists interested in Pleistocene hunters, the curtain of civilisation might fall a little sooner, but it still falls. This is shown by the Moderns, some of whom have now been rehabilitated as complex rather than savage hunters. History, in the sense of self-determination, has been returned to them. They are now part of modern humanity, separated by a rapid transformation, seen by some as the Human Revolution, from the earlier Ancients and Pioneers. The division between "us" and "them", the ancestors, thus falls some 50,000 rather than 10 or even 5,000 years ago (1994:244).

Before we discuss the early examples of hominids, it may be worthwhile heeding to the warnings of Clive Gamble:

> A world prehistory must be interested in origins, but not the quest for origins which by dating and classifying ancestors seeks to establish in deep time and from natural principles the antiquity of exclusion, the fragmentation of humanity for whatever purposes and motives. The goal should instead be an interest in diversity in order to encompass and enrich rather than reject. If we cannot acquire self-knowledge via the study of our ancestors then what hope for the study of other animals and habitats, which we also use to construct our worlds? The global time-walkers are likewise trapped in amber so long as we regard them as natural rather than cultural beings. We do not need to humanise them in our form to understand them. We just have to ask different questions. The when, why, and how of global colonisation pose many such questions for the future development of a truly world prehistory (1994: 248).

With this backdrop we will briefly discuss the early hominid finds in this section. We do not propose to give a connected story of these exciting finds, but only representative examples of more recent discoveries. Basically this is to provide a perspective to Indian Stone Age. In India we have only one hominid skull reported from the Narmada valley, probably of *Homo erectus* lineage, though the dating is not firm. But in Africa, the source of probably all humanity, the dates are going beyond 4 My.

LUCY AND OTHER EARLIEST HOMINIDS: AUSTRALOPITHECUS

Donald Johanson named his new finds from Hadar area as *Australopithecus afarensis*. Dating back more than three million years, Lucy was the oldest, most complete hominid fossil ever found. She was only a metre tall, with a mixture of ape and human features. Lovejoy suggests that smaller canines mean that there was much less competition for females among *afarensis* - an indication that monogamy may have been evolving more than 3 million years ago. Lucy's skull probably exceeded 500 cc. By comparison, the brain of *Homo habilis*, one of the earliest members of our own genus, averaged about 630 cc. Using a new dating technology using lasers, Bob Walter could determine the age of most of the fossils at Hadar. Lucy lived 3.18 million ± 10,000 years ago. The first family assemblage turned out to be slightly older than Lucy - about 3.2 million years, which indicates that *afarensis* persisted relatively unchanged a long time at Hadar - at least 400,000 years. Another skull fragment found in 1981 was 3.9 million years old, from a site about 60 km south of Hadar; it may also be *afarensis*. If so, Lucy's species would have survived almost unchanged for 900,000 years. Her longer arms would have certainly helped her climb between branches.

Working at a site called Kanapoi near Lake Turkana, they found pieces of a new 4.1 million years old bipedal species named *Australopithecus anamensis*. The new species has many features in common with Lucy, but it is significantly more primitive and ape-like in its teeth. *Anamensis*, Johanson suspects, gave rise to *afarensis*. Tim White announced in 1994 that they had found bones of an even earlier hominid at a site in Ethiopia called *Aranasis*. Tim and his Ethiopian colleagues have since unearthed a nearly complete skeleton of the same hominid dated to 4.4 Myr ago. Its position on the human family tree is in question. It has many chimp-like features - enough that Tim decided to create an entirely new genus for it, naming the animal *Ardipithecus ramidus.*

Johanson thinks that Lucy was the ancestor of all humanity, though not all agree. About the human ancestory, the famous Darwinian biologist Dawkins says,

> It is...certain that there existed one female, whom we may call Mitochondrial Eve, who is the most recent common ancestor of all modern humans down the female only pathway.... Although it is possible that Mitochondrial eve and the Focal ancestor are one and the same, it is vanishingly unlikely that this is so. It is somewhat more likely that the focal ancestor was a male than a female.... There is disagreement over where Mitochondrial Eve lived but the balance of informed opinion still favour Africa (Dawkins 1995:192).

Early Homo

Olduvai Gorge, in Africa, has become famous for its early hominid discoveries. Though Mary Leakey had found *Zinjanthropus* at Olduvai Gorge and Louis Leakey had initially pronounced it to be the maker of the gorge's stone tools, later fossils discovered at the site turned out to be slightly older than *Zinjanthropus* and belonged to the real tool-makers. These fossils were older than 1.75 million years, and the brain was significantly larger, with a volume estimated at 640 cc. Despite initial opposition, Leakey and others decided to call it *Homo habilis* in 1964, and put 600 cc as the qualifying size of the brain for admission to genus Homo. It created a great furore among anthropologists. Eventually though *Homo habilis* was accepted by most anthropologists as a valid species (Levin 1998).

Near Lake Baringo in Kenya, a temporal bone was discovered in 1967 and was securely dated to 2.4 My, which meant that this find represented the oldest-known specimen of Homo. In 1972 Richard Leakey discovered another Homo skull (KNM-ER 1470), with a large cranium of about 750 cc. It also turned out to be 1.9 My old, though with a much larger skull than the Olduvai specimen. Another cranium with only 500 cc capacity from Lake Turkana was identified as a female *Homo habilis*.

An international team reported, in 1993, a partial hominid mandible from near Lake Malawi. The authors assigned the Malawi specimen to *Homo rudolfensis*, a contemporary of *Homo habilis* that is also found at Lake Turkana. The evolution of Homo has been associated with the climatic cooling that occurred approximately 2.5 million years ago, and these two early specimens are consistent with that hypothesis (Levin 1998). Levin suggests that it is useful to think of *Homo habilis* as a smaller-brained creature with an archaic post-cranium, and *H. rudolfensis* as larger-brained with a more modern post-cranium.

In 1986, Donald Johanson, Tim White, and a large team of colleagues discovered an extremely fragmented hominid skeleton (called OH 62) at Olduvai Gorge, comprising part of the upper jaw, some cranial fragments, most of the right arm, and parts of both legs. OH 62 was a small, mature female, comparable to Lucy in being approximately one metre tall. As with Lucy, the arms were long and the legs short, compared with later Homo. OH 62 was found in the lowest layers of Olduvai Gorge, and was dated at between 1.85 and 1.75 million years old. Around the same time another fossil from Lake Turkana was found and was termed *Homo erectus*. It was almost 2 metres and had very humanlike limb proportions, but lived only 200,000 years later than OH 62. This would mean that if *Homo habilis* is ancestral to *Homo erectus* then evolution from an ape-like to a humanlike condition must have occurred very rapidly.

Recently there has been much excitement at the news of the Gona tools pushing the antiquity of hominid artefacts to beyond 2.5 Myr. Semaw says:

> Palaeoanthropological investigations in the Hadar region of the Awash valley of Ethiopia between

1992 and 1994 resulted in additional archaeological discoveries as well as radioisotopic age control and a magnetic polarity stratigraphy of the Gona sequence. These occurrences are now securely dated between 2.6-2.5 Myr. The stone tools are thus the oldest known artefacts from anywhere in the world. The artefacts show surprisingly sophisticated control of stone fracture mechanics equivalent to much younger Oldowan assemblages of Early Pleistocene age. This indicates an unexpectedly long period of technological stasis in the Oldowan.... The excavated and surface artefact assemblages at EG10 and EG12 primarily comprise simple cores, whole flakes and flaking debris unifacially and bifacially flaked cores comprise the 'flaked pieces' category. There are numerous examples of several generations of flake scars on the cores, indicating that Late Pliocene hominids had mastered the skill of basic stone knapping. Moreover, the large number of well struck flakes with conspicuous bulbs of percussion indicate a clear understanding of conchoidal fracture mechanics....The artefact collections from Olduvai Gorge, Koobi Fora and the Omo are the largest and best-studied samples of Oldowan artefacts. The oldest reliably dated among these are those from Lokalalei, which are constrained to be younger than the Kalochoro Tuff (=Tuff F of the Shungura Fm) at 2.36± 0.05 Myr. The Gona artefacts are thus at least 160Kyr ± 90Kyr older than these, the ages being distinguishable with greater than 92% confidence....The Gona evidence extends the known age of the Oldowan Industrial Complex to 2.5 Myr and obviates the need to posit a 'pre-Oldowan' or an early facies of the Omo industrial complex....The very early age of the Gona artefacts shows a technological stasis in the Oldowan industrial complex for over a period of 1 million years. The Acheulean appears abruptly at about 1.6-1.5 Myr with large bifacial tool forms such as hand-axes and cleavers that were unknown in the Oldowan (*sensu stricto*).... There is, as yet, no evidence of stone artefacts in sediments older than 2.6 Myr within the Gona. Two contemporaneous hominid species Homo and *A. aethiopicus* are known elsewhere in eastern Africa from deposits that are comparable in age with the Gona. However, no hominid specimens have yet been found associated with Late Pliocene stone tools.... The sophisticated understanding of conchoidal fracture evidence at Gona implies that the hominids that lived about 2.5 Myr ago were not novices to lithic technology. We predict that even older artefacts will be found (Semaw 1997:333-36).

Bernard Wood suggests that the maker of the Gona tools was *Paranthropus*. There is evidence that *Paranthropus aethiopicus/boisei* existed in the Omo region of Ethiopia across the same approximate time range, 2.5-1.5 Myr ago (Wood 1997: 292-293). Semaw however does not agree with this identification. About the *P. boisei*, Deison (1997: 445) says that as with many early human species, *P. boisei* occurs at only a few sites: Olduvai Gorge and Peninj (Tanzania), Chesowanja (Kenya) and, especially, in the Lake Turkana basin (in the Shungura, Koobi Fora and Nachukui/West Turkana zones on the Kenya-Ethiopia border), mainly between 2.2 and 1.6 Myr. A partial upper jaw has also been recovered from the Chiwondo Formation in Malawi. This discovery of a *P. boisei* skull by Suwa *et al.* (1997: 489-92) now extends the geographical range to the north-east. Temporally, with a firm date of 1.4 Myr, it is near the previously extrapolated latest occurrence of the species. Most of the other finds are associated with relatively moist and wooded habitats, but the Konso deposits yielding the new specimens indicate a more open, drier palaeoenvironment (although nearby sites were also moist and wooded). In the same bed at Konso are a mandible of *Homo erectus* and an assemblage of artefacts referred to the earliest Acheulean (hand-axe) industry. In fact, revised calibration of the Olduvai Gorge sequence indicates that the oldest Acheulean sites there (EF-HR and MNK) probably date to 1.6-1.5 Myr.

Homo erectus

There are two theories about early human expansion. The first, known as "out-of-Africa", postulates that human migration began about 1.8 million years ago, when *Homo erectus* left the African continent and colonised Europe, the Middle East and Asia. Roughly 1.6 million years later, anatomically modern *Homo sapiens* appeared in Africa, and eventually migrated out too, displacing the pre-humans who preceded them. The second theory, known as multi-regionalism, has no quarrel with the first wave of *Homo erectus* expansion, but argues that the subsequent *Homo sapiens* emigration never took place. Rather, it holds that *Homo sapiens* sprang up in many spots throughout the Old World, evolving from *Homo erectus* colonies already in place.

In a summary review of early hominids (*Time*, December 13, 1996 issue) the writer agreed that paleontologists do not pretend to know everything about how *Homo erectus* lived.

> Their skill in making tools was limited: a flaked stone or a crude axe was probably as good as it got. They arose in Africa about 1.8 million years ago and later ranged over an impressive expanse of land that included the Middle East, China, Southeast Asia and possibly Europe. But *Homo erectus* was no match for our species, the glamorous *Homo sapiens*, and not long after anatomically modern humans appeared some 200,000 years ago, the more primitive hominid died out.... According to research published last week in the journal *Science*, *Homo erectus* may not have gone so quietly into that good night. On the Indonesian island of Java, it now appears, a small group of hangers-on may have lived as recently as 27,000 years ago, thriving in a world that *Homo sapiens* had long before claimed as its own.

The *Time* further reports :

> The study, based on a new analysis of fossil sites, has created a tempest in the paleontological community. Now researchers not only must explain how a single prehuman population could remain frozen in evolutionary amber for so long after its species went extinct elsewhere in the world, but also must revisit two of science's most hotly debated questions: Where on the habitable continents did modern humans first emerge, and how did they come to dominate the world? 'These dates will stir up a lot of controversy', says geochronologist Carl Swisher of the Berkeley Geochronology Centre in Berkeley, California, who headed the study. 'Some people definitely won't believe them'.

Scientists were particularly intrigued by more than a dozen partial skulls found near the villages of Ngandong and Sambungmacan in the 1930s and 1970s. The skulls had unusually large brain-cases, and so were estimated to be anywhere from 100,000 to 400,000 years old, among the youngest *Homo erectus* remains ever found. For more than a generation, those estimates stood.

As Swisher *et al.* (1994) was denied access to the fossil specimens for dating, so he had to collect his own samples. Luckily he found some teeth from the same levels. When Swisher and his colleagues dated the teeth, they were stunned at the results: the dental remains were only 27,000 to 53,000 years old, suggesting that the hominid skulls were too. "We never expected to find dates this young", Swisher says. " These dates must be wrong", says paleontologist John de Vos of Holland's National Museum of Natural History. "They just threw the fossils into a machine, and out rolled a date".

Scholars doubted the stratigraphic location of the dated teeth. It was suggested that flooding, for example, could have washed the *Homo erectus* remains into a younger fossil bed. Swisher *et al.* (1994) disagrees, arguing that the remains are too well preserved—its fragile structures are generally intact - to have been bumped around in a flood. Once Java's last land bridge disappeared, the island was separated from the Asian mainland by hundreds of miles; any population that took root there would thus have been well protected from interlopers. More troubling are the questions the new study raises about human evolution in general.

The new findings provided a boost to the out-of-Africa camp. If *Homo erectus* really became *Homo sapiens* in several places at once, they argue, why would such an evolutionary wave have simply skipped Java? What is more, multi-regionalists have long contended that Javan *Homo erectus* gave rise to modern Australians, but if the older and newer species in fact overlapped, this becomes unlikely.

The controversy continues. "*Homo erectus* and *Homo sapiens* could never have lived together", De Vos maintains. May be not, counter Swisher *et al.* (1994), but for now the fossils say they did.

Pitts and Roberts (1997) have reported Palaeoliths from 400,000 BP horizons from Boxgrove, Britain. The use of soft hammers provides important evidence for technological sophistication, suggesting that these early humans planned their tasks and prepared implements accordingly. The recent discovery of the spectacular long, wooden spears from Schoningen, Germany, also dating to about 400,000 years ago, comes as a timely confirmation of what the Boxgrove finds had already suggested - that these early humans were hunters of large, fit, mature animals. They also carried out the butchery of the carcasses in an unhurried, efficient and cooperative manner.

Thieme created a stir by reporting Lower Palaeolithic hunting spears from Germany. He reports:

> Found in association with stone tools and the butchered remains of more than 10 horses, the spears strongly suggest that systematic hunting, involving foresight, planning and the use of appropriate technology, was part of the behavioural repertoire of pre-modern hominids. The use of sophisticated spears as early as the Middle Pleistocene may mean that many current theories on early human behaviour and culture must be revised.... It is postulated that the grooves were for holding flint tools or flakes; if this supposition is correct, these implements represent the oldest composite tools yet discovered. Associated with these finds were more than a thousand large mammal bones, some of which exhibit cut-marks from butchery. The fauna includes straight-tusked elephant *Palaeoloxodon antiquus*, rhinoceros *Stephanorhinus kirchbergensis*, red deer, *Cervus elaphus*, bear and horse (1997: 807-10).

Thieme further claims that these finds are thought to be the oldest wooden throwing spears yet discovered. As they are sandwiched between deposits of the Elsterian and the Saalian glaciations, and situated within a well-studied sedimentary sequence, their age can be estimated as probably 400 Kyr. The discovery of spears designed for throwing means that theories of the development of hunting capacities and subsistence strategies of Middle Pleistocene hominids must be revised, as well balanced, sophisticated hunting weapons were common from an early period of the Middle Pleistocene onwards. Accordingly, meat from hunting may have provided a large dietary contribution than has previously been acknowledged. The Schoningen evidence also illustrates how little is known about the 'organic' component of early hominid material culture (Thieme 1997).

China: In China, the dates of the *Homo erectus* appear to be too old. An Zhisheng and Ho Chuan Kun (1989: 213-21) assign a high antiquity to the *Homo erectus* finds from China. They say that skeletal remains of *Homo erectus* found in Pleistocene loess at two sites near Lantian in central China are of greatly different geologic age. The cranium found in the fossil-bearing strata at Gongwangling is about 1.15 Myr old whereas the remains found at the Chenjiawo locality in Middle Pleistocene loess are about 0.65 Myr old. The dating is based on new paleomagnetic polarity determinations and on the lithostratigraphic position of the fossils in the loess-paleosol sequence. Our results confirm that both localities are older than the first occupation of Zhoukoudian. New dates, palaeoenvironmental settings, and morphological features of the hominids from Lantian localities have significant bearing on the understanding of adaptive radiations of the middle and late hominids in Asia.

Wanpo *et al.* (1995: 275-78) report that the site of Longgupo cave was discovered in 1984 and excavated in 1985-88 by the Institute of Vertebrate Paleontology and Paleoanthropology (Beijing) and the Chongqing National Museum (Sichuan Province).

> Important finds include very archaic hominid dental fragments, *Gigantopithecus* teeth and primitive stone tools. Palaeomagnetic analysis and the presence of *Ailuropoda microta* (pygmy giant panda) suggested that the hominid-bearing levels dated to the earliest Pleistocene. In 1992, a joint Chinese-

> American-Canadian geochronological research corroborated the age using electron spin resonance (ESR) analysis. We report here that the hominid dentition and stone tools from Longgupo cave are comparable in age and morphology with early representatives of the genus *Homo* (*H. habilis* and *H. ergaster*) and the Oldowan technology in East Africa. The Longgupo dentition is demonstrably more primitive than that seen in Asian *Homo erectus*. Longgupo's diverse and well preserved Plio-Pleistocene fauna of 116 species provide a sensitive contextual base for interpreting the early arrival of the genus *Homo* in Asia.

They have estimated the age on three parametres: 1. The co-occurrence of *Sinomastodon, Nestoritherium, Equus yummanensis, Ailuropoda microta* and *Mimomys peii* place the middle zone clay facies in the late Pliocene and earliest Pleistocene. 2. Palaeomagnetic data place the 7-8 levels within the Olduvai chron, 1.96 to 1.78 Myr. 3. The ESR determination of 1.02 ± 0.1 Myr, on material from level 4 (3m above levels 7-8), constrains and reinforces these interpretations. "The Longgupo specimens are therefore older than any reported for China and at least as old as Indonesian *Homo erectus*. The Longgupo specimens closely resemble East African fossils representing the earliest-species of the genus *Homo*. They share few characters in common with Asian *Homo erectus*. As their incompleteness precludes designating a new species, we assign the Longgupo hominids to *Homo species* indeterminate, while noting affinities with *H. habilis* and *H. ergaster*. The stone tools are consistent with this interpretation. Given the early date and primitive morphology for the Longgupo specimens, and the older age estimates for *H. erectus* in Java, we must recognize more than one Plio-Pleistocene hominid species in east Asia. The new evidence suggests that hominids entered Asia before 2 Myr, coincident with the earliest diversification of genus *Homo* in Africa. Clearly, the first hominid to arrive in Asia was a species other than true *H. erectus*, and one that possessed a stone-based technology. A pre-*erectus* hominid in China as early as 1.9 Myr provides the most likely antecedents for the in situ evolution of *Homo erectus* in Asia" (Wanpo *et al.* 1995: 275-278).

Australia: The antiquity of the Australian man seems to be pushed back everytime. Dayton and Woodford (1996) have again pushed back the date of early humans in Australia. Jinmium is located just inside the western border of Australia's wild Northern Territory.

> It has a stone monolith rising 40 metres above the sandy floodplain. Surrounding this impressive hunk of sandstone are smaller, but still enormous boulders, poised like patient attendants. The arrangement of the stones is natural, but what has been carved and painted on them is not. The layers of rock art covering the monolith and its companions betray Jinmium as an ancient cultural centre. Recently painted spirits and other mysterious figures lie over earlier images are nearly 10,000 carved circular engravings, known as cupules. Richard Fullagar, David Price and Lesley Head of the Australian Museum say that stone tools at Jinmium could date back 176,000 years and its rock art 7,5000 years. If true, this means the team has pushed back the date for the settlement of Australia by about 100,000 years, and added an extra dimension to the long-standing controversy over the origin of modern humans. The researchers could also have identified the oldest known art in the world. Ochre, the iron-oxide based pigment, first appears in sediment dated to between 75,000 and 11,16,000 years of age. Nearby, a sandstone fragment with characteristic pit marks was found in sediments between 58,000 and 75,000 years old. Tacon, a rock art expert, concludes that the fragment fell from the cupule-covered wall of a rock shelter in the site's central outcrop. And starch grains found in association with 60,000 years old pounding tools suggest that around this time inhabitants process plant food, probably tubers. All up, the findings indicate that people were living a rich life at the site much longer ago than most archaeologists had suspected. Kershaw says that palynologist Sander van der Kaars, now at Monash, has unpublished evidence from a core taken off Lombok, Indonesia, of a change from forest to grassland vegetation about 190,000 years ago, and a telltale charcoal park 200,000 years ago. Kershaw argues that human activity is the only reasonable explanation for these changes (Dayton and Woodford 1996: 28-31).

Any date beyond 120,000 years makes it difficult for the out-of-Africa theorists. Fullagar and his colleagues point out that before 135,000 years ago, the sea-level fell dramatically, which could have made the sea voyage from mainland Asia to Australia easier. The date at which humans arrived in Australia, and whether they were ancient or modern, has big implications for these two competing theories, says Alan Thorne, a palaeoanthropologist at the ANU and an advocate of the multi-regional hypothesis. Somehow the human skeletal remains or teeth have been conspicuously absent from early Australian sites. The next best thing would be to firm up the Jinmium dates. Until then, all the implications of Fullagar and his team's research will be in doubt. As Stringer says: "I'm holding back to wait for these dates to be confirmed by another lab". (Dayton and Woodford 1996: 28-31).

In this connection, it may be relevant to recall the observations made by Singhvi *et al.* (1998) in their review paper:

> In the earliest African studies, the focus was on the limestone caves in South Africa and the East African Rift. An increasing number of sites in these areas competed with one another in providing older and newer hominid fossils. The great number of finds in well established chronological contexts led to recognising East Africa as the original habitat of hominids. This gave rise to the 'East African Rift Centric' (EARC) theory of human origin, based on a reasonably secure foundation of numerical dates....Reinvestigation of Longgupo cave in central China has fuelled the debate on the timing of the movement of Homo out of Africa, and supported the idea of multiregional evolution (Huang *et al.* 1995). Based on these new finds and their associated dates, it appears that the spread of Homo may have happened much earlier than has been assumed today. The ESP dates, the palaeomagnetic sequence, and the fauna of the Longgupo cave deposits have placed the hominid bearing levels to the earliest Pleistocene. Age determinations suggest that hominids were established in Asia just after 2 Myr, and, given the primitive nature of the hominid dentition from Longgupo, it is possible that the first hominids to occupy Asia may have been *erectus* variants such as *Homo ergaster* or perhaps *Homo habilis*. The dental remains share morphological similarity with the early representatives of the genus Homo in Africa, and the stone tools share similarity with the earliest Oldowan technologies of East Africa. These results indirectly support an early age of the Javanese *Homo erectus* fossils. The basic question of 'When did hominids move out of Africa?' still remains enigmatic. At this stage, the most probable answer is that hominids migrated out of Africa at the *erectus* stage. On the basis of the foregoing discussion on the chronometry of the Lower Palaeolithic, it appears that early technology began in Africa, evolved slowly, and eventually spread widely in the Old World (Singhvi *et al.* 1998).

Neanderthals

In the Croatian cave, known as Vindija, the bones belonged mostly to Neanderthals (in German tal means valley, so it should be Neandertal, though Neanderthal is more common), a people who inhabited Europe from about 230,000 years ago until they vanished around 30,000 years ago. Analysis of Neanderthal bones discovered here in the 1970s has yielded provocative clues to the lives of these hunter-gatherers, who occupied this cave some fifty millennia ago. Fine cut-marks and unusual fractures—similar to those made on the bones of butchered animals—suggest that Neanderthals practised cannibalism, either from hunger or as some kind of death ritual.

Cannibalism seems far more likely in Croatia, where cut-marks scar many of the bones from Krapina and Vindija. Here, Neanderthals had smashed the bones of many of their dead. "We simply do not know whether this represents a ritualistic cannibalism or whether these people had a taste for their fellow men, so to speak", says Smith.

Rick Gore (in *National Geographic* 1996:4-35. Quotations given below are from Gore's interviews of the experts) finds others who disagree. "I think they wanted the meat and the marrow", argues Tim White, a paleoanthropologist at the University of California at Berkeley who has studied the Croatian collection. "If it were part of a ritual to break open the bones, then all the bones would have been broken. But they smashed open only the large bones of the limbs—the ones with lots of marrow". White also points out that the Neanderthals made the same patterns of cut-marks on their fellow humans as they did on their animal prey. Moreover, those marks recur on bones from both Vindija and Krapina, sites occupied at intervals thousands of years apart. He sees cannibalism as one of a variety of ways Neanderthals sustained themselves rather than an occasional act of desperation by starving humans.

But finds at other Croatian caves suggest another, more compassionate side to the Neanderthals. A skull fragment found at a nearby Neanderthal rock-shelter shows evidence of a serious head wound that had healed. Someone had taken care of the victim for a long time.

Gore (ibid.) says, Neanderthals have been generally considered almost sub-humans, bereft of any intelligence or language skills. Neanderthals left scant evidence that they could create art. They appeared uninventive; their tool-making skills seemed primitive.

These misconceptions are changing now. "Neanderthals were highly resourceful, highly intelligent creatures", says Fred Smith, a Neanderthal specialist at Northern Illinois University. "They were not big, dumb brutes by any stretch of the imagination. They were us—only different". The recent excavations and analysis have demonstrated that Neanderthal tools in fact required a high level of craftsmanship and mental skills as adept as modern humans. Neanderthals deftly worked pieces of flint into knives, scrapers, points, and blades. They organised group hunts and took care of the weak and the sick, which suggests a social organisation more complex than previously believed. Most scholars now accept the idea that Neanderthals spoke at least a rudimentary language.

Found by quarry workers near Düsseldorf, the original Neanderthal man was proclaimed by some to be the missing link between apes and humans. Others argued that this odd specimen with the ape-like brow-ridges was simply a misshapen freak from the Middle Ages. But soon more bones with the same strange features were unearthed in Belgium, France, and other parts of Europe. Then, at the turn of the century, the bones of as many as 80 Neanderthals were discovered in a cave in the Croatian village of Krapina. The origins of the Neanderthals are uncertain, but scientists suspect that they share a common ancestor with modern humans: a tall, slender species known as *Homo erectus*, which migrated into Europe probably from Africa through West Asia between 700,000 and a million years ago.

It is not clear why Neanderthals disappeared. Around 40,000 years ago modern humans began spreading through Europe. By about 10,000 years after their arrival, all record of Neanderthal life ends. Perhaps the modern humans conquered and destroyed the Neanderthals. Perhaps the newcomers introduced deadly new diseases, much as Europeans carried smallpox to the New World. The Neanderthals might have interbred with the modern humans. Or may be the Neanderthals slowly died off, unable to compete with the more adaptable moderns (Gore 1996).

Their powerful musculature enabled them to bring down big game, such as bison or elk. Their noses were broad, possibly to provide more inner surface area to add moisture to the frigid, dry air they had to breathe. On average they had even larger brains than people do today, but in this case it seems that bigger did not necessarily mean smarter. Because we are smaller in physique, our brains are relatively larger. Some experts speculate that Neanderthals needed more brain cells to co-ordinate their extra body mass.

These Neanderthal traits probably began emerging between 230,000 and 300,000 years ago. Evidence of their antiquity has recently been discovered in the muddy floor of a cave in the Sierra de Atapuerca of northern Spain. Arsuaga believes these people lived here about 300,000 years.

Grafting images of living humans onto Neanderthal skulls, computer experts at the University of Illinois at Chicago have resurrected their faces.

Rightmire (1997: 917-18) reports that this assemblage from the Sima de los Huesos ('Pit of Bones') includes several well-preserved crania, along with jaws, teeth and other body parts of at least 32 individuals. The site and its contents reveal much about the people who preceded the Neanderthals, and the course of human evolution in the Middle Pleistocene. The bones are ancient. Both human and bear fragments have been dated using electron-spin resonance and analysis of uranium isotopes. The results indicate a minimum age of about 200,000 years, although some of the remains could be in excess of 300,000 years. Although the Spanish researchers feel that there is little basis for splitting this long lineage into discrete segments, they elect to lump the Sima material - along with the more ancient remains - in the species *Homo heidelbergensis.*

Why the remains of so many people lie clustered here is unknown. Perhaps the cave collapsed or a catastrophic flood swept the bodies here. May be the cave was a favourite feasting site for predators. But they have offered a more intriguing possibility.

"They were not brought here by carnivores", says Jose Miguel Carretero, a paleoanthropologist. "None of the bones have tooth marks, and there are no remains of other species carnivores prey on. Whatever the reason, they gave their dead special treatment. This tells us something about how their minds had evolved. Animals do not take care of their dead. This practice was a harbinger of the simple grave offerings of the later Neanderthals—perhaps one of many cultural behaviors they inherited. Meanwhile recent dating has pushed back the age of the first people generally accepted as true Neanderthals by 100,000 years - to 230,000 years ago".

An important cache of these early Neanderthals was unearthed in 1976 at Biache-Saint Vaast in northern France by workers excavating the foundation for a new steel mill. They found two partial Neanderthal skulls, along with hundreds of flint tools and animal bones. The workers had apparently stumbled across a camp where Neanderthals butchered animals. French scientists see evidence in these artifacts of a surprisingly advanced toolkit. A decade ago these early Neanderthals found at Biache-Saint Vaast in northern France were widely viewed as scavengers, incapable of planning an activity as complex as a hunt, much less one involving such fierce quarry. But Alain Tuffreau, an archaeologist at the University of Science and Technology of Lille, says such slaughters show that these people were more advanced. "I think it is evident that they were hunting in groups", he says. "Many of the bones belonged to young adult aurochs. They were very strong and dangerous. Animals of that age do not normally die together in such large numbers. For humans to kill such big mammals before bows and arrows were invented, they needed a group and a strategy".

The Neanderthals of Krapina, the Croatian cave discovered around the turn of the century and now dated at 130,000 years ago, had the barrel chest, robust limbs, broad, short body, and "occipital bun"—a bulge at the base of the skull—typical of classic Neanderthals.

"Certainly by 125,000 years ago they had become formidable hunters as well as gatherers of edible plants, shellfish, and small reptiles", says Mary Stiner. Neanderthals, Stiner explains, had been competing for food with other predators - wolves, hyenas, and lions. As their hunting skills developed, Neanderthals could start going after prey the other carnivores avoided—big, prime-age elk, bison, or even mammoths, whose meat provided more energy-laden fat. With enriched diets, Neanderthal populations probably expanded, increasing their impact on other species.

But the Neanderthals lacked elaborate weapons; they had to kill through co-operation. "Surrounding and confusing prey is a classic predatory tactic", says Kuhn. "A few co-operating hunters could have exploited natural landscape features like bogs and deep stream banks that put large animals at a disadvantage. They probably killed at close range with wooden spears that perhaps had a sharp stone point". A wooden spear nearly 8 feet long was found among the bones of a fossil elephant discovered in 1948 in a bog in Germany.

Hunting was not the only form of co-operation Neanderthals practised. They bonded into close social groups, as a collection of skeletons from a cave called Shanidar in Iraq poignantly illustrates. There, around 100,000 years ago, a man, two women, and an infant were buried together. Excavators found the pollen of early spring wildflowers in the soil around the corpses.

"I suspect they died of starvation in the late winter, when the stresses were greatest and the food resources leanest", says Erik Trinkaus, who spent the late 1970s studying the Shanidar specimens. Possibly the flowers were set around them by the rest of their social group, which suggests that they were thinking and caring about their dead.

We know they had fire to keep warm. Some cave floors are made almost entirely from compressed layers of ash many feet thick. Their hearths were simple, resembling camp-fires rather than the efficient, rock-lined fireplaces made by later humans.

From studies of the tools Neanderthals did use, researchers have begun to fill in the details of their technological skills. This is one of the few windows into the Neanderthal mind. To the uninitiated, Neanderthal tools-mostly sharp-edged flakes of stone that can be held in the hand—look as if they had been casually knapped off a piece of convenient rock with another stone. It was not so. Neanderthals might have travelled many miles to procure just the right pieces of flint. Sometimes they would carry their kill to sites near those rock sources.

"You need a lot of brains for flint knapping", says Jacques Pelegrin of the French Centre for Archaeological Research. "It would be like playing chess for us. You have to plan and organise how you are going to flake off each piece from the core rock ahead of time. Rocks are never standard. You have to adjust to the differences. Flint breaks under certain conditions. You have to learn those. It takes months, if not years, to learn to do it well. I have worked flint for years now and can say the techniques used by the Neanderthals are no less difficult than those used later by modern humans".

"The axe was perhaps a multipurpose tool", Pelegrin says. "Different edges of it were used for different purposes—cutting, butchering, scraping, defleshing. It was the Swiss army knife of its day. We get lots of information out of these. We might detect 300 scars on an axe, each made Neanderthals during its shaping. We know how to read the scars and then reconstruct how the axe was made. If I have only the by-products flaked off a piece of rock, I can tell you what kind of tool was made".

To make such tools, as well as to organise a co-operative hunt, Neanderthals must have been able to communicate and pass on their knowledge. Scientists have long argued about whether Neanderthals had the anatomical equipment for speech. Voice boxes and vocal tracts do not fossilise, but a small structure called the hyoid bone at the back of the tongue does. In modern humans the voice box hangs from this bone. In 1983 an intact hyoid bone was discovered in a 60,000-year-old Neanderthal skeleton excavated from a cave called Kebara in Israel.

"There's no way to distinguish this from one of our hyoid bones", says Rak. "So we can infer that Neanderthal voice boxes looked very much like ours and could make the same sounds".

But did they have language—the critical tool we use to store and pass on information and make sense of our world? "They may not have had a language as complex as ours", says Christopher Stringer, a paleoanthropologist at the Natural History Museum in London. "We have past, present, and future tenses. We have symbolism. They may not have had all that, but at least they could talk to each other". People of the past often speak most eloquently to us through their art. And here again the Neanderthals frustrate us. Before the last Neanderthal disappeared, modern humans were carving exquisite bone ornaments to adorn their bodies and painting the caves of southern France with magical, hypnotic portraits of wild animals.

Yet many scientists now suspect that the Neanderthals' ability to create art has been underestimated. They might have put their creativity into dance, costume, or carving wood, which usually decomposes. One of the few surviving Neanderthal "art objects"—a carved and polished ivory tooth from a baby mammoth—was excavated in 1958 at Tata in Hungary, a region that in Neanderthal times was a rich grassland.

Perhaps the two peoples (*Homo neanderthal* and *sapiens*) lived side by side for tens of thousands of years. Yet, during that time, the modern humans showed no signs that they had superior technology. Then, around 50,000 years ago, something profound happened. New technologies associated with modern humans—finer blades and projectile weapons—began to appear.

Scientists can only speculate on what triggered this technological spurt. "I think there was a mutation in the brains of a group of anatomically modern humans living either in Africa or the Middle East", says Richard Klein, an anthropologist at Stanford University. "Some new neurological connections let them behave in a modern way. May be it permitted fully articulate speech, so that they could pass on information more efficiently". Whatever the cause, around 40,000 years ago modern humans moved into Europe, armed with innovations—such as tailored clothing, better shelters, and more efficient hearths—that let them survive the cold of glacial Europe, previously the exclusive domain of Neanderthals. Nineteenth-century scientists named these newcomers the Cro-Magnon people, after a French rock-shelter by that name where three anatomically modern human skeletons were discovered in 1868.

What happened when this new culture met the Neanderthals remains a hotly debated mystery. Our own recent history suggests that there would have been some violence.

A woman's skull, some flaked tools, and the bones of an ibex—a wild goat—offer mute testimony to the Neanderthal presence on Gibraltar. The Iberian peninsula may have been the last refuge of these enigmatic people. Not so long ago in our history, humans of another kind walked the glacial shores here. And looking back, we can almost make out their footprints, hear their voices fade.

Some bones at Vindija, for instance, appear slightly more slender and graceful than classic Neanderthal bones. Does that imply that Neanderthals in central Europe were beginning to interbreed with groups of modern humans arriving from the Middle East? While some scholars think that "Neanderthal genes persist in modern Europeans today", others like Spoor reject this idea: "They were a different species". (Quoatations from Gore in *National Geographic* 1996: 4-35.)

Ward and Stringer (1997: 225-26) admit that the sequencing of mitochondrial DNA from Neanderthal fossil bone is a terrific achievement. Among the conclusions to be drawn from the data is that there was a period of more than 500,000 years during which Neanderthals and the line leading to modern humans evolved independently.

This implies that the Neanderthals' divergence is of considerable antiquity, dating 555,000 to 690,000 years ago. This is about four times greater than the time back to the common ancestor of modern human mtDNA (120,000 to 150,000 years). These molecular results, then, imply that there was a period of roughly half a million years of independent evolution of Neanderthals and the line leading to modern humans. This, in turn, suggests that the divergence might have occurred at about the time that the two main lines of *Homo heidelbergensis* became distinct in Europe and Africa respectively. Such a scheme of events implies that the Mid-Pleistocene forms of *H. heidelbergensis* in Europe may have eventually led to early Neanderthals, such as the specimens from Atapuerca in Spain, and ultimately to the 'classic' forms found at Krapina, in

Croatia, and at Neander itself. Conversely, modern humans are likely to have evolved from transitional groups of archaic *Homo sapiens*, such as those found at Guomde and Floisbad, in East and South Africa respectively, which in turn were independently derived from later *H. heidelbergensis* forms in Africa. Intriguingly, still other forms of humans may have survived in Southeast Asia.

Given the quality of the new molecular findings, the study of ancient human DNA can, at long last, be said to be on a secure footing. As additional molecular data of increasing complexity are produced, the near future looks set to be truly revolutionary time for students of human evolution (Ward and Stringer 1997: 225-26).

Homo sapiens

The Neanderthal origins are dated to about 130,000 BP, and *Homo sapiens* are considered younger than them. But the findings from Ethiopia show that the so-called Kibish man may be equally old. It is interesting to quote Stringer and Mackie (1996) about these discoveries. They say that the Kibish man's bones remained in Addis Ababa and "Researchers did not realise it at the time, but scrutiny of those few bone fragments would prove to be crucial in a fundamental rethink about the evolution of our species".

Stringer and Mackie describe the man from Kibish to be quite different from Neanderthals - and that is because he was a member of our own species, *Homo sapiens*. And give or take some fragmentary bones from other parts of Africa, he is the most ancient direct kin for which fossils have been discovered. His bones were found by an expedition led by Richard Leakey. His subsequent discoveries have provided science with significant insights into our very distant past and have quite overshadowed Leakey's own work at Kibish, one of his earliest expeditions. At the time, he was acting on behalf of his father, Louis, and was leading the Kenyan contingent of a joint French-American-Kenyan trek to the Omo-Kibish region. Its aim was to investigate the sediments lying on either side of the lower reaches of the Omo river where it widens and flows south towards Lake Turkana in north Kenya.... No volcanic rocks, which often supply important geological and chronological data, were found around the site. However, samples of shells collected from well above the level of the Kibish dig were dated to around 40,000 years ago, indicating that the bones, which were found far below this sequence of beds, must be far older. In addition, shells from the same level as the Kibish site were dated - using a special technique known as uranium-series dating - to around 130,000 years old.

At the time, by the standards of other African finds, this seemed an unremarkable date for a supposedly primitive human being. However, after proper studies had been carried out, researchers found that the ancient skull and skeleton of Kibish man resembled those of modern humans in a number of ways. It was then that the importance of the find began to be appreciated, as Leakey (1983) recalls in *One Life*: "Geological investigations and dating have shown that the two skulls are about 130,000 years old, yet despite their antiquity they are both clearly identifiable as *Homo sapiens*, our own species. At the time of their discovery, scientists generally believed that our species had only emerged in the last 60,000 years and many considered the famous Neanderthal Man to be the immediate precursor to ourselves. The Omo fossils thus provided important evidence that this was not so".

These discoveries led a few researchers in the 1970s to conclude that the Kibish man was a far more likely ancestor for the Cro-Magnons, a race of early Europeans who thrived about 23,000 years ago, than their immediate predecessors, the heavy-set Neanderthal. Then in the 1980s, a new reconstruction and study of the Kibish Man revealed an even more startling possibility - that he was a far better candidate as the forebear, not just for the Cro-Magnons but for every one of us alive today, not just Europeans but all the other peoples of the world, from the Eskimos of Greenland to the pygmies of Africa, and from Australian aborigines to native Americans. In other words, the Kibish man acted as pathfinder for a new genesis for the human species.... Many palaeontologists, anthropologists and geneticists have come to agree that this ancient resident of the river-banks of Ethiopia and all his Kibish kin - both far and near - could indeed be one of our ancestors. However, it has also become clear that the evolutionary pathway of these fledgling modern humans was not an easy one. At one stage, according to genetic data, our species became as endangered as the mountain gorilla is today, its population reduced to only about 10,000 adults. Restricted to one region of Africa, but tempered in the flames of near extinction, this population went on to make a remarkable comeback. It then spread across Africa until - by about 100,000 years ago - it had colonised much of the continent's savannahs and woodlands. We see the imprint of this spread in biological studies which have revealed that races within Africa are genetically the most disparate on the planet, indicating that modern humans have existed there in larger numbers, for a longer time than anywhere else (Stringer and MacKie 1996).

In the neglected western branch of the African Rift valley, at the town of Katanda erosion has produced an archaeological treasure-trove: thousands of artefacts, mostly stone tools, plus a few bone implements that quite astonished the archaeologists led by the husband-and-wife team of John Yellen, of the National Science Foundation, Washington, and Alison Brooks, of the George Washington University. Among the wonders they have uncovered are sophisticated bone harpoons and knives. Previously it was thought that the Cro-Magnons were the first humans to develop such delicate carving skills—50,000 years later. Yet this very much older group of *Homo sapiens*, living in the heartland of Africa, displayed the same extraordinary skills as craftsmen. It was as if, said one observer, a prototype Pontiac car had been found in the attic of Leonardo da Vinci (Stringer & MacKie 1996).

As we mentioned above, except for the skull-cap from the Narmada valley, India does not have any hominid remains to boast of. Of course, M. Singh of Chandigarh has claimed discoveries of hominid teeth, etc. from the Siwaliks, but there are still controversies about their true affiliation. Also Sri Lanka has yielded hominid fossils, though of more recent age.

SOUTH ASIAN PALAEOLITHIC CULTURES

Introduction

Robert Brucefoot was the first to discover a Palaeolith in India in 1863. Palaeolithic research in India is, therefore, 140 years' old. But it got a real fillip only with the coming of the Yale-Cambridge Expedition of 1935. Today quite a few organisations and universities are working on Stone Age research, yet the evidence is very scanty compared to the European or African situation, while publications are few and far between. The Stone Age has been divided in various ways, each with its different nomenclature: Series I, II, III; Early, Middle and Upper Palaeolithic; and Early, Middle and Late Stone Age. The term Palaeolithic is now widely accepted and has been adopted here.

In the nineteenth century a large number of Palaeolithic sites were discovered all over India excepting the northern alluvial corridor and Kerala. For the absence of traces of early humans in these two regions there could be two main reasons. Either they avoided this area because of dense forests and lack of raw material, or the recent alluvium has covered the older sites. In other regions, Palaeolithic tools have been found from plateaus, river terraces and even hill slopes - thus no ecological preferences can be discerned. Kashmir was thought to be devoid of the tools of Palaeolithic man until recently when there also some artifacts have been reported, though our extensive work in the 1980s in the valley did not produce any definitive evidence of Palaeoliths

(Agrawal 1992).

For long it was thought that cave sites were only casually used by Palaeolithic humans in India but in recent years some rich habitation sites have come to light (Map 3-2). Sanghao (Parkho Darra cave), north of Peshawar in Pakistan, yielded the Middle Palaeolithic tools, bones and charcoal in plenty from a deposit 3m deep. Better documented is the site of Bhimbetka on the Vindhyas near Bhopal (MP). A large number of cave shelters were occupied here from the Early Palaeolithic to Mesolithic times but unfortunately no faunal or floral remains have survived. Renigunta in Andhra is also an important Upper Palaeolithic site with a rich repertoire of stone and bone tools and remains of animals.

To define the start of the Early Palaeolithic, we will have to first define the boundary between the Pliocene and Pleistocene epochs, referred to as N/Q (Neogene/Quaternary) boundary in geological parlance. It may however be noted that now that hominid antiquity is going back beyond 2 Myr, N/Q boundary is no more that important for the study of early humans.

N/Q Boundary

Lyell (1839) had replaced the older term "newer Pliocene" by Pleistocene and included in it the sediments which yielded 90-95% molluscan species which are still living. Now the term "Neogene/Quaternary" (N/Q) boundary is preferred. In 1948, the International Geological Congress placed the N/Q boundary at the base of the 1600m thick sediment section at Le Castella in Calabria (Italy), marking the first appearance of deep water foraminifera *Hyalinea balthica* and the mollusc, *Arctica islandica*. And for the continental sequences, appearance of *Elephas, Leptobos, Equus*, etc., were considered the markers of the N/Q boundary.

The following criteria for the marine sediments are now accepted more universally:

1. Extinction of the Discosters which had flourished during the previous 75 Myr.
2. Extinction of *Globigerinoides sacculifer fistulosus* above the N/Q boundary.
3. First appearance of *Globorotalia truncatulinoides*.
4. Ninety-five per cent of the *Globorotalia menardii* left coiling above the N/Q boundary and 95% right coiling below the boundary.
5. Olduvai sub-chron on the magnetic polarity scale dated 1.8 to 1.6 Myr.

The situation is a bit more complex on the continents as the Pleistocene mammals could not have made a simultaneous appearance all over the world. The Russian palaeontologists prefer the term Anthropogene (marking the advent of humans) to Quaternary and include in it Eopleistocene and Pleistocene; the latter term there includes only the Brunhes chron (< 730 Kyr). Now that hominid antiquity has gone back to 4.3 Myr in Ethiopia, demarcating Anthropogene at 1.8 Myr does not make much sense. In Russia the Anthropogene boundary is marked by the end of the Kuruksay suite fauna and the advent of the Kayrubak suite.

In North America the N/Q boundary is marked by the end of the Biancan and the emergence of the lrvingtonian fauna which includes *Mammuthus, Lepus, Dipodomys, Ondatra*, etc. In Europe, on the other hand, quite a few species appear at the Olduvai sub-chron. The Biharian faunas mark the generally accepted N/Q boundary in Europe, for example, *Eucladocerus tetraceros* and *Cervus prolensis*. The species that come to an extinction around this time are: *Eucladocerus sene, Cervus philisi philisi, Croizet ramosus minor, C. ramosus medius*, gazella and antelopes. We thus see that on the basis of appearance or disappearance of certain fauna it is not possible to define N/Q boundary on land for the whole globe. It is therefore better to have an absolute time marker as the N/Q boundary and not any faunal succession.

With this background we will now examine the problem of the N/Q boundary in the Indian context.

Zeuner (1946) had based his definition of the Plio-Pleistocene boundary on three main criteria: 1. The changes in marine fauna. 2. The appearance of *Equus* (horse), *Bos* (cattle) and *Elephas* (elephant). 3. The advent of the first major glaciation, the Alpine Gunz. In India, traditionally, the advent of *Equus, Bos, Rhinoceros, Elephas*, etc. was taken as the beginning of the Lower Pleistocene. But in terms of absolute time this boundary is not defined, at least unanimously. We will first review the palaeontological findings in terms of traditional Plio-Pleistocene and then discuss the problem of the Plio-Pleistocene boundary in absolute temporal scales.

There have been extensive surveys of fossils in the Karewas of Kashmir, the Narmada basin, the Siwaliks, the Deccan river valleys and the Kurnool caves. But in view of the large size of the subcontinent, the fossiliferous sites are meagre due to erosion in the Himalayan foothills and presence of few sedimentary troughs in the subcontinent.

One of the richest fossiliferous basins is that of the Narmada in Central India. Till recently, the Narmada alluvium was considered a type-site for post-Villafranchian fauna in India. Recent work in the peninsular valleys of the Godavary, the Bhima, the Pravara, etc., has shown that the so-called Middle Pleistocene fauna (*Equus namadicus, Bos namadicus, Elephas hysudricus, Stegodon insignis*-ganesa) in fact continues into the Upper Pleistocene. *Stegodon insignis*-ganesa, *Equus namadicus* and *Elephas hysudricus* also occur in the Lower Pleistocene levels of the Siwaliks. *Bos namadicus* survives into the Holocene and has been reported from Langhnaj; so also the species like *Elephas maximus, Cervus duvauceli* and *Rhinoceros unicornis*. Therefore only *Hexaprotodon namadicus* and *Sus namadicus* may be considered as the Middle Pleistocene index fossils.

The situation becomes a bit more complicated as Lower Palaeolithic stone tools have been assigned, on the grounds of faunal associations, a Middle Pleistocene age in the Narmada valley. But some of the Middle Palaeolithic sites have been ^{14}C dated to younger than 40 Kyr in the Narmada basin. On the other hand, the whole of the Narmada sequence has shown a normal polarity as a result of our recent work, which means that the Narmada is not older than 700 Kyr (Brunhes chron). The Boulder Conglomerate (1) Zone of the Narmada has also yielded a scull cap of *Homo erectus* (Sonakia 1985). A little contamination in the old ^{14}C samples can bring them into the dating range but actually they may be beyond the ^{14}C range and therefore the available ^{14}C dates need not be taken as evidence of accurate dates for the Narmada formations.

The evidence from Kashmir, as will be discussed below, and from the Pakistan Siwaliks (Opdyke *et al.* 1979), is now clear, as a result of palaeomagnetic and fission track dating, that the so-called Lower Pleistocene fauna *(Equus sivalensis, Cervus s., Elephas,* etc.) can now be securely dated to the Matuyama chron (2.4 Myr).

Of the Indian fauna, the progressive groups, possibly of local origins, were the primates, giraffe-like forms, musk deer, goats, buffaloes, bovids and pigs. The fauna that were common with Europe are the sabre-toothed cats, hyena, wolves, rhinoceros, genus *Equus*, various deer, antelopes and hippopotamia. The migratory routes lay east and west of the Himalayas, and most of the larger animals migrated from Egypt, Arabia, Central Asia and North America through passes across Alaska, Siberia and Mongolia (Pilgrim 1925) and the animals came through Burma and China in the east and through Baluchistan from the west.

Recent work in Nepal provides better chronological controls. Yoshida and Gautam (1988) have dated the deposits in Nepal using palaeomagnetic techniques. There the Lukundol Formation spans a long period: covering both Pliocene and the Pleistocene. The Members I and II cover the uppermost part of the Gauss chron (3-2.5 Myr); the Members III to VII span both Matuyama and Brunhes chrons. From Members II to IV (circa 2.9 to 1 Myr) were recovered *Elephas planifrons, Stegodon ganesa, Hexaprotodon sivalensis, Elephas hysudricus* and *Crocodylits* sp.

The Lukundol fauna corresponds to the Pinjor fauna of the Siwaliks and does not appear after Member IV, around 0.9 Myr. In the Siwaliks also such fauna does not occur after the Jaramillo sub-chron (0.9 Myr). Yoshida and Gautam (1988) place the Plio-Pleistocene boundary in the silt bed 25m below the base of Member V coinciding with the Olduvai sub-chron of the Matuyama chron.

The Yale-Cambridge Expedition led by de Terra and Paterson (1939) connected the Kashmir glacial deposits with the alluvial sediments of the Potwar area in West Punjab by correlating the outwash of the II Glaciation with the Potwar Boulder Conglomerate. de Terra assigned Dhok Pathan beds to Pliocene and Tatrot to Lower Pleistocene. *Equus* and *Elephas* appear first in the Tatrot beds. Later workers like Gill, Gannser, Sahni and Khan have disagreed with de Terra and Paterson's findings. Sahni and Khan assigned the Pinjor beds to Early Pleistocene because of the association of *Equus*, *Bubalus* and *Rhinoceroses*. They find an unconformity between the Lower and the Upper Conglomerate; the latter is equated with the II Glaciation and ascribed to the Middle Pleistocene.

de Terra and Paterson applied the fourfold Alpine glacial sequence to Kashmir too. Later workers have, however, suggested three to 8 cycles of glaciation. Porter (1970: 1421-26) worked in Swat Kohistan in Pakistan, which is almost the counterpart of Kashmir, and gave (see Table 3.1) the following threefold sequence.

TABLE 3.1 PORTER'S (1970) STRATIGRAPHY FOR SWAT VALLEY

Stratigraphic Units	*Climatic*
Kalam Drift (K) Glaciation	Kalam
Kalam I Drift	Early Stade
Kalam II Drift	Intermediate Stade
Kalam III Drift	Late Stade
Gabral Drift (G)	Gabral Glaciation
Gabral I Drift	Early Stade
Gabral II Drift	Late Stade
Laikot Drift (L)	Laikot Glaciation

Porter's threefold glacial sequence does not recognise any interglacials but only stadial periods, which means that warmer conditions never prevailed for any length of time.

In Kashmir both plant and animal fossils have been reported for the last 150 years but with our recent work (Agrawal *et al.* 1989; Agrawal 1992) mega-vertebrates have been put into an absolute time bracket. *Cervus punjabiensis*, *C. sivalensis*, *Equus sivalensis*, *Elephas hysudricus*, *Canis vitasternsis*, etc. employing both palaeomagnetic and fission track techniques have been dated to the beginning of the Matuyama chron (2.4 Myr). Other fauna and macro-vertebrates have also been dated there but we need not go into these details here.

When Kashmir and the north was under glacial ice, what was happening in the rest of the subcontinent? Did rainy or dry conditions prevail there? This problem of correlating glacials and pluvials (rainy conditions) has been a subject of polemics the world over, though now there is some consensus that the glacials were coeval with dry periods in the lower latitudes.

In peninsular India river deposits indicate only one intense pluvial period marked by the lower boulder gravel which also contains the Early Palaeolithic tools. Thereafter, there were only one or more minor pluvials. The same story is repeated in Saurashtra, Gujarat. Rajaguru and Joshi suggested a correlation between pluvials and glacials. Increased rainfall requires more heat to warm up the subcontinent, but the glaciation in the north must have led to a lowering of temperature further south which would attract a less powerful monsoon. This model would equate glacials in the north with an interpluvial (dry) phase in the south. Singh's pollen studies of Rajasthan lakes also indicate an intense pre-Holocene aridity which may be equated with the last glaciation of Kashmir and the north.

Zeuner had once suggested that changing sea-levels may provide a basis for such correlations, as the sea-level will fall when a lot of water is locked up during glaciation in the form of ice in the glaciers. We have shown that the sea-level on the west coast of India rose by 5m at around 5000 BP. It is interesting to find that a wetter phase (pollen zone C) occurred in Rajasthan about that time. Gupta has reported two more rises of the sea-level in Saurashtra at 30,000 and 120,000 BP. Did they correspond to interglacials or stadials in Kashmir?

Below we shall discuss the Palaeolithic cultures in India, which for convenience we have divided into five zones: north, west, central, east and south. The earliest human occupation of India known to us at present belongs to the Lower Palaeolithic stage of prehistory. Two cultures or technological traditions are known from this stage. These are: (1) the Sohanian, represented by pebble tools (choppers and chopping tools), flakes and cores, and (2) the Acheulian, represented by bifaces (hand-axes and cleavers), a variety of scrapers, flakes, blades, and cores.

PALAEOLITHIC CULTURES OF THE NORTH

Kashmir

The Kashmir valley is separated from the plains by the steeply-rising Pir Panjal range. Pir Panjal was uplifted to 5,000m during the Pleistocene period itself. Today it grows paper birch, rhododendron and juniper, but no trees grow above 4,000 m. The rolling upland is covered by alpine type meadows, termed *marg* in the local dialect. The boat-shaped vale of Kashmir is surrounded by the steep Pir Panjal hills on the south-west and the Himalayas on the north-east. As one enters the valley, the cultivated fields of maize and rice appear rather abruptly after the forested hills at 2,000 m. The Karewas, terraced foothills, are the remnants of lake beds of the N/Q period, divisible into the Lower and the Upper Karewas. The Karewas gently merge into the valley proper at about 1800 m. Up to 2,300m deodar (*Cedrus deodara*), pine and walnut mingle with poplar, willow, elm and horse chestnut. It is said that some of the tree species were imported into Kashmir by the Mughals. The moraines of the Pleistocene glaciations are well preserved on the Sind and Liddar river valleys. de Terra and Paterson discovered five terraces in the Kashmir valley. Terraces I and III were caused by erosion during interglacial periods when the ice melted and great streams of water were released. Terraces II, IV and V were aggradational and were formed due to the filling up of the valley by ice.

The only radiocarbon-dated pollen sequence from the bogs of Toshmaidan in Kashmir shows that deglaciation here started around 15,000 BP (Singh & Agrawal 1976: 232). The pollen data yield a cold-warm-cold sequence starting from the date of deglaciation.

The complete absence of Palaeoliths from Kashmir appeared quite understandable as it was an intensely cold region during glacial times. Moreover, the Pir Panjal range of the Outer Himalayas was continuously rising and causing violent tectonic disturbances. But in 1969, Sankalia *et al.* reported Palaeoliths from Kashmir.

The first discovery of a massive flake and a crude hand-axe was made near Pahalgam, 65 km east of Srinagar. The massive flake (26 x 17 x 6 cm) showed stepped flaking on one side only and was found in the Boulder Conglomerate of the Liddar valley, dateable to the II glacial. Sankalia, however, feels that it should belong to the I Interglacial. This would make it the earliest industry in the subcontinent, as it should then fall in the Lower Pleistocene period. A crude hand-axe was also discovered from the boundary of Boulder Conglomerate and Brown Clay and thus both on technological and stratigraphic grounds it may be considered the earliest hand-axe in Asia. Whether both this flake and the hand-axe are products of the culture or are separate entities cannot be resolved at this stage.

A variety of scrapers made of quartzite, three borers of quartz schist, a roughly rectangular quartzite core and a hand-axe-cum-chopper, were found later by Sankalia *et al.* from the deposits on the river Liddar, near Pahalgam, dating variously to II Glacial, II Interglacial and III Glacial. There is a total of only 10 tools covering hundreds of thousands of years, but one would need a larger number of indubitable tools to accept the presence of Palaeolithic man in inhospitable Kashmir. We also collected some Palaeolith-like objects from Kashmir but later on discarded them as despite our 10 years' survey in the region we could not find a factory-site or primary site in Kashmir.

Potwar and Sohan valley

The glacial sequence had to be correlated with that of the plains and de Terra and Paterson found the Potwar region (West Punjab, Pakistan) ideally suited for this purpose. The river valleys were also rich in Palaeoliths. Potwar is an elevated undulating land, lying between Pir Panjal and the Salt Range. (We have used here de Terra and Paterson's terminology and chronology, but recent work in Pakistan by Rendell *et al.* has found many of their conclusions untenable, as we will discuss below.)

The upper Siwaliks in Jammu are formed by the Boulder Conglomerate. This is a glacial deposit comprising faceted rocks and erratic in the valleys of Tawi and Poonch, belonging to the II Glaciation. The Boulder Conglomerate forms the topmost surface in the Indus and Sohan valleys in the Potwar area and provides the link with the II Glaciation of Kashmir. The bones of *Elephas namadicus* would place the deposit around the Middle Pleistocene date.

As mentioned earlier, this whole area was experiencing tectonic movements. In the vale of Kashmir the lake was cut up and the river Jhelum emerged during II Interglacial, but now dated by us to about 85 Kyr. The Boulder Conglomerate formation in Potwar area also became tilted and the rivers started cutting into the conglomerate and thus originated the rivers Indus and Sohan. In this process was formed Terrace I, a thin re-deposit of the Boulder Conglomerate. A pebble-culture industry (chopper-chopping complex of Sohan industry) was reported from Terrace I, which also contained hand-axes.

It may be recalled that the hand-axe is common to both European and African Palaeolithic cultures. Pebble tools and cleavers are absent in Europe, but present both in Africa and India. In Central Asia and China no hand-axes have ever been found, only pebble tools occur there. Did the hand-axe and the pebble tool traditions meet in the Potwar area for the first time? Or are they part of the same culture here?

Sohan Culture

A pebble tool is made from split pebbles by flaking them, and these pebble tools abound in the Potwar area. The early Sohan (Fig. 3-1) culture, named after the Sohan river, is marked by choppers and Clacton flakes, named after Clacton-on-Sea, England, where they were first found (the latter are detached by a swinging blow resulting in an angle of about 120° between the striking platform and the flake surface). The Late Sohan shows prepared cores and parallel-sided flakes (Fig. 3-2). According to the degree of patination (weathering) the Early Sohan industry of Terrace I has been divided into A, B and C groups. Group A is associated with the flakes which still have the original cortex and the striking platform is unprepared. Group C flakes show extensive primary flaking and prepared platforms. The pebble choppers are made on quartzite or trap.

Pl. 3-1. Isampur, Lower Palaeolithic site. Trench 1, 45cm depth

Pl. 3-2. Hammer stones from Isampur Excavations. Left to right: chert, quartzite, basalt. Lower Palaeolithic

Pl. 3-3. Limestone bifaces from Isampur excavations. Lower Palaeolithic site

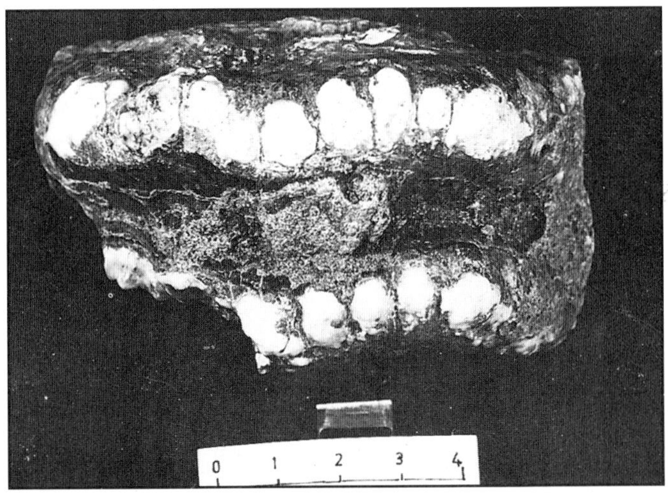

Pl. 3-4. Tooth fragment of extinct elephant (*Stegodon insignis ganesa*). Manjra valley, dist. Beed, Maharashtra

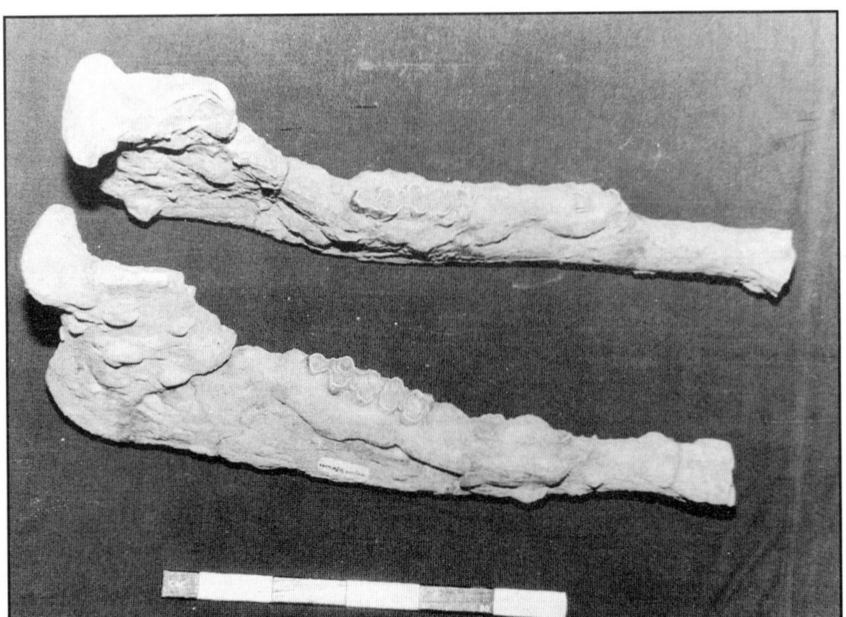

Pl. 3-5. Lower jaw of extinct buffalo, Barmanghat, central Narmada, MP. Lower Middle Pleistocene

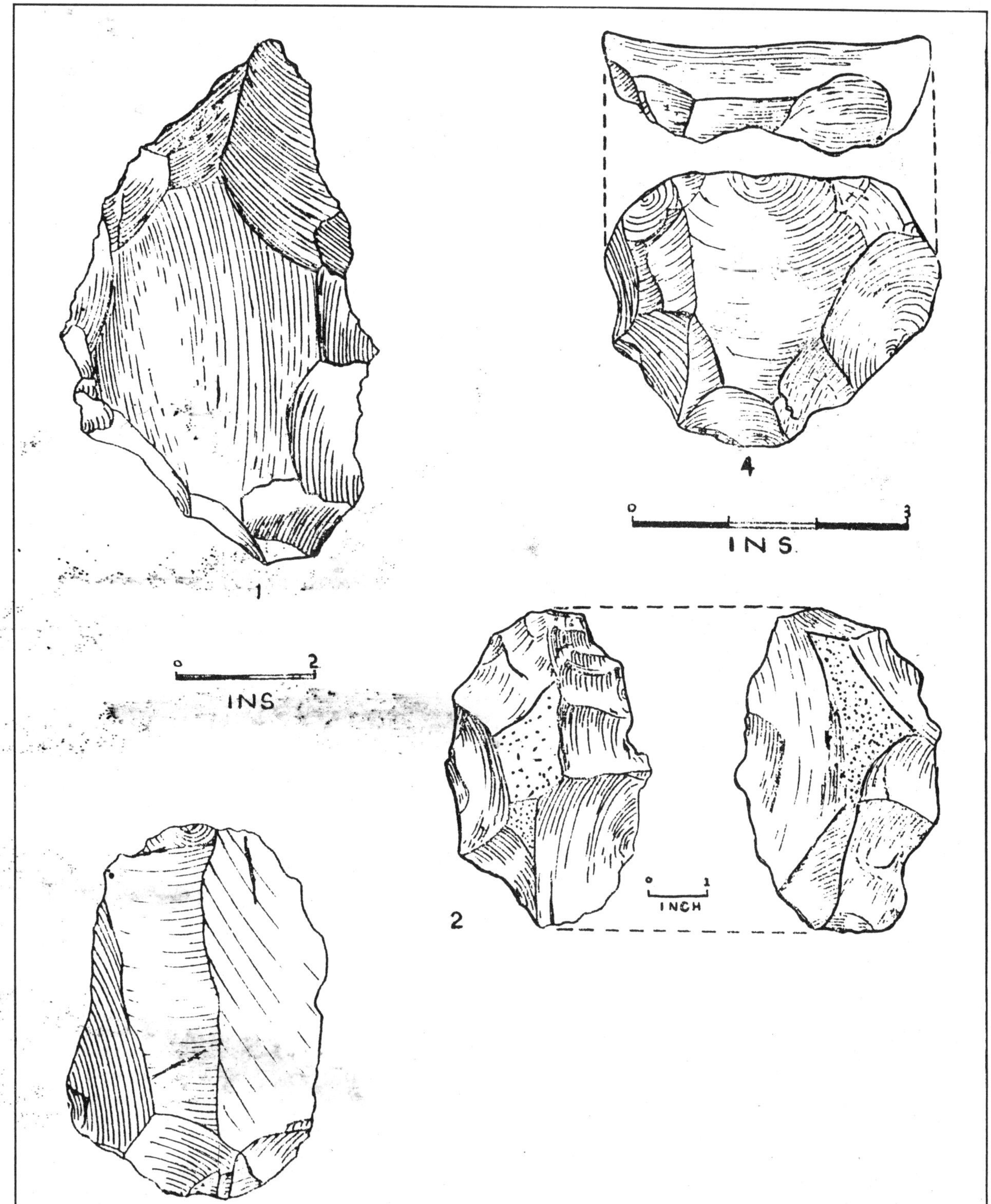

Fig. 3-1. Early Sohan flakes and cores (after Sankalia 1974)

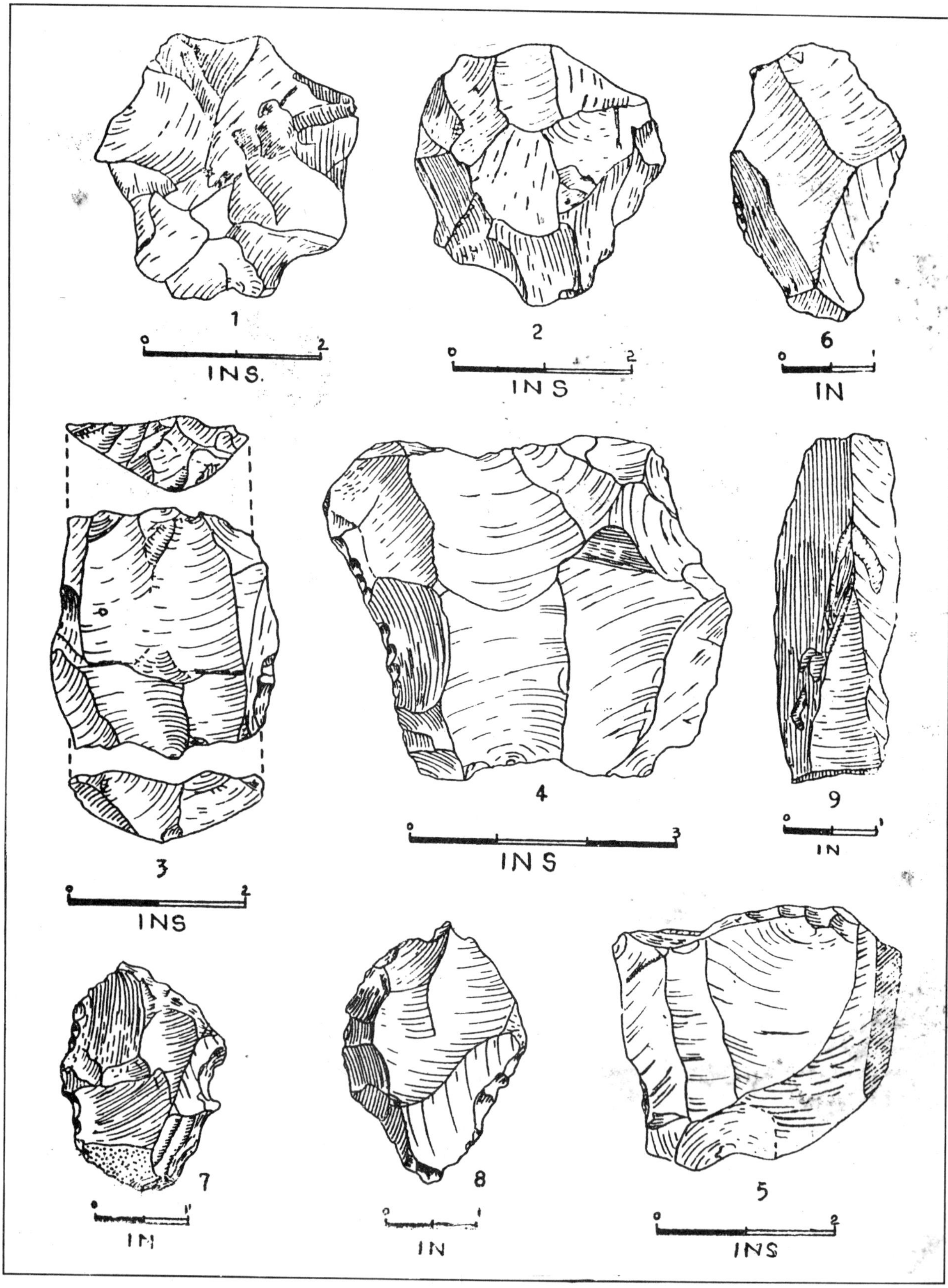

Fig. 3-2. Late Sohan flakes and cores (after Sankalia 1974)

Terrace II, correspon-ding to III Glaciation, still continues to yield pebble tools and Clacton flakes, though some carefully prepared cores and parallel-sided and elongated flakes are found along with them. On the basis of its Levallo-isean character, the Late Sohan A industry is said to belong to the Middle Pleistocene. (In the Levallo-isean technique the core is dressed to obtain a flat surface, then a blow is struck resulting in thin broad flakes. It was named after a suburb of Paris where the technique was first recognised.) In the Late Sohan B almost half of the flakes have trimmed surfaces and faceted striking platforms, analogo-us to the Late Levalloisean industry of Europe. The Late Sohan B industry appears in the upper part of the Potwar loess; Terrace II and the Late Sohan A occurs in the underlying gravel of this terrace. More than a score of the Late Sohan B sites are known. Near Pindi Gheb, a similar industry was reported from Dhok Patan.

The Sohan valley also yielded hand-axes or bifaces from stratigraphical contexts of II Interglacial (Terrace I) and III Glacial (Terrace II). Only at a site near Rawalpindi were found hand-axes from the earliest level, unmixed with the Sohan industry. At other sites like Adial, Balwal and Chauntra, hand-axes occur with the Early and the Late Sohan artifacts. Later discoveries have shown that both hand-axes and the Sohan industries are associated with similar horizons and, therefore, it is difficult to say which industry is earlier if they are separate industries at all! Both crude, massive and round butted forms (Abbevillian) and more refined, heart-shaped types (Acheulian) with the cortex completely stripped off are found together from the earliest levels and therefore no time-gap can be postulated for the evolution of the hand-axe industry from the Abevillian to the Acheulian stages.

To sum, de Terra and Paterson (1939) reported Early Sohan tools from Terrace I (T1) of the Sohan river (a tributary of the Indus river) cut into the Boulder Conglomerate of Second Glacial Age in the Potwar plateau of Pakistan. They also found Acheulian tools in the same deposit, though at discrete localities. They dated T1 to the Second Interglacial age in the fourfold scheme of Pleistocene glaciation that they had proposed for the Himalayas. The faunal remains from this deposit included the horse, buffalo, straight-tusked elephant and hippopotamus, suggesting an environment characterised by perennial water sources, tree vegetation and grass steppes. Younger deposits showed the Sohan industry to have evolved over time. T2, with gravel at the base and loess on top, and dating to the Third Glacial period, yielded Acheulian and Late Sohan A industries from the basal gravels. Late Sohan A comprised refined pebble choppers and Levallois flakes. The overlying loess of the same terrace produced the Late Sohan B industry, characterised by Levallois flakes and blades and by the complete absence of Acheulian elements. The fauna of this horizon included horse, bovids, camel and wolf (Wadia 1928:287).

The two tool traditions of chopper chopping tools and hand-axes (Acheulian) have been generally considered quite separate. Sheila Misra (1994) mentions that the Sub-Himalayan region has been considered a region of the non-Acheulian Lower Palaeolithic industries, the Sohan. A major focus of work on the Lower Palaeolithic in this region, therefore, has been to understand the Sohan phenomenon in relation to the Acheulian. Most workers consider that the Sohan/ Acheulian differences are related to biocultural differences, or adaptations to different environments. The discovery of a number of Acheulian sites in the Sub- Himalayan region, has destroyed the geographical identity of the Sohan (Mohapatra 1982; Corvinus 1990). Rendell and Dennell (1985) have found hand-axes at Jalapur and Dina in the Jhelum basin in sediments just above the Bruhnes/Matuyama boundary, and date them to between 0.5 and 0.7 Myr. Mohapatra, finds that the Acheulian industry occurs in a geomorphic context which is later than the Sohan, and considers that the Acheulian "just touched the outer fringe of the western Sub-Himalayas for a short while" (Mohapatra 1990: 257). He notices that while the Sohanian artefacts are mainly made on cobbles, the Acheulian utilised large flakes detached from boulders for preparing bifaces. Gaillard (1994) has contrasted the reduction sequences of the Early Acheulian from Singi Talav Rajasthan with some of the Sohan assemblages, and finds the technologies are distinctive, although at the same level of complexity. Recently, Corvinus (1994) has located two Acheulian sites in Nepal. The Acheulian in Nepal occurs in the earliest post-Siwalik sediments. While the distinctiveness of the Sohan tradition is fairly well documented, the explanation for this variation is not well understood. Archaeologists have traditionally attributed differences in artefacts to differences in cultures, and have only gradually realised that in the Lower Palaeolithic period we do not know if cultural differences existed. Presently, differences in raw material and preservation along with functional and use history of the artefacts are considered more important factors in explaining variations in the Lower Palaeolithic. Dennell and Rendell (1991) do not consider the Sohan as forming a distinct entity from the Acheulian. Jayaswal (1982) shows that pebble tools are a part of many of the Acheulian industries from the peninsular region (Sheila Mishra 1994: 57-64).

V.N. Misra (1989: 17-27) also says that many archaeologists have found it difficult to accept the coexistence of two distinct technological traditions in close proximity without any influence on each other. Salim's recent work also confirms these observations. The Sohan terraces turn out to be erosional features rather than true depositional terraces. As the archaeological material found by de Terra and Paterson all came from the surface, it cannot be associated with any specific deposit nor for the same reason can it be dated. The Mission members were unable to corroborate the existence of an independent Sohanian technological tradition though they found artefacts of Acheulian and other traditions. Misra, however, thinks that geological and archaeological findings on the Indian side appear to agree with de Terra and Paterson's observations in Pakistan. Five terraces similar to those of the Indus-Sohan in the Potwar region have been recognised in the valleys of the Sutlej, Beas, Banganga and other rivers in the Punjab-Himachal Pradesh region. Pebble tools of Sohanian style have been collected on the older of these terraces (Lal 1956). Mohapatra (1976), who has discovered both Sohanian and Acheulian sites in the Hoshiarpur-Chandigarh sector of the Siwalik hills, has argued that the Acheulian and Sohanian populations inhabited two distinct types of environment, the former occupying the flat surfaces of the Siwalik frontal range and the latter the duns or valleys of the Himalayan flank (Misra 1989:17-27).

Reporting on his recent explorations in the Sohan valley in Rawalpindi, Salim (1992: 83-86) says that many collections of Lower and Middle Palaeolithic were observed and recorded. "In August 1993 near Gurha Shahan, while examining quartzitic Upper Siwalik Conglomerate and silts and sands, artefacts were recorded from both these geological deposits. The silts and sands are labelled by de Terra and Paterson (1939: 281, Fig. 162) as Pinjor, underlying the conglomerate. This stratigraphic position and succession of Palaeolithic cultures is illustrated here, where Pinjor deposits are sandwiched between Tatrot below and conglomerate above. No previous worker had reported any artefacts from Pinjor zone from Potwar. The Stratigraphic Committee of Pakistan (Fatmi 1974) had accepted to adopt Sohan formation terminology for Tatrot-Pinjor-Conglomerate stages. The Sohan formation was originally proposed by Kravtchenko (1964: 230) for Upper Siwalik deposits in the Sohan valley. For archaeological purposes, it can be regarded as a separate unit, from where one can study variations in Palaeolithic assemblages. The importance of these finds is that at present they are the earliest in Pakistan coming from within the old geological deposits, which lie below the Conglomerate". On the basis of palaeomagnetic dating he places them between 2 and 2.4 million years (Salim 1992: 83-86). Salim visited the Gurha Shahan area and studied geological sections to determine the stratigraphic position of sands and silts. These silts along with Conglomerate deposits were examined near Dhok Kantral and Bhandar Nala and Shami confirmed that silts and sands represent Pinjor and they lie at the base of Upper Siwalik Conglomerate (Salim 1992). Salim has also briefly reported the Pinjor and Upper Siwalik Conglomerate sites. He says that the Boulder Conglomerate of de Terra and Paterson (1939: 28 -82) is now called Upper Siwalik Conglomerate consisting of quartzite, sandstone, limestone and other rocks. It is different in age and composition from the Lei Conglomerate of limestone, which lies above it. From milestone 163, G.T. Road site, de Terra and Paterson (1939: 282) had reported pre-Sohan flakes from this quartzitic Conglomerate. Recent building activity has exposed a large area of this Conglomerate. From within this deposit not only rolled flakes and cores but also typical Acheulian cleavers, hand-axes, and scrapers were collected. During their survey of Potwar, de Terra and Paterson collected a few artefacts in rolled condition, which according to them were typologically different. Salim thinks that with such recent finds the pre-Sohan label can be discarded and in its place Acheulian terminology could be retained. It is from the same Conglomerate, a core was reported and dated to 2 Myr by Rendell *et al.* (1987: 488).

Pinjor site PS-55 is located 300 metres to the south of G.T. Road near the 265 km milestone. The silts are about 18m in height from the ground level with horizontal layers of silt sand and thin layers of conglomerate at the top. Artefacts were collected from the conglomerate Layers 1 and 2. Layer 1 is recognised within silts, 6m below the top surface. According to Salim it is a graded 3m thick sediment. The bigger pebbles were employed for tool manufacture. Below this is a 15m silt and sand layer and in this layer, an animal tooth was collected. Layer 2 thickness varies from 1m to 2 m, with bigger pebbles sometimes embedded in a hard sandstone. Artefacts are between 2.5 cm and 15cm in length. Pinjor site PS-56 Fatima Villa is located some 250 metres to the north-west of Gurha Shahan, adjacent to the G.T. Road. The site is represented by a 6m high hillock, part of which is being levelled and a wall is built by Fatima Villa owner. About 7 m of silt-sand deposits are exposed, 4m below the surface artefacts are found in a conglomerate layer. At the ground level bovid teeth were also collected. At Pinjor site PS-57 (opposite Fatima Villa) the silts continue across and to the north of G.T. Road, where a hillock has preserved the artefacts. The silt is about 7 m high. At the exposed base animal bones were collected.

Salim (1992) reported the artefacts from the explored sites as follows:

Site PS-55	*Artefacts*
Layer 1	52
Layer 2	17
PS-56	31
PS-57	9
Total	109

The size of artefacts is determined by the small dimensions (1 cm-15cm) of pebbles available in Pinjor sands. However they are much smaller than those pebbles from the overlying Upper Siwalik Conglomerate, where large boulders of 25cm diametre are common. Pinjor deposits provided small pebbles of quartzite, quartz and sandstone to the prehistoric man, who flaked them to obtain sharp-edged pieces. Preliminary study of such lithics indicates that artefacts such as cores and flakes were prepared and were used as tools or later converted into tools. There are pebble tools, scrapers and utilised fragments. Some artefacts are abraded indicating rolling by water, whereas others are fresh. The artefacts with sharp ridges and edges must have been made in the adjacent area suggesting that we are dealing with original Palaeolithic sites, working floors. Stone hammer technique is observed due to prominent bulbs on flakes and deep scars on cores. However, such artefacts are much smaller and weigh less than the Acheulian tools from overlying Upper Siwalik Conglomerate. Salim cautions that at present we can label Pinjor finds as a core-flake assemblage, and only future studies can determine whether it represents a pebble tool tradition or otherwise. Palaeolithic artefacts have already been reported from Pinjor sediments in Sirmur district, Himachal Pradesh, India (Verma and Srivasta 1984: 13-19). In the adjacent area of Haryana, M.P. Singh has reported a hominid incisor from Nadah, near Chandigarh from the Pinjor deposits.

Salim (1997: 152), summarising his views on the Lower Palaeolithic of Pakistan, says that we now can study not only the Palaeolithic cultures but also social context of hominids in this region. We must venture further into underlying sediments such as Tatrot for hominid activities. The oldest tools at present come from Pinjor silts and sands and represent a pebble core-flake assemblage made on small quartzite pebbles. No new name is given to them as the research work continues. Future work can determine their status whether they belong to Asian pebble tool tradition or core-flake assemblages of East Africa such as at lake Turkana. The search for hominid remains continues now both from Pinjor and other Upper Siwalik Conglomerates. The Acheulian toolkits have been recovered and analysed and based on stratigraphy two Lower Palaeolithic collections can be distinguished. Those from within quartzite Upper Siwalik conglomerate are rolled and abraded, and smaller in size. The youngest Acheulian comes from the surface of quartzitic as well as Lei Conglomerate; tools are patinated with sharp edges and ridges, but larger in size with an approximate 3-4 Myr age. The third collection consists of fresh Acheulian tools with cordiform hand-axes of Middle Palaeolithic age. These Palaeolithic cultures can be studied against palaeoenvironmental conditions with new dating techniques such as Palaeomagnetism for a more refined chronology.

In contrast, Mohapatra (1976), using several sets of magnetic polarity data from the Upper Siwalik beds of both India and Pakistan, has tentatively tried to date the two sets of Palaeolithic industries. The Sohanian tradition, according to him, appeared in the Mindel-Riss Interglacial (300-400,000 BP) and continued evolving up to the end of the Pleistocene. The Acheulian tradition, on the other hand, cannot be older than 200,000 BP because it is only around this time that the range became sufficiently stable to support human population.

Occasional claims have been made for the existence of a pre-Acheulian Sohanian tradition in peninsular India but Misra thinks that they remain to be substantiated by unequivocal stratigraphic evidence.

Sanghao: Dani (1964:1-50) excavated a Palaeolithic site at Sanghao near Mardan, in the former North-west Frontier province of Pakistan. The cave lies at 600m within a cemented limestone conglomerate, which Dani has correlated with Terrace I of Kashmir. The Sanghao valley is a rugged area of undulating plains broken up by *khwars* (torrents) and the sides shredded by piercing spurs. There are a large number of *darras* (canyons) in the valley. Rainfall is scanty and a few natural springs provide oases for flora and fauna. Nearby there is an affluent of the Swat.

Dani reported a deposit 3m thick with 12 layers. Layers 12 to 6 are Palaeolithic. Quartz is the raw material used as it occurs as a vein in the nearby limestones. A small hand-axe, scrapers, awls and Mousterian cores from the lowest layers obviously connect it to the Middle Palaeolithic. Blades and burins (5% of the tools) have also been reported, thus an Upper Palaeolithic horizon is indicated.

At Rohri, perhaps the Harappans had cleared the Palaeolithic debris from many sites. The chert used by Palaeolithic man was dark and patinated unlike the light coloured Harappan material. At Rohri only the Upper and the Middle Palaeolithic artifacts are found, but at milestone 101 even the Lower Palaeolithic material occurs. As the same outcrops have been used from the Early Palaeolithic to the Harappan times, it is difficult to distinguish pure single-culture sites. Recent alluvium has covered the sites that may have been on the alluvial plains.

Before we leave the Sohanians, it is necesary to take note of the recent work of the British archaeologists in Pakistan. We would like to quote verbatim the summary of their expedition, as it totally subverts what de Terra & Paterson (1939) had observed earlier. Moreover, it gives a new perspective to the Palaeolithic studies in South Asia.

In their report Rendell *et al.* give the following conclusions:

> We began this report with a review of de Terra and Paterson's (1939) *Studies of the Ice Age of India and Associated Human Cultures*, published 50 years ago under academic and logistic circumstances that are virtually unrecognisable today. In evaluating their work, we have often been critical of their methodology and results, and we have shown that almost all of their conclusions have been untenable for some time. In de Terra's case, he was at fault in assuming that the geological record of the Sohan valley and Kashmir showed an essentially climatic rather than tectonic record; he made serious errors in the field in imposing a sequence of river terraces on the Sohan valley landscape, and in assuming that this sequence would provide a complete record of changes in Pleistocene climate. He made a major error in following Wadia's (1928) mistaken view of the relationship between the northern and southern limb of the Sohan syncline, and consequently of the relationship between Siwalik and post-Siwalik strata on the southern limb of the fold. His attempts at correlating glacials and interglacials, deduced from his supposed terrace sequence, with a four-fold sequence of world-wide glaciations are also untenable, not least because of what has since been learnt about the glacial record of the Pleistocene. Unknown to him, his main error was in assuming that the Upper Siwalik 'Boulder Conglomerate Stage' represented a single time unit within the Pleistocene, which he then correlated with the "Great Glaciation" (i.e. the "Mindel" glacial of the Alps). Recent work has demonstrated that the Upper Siwalik Boulder Conglomerate is time-transgressive, and cannot therefore be correlated with any single event elsewhere. de Terra compounded his mistake within the Sohan valley by mapping the post-Siwalik Lei Conglomerate as Upper Siwalik, an error that sowed seeds of confusion for subsequent studies because the former is around a million years younger than the latter. Paterson's work was no less faulty in several important respects. We have shown how his approach to the Sohan valley in particular was pre-conditioned by his main research on the Clactonian assemblages of southern England, and how he was influenced by current French views of gradual, "progressive" evolution in the Palaeolithic that have been obsolete for many years now. We have shown that few of his assemblages can be dated, either relatively to one another or absolutely, and that most are probably mixed and derived from long and perhaps intermittent use of conglomerate exposures as sources of raw material. Most importantly of all, we doubt his identification of a pre-, an Early and a Late Sohan, and his conclusion that the Sohan Flake Tradition existed alongside, and independently of, the Acheulean bifacial tradition.
>
> These are harsh conclusions, but ones that we feel are fair. This is not to belittle de Terra and Paterson's achievements, provided that their work is judged in the context of its time. We have tried to tease out the reasons why they worked the way they did; to identify the ingredients that shaped their view of the past, and to understand why they used the methods that they did. To that extent, our appraisal of their work is also an enquiry into the history of Pleistocene geology and Palaeolithic archaeology. If their work was at fault, so too was most of that of their peers and contemporaries, including figures that were, or later became, more important, such as the Abbe Breuil and Louis Leakey. Had we been working in the 1930's, we doubt whether we would have approached the Sohan valley very differently; similarly we hope that putative judges of our work will attempt to set it in the context of the 1980's. Having lived in de Terra and Paterson's shadow for several years, we cannot but admire their breadth of vision, their energy and self-confidence, however wrong their conclusions may now appear.
>
> What we have attempted to do in the second part of this monograph is to put something in place of studies of the Ice Ages of India. As is evident, we have worked on a totally different scale, with totally different field and laboratory techniques, and wholly different perceptions of the past. Instead of attempting to cover the whole of northern Pakistan and India in one five-month field season, we have spent 12 months between us, over 10 seasons, in one tiny part of the Sohan valley, examining an area that de Terra and Paterson would probably have exhausted in a matter of days. Unlike de Terra and Paterson, our main geological concerns have been with sequences rather than

with landforms; and unlike them, we have had to grapple with a glacial-interglacial sequence that is far more complex than the appealing simplicity of only four world-wide glaciations. Thanks to palaeomagnetism and radiometric dating techniques, we have been able first to date absolutely sections and exposures that were undatable to them; and secondly to appreciate the recent nature and extent of tectonic changes in the Sohan valley. Unlike them, we can accept and demonstrate that major geological units are time-transgressive, and we do not need to be unduly pre-occupied with large-scale regional correlations as a way of establishing a chronological framework. Archaeologically speaking, we have concentrated on finding small amounts of well-dated material, and paid scant attention to the type of surface collections that constituted the bulk of Paterson's evidence. Absolute dating has relieved us of the need to devise typological sequences based on notions of gradual, progressive change; and research into the early Palaeolithic in the last few decades has shown how inter-assemblage variability within a given period frustrates most attempts to show simple, unidirectional change through time. This is not to say, of course, that change did not occur in the lower Palaeolithic; merely that other factors such as the circumstances and location of tool use and discard, the type of raw materials used, and the taphonomic history of each assemblage need to be considered before such changes can be identified.

Not surprisingly, our results are very different from those that de Terra and Paterson published in 1939, but we hope, no less fascinating. As we hope to have shown, the Plio-Pleistocene history of the Sohan valley is just as enthralling and exciting as it must have appeared to them, even if it must now be seen in terms of tectonic as well as climatic change. As reviewed in chapter 3, the Upper Siwaliks have been investigated longer and in greater depth than any other Neogene sequence, and in the last decade, our understanding of it has advanced enormously through the application of palaeomagnetic and radiometric work. Our debt to that work, particularly that undertaken by the Dartmouth – Peshawar group is immense, and much of what we have attempted would not have been possible without their programme of palaeomagnetic dating. In particular, their provision of a chronological framework for the Upper Siwalik, and their demonstration that the "Boulder Conglomerate" is not a "stage" but is in fact time-transgressive were major breakthroughs in developing an understanding of the Pleistocene geology of the Potwar.

The post-Siwalik record tends to be overshadowed by the fascinations of the Upper Siwaliks, but should be treated as being of equal interest. Much of our work has been on the Upper Pleistocene, and particularly on the so-called "Potwar loessic silt". We have shown that much of this is true loess, and that much of it was deposited during the last glaciation (i.e. between 75 ka and 18 ka), and not during the penultimate (Riss) glaciation, as supposed by de Terra and Paterson. Where we have been fortunate is that our work coincided with the development of TL as a way of dating loessic deposits. This technique was developed during this current project, and the opportunities of sampling extensive and thick loess deposits at Riwat also led to some innovative and useful contributions that have helped establish TL as a useful and viable dating technique. In methodological terms, one of the most rewarding parts of this study for the principal geologist was the opportunity to participate in the development of a laboratory technique that could be used to date the deposits under investigation in the field.

Our archaeological results from an area less than 3 km by 1 km fall far short of replacing Paterson's sequence with another of equal breadth, but hopefully provide a series of starting points for future workers. Three sets of discoveries have been presented in this volume, of very different ages and type. Each can be briefly reviewed in turn:

i) The initial upper Palaeolithic or late early Palaeolithic

By far the largest amount of archaeological evidence presented in this volume is from site 55, dated by TL to ca. 45,000 years BP. As shown from the numbers of conjoining pieces, this assemblage has a high integrity, and probably relates to a very short period of use and discard, perhaps in the order of weeks rather than years. By excavating a large area of up to 200 m^2, spatial variability in the distribution of different types of flaked stone could be shown. In particular, it was demonstrated that a smaller excavation might have inadvertently over- or under-estimated the importance of blade manufacture. What was of interest was the presence of small blade elements in an assemblage otherwise dominated by flakes, but made without elaborate core preparation. Unfortunately, the regional status of this assemblage cannot be assessed until more is published on comparable assemblages from elsewhere in Pakistan, northern India, Afghanistan and Iran. In following recent trends, we have avoided terms such as Middle Palaeolithic or Middle Stone Age; for reasons evident in chapter 2, we cannot retain Paterson's concept of a late Sohan, as that was poorly defined and is largely undated, and perhaps even undatable. Future work may clarify whether the site 55 assemblage is classed as "initial upper Palaeolithic", or as "late early Palaeolithic"; however, the distinction between the two is likely to be blurred, and a lengthy terminological debate over this point at this stage is probably of little value.

As is evident in chapters 8 and 11, explanations of the distribution and type of material found at site 55 have been cautious, given ongoing and long-term uncertainties over the interpretation of Palaeolithic sites in general. The most definite conclusion that can be reached is that it does not represent a living site, as normally defined. Other suggestions are inevitably more tentative. A structure of some kind existed there, but we have resisted temptations to foist yet another hut on the Palaeolithic from the evidence at hand. The suggestion that the site was used for a specific function such as skin working is one that needs further enquiry. One line is through wear analysis of some of the artefacts; another is to compare site 55 with other Palaeolithic examples in better documented areas. A third approach that could not be tried here would be to excavate other contemporaneous sites in the Riwat area to assess the degree and type of inter-assemblage variability. If, however, the site was one with a special function, it is of interest to debates over the advent of modern human beings, and a recognisably modern way of hunter-gatherer behaviour. Neanderthal behaviour is commonly presented these days as "pre-human" in the sense that they did not have the type or depth of advance planning seen in Europe in the later Upper Palaeolithic with *Homo sapiens sapiens* (see e.g. Dennell, 1983: 79-102). Site 55 is intriguing in that (assuming, as always, that the dating is correct!) it implies that this type of behaviour was being practised whilst Neanderthals were still inhabiting Europe. It remains to be seen how typical or atypical site 55 is of its period in Asia.

ii) The Middle and Early Upper Pleistocene

Undoubtedly the largest gap in our present knowledge of the Pleistocene of northern Pakistan concerns the Middle and early Upper Pleistocene (i.e. between 700 ka and 45 ka). Unsurprisingly, therefore, next to nothing is known of the Palaeolithic record of this period. In European terms, this time-span corresponds to most of the Lower and almost all the Middle Palaeolithic. At present, the only securely-dated material that we know of in northern Pakistan from this 600,000 year period are the three hand-axes and a few flakes from Dina and Jalalpur; and the hand-axe and disc core from the upper conglomerate at Riwat. Five pieces of stratified material from 600,000 years is an obvious invitation and plea for future fieldwork. What can be suggested as possible pointers to the future are that on historical grounds (see Chapter 2), we see no reason to accept Paterson's assertion that there were two independent traditions of hand-axe and flake-users in the Punjab during this time. Instead, we would offer a more parsimonious suggestion, that there was only one Middle Pleistocene tradition in the Punjab, and this used and discarded both hand-axes and flakes. Given that four of the five artefacts known from secure contexts from this period are bifaces, and that the Acheulean is very well-documented in India, we feel it is also likely that northern Pakistan has a Middle Pleistocene Acheulean awaiting discovery. It is unfortunately too early to speculate on the age and significance of the type of Levallois cores and flakes that we have noticed on erosional surfaces in the Riwat area.

iii) A pre-Acheulean?

By far the most surprising discovery we made was that of hominid-struck pieces in the lower conglomerate horizon at Riwat that we have subsequently dated to ca. 2.0 Myr. We recognise fully that this is the most contentious part of our results, since this impinges directly upon prevailing views of human origins and Eurasian colonisation. We do not see at present how we could have reached any other conclusion over this material. We remain satisfied that R001, R014 and R88/1 were deliberately struck, and that they are wholly different from the overwhelming amount of naturally-modified clasts that we have observed in this and other conglomerate horizons. Although other pieces are more debatable as instances of hominid-flaking, the point remains that in our view - and in the view of most of those who have seen the replica or original of R001 - at least one piece was deliberately flaked. It thus has to be explained, however awkwardly. We have shown that flaking occurred before incorporation into that horizon; and we think also that the context has not subsequently been reworked. There is no doubt in our minds that the lower conglomerate horizon is overlain by 70m of Upper Siwalik deposits, and we have shown that these must be between 0.9 and 2.47 Myr old on palaeomagnetic grounds. We also have no doubts that the section at Riwat is an integral part of the Sohan Syncline. The dating of that folding to 1.9 Myr is the result of the work of other investigators, but we see no reason to disbelieve their conclusion.

If our conclusion that artefacts were being flaked in Pakistan ca. 2 Myr ago is rejected on the grounds that the dating is subsequently proven to be too old, then we have no cause for complaint. Where we would complain is if it is rejected simply on the ground that is at odds with current models of human origins. Models should encourage rather than restrict further work; a discovery should not be rejected or ignored simply on grounds of inconvenience or unpopularity.

Our overall feeling after 10 field seasons in northern Pakistan is one of humility towards the landscape we have been investigating. It is not a landscape (contra de Terra and Paterson) that yields quick and easy answers; it is fascinating and complicated, but often deceptive and unyielding. Rewards can often seem scant when set against the amount of time and effort required to obtain them. In many ways, these feelings should be evident in this study. Rather than providing a large set of answers to the problems initiated by and resulting from de Terra and Paterson, we feel we have probably ended with a longer and more thorough set of questions. There has clearly been some useful progress in recent years in unravelling the Plio-Pleistocene geology and chronology of the Upper and post-Siwaliks. What is singularly lacking from current research on both the Siwaliks and post-Siwaliks is a climatic record that can stand independently, and be compared with what is now known from deep-sea cores and other sources. The work presented here on the loess sequence of the Potwar and Sohan valley goes some way towards providing a climatic record for the Late Pleistocene, but obviously needs to be extended back in time, and supplemented by other kinds of data. Probably the greatest geological challenge now facing researchers in this area is to identify, and to gauge the effects of, the numerous climatic changes of the last 2-3 million years, especially in a region so dramatically affected by the recent uplift of the Himalayas. As stated earlier, the fascination of this region during the Pleistocene lies in the study of the interplay between climatic change and tectonic instability, and particularly in the way these two factors affected the hydrological regimes of streams and rivers, and vegetational and faunal communities. Another major problem is that the geological sequence of the Potwar contains some enormous gaps and discontinuities that were signally ignored or overlooked by de Terra when he placed his erosional unconformity in the Sohan area between the Middle and Upper Siwaliks. In so doing, he gave the misleading impression that the Upper Siwalik record of this area was far more continuous than it now appears to have been. One hiatus that is particularly relevant here is between the end of the folding of the Sohan valley ca. 1.9 Myr ago, and the oldest-surviving post-Siwalik deposits that in some parts of the valley may be a million or more years younger. Palaeolithic archaeologists are inevitably entrapped in such problems. If there is a pre-Acheulean in Pakistan and India, it is clearly of great general significance, but equally clearly, it will be difficult to isolate in an area where the landscape has changed so profoundly, and where so much has been eroded. The present scarcity of evidence for whatever constitutes the Palaeolithic of the Middle Pleistocene is considerably bound up with the scarcity of evidence for landscapes of this period. Although the loess landscape of the Potwar is one of the best-preserved upper Pleistocene landscapes in the Old World, it also masks a hunter-gatherer landscape that is at present represented only by one excavated site, and hardly anything is yet known of what preceded or followed it. If this volume encourages others to supplement or even refute some of the conclusions that we have reached, it will have had some value (Rendell *et al.* 1989: 202-6).

In view of the unconventional conclusions of Rendell *et al.*'s work, we had to quote it extensiverly to avoid misrepresentation. We are a bit surprised that they have totally ignored the Neogene climatic sequence worked out by our multidisciplinary teams in Kashmir (Agrawal *et al.* 1988, 1989; Agrawal 1992).

Punjab and Himachal

Eastwards are the provinces of East Punjab and Himachal Pradesh. Palaeoliths were found in this area on the terraces of the Beas, the Banganga and the Sirsa rivers. The region is included under the Siwalik foothills (600-1,000 m) and behind these are the Himalayan ranges of Dholadhar and Shimla hills. The Siwalik hills are denuded of forests today and are severely eroding, creating havoc for the plains below.

At Nalagarh, there are three terraces on the river Sirsa at 21, 12, 3 m. The Upper Terrace gravel is cemented in places; in the Middle Terrace it is loose and has a thin mantle of silt; both these terraces yielded choppers and scrapers made from pebbles. An awl flaked all over was found as well, a far advanced tool to be here in the company of the Early Sohan artifacts. There is not much difference between the tool typology of the two terraces.

Lal (1956) reported Sohan type tools from the five terraces of the Beas and the Banganga valleys in the Kangra district (Himachal Pradesh). Later Joshi and some Polish workers discovered that these terraces are not due to glacial action, but have been formed by the erosion of the cones in the foothills. The mountain-building processes raised these terraces higher, and while the exact cause of the formation of such cones is not known, the role played by climatic events must be taken into consideration. There seems to be an evolutionary trend in the tools discovered from the five terraces at Guler (Fig. 3-3), in Kangra, but they can all be grouped under the Early Sohan category with the chopper-chopping tools, Clacton and proto-Levalloisean flakes.

Mohapatra (1966) carried out excavations at Dehra Gopipur and found both unifacial and bifacial choppers, but the pebble tools were confined to the silt of Terrace III. At places choppers are found with flakes, cores and points made from chert. It may be noted that the pebble element continues from the Early Palaeolithic to the Neolithic as shown by Ranov's work at Kara-Maidan, Lakhuti and Karatau sites in Tadjikistan. It will be useful to look for pebble tools in association with the Neolithic cultures in this region too.

Hand-axes and cleavers have also been reported from Nandrul, Kofla, Dhavala Thana and other places in Himachal Pradesh. With hand-axes from the early context and bifacial flaking of choppers in Kangra region, there does not seem to be much point in emphasising the distinctive identities of the Sohan and the hand-axe cultures in this area.

PALAEOLITHIC CULTURES OF WESTERN INDIA

In this section we have included the present Indian states of Rajasthan and Gujarat.

Rajasthan

In 1917 Brown reported the first Acheulian tools from Jaipur, in Rajasthan, and in the same year Heron noted the evidence of climatic change in the sand-dunes of the area. Since then several workers have investigated Rajasthan and it is, therefore, a better studied area than most others in the subcontinent.

The Aravalli ranges running NE-SW dissect the area diagonally into two unequal parts. The western part is a vast flat expanse of alluvial sand called Marwar (old *Marubhumi*, desert land). Relief is provided by isolated low hills and sand-dune formations. The river Luni, along with

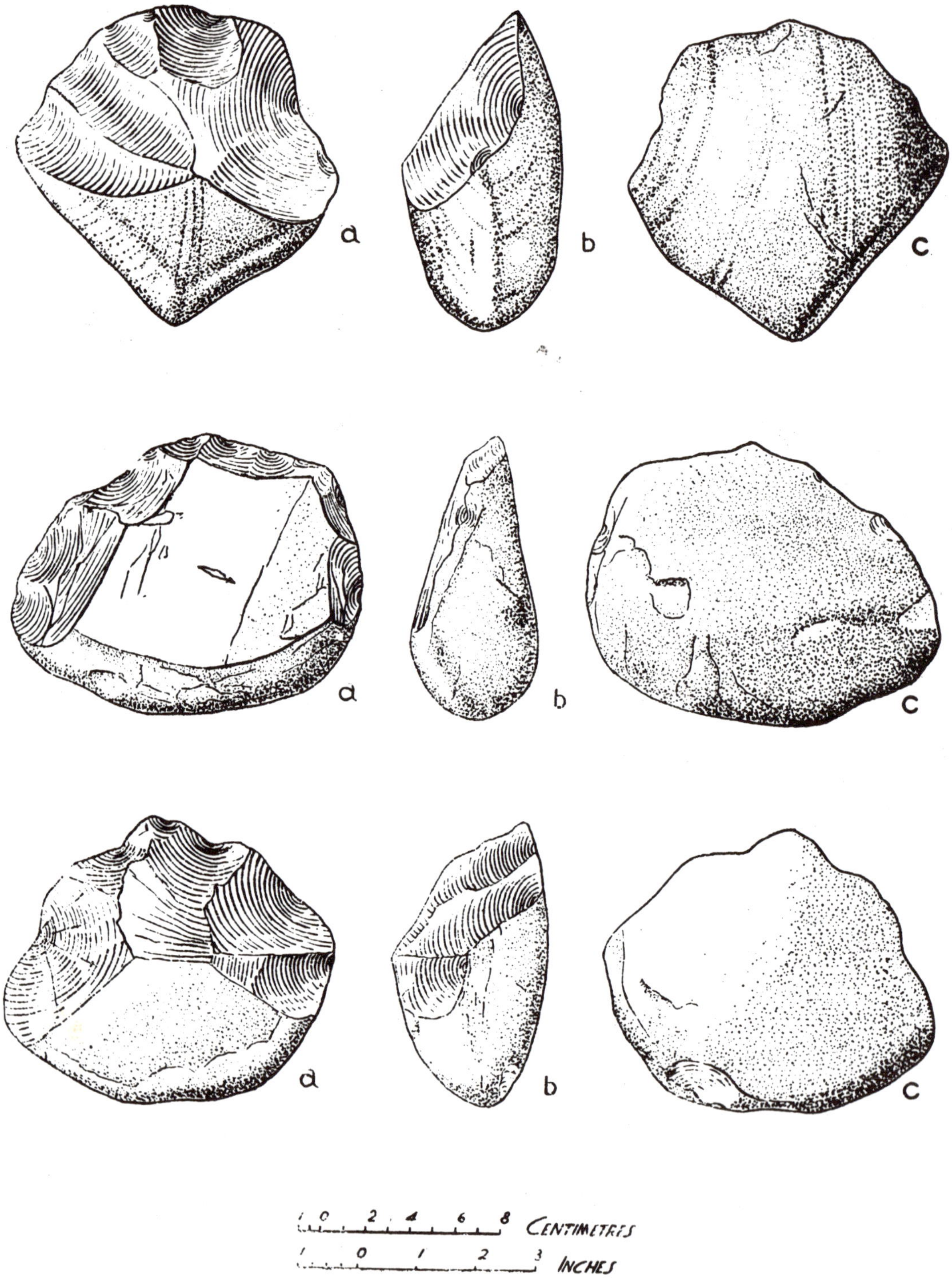

Fig. 3-3. Chopper chopping tools from Guler, Himachal Pradesh

its several tributaries, drained the area in the past; now it is an ephemeral stream that flows only during the monsoon. Due to uncertain and scarce rainfall, cultivation today is possible only in the monsoon season. This compels the local people to supplement their livelihood with herds of cattle, sheep and camel. It is no surprise, therefore, that the nomadic way of life is quite common in these parts and the population is very thin.

The situation markedly changes in the eastern part of the Aravallis. This area, called Mewar, is more rocky and hilly, yet rainfall is much greater, 60 to 100 cm. The rivers Banas and Chambal flow through the region almost all the year round, and as a result, Mewar is greener and agriculturally richer than Marwar, a difference that is also reflected in population density.

There are clear indications, at least in the western part (Marwar), that ecological conditions have not remained the same; Rajasthan being located in a semi-arid zone is more sensitive to climatic change. The interplay of windborne and riverborne sediments provides an alternation of arid and humid conditions. Unlike the rivers originating in the Himalayas, the river Luni has its source in the Aravallis and therefore reflects only the regional climatic changes. Archaeological evidence also shows some cyclic fluctuations in the occurrence of human population in this area. For example, the Harappan settlements come to an end around 1800 BC; the next important group of cultures is black-and-red and painted grey ware (PGW) cultures which appear only at the beginning of the first millennium BC; after this the Rangmahal culture with its wide distribution, particularly along the Ghaggar, appears in about the second century AD. The rivers Ghaggar and the Drishadvati are dry today; but extensive and high Harappan mounds can be seen on their banks. The PGW sites occur within the channel itself, perhaps indicating a dwindling water supply. It has been suggested that the Ghaggar and the Drishadvati were part of the main Indus system. This would make a uniform ecological zone, drained by the Indus system of semi-arid alluvial tracts occupied by the Harappa culture.

In the 1960s Verstappan initiated the modern Palaeoclimatic studies in Rajasthan. In recent years Ghose and Singh, Allchin, Goudie and Hegde, Dhir, Ghosh, Misra, Sinha, Sural, Singhvi and the senior author have worked extensively on the Luni basin and also on the dunefields. G. Singh provided a vegetational history of the past 10,000 years from the lake sediments of Sambhar, Didwana, Pushkar and Lunkaransar. The diverse climatic data from Rajasthan are tabulated in Table 3.2.

The Luni river complex shows an old integrated drainage system indicating that at one time the river carried a lot of water and sediment load. At a later date, the channels were choked by sand-dunes. On the basis of the present rainfall patterns, Goudie has shown that below 250-300 mm annual rainfall sand-dunes are active and mobile and above this vegetation stabilises them. Four horizons have been recognised in these sand deposits. The bottom-most sand-dunes even now are exposed at places to a height of 25 m. A deeply weathered reddish horizon was developed after this dune-building activity. These reddish-topped dunes are compacted and gullied. Over this is a kankarised horizon with its root casts. Finally these are capped by the modern loose yellowish sand. The first dune activity has been attributed to an arid phase. The red weathered horizon with its acidity and decalcification implies formation of acids due to richer vegetation under wetter conditions. The calcreted horizon, moreover, indicates more rainfall than today. This is the climatic interpretation of most of the workers.

Let us now turn to the Palaeolithic cultures of the area.

Pioneering work on the Palaeolithic in the Rajasthan desert was done by Misra, who identified Lower Palaeolithic assemblages from the Luni, Berach and Gambhiri river basins in the 1960s (Misra 1961, 1962, 1967) (Fig. 3-4).

TABLE 3.2 HOLOCENE CLIMATIC PHASES AND CULTURES IN SOUTH ASIA

Evidence	*Climatic Phase*	*Dated Culture*
Pollen Profiles	Aridity sets in	Late Phase 3,000 BP onwards Harappan Culture vanishes
Pollen Profiles	Moist conditions	Phase IV 5,000 - 3,000 BP Pre-Harappan and Harappan Cultures
Pollen Profiles		Moister than now Phase III c. 9,500 - 5,000 BP Microlithic settlements
Pollen Profiles	Intensely Moist conditions	Phase II c. 10,000- 9,500 BP Microlithic Settlements
Pollen Profiles	Severely arid Windy	
Deep - weathered Profiles	Major Wet Phase	Integrated drainage Channels of River Luni
Major dune Formation	Major Dry Phase	Singh's Phase I c. pre-10,000 BP Middle Palaeolithic
Upper Palaeolithic		No human Cultures

In 1980 Agrawal, Misra and Rajaguru began a project in the Thar desert. This project involved the collaboration of scientists from many other institutions. The success of this project was largely due to the concentration of resources at a number of localities around Didwana and the collaboration of a team of workers. Two major localities were excavated, 16R a sand-dune and Singi Talav, a playa. While 16R provided a good palaeoclimatic record, Singi Talav provided an excellently documented Early Acheulian assemblage (Gaillard *et al.* 1986). The Didwana lake core provided an excellent Holocene palaeoclimatic record (Wasson *et al.* 1984). In the 16R dune, a 20m exposure revealed the alternation of stabilised/pedogenised dune surfaces with zones of active sand accumulation. Artefacts were found in a number of horizons within the dune (Misra 1987b; Misra and Rajaguru 1989; Misra *et al.* 1982). Th/U and TL dating of the dune sand and calcrete was carried out (Raghavan *et al.* 1989; Chawla *et al.* 1990). This section gives us a very detailed record of the last glacial-interglacial and earlier cycles. The Early Acheulian from Singi Talav showed that man had adapted to a desert environment during the Lower Palaeolithic. The Th/U date of > 390 Kyr from the lithounit III of the 16R dune indirectly indicates an early date for the Singi Talav assemblage.

As mentioned earlier, a few sites with Acheulian tools have been discovered in the Jaipur, Bundi and Alwar districts. Though Acheulian hand-axes have recently been found north of Luni near Jayal, Marwar is largely poorer than the valleys of Mewar in Early Palaeolithic sites. In fact, Chittorgarh (Gambhiri basin), Kota (Chambal basin) and Nagari (Berach basin) are some of the richest Palaeolithic sites in the country. Udaipur, a hilly district, however, has not produced any stone tools so far. The valleys were wetter and more favourable for both Palaeolithic man and animal; the thickly forested foothills of Udaipur were not inhabited. The toolkit comprises hand-axes, cleavers (Fig. 3-5), Levallois flakes, blades and scrapers, chopper and chopping tools. Artifacts are mostly made from quartzite, recovered from the river beds as pebbles.

Palaeolithic research in Rajasthan in recent years owes much to Misra who has worked out the following stratigraphy bottom upwards of the various sediments and their cultural association:

Lithological Units	*Cultural Association*
Basal rock (shale, schist or granite)	
Mottled clay (kankarized layer?)	
Bouldery pebbly gravel	Acheulian Assemblage
Mottled clay or silt	
Sandy Pebbly gravel (cemented)	Middle Palaeolithic
Silt	Microliths on its surface
Sand-dune	Mesolithic

As this table shows, Middle Palaeolithic tools are found cemented in the sandy pebbly gravel, underlying the mottled clay. Several Middle Palaeolithic sites have been found in Wagaon and Kadamali river valleys in Mewar. There is a distinct change in the toolkit. Now the tools are smaller than the Early Palaeolithic ones; they are largely made on finer-grained material like agate, jasper and chert. Hand-axes and cleavers become rare; chopper-chopping tools are absent altogether. The Levallois and discoidal core techniques are more predominant now. The assemblage comprises a variety of scrapers, borers and points besides flakes and blades.

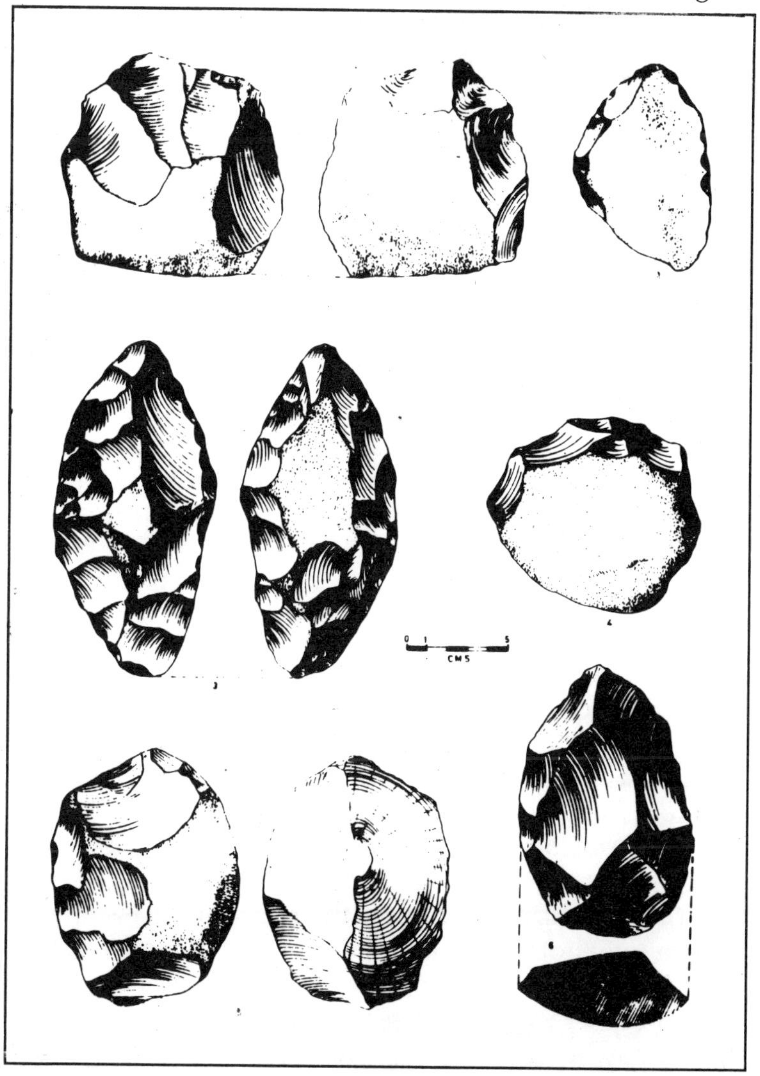

Fig. 3-4. Early Palaeolithic choppers and hand-axes from Berach and Gambhiri valleys, Rajasthan (courtesy V.N. Misra)

In western Rajasthan (Marwar) as well many Middle Palaeolithic sites have been discovered in the valley of the Luni and its tributaries. These tools derive from the cemented gravel and they seem to be in places on the limestone hills from Sojat to Bilara. In the Luni valley, a greater variety of material has been employed, e.g., silicified wood, rhyolite, porphyry, etc. Hand-axes and cleavers still persist and the Levallois technique is more dominant. The assemblage here seems to have evolved clearly out of the Acheulian tradition.

From near the freshwater lake

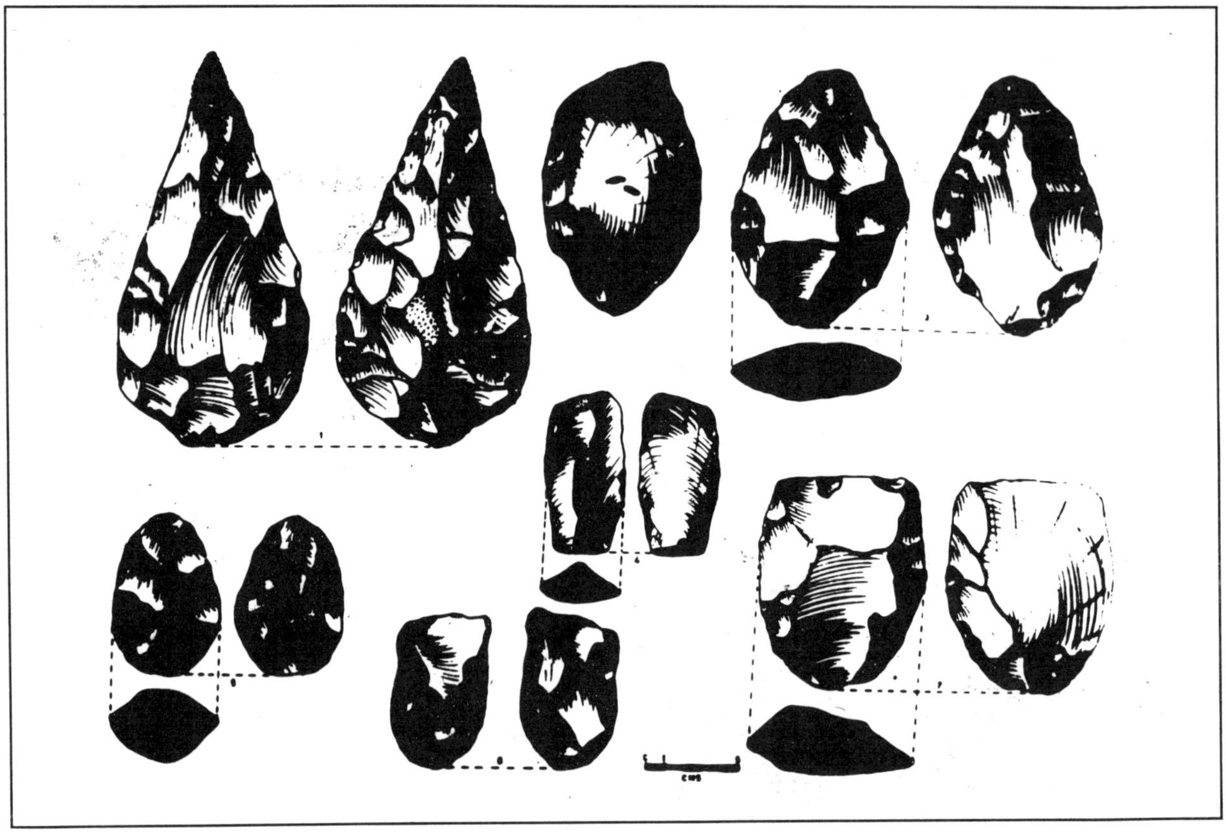

Fig. 3-5. Acheulian hand-axes and cleavers from Berach and Gambhiri, Rajasthan (courtesy V.N. Misra)

of Budha Pushkar (Alwar district), a Middle Palaeolithic industry comprising scrapers, chopping tools, cleavers, blades, burins and prepared flakes has been reported. These tools belong to the weathered soil horizon representing, it is believed, a wet phase. Slender blades and cores of the Upper Palaeolithic tradition have also been found in the limestone hills of Sojat and from the Luni valley.

Gujarat

Gujarat is a great alluvial tract drained by the Sabarmati, Mahi and their affluents. The coastal area in south-west of Rajasthan is marshy. Rainfall decreases rapidly from 150-175cm in the South to Surat where it is 100cm and at Ahmedabad only 70 cm. The higher, forested eastern region gets more rainfall but the terrain is broken and has poor soils. The Saurashtra or Kathiawad peninsula, a tract of 119,000 sq. km between the Rann of Kutch and the Gulf of Cambay, is very different from the Sabarmati and Mahi basins. The Rann is a vast expanse of bare tidal mud flats, a black desolation flecked with saline efflorescences. The monotony is relieved by the sudden flights of great flocks of flamingoes. In the north, the mud desert merges with the Thar sand desert. The Deccan lava forms the main landmass of Saurashtra and the Tertiary miliolitic and most alluvial deposits flank this basaltic platform. Kathiawar has an altitude lower than 300-600 m. The Gir forest sanctuary today protects the only surviving species of the Asian lion.

The river Sabarmati rises in the Aravallis and flows north-south, debauching into the Gulf of Cambay. It has three deposits exposed over the basal rock of granite, and at the bottom is a gravel conglomerate, overlying it a reddish silt and on top a yellowish sandy silt. The Early Palaeolithic industry (Fig. 3-6), comprising hand-axes and cleavers, and cores with pebble

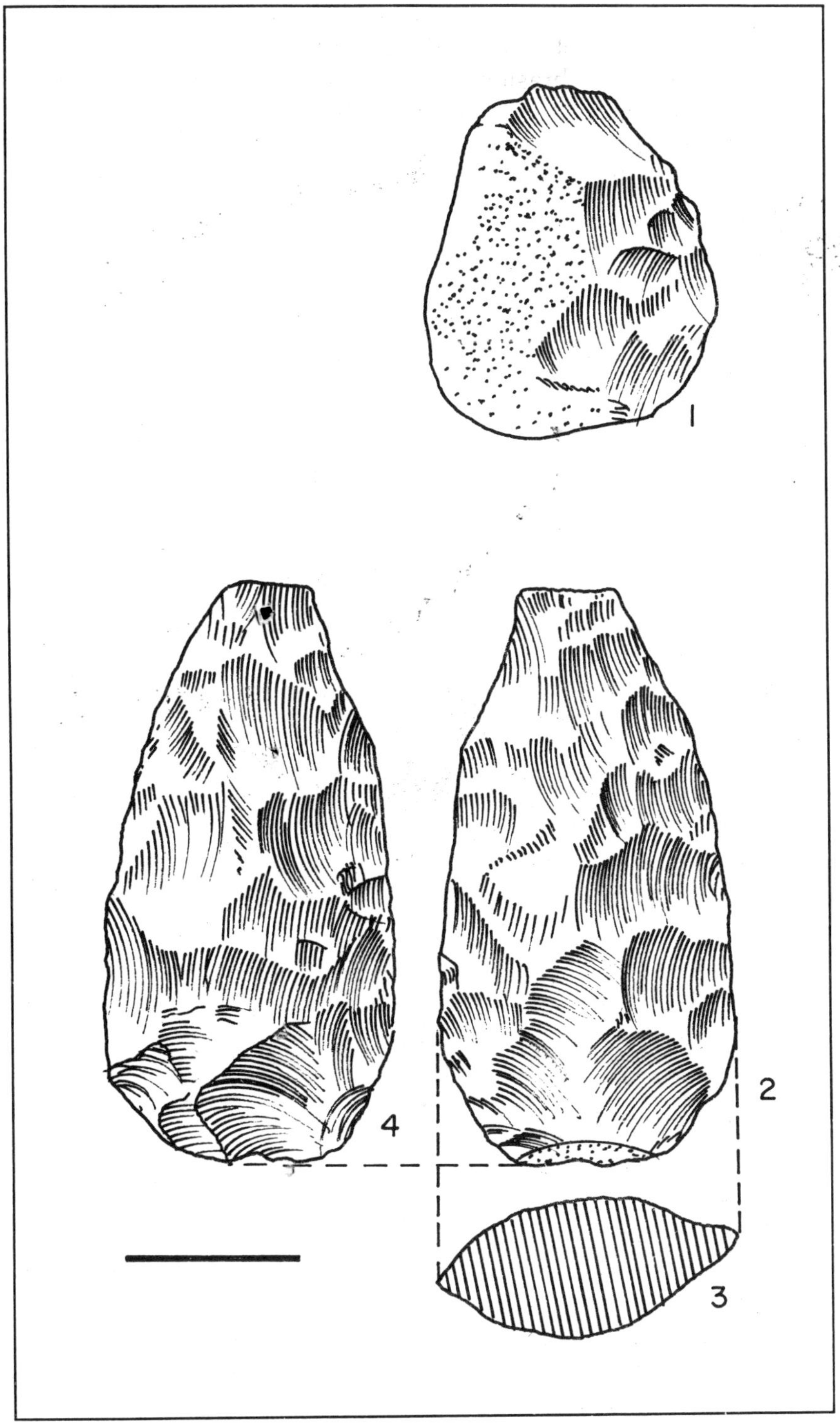

Fig. 3-6. Early Stone Age tools from the Sabarmati valley, Gujarat (after Sankalia 1974)

surfaces, is confined to the gravel conglomerate and the flakes show high-angled striking platforms but none has true Levallois features. There are also a few pebble tools.

Further south, the Orsang valley contains many sites. Sankalia (1974) reports a Middle and Upper Palaeolithic industry from Bhandarpur, while a beautiful hand-axe was also found at the site. At Visadi, in the same valley, Allchin (1973) came across an Upper Palaeolithic assemblage in a sand-dune. It comprises blade cores, blades and burins made from quartz; there is a complete absence of the Indian Middle Palaeolithic type of cores (Levallois-Mousterian). Allchin (1973) compares the Visadi industry with those of Sanghao and Renigunta. It is interesting to note that today the annual rainfall in this area is 84cm and therefore no active dunes can form. The discovery of this Upper Palaeolithic industry in the body of a dune has been taken to denote arid conditions.

In Saurashtra the terraces of the river Bhadar have produced both the Early and Middle Palaeolithic tools from the pebble conglomerate (Sankalia 1965a: 327). One finds hand-axes, cleavers, chopping tools, points, borers and scrapers in this assemblage. Though earlier it was thought that there were two major cycles of erosion, later work has shown only one major cycle. There have been reports from the Kutch area of cleavers, hand-axes and choppers, with a lot of cortex still intact, and the Middle Palaeolithic tools from Dokamardo in Saurashtra.

Chakrabarti excavated a Late Acheulian gravel context at Samadhialia, in Saurashtra. The artefacts were of volcanic rocks and showed little abrasion and were recovered from a colluvial gravel deposit about 1.20m thick. In comparison to the surface Acheulian assemblages there was a much lower proportion of finished tools to waste products showing that the context was comparatively less modified (Chakrabarti 1979).

In Saurashtra, Lele (1989) tried to relate the archaeological evidence to the miliolite stratigraphy and ultimately to the record of Quaternary sea-level fluctuations. They located in situ Acheulian tools in gravels at Junagarh and Umrethi which are graded to a low sea-level. Miliolite was dated by the Th/U method at Umrethi and Junagarh to 95 Kyr and 67 Kyr. It was the first application of absolute dating to the Lower Palaeolithic in India (Baskaran *et al.* 1986).

As described by Mishra (1994), Chitale has reported a number of non-biface stone tool assemblages in the Dangs area of the south Gujarat coast. These are dominated by choppers. Joshi and Bopardikar discovered a number of chopper assemblages in the Konkan. Guzder discovered four sites in the Malvan-Ratnagiri region, which had assemblages of quartzite flakes. She excavated the site of Haddi near Malvan, close to the present sea-level. Rajendran has reported quartz pebble tools from the Kerala coast. Recently Goudeller and Korisettar have reported Acheulian bifaces from four localities in the Dudhsagar basin of Goa (references in Mishra 1994).

For dating the Palaeolithic industries in Gujarat only three types of evidence are available: sea-level changes; river morphology; and miliolite formations. Dating of the miliolite by Th/U method is fraught with problems, though it has been tried in Saurashtra (Baskaran *et al.* 1986).

The sea-level oscillated during the Quaternary period, mainly due to the locking of vast amounts of water in the extensive glaciers. During Ice Ages sea-levels fell by more than 100 metres. On the Saurashtra coast clear evidence of high sea-level up to 5 ± 3m is provided by inland oyster beds, coral reefs, coastal miliolites, high strand-lines, etc. The west coast of Maharashtra also shows these sea-level changes and a ^{14}C and $^{230}Th/^{234}U$ dated sea-level curve has been worked out (Agrawal *et al.* 1973: 3-17; Gupta & Amin 1974: 79-83). It shows that there were three marine transgressions at about 5,000, 35,000 and 130,000 BP. On Bhadar there is only one major aggradation cycle.

Rajaguru and Hegde (1972) have shown that the Middle Palaeolithic tools are found in an inset terrace cut into miliolite rocks. Near Junagadh, they have found Early Palaeolithic artifacts from a pre-miliolitic gravel. The miliolite rocks have been attributed different origins by different workers. One view holds that the miliolite is formed by foramanifera blown inland from the exposed continental shelf. It is not a reliable material for ^{14}C dating and the available dates range from 14,000 to 30,000 BP. The oyster shells from Badalpur and Hiran gave an age of about 22,000 ± 2,000 BP. These dates could represent the upper limits of the 30,000-35,000 BP marine transgression. The available evidence suggests that there are two miliolite formations. One formed after the 120,000 BP incursion and the other after the 35,000 BP rise in sea-level. This would give an upper date of 120,000 years to the Early Palaeolithic artifacts as they are pre-miliolite, and to the Middle Palaeolithic a post-35,000 BP date, as they are post-miliolite. These estimates are obviously based on tenuous arguments and need to be checked by more direct evidence.

PALAEOLITHIC CULTURES OF CENTRAL INDIA

Ganga valley and the Vindhyas

Between the Himalayas and the Vindhyan range is a trough, several thousand metres deep. The Ganga and its affluents filled this up to form the present vast alluvial plain. Owing to the heavy rainfall (100-200 cm/year), it developed into a thickly wooded area, the *mahavana* of the epics. It appears that Palaeolithic man avoided this area for it was a tangled forest and had no rock outcrops for his tools.

But in Mirzapur district where the Kaimur range of the central massif penetrates Uttar Pradesh Palaeoliths were reported by Cockburn as early as 1883. We have included it in Central India as geologically it is part of the Deccan plateau. Most of the tributaries of the Ganga originating in the Central massif are implimentiferous, whereas those rising in the Himalayas are sterile. These tributaries of Ganga show a twofold aggradation-erosion cycle. The lower gravel is pebbly and the upper gravel is finer, and both are capped by silt. The lower gravel incorporates Palaeoliths made on a coarse grained quartzite and sandstone. These include both crude and fine hand-axes, cleavers, cores, choppers and Levallois flakes. Tangs for hafting are a peculiar feature of the hand-axes of this area.

Where prehistory is concerned, Sharma's team struck a 'gold mine' on the river Belan (Kaimur range). The basin has been studied for a number of years and has produced thousands of stratified tools and fossils; however only brief reports are available so far (Sharma 1973:106).

Satsangi and Dutta (1967-68) ascribe the fossils found here to the Middle Pleistocene. The Narmada and Godavari alluvia contain similar fossilised fauna, e.g., *Elephas, Bos, Bubalus* and *Cervus* and suggest contemporaneity. But the absence of some extinct forms (e.g. *Hippopotamus palaeindndicus, Stegodon insignis, Helarctos namadicus*) and the presence of some species of ox and buffalo which are similar to the present-day forms, may indicate a younger age for the Belan sediments.

Varma (1999:175-204) has recently given a comprehensive summary of the Palaeolithic cultures in the Vindhyan-Ganga region. He reports that the Palaeolithic man during the Lower and Middle Palaeolithic, in the Vindhyan region, primarily used hand-axes, cleavers, scrapers and tools made on pebbles. A study of the tools recovered in situ from the sections revealed that pebble tools were the earliest to be used, followed by hand-axes, scrapers and, last, cleavers. Generally, crude and evolved tools are found mixed together at factory sites. Hand-axes of almost all the known types have been found. The largest measures nearly 38.5cm and smallest 9 cm. The average length is 15 cm. Cleavers and scrapers taken together constitute only 30 per cent of the total assemblage. Scrapers are normally made on flakes. The cleavers are also found to be made on flakes. Their length varies from 17.5 to 11.5 cm, the average being 14 cm.

Varma (1999) remarks that among the tool assemblages of the Vindhyan region, special mention may be made of chunk tools which are made on pieces of flat stone slabs by marginal retouching by removing flakes by centrally directed alternate flaking technique. These tools indicate that the man of the Vindhyan region was experimenting with different types of stone material and was also trying to make multifunctional tools. Some tools as such have typical characteristics of both hand-axe and cleaver, even of a scraper. Such tools may be called hand-axe-scraper or cleaver-scraper. Of all the tools of the Lower Palaeolithic, the cleaver, which was a later addition, was the most specialised tool type because it could be used in a variety of ways. Cleavers with concave working edges can be used only for scraping or peeling objects, which are cylindrical in section, such as tree branches or bones of large animals. In such cases shafts are attached at a right angle to the working edge. Cleavers that have a convex working edge are most suitable for cleaning hides and for leather work. Varma thinks that there is hardly any doubt that Palaeolithic man in the Vindhyan region had started hafting his tools. Hand-axes or cleavers meant for hafting had a developed tang in place of a butt-end along with shoulder-like projections. Cleavers were hafted in a variety of ways, according to need. A cleaver if hafted parallel to the working edge can be used as a woodcutter's axe (*kulhari*); if it is hafted at right angle to the working edge, it can be used as a *kudal* or *faurah*. If the cleaver is used as a woodcutter's axe, the proximal edge will show more wear and tear and the working edge will become slightly oblique. In the largest number of cleavers the working edge is usually oblique, which indicates that people must have been using them for cutting trees, etc.

Varma thinks that Palaeolithic man had learnt to cut, clean and make tools of timber also. The evidence of hafting in some of the stone tools and the working edge of cleavers supports the idea that man during this period utilised wood also for making his tools more effective (Varma 1999).

The gradual refinement in flaking technique and in the selection of stones for the manufacture of tools indicate how, through trial and error, Palaeolithic man was acquiring knowledge and how the knowledge thus acquired was being passed over to the succeeding generations, which made development in technology possible. The earliest pebble tools - Abevillian and Early Clactonian tools - were made primarily from utilitarian point of view, but gradually aspects other than utilitarian were also taken care of. As a result, finely flaked tools came to be prepared. Tools gradually become smaller, regular in outline, with shallow flake scars. This indicated man's mastery over flaking techniques. In the earliest or Abevillian tools he used a stone hammer and direct percussion technique. The developed Acheulean tools made by Levalloisian technique indicate that the tools were carved out of the core with a preconceived idea.

No primary habitation site of the Lower Palaeolithic period in the Vindhyan region has so far been excavated. No knowledge of fire making has been noticed so far in this region. Hence, we are not in a position to say anything regarding the pattern of their life.

Technologically speaking, there is a marked difference between the tool typology of the Lower and Middle Palaeolithic. On the basis of the evidence of the Belan valley, we can safely say that the change was a gradual process. In the Middle Palaeolithic tools are based on flakes; small scrapers, points, blades, etc. comprise the main tool types. So far no skeletal remains of Lower or Middle Palaeolithic man have been recovered, nor has any grave site been excavated. Hence, we are not in a position to shed any light on the human life pattern of the period. Nor any Upper Palaeolithic skeletal remains have been found in the Vindhyan region. The tools are now based completely on blades and a number of new types of tool emerge such as burins, awls, various types of scrapers, points, lunates, etc. This does indicate the emergence of a new type of society. The effective use of bows and arrows must have started from this time. It is difficult to trace the evolution of Stone Age industries without excavations and so far the material has been collected mostly from the surface. Sharma claims a distinct Upper Palaeolithic industry in Belan Gravel III. A ^{14}C date for shell from this gravel gives an age of 18,000 BP. The reported discovery of a mother-goddess figurine from these levels lends it a European flavour. Sankalia and Misra however doubt that the Belan finds indicate a classical blade and burin industry.

Narmada region

The present Madhya Pradesh is essentially an extension of the Deccan Plateau separated by the river Tapti. Most of the plateau has an altitude of 300 m, with the Vindhyas and the Maikal range reaching more than 500 m. It is drained by the affluents of the Yamuna which rise in the Vindhyas and flow northwards into the Gangetic system. Cutting east-west across the plateau, the Narmada with its source in the Maikal range flows westwards into the Gulf of Cambay. Not only the drainage but also the geology and the vegetation of this region too are very complex. Some of the primeval original forests are preserved here and many primitive tribes occupy remote areas, which were termed *cul-de-sac* by Subbarao. The rivers Chambal, Son and Betwa belong to the Gangetic system and all these river valleys have yielded Early Palaeolithic tools. Deccan trap, gneiss, granite, quartz and sandstone are abundant in this area. Quite often tools are made from granite (e.g., the Betwa valley) but at some places sandstone has been preferred. A variety of hand-axes and cleavers are reported from the area. The Biana Nala site shows that the tools were made by the Vaal technique. Nearer Bihar, tools show a transition from the Early to the Middle Palaeolithic stage.

The central reaches of the Narmada comprising the Hoshangabad, Narsimhapur and Japaipur districts have been quite extensively explored by several workers. The pebble bed on the Narmada terraces has yielded hand-axes and cleavers. The pebbles of the bed cannot be local because they are quartzitic and the region is basaltic, and this could be explained only through river aggradation. The deposit with big boulders (30 x 30 x 50 cm) could not have been carried by the river unless the conditions were much wetter than today. Embedded in this layer are massive unifacial and bifacial cores, but occasionally hand-axes and cleavers too are encountered. The bouldery bed is capped by a pinkish calcareous clay.

The second bouldery layer, overlying the first, is little finer but it also produced the same type of deeply-scarred flakes and cleavers. A 12 metre thick silty deposit lies over this bed. A deposit of still finer thin gravel of about the same depth was deposited against the second gravel. Scrapers, points and other Middle Palaeolithic tools are found in the third gravel. These tools are now made from finer material like jasper and agate.

Sheila Mishra (1994) in a recent review has summarised the Palaeolithic evidence from the Narmada and Tapi basins. The Narmada, along with the Tapi, flows in the opposite direction to the easterly flowing peninsular drainage, and traditionally divides the Indian subcontinent into northern and southern halves. A number of alluvial basins are separated by gorges along its course. Lower Palaeolithic artefacts are found in the ancient alluvial deposits as well as on bedrock surfaces away from the river. In the central Narmada, Supekar's excavation of Mahadeo Piparia in the 1960s ended a phase of work there. In recent years, Misra, Rajaguru and Badam along with some students have been working in the area (Misra *et al.* 1989, 1990). The excavation of the site of Samnapur, although Middle Palaeolithic, may be mentioned here (Misra *et al.* 1989). Ahasan (1993) has studied the site formation processes of this site. Away from the river towards the divides, wherever quartzite is exposed, Acheulian artefacts have been found in the surface/ rubble context.

There are 90 sites in Raisen district in the divide between the Narmada and Betwa. He considered that these sites were probably never buried. Very few hand-axes were recovered from these assemblages which were dominated by flake scrapers, Levailvois and disc cores. The cave sites of Adamgarh and Bhimbetka also yielded similar material. Recently the Archaeological Survey of India (ASI) has undertaken exploration of the region to be submerged by the Indira Sagar Dam on the Narmada at Punasa. Some new sites have been reported in IAR (1987-88: 43-44; 1988-89: 43-44), and excavations were carried out in a number of localities around the village of Balwada (Ota 1992). In the downstream region, a second alluvial basin, the Nimar plains, was studied by Sheila Mishra. Mishra developed the methodology of relative dating for building up Quaternary stratigraphy during this study (Mishra 1985; Mishra *et al.* 1988). A Late Acheulian assemblage was associated with a weathered gravel at Gangatkheri, while at Mehtakheri large quartzite flakes were recovered from a similar gravel. Recently Chamyal and Merh (1992) have studied the Quaternary stratigraphy, with an emphasis on palaeosols (see the references in Mishra 1994).

Sali did extensive explorations in the Tapi basin, and discovered a number of Lower Palaeolithic sites of which the site of Yesar-Bhadne (Sali 1973-74) is the most important. This site yielded a Late Acheulian assemblage from an alluvial context (Mishra 1994).

Bhimbetka: Very few real Palaeolithic dwelling sites have been excavated in India and still fewer have been properly published. The other known and published sites, besides Bhimbetka, are

Lalitpur (U.P.), Chirki (Maharashtra), Isampur and Anagawadi (Karnataka). Bhimbetka has some unique features: the location of sites in rock shelters; a rich repertoire of paintings on the rocks; a congenial ecological setting; and a continuous succession of cultures from the Acheulian to the Mesolithic.

Bhimbetka is located on the Vindhyan range about 600m above sea-level and 100m above the nearby plains in the Raisen district of Madhya Pradesh and 50 km from Bhopal. Here, unlike at other places, the Vindhyas are not composed of the Deccan lavas but of sandstone and quartzite. The annual rainfall in the area at the present time is about 120 cm. These hills form a watershed: on the northern side it drains through Betwa to the Ganga and the southern slopes drain into the Narmada which is about 25 km away from Bhimbetka. Though the small stream near the site is intermittent nowadays, there are a number of perennial freshwater springs in the area. More than 200 rock shelters and caves are located on the Bhimbetka hills and over 750 in the entire area. One of the caves measures 40 x 12 x 15 m. Over 500 caves are decorated; the total of paintings runs into several thousand. Perhaps this is the richest rock painting site, not only in India but possibly in the world, ranging in date from the Medieval to Mesolithic times. Quite a few of the rock shelters have occupational debris in them. Misra and Wakankar have excavated a few of them.

Misra (1976a: 28-50) has studied the flora and fauna of the site extensively. He finds that at least 30 plants yield edible flowers, fruits, seeds, roots and tubers. Even today, these plants are used by the local population. The hills are covered with a thick deciduous forest except where it has been cleared by man in recent times. A variety of deer (sambhar, chital, black buck), boar, nilgai, leopard, sloth bear, wolf, hare, fox and langur inhabit these hills. Thus the site provided game, vegetable food, water, shelter, raw material for tools and high advantage points to watch out for the game. No wonder that prehistoric man occupied these surroundings for a long period.

Misra says that it is obvious that the tools were made in the rock shelter as evidenced by the presence of fabrication debris. Material used throughout was orthoquartzite. A distinct preference was shown for iron-rich, tough purple quartzite for making hand-axes and cleavers; the other tools were made on yellowish quartzite which weathers faster. About 5,000 artifacts were recovered by Misra from his excavations. The pattern of horizontal and vertical distribution of tools indicates that no one particular area was used for tool fabrication. Sixty-eight per cent of the artifacts were waste products and 32% tools, and of the latter, side scrapers and other non-biface tools constitute 28%, bifaces only 4%. Levallois flakes make up 12% and end scrapers 10% while the ratio of cleavers to hand-axes is 3: 1. Misra, therefore, considers it a late (Mousterian) stage of the Acheulian industry representing the terminal phase of this tradition. The Lalitpur, Chirki, Anagawadi industries, in comparison, are marked by a predominance of chopper-chopping tools and bifaces; low incidence of Levallois flakes; and a low ratio of cleavers to hand-axes. These are all markers of early date. In contrast, the Bhimbetka assemblage is typologically a later industry. At Bhimbetka one can see the gradual replacement of the Acheulian tradition by the Middle Palaeolithic culture.

Unfortunately, nothing much has survived of the organic remains. No bones at all have been found yet; their absence is attributed to the acidic nature of the soil. Apparently, no pollen has been examined. A number of hand-axes and cleavers show edge damage and even breakage, clearly indicating their use in rock-shelters, as the broken pieces were still lying around. A series of five stone-paved floors further proves that the site was being used for living.

Misra (1989) has pointed out that Acheulian sites are particularly densely concentrated and are richer in Central India and the southern Eastern Ghats. Both these regions today receive adequate rainfall, have a thick vegetation cover, and are rich in wild plant and animal food resources. Chemical analysis of sediments from Bhimbetka shelters in Central India suggests that conditions in the past were as humid, if not more humid, than they are today. Both plant and animal life must therefore have been abundant. Fossil faunal evidence from the alluvium of the Narmada, Godavari and their tributaries supports this inference.

At Bhimbetka, one shelter IIIF-23, revealed a 2.5m thick Acheulian occupation without any perceptible break. A few other shelters produced evidence of only short-term occupation. Today there are perennial water springs at Bhimbetka which are the only source of water for human as well as animal populations, both domestic and wild. If these springs were also active during the Pleistocene, occupation of the shelters would have been possible throughout the year. However, stone tool industries found in the rock shelters and nearby open-air sites, as at Barkhera near Bhimbetka and Putli Karar area, both in the Raisen district, are so closely similar as to be the work of one and the same people. It would appear that these two locations represent seasonal camping places of the same populations, the rock shelters being used during the rainy season and the open-air sites during the winter months. Over most of the country, however, the hunter-gatherers lived in the open, along perennial as well as seasonal streams. In the latter context the occupation probably took place only during the rainy season and early winter months when water would have been available in the streams and local pools. During the summer months, when water in seasonal streams and pools dried up, all human groups must have been forced to congregate along perennial rivers (Misra 1989).

Acheulian artefacts here are usually found buried in bouldery and pebbly gravels of the Son, Chambal, Narmada, Godavari and other rivers and their tributaries. These gravels are believed to have been deposited in a semi-arid climate with intermittent, erratic rainfall and sparse to absent plant cover. These gravels are invariably covered by fine silts and silty clays, which are usually devoid of archaeological material. Misra thinks that this situation is almost certainly due to the fact that such sediments were deposited by low energy streams, which were unable to carry coarser material including stone artefacts. Acheulian occupations contemporary with the deposition of fine sediments have to be searched for outside fluvial deposits. Numerous Acheulian sites (surface) found in Central India and the Eastern Ghats are probably such occurrences. Faunal remains have been preserved in Acheulian-bearing gravels in some of the peninsular rivers. The Lower Group of the Narmada stratigraphy which has yielded Acheulian tools contains fossils of *Sus namadicus, Bos namadicus, Elephas hysudricus, Equus namadicus, Hexaprotodon namadicus, Stegodon insignis*-ganesa which are all believed to be of Middle Pleistocene age. Some of these fossils types have been dated by us in the Kashmir Karewas to a period younger than 2.4 Myr (Agrawal 1992). The coarse gravel unit of the Pravara river, a tributary of the Godavari, has yielded fossil of *Bos namadicus, Equus namadicus* and *Elephas namadicus* as well as pieces of fossilised tree trunks and branches in association with Acheulian assemblages. These animals indicate the existence of both forest and open grassland environments and the availability of plentiful water round the year. There is little doubt that all these animals formed a source of food for Acheulian populations but whether they were hunted or scavenged or exploited in both these ways can be ascertained only when faunal remains are found in association with undisturbed occupation sites. At the moment such occurrences are conspicuous by their absence (Misra 1989).

Misra reports that the stone industry is marked by the low proportion of bifaces, the high ratio of cleavers to hand-axes, the very high proportion of flake tools like scrapers, the extensive use of the soft hammer technique, and the knowledge of the Levallois and discoid core techniques. This stage is best represented in the rock shelters of Bhimbetka and the open-air sites in Raisen district of Madhya Pradesh and the Tirupati valley in Andhra Pradesh.

As mentioned in the section on "Our Ancestors", a cranium of advanced *Homo erectus* has been discovered in the basal gravels of the Narmada river at Hathnora near Hoshangabad in

Madhya Pradesh. From the same deposit Acheulian tools, some of them typologically and technologically similar to those of the Bhimbetka rock shelters, have also been found (Sonakia 1985). Although both the hominid fossil and the tools come from a secondary archaeological context, their association appears quite plausible considering that elsewhere in the Old World too the Acheulian culture is associated with *Homo erectus* fossils (Misra 1989).

Narmada hominid skull: Sonakia made this momentous discovery of early man in India. As this is the only hominid skull in India, we will describe this find in some detail (for the specialist) in his own words:

> The hominid site is located near Hathnora, a village on the northern bank of the Narmada river, and 40 km north-east of Hoshangabad town in Madhya Pradesh state (22° 40' N: 81° 40' E). The Narmada river follows a westerly course across the Indian subcontinent for a length of nearly 1,300 km.... The main Pleistocene and Holocene alluvial deposits occupy a trough about 320 km in length and 20-50 km in width between Jabalpur to the east and Hardalo the west. These deposits have brought to light one of the richest Pleistocene mammalian assemblages in India.
>
> The Narmada alluvium is nearly 18m thick at the locality of the hominid find. The fossilised skull cap was removed from its basal gravel-conglomerate bed, which was exposed as a 100 X 70m wide erosional platform. This bed is nearly 3m thick and it directly overlies the Deccan Trap basalts of Eocene age exposed in the river-bed. The skull cap lay embedded in the gravel with its right temporal bone resting on the base of the deposit. Well preserved mammalian skeletal remains, including *Bos namadicus, Stegodon ganesa, Stegodon insignis, Hippopotamus namadicus, Equus namadicus,* and *Cervus* sp., were found associated with the skull in the gravel conglomerate horizon. In the immediate area were stone implements, including large and medium-sized hand-axes, flakes, cleavers, and choppers made of compact quartzite. In addition, medium-sized flint and chert scrapers were present. These tools resemble those of an Acheulian industry. The implements were embedded in the basal conglomerate.... The gravel conglomerate layer is overlaid by a nearly 2 m thick pink clay layer rich in calcareous concretions. It also contains medium-sized flakes and mammalian fossils. This pink clay is overlaid by an incoherent gravel/pebble bed of about 1-1.5 m thickness and a 10-12 m thick layer of pinkish and yellowish clay with occasional sand silt interlayers.
>
> The hominid fossil specimen, presently designated as "Narmada Man", is represented by a complete right half of the skull cap, to which a part of the left parietal is attached. It lacks a mandible, maxillary bones, and teeth. Much of the left half of the skull is missing. It is possible to locate the landmarks of Bregma, Lambda, and Asterion. The degree of suture closure is comparable to that often found in skulls of aged individuals. The cranium is robust. Its general form is dolichocranic. Its greatest length (Glabella/Opisthocranion, minimally reconstructed) is 198 mm; its greatest breadth (Bimastoid, minimally reconstructed) is 142 mm; its cranial index is 71.7; and its cranial capacity, as estimated on the basis of outer dimensions utilising the formula of Dudley Buxton, would fall around 1,200 cc.
>
> The specimen has several striking features, the most outstanding of which are the massive projecting and rounded supraorbital torus, receding frontal region, presence of a sagittal keel, a slight parasagittal depression, and a moderately prominent external occipital protuberance. The vault bones are remarkably thick, nearly 11 mm thick at Bregma. The outline of the vault appears to slope directly backward from the region of the reconstructed Glabella, the curve smoothly increasing to Bregma. Posterior to Venex, the profile of the vault is flat but becomes depressed toward the region of the external occipital protruberance. Temporal lines are marked as slightly elevated ridges that curve posteriorly to form a prominent angular torus. The remanent root of the zygomatic arch is massive. In basalar aspect the mandibular fossa is broad and shallow. The tympanic plate in the acoustic meatus is thick and tilled. The right temporal bone is flat and stout. The maximum width of skull is in the temporal region, and the supramastoid crest is prominent. Mastoid process, although broken, is small.
>
> The Narmada hominid specimen bears a number of similarities to skulls of Asian *Homo erectus,*

hence an affinity of "Narmada Man" to *Homo erectus* is suggested, pending further research. In absence of radiometric dating, the faunal assemblages, and Palaeolithic stone tools assume special significance. According to Pascoe (1931:674-91) the age of the fauna of the Narmada valley alluvium "appears to be Middle Pleistocene, and equivalent to that of the Boulder Conglomerate stage of the Siwalik". Pilgrim (1910) equated the Narmada alluvium with the Trinil beds of Java, which yielded *Pithecanthropus erectus (Homo erectus)* fossils associated with *Stegodon, Elephas hysudridicus, Hexaprotodon, Bubalus, Bos, Crocuta crocuta, Tapirus*, and Rhinoceros (Sonakia 1985: 612-16; and references therein).

Kennedy (1992) gives the following opinion on these finds:

> We conclude that employment of the Bayes factor in this multivariate analysis erodes the initial confidence in assignment of Narmada Man to the taxon *Homo erectus*. This confirms the independent results of our morphometric univariate analysis. That Narmada Man does not fit easily within the suite of morphometric characters of Asian *Homo erectus*. It is correlated with the extremely high incidence of characters that are found in middle Pleistocene hominid specimens variously labeled as "archaic" *Homo sapiens*, pre-Neanderthals and ante-Neanderthals.
>
> The Narmada calvaria is the only preserved and authenticated discovery of a middle Pleistocene fossil hominid recovered from the Indian subcontinent, and its geographical mid-point situation between the regions of relatively richer fossil hominid sites in the Far East and Southeast Asia and in the Eurasian and African landmasses afford it a unique place. However, its advent occurs in the present world of palaeo-anthropological controversy. To some investigators, *Homo erectus* is a valid taxon while to others it is a grade, a population, a palaeospecies, or even a collection of specimens some investigator decides belong together. This means that its taxonomic status will be debated for some time into the future. Those who insist that Narmada Man is an Indian *Homo erectus* find support among their colleagues who accept the validity of this taxon for widely distributed hominid populations of the middle Pleistocene. In calling it an "evolved" form, there is the assumption that *Homo erectus* is ancestral to all modern humans. Rather, we conclude that the Narmada calvaria is that of *Homo sapiens*, a hominid which exhibits a broad range of morphological traits that occur in highest frequencies in specimens from Arago 21-47, Petralona and Bilzingsieben, but are reflected, too, in possible Neanderthal antecedents such as Steinheim, Swanscombe, Ehringsdorf and Fontéchevade. Affinities with so-called *Homo erectus* and other fossil specimens from Africa (Kabwe, Elandsfontein) appear to be less obvious from our comparative analysis, and the Far Eastern and Southeast Asian Middle Pleistocene fossils share the least number of parallels with Narmada. Results of our morphometric and Bayesian statistical analyses suggest that Narmada Man shares an impressive suite of anatomical features with earlier *Homo sapiens* fossils from Eurasia and Africa (Kennedy 1992).

Thus the taxonomic assignment of the Narmada man remains uncertain.
In his new and exciting book, *God-Apes and Fossil Men*, Kennedy says:

> While Africa holds just claims today as the continent on which our earliest human ancestors evolved, the vast sub-Himalaya landmass offers scientists the challenge of discovering the evolutionary diversity and adaptations of those human ancestors who moved out of Africa and into Asia some two million years ago. Their settlement in India has been stabilised by the recovery of a middle Pleistocene fossil hominid specimen from the Narmada valley. The 34,000 years old skeleton of anatomically modern humans, who were contemporaries of the Cro-Magnon people of Europe, has been found in a cave site in Sri Lanka. Prospects of finding Neanderthals, or their collaterals, in the north-west frontier area of Pakistan are excellent (Kennedy 2000: xv).

TABLE 3.3 ^{14}C DATES OF MIDDLE PALAEOLITHIC SITES

All BP ages are based on 5568 yr half-life of radiocarbon. Calibrated ages are given in bc (after Possehl 1993).

Site	*Sample No.*	*5568 YRS.BP*	*Calib. Dates*	*Culture*	*Material*
Bhimbetka	PRL-787	15370+570, -530 BP	None	Middle Palaeolithic	Charcoal
Bhimbetka	PRL-789	17670+490, -460BP	None	Middle Palaeolithic	Charcoal
Bhimbetka	PRL-788	17230+480, -440 BP	None	Middle Palaeolithic	Charcoal
Dhamner	PRL-143	10130±250BP	None	Middle Palaeolithic	Shell
Dhom Dam	TF-1004	37,640+5200, -4245BP	None	Middle Palaeolithic	Unknown
Didwana	PRL-911	26215+2200, -1700BP	None	Middle/Lower Palaeolithic	Organic Matter
Gerwal Well	PRL-710	26090+800, -720BP	None	Middle Palaeolithic	Calcium Carbonate
Kaldevan Halli	PRL-79	1560±120BP	463,478, 530 cal.ad	Middle Plaleolithic?	Shell
Muladam	TF-217	>39000 BP	None	Middle Palaeolithic	Wood
Muladam	TF-345	31075+5550, -3254 BP	None	Middle Palaeolithic	Wood
Nandipali	PRL-293	23670+690, -690 BP	None	Middle Palaeolithic	Shell
Nandur Madmesh	BS-163	26600±430BP	None	Middle Palaeolithic	Shell
Prabhas Patan	PRL-30	20825+670, -540 BP	None	Middle Palaeolithic	Shell

Maharashtra

Maharashtra occupies the same Central plateau but is separated from Madhya Pradesh by the river Tapi (or Tapti). The political boundary of Maharashtra is roughly coterminous with the main mass of the Deccan lavas. In fact, the eastern linguistic boundary between Marathwada and Telengana is demarcated almost exactly by the edge of the lavas. On the west, beyond the Ghats, is Konkan - a thin strip of coastal lowland. The main tableland of Maharashtra is traditionally called Desh, and the Desh terrain is surprisingly homogeneous, the only variation being provided by erosional features, different soils, etc. The Tapti trough has deep regur (black soil); the rest of the area is mostly covered by medium regur. Most of Desh lies in the rain-shadow of the Ghats. The spillover of rains beyond the Ghats reaches only up to Poona and Belgaum. Deccan is drained by the rivers Tapti, Godavari, Bhima and Krishna.

Konkan, a coastal lowland, is riven with hills. This lowland is about 500 km long and 50 km wide and is watered by the rivers Ulhas, Vaitarna and Amba. With the rainfall exceeding 200 cm, today rice is the main crop in Konkan.

A fairly large number of Palaeolithic sites are known from Maharashtra (Sankalia 1974). The main emphasis in these studies was on chrono-stratigraphic correlations of stone industries. The distribution of Palaeolithic sites shows that early man occupied a variety of ecological niches: from heavy rainfall areas to semi-arid regions. The determining factor seems to have been availability of raw material. In Maharashtra this is reflected in the scarcity of Palaeoliths from the upper reaches of the rivers Bhima and Krishna. One has however to bear in mind that most of the tools have been recovered from river gravels where they may occur as secondary deposits, and one does not know how far away they are from the primary sites.

In general, the rivers of the Deccan seem originally to have had a much wider bed. On the basaltic bed a fairly thick deposit of a pebbly gravel has been taken to indicate a much wetter climate. The associated remains of elephant (*Elephas antiquus*), cattle (*Bos namadicus*) and rhinoceros, even from the sediments of the present day semi-arid tract of Poona and Nasik, do support such an interpretation (Figs. 3-7 and 3-8). The Palaeoliths from these gravels are of an advanced type (e.g. pointed hand-axes) and may represent a Late Acheulian stage. Over the pebbly gravel lies a thick clayey silt which after weathering appears as a calcareous formation which has been variously interpreted as depicting wetter regimes or still-water conditions. When the average deposit was about 10m, the rivers started cutting their beds. The next phase of deposition shows a much finer sandy cross-bedded gravel. The gravel has been radiocarbon-dated and is older than 30,000 BP; it is capped by a yellowish silt, and the topmost surface is mostly regur, which became the base for the Chalcolithic settlements. The stratigraphy of the Deccan river sections is as given in Table 3.4.

TABLE 3.4 STRATIGRAPHY OF THE RIVERS VALLEYS IN THE DECCAN

General Stratigraphic Unit	*Culture*
Pebbly gravel artifacts	Late Acheulian
Silty clay	Middle Palaeolithic
Cross-bedded sandy gravel	Blade and burin industry
Yellowish silt	Microliths
Blackish soil	Chalcolithic cultures

Climatic interpretation of the data is difficult and requires consideration of several parametres. Kajale, Badam and Rajaguru (1976:122-32) have analysed pollen, fossil, geomorphic, mineralogical and archaeological evidence from the sediments of the river Ghod to reconstruct the palaeoenvironment. Here they get only the upper units of lithostratigraphy. Their upper Bhima formation is equivalent to the cross-bedded sandy deposit; the vertisol is equivalent to the yellowish silt; and the top soil is the same.

There is a concentration of Palaeolithic finds where basalt dykes were available for tool-making. The so-called camp sites are actually workshops where early man made his tools, and there is no other sign of his settlement. A workshop site on the Chirki (an affluent of the Pravara) near Nevasa has been intensively studied. Corvinus (1983) collected more than 2,000 artifacts from this site. Heavy tools, like hand-axes and choppers were made from pebbles and lighter tools like cleavers, scrapers and borers from flakes (Pl. 3-1). The peculiarity here is that 90% of the flakes are side struck and not end struck. Besides dyke basalt, chalcedony and quartz have also been used.

Sheila Mishra (1986: 91-96) however, observes that:

1. Typologically the Nevasian does not resemble a Middle Palaeolithic industry but fits very well into the flake component of the Early Acheulian. In fact, the light duty component of the Acheulian at Chirki is identical typologically to the Nevasian.
2. The rare occurrence of the heavy duty, typical Acheulian forms such as hand-axes, cleavers, choppers and polyhedrons from the alluvial gravels which are rich in Nevasian tools, can be explained by the fact that most of the heavy duty tools were

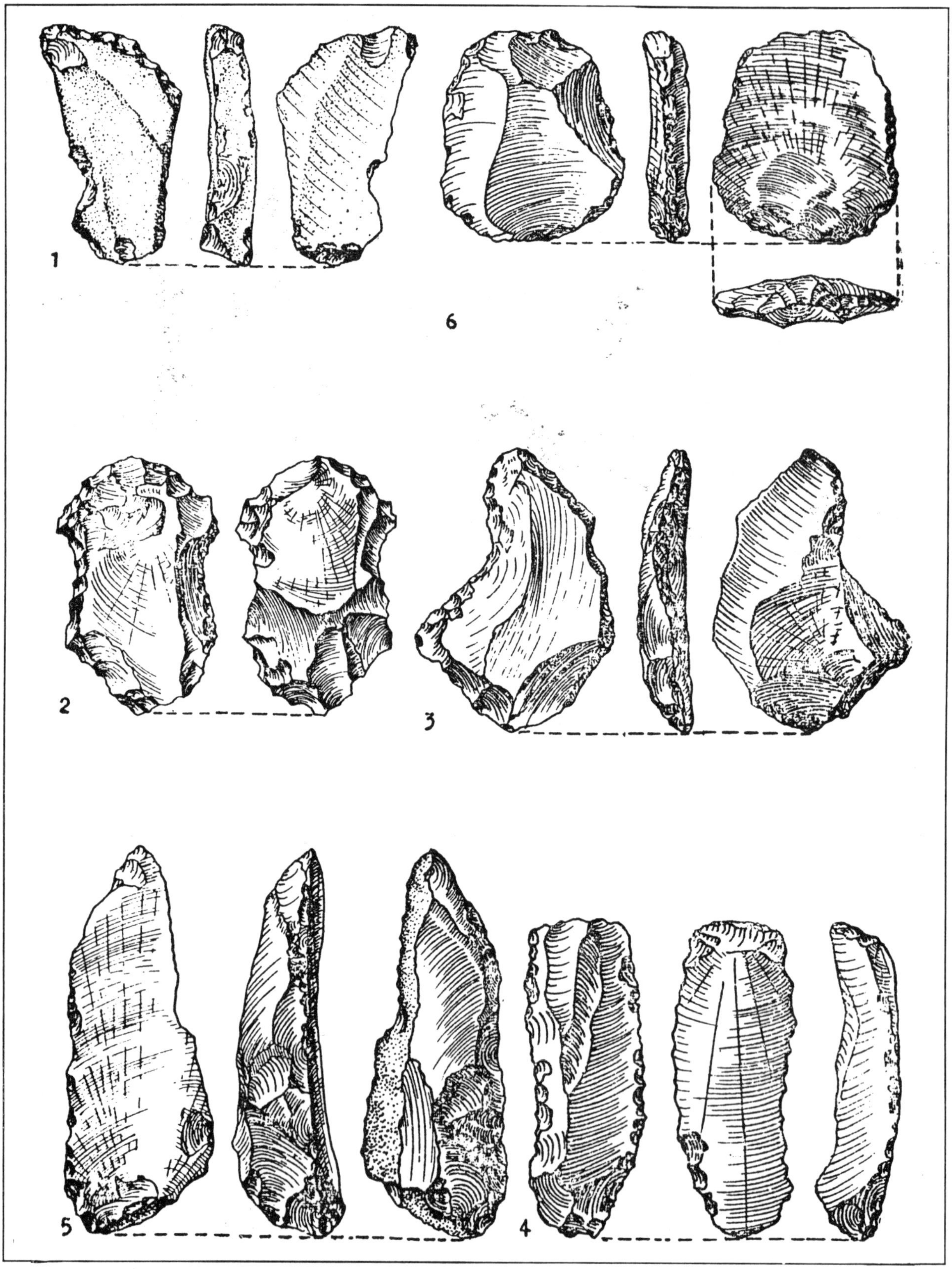

Fig. 3-7. Scrapers from Bel Pandhari and Nevasa, Maharashtra (after Sankalia 1974)

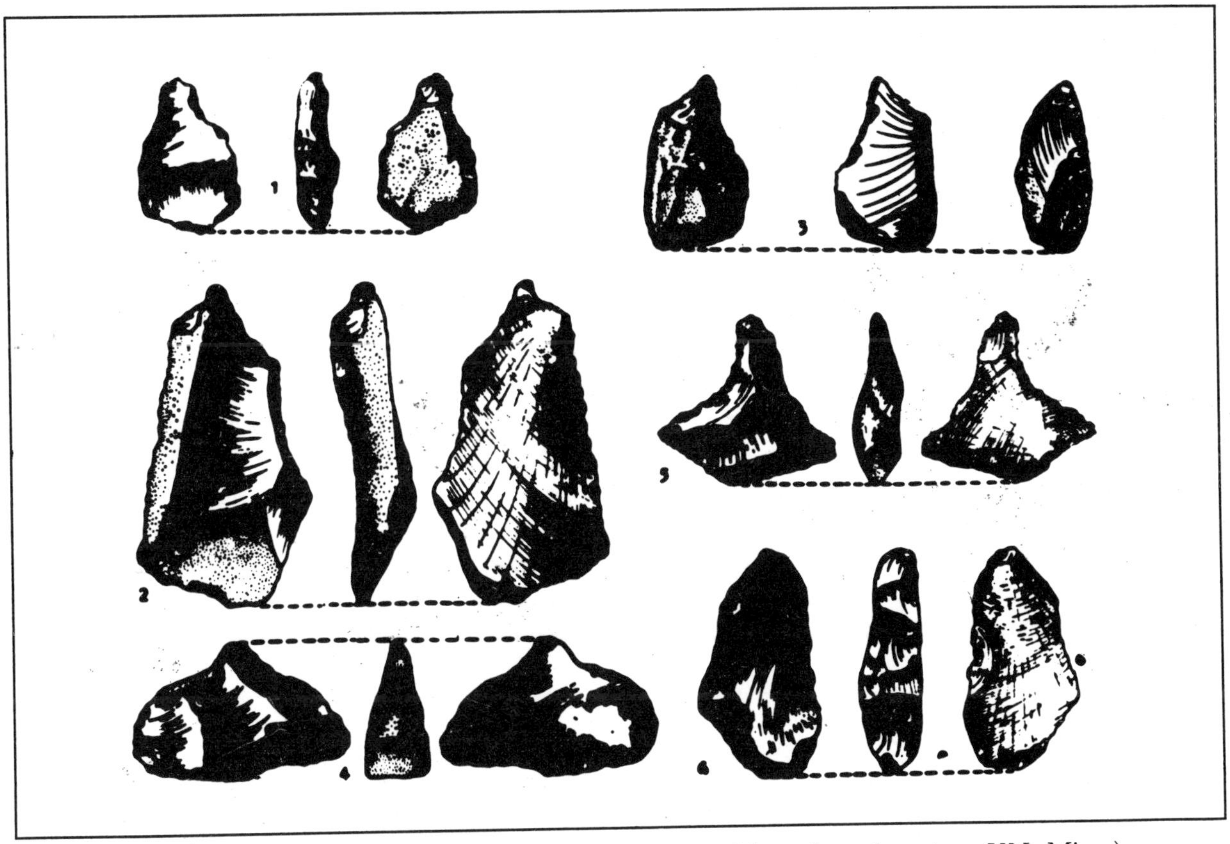

Fig. 3-8. Middle Palaeolithic borers and scrapers, Maharashtra (courtesy V.N. Misra)

made on basalt since other rock types rarely occur in large enough nodules. Basalt weathers rapidly in comparison to other rock types. Therefore the basalt component of the Acheulian has not survived re-deposition into a much later secondary context.

3. The lithological composition of the tool assemblages at Chirki primarily reflects differing intensity of disturbance. In the rubble gravel small basalt flakes appear to be under-represented. In the alluvial gravel only the silica component has survived. In the Chirki D locality the assemblage appears to be mostly intact.
4. The least disturbed locality at Chirki, based on the high rate of survival of the most easily weathered component, that is basalt flakes resembles in context Acheulian sites reported from other parts of India such as Hunsgi and Lalitpur.

For the most part, Early Palaeolithic artifacts from Maharashtra comprise chopper-chopping tools, a variety of hand-axes and cleavers and discoids. On the basis of evolved tool-types like pointed hand-axes, etc., Sankalia places the Chirki industry very near to the Middle Palaeolithic. Even the choppers from the Konkan area show fine working typical of the Middle Palaeolithic scrapers and have, therefore, been assigned to the early Middle Palaeolithic. In the early stages, the Middle Palaeolithic tools were found only in western Maharashtra but subsequent discoveries show that they occur all over the state. Stratified tools come from Gravel II, which is also rich in nodules of jasper, chalcedony, etc., which were used for the Middle Palaeolithic tools. The main sites are Koregaon, Chandoh and Shikarpur (all in the Poona district); Rankenala in the Kan valley; Nevasa and Kalegaon in the Ahmednagar district; and Khandivalli near Bombay. The Middle Palaeolithic industry is dominated by a variety of scrapers (57%), borers (25%) and points (15%). Points with single or double tang are unique to Maharashtra. Scrapers are of a great variety: hollow, double-edged and round (Pl. 3-2). No true burins are known from here.

The Upper Palaeolithic is not well represented in reports from Maharashtra though Todd had recorded an Upper Palaeolithic assemblage from Khandivalli, near Bombay. The Patne assemblage shows a clear transition from the Middle Palaeolithic to the Upper Palaeolithic. In the Upper Palaeolithic industry, unlike the thick Middle Palaeolithic backed blades made from jasper, one gets finer blades and burins made from chalcedony. The final phase here culminates in the Microlithic facies.

PALAEOLITHIC CULTURES OF THE EAST

Assam, Bihar, Bengal and Orissa have been grouped together in the Eastern Zone. Bihar and Bengal form the eastern extension of the alluvial corridor but Assam and Orissa are mostly hilly. Eastern Uttar Pradesh and Bihar comprise the middle Ganga valley. In the alluvial plains of Bihar, Palaeoliths are rare and confined to areas where rock outcrops occur. The Chhota Nagpur plateau forming the south-eastern part of Bihar, and an extension of the peninsular Indian massif, is richer in the Palaeolithic remains. These undulating, lateritic plains have a mixed geology. The old granites and gneiss occur with younger Vindhyan sandstone and basalt. Sal and bamboo forests exist only in patches today. Though Anderson had reported the first Palaeoliths from the region as early as 1917, modern research in this region is just a decade old.

Bihar

Sen and Ghosh (1960: 178-91) reported two tool-bearing terraces on the river Raro in the Singbhum district. The collection comprised pebble hand-axes, bifacial chopping tools and flakes. Though a variety of raw material has been used, jasper seems to have been preferred as there was a quarry available nearby. In Singbhum about 40 Palaeolithic sites have been reported by Ghosh. Hand-axes and choppers are the main tools. Palaeoliths were found also in the Monghyr district from the Bhimbandh and Chormara valleys. If the present conditions are anything to go by, these hill-girt forested valleys must have been ideal habitats as they provide game, fruits, tubers, raw material for tools and protection against elements and enemies. The Jethia valley, near Rajgir, has also provided evidence of early man from the earliest to the Mesolithic times.

Stratigraphically, the Early Palaeolithic tools are found in the Pebble Conglomerate but those from the Middle Palaeolithic occur at the junction of the Upper Loose Gravel and the Upper Clay. The Middle Palaeolithic is represented by a flake industry dominated by scrapers produced by the Levallois technique; a few small hand-axes also are associated. The Upper Clay assemblage is still dominated by scrapers (75%). Blades (9%) and burins (10%) appear for the first time in this horizon. The industry thus seems to be at the initial stages of the Upper Palaeolithic rather than a developed one.

Bengal

Bengal represents the eastern end of the alluvial corridor formed by the Ganga and the Brahmaputra. "New mud, old mud and marsh", aptly describes Bengal. The modern delta is recent and therefore devoid of stone tools. There are four terraces formed by the old delta, which is much higher than the modern one, and belongs to the Pleistocene age. The Pleistocene terraces can be distinguished from the dark loosely-compacted sediments of the recent delta by their reddish brown mottled colour. But not all Bengal is deltaic; the Chhota Nagpur plateau extends into its western part. Then there are the northern hills. Geologically the area has very old rocks: Archeans, Puranas, etc., which have been laterised and eroded giving rise to secondary laterite.

The valleys of the Damodar and the Suvarnarekha, along with their affluents, are rich in Palaeolithic tools. There seems to be a topographic control here on the distribution of Palaeoliths. They are found on hill slopes, foothills, elevated tracts and river banks, but the elevated tract alone is the richest in tools.

Tool collections have been made from the districts of Midnapore, Purulia, Bankura and Birbhum. In the Midnapore district there is a clear depositional cycle. The weathered bedrock is overlain by a lateritic gravel conglomerate containing Early Palaeolithic material. In the lateritic grit and silt over this deposit are found the Middle Palaeolithic tools. Hand-axes, choppers and scrapers, made both from pebble cores and flakes of quartzite, comprise the Early Palaeolithic assemblage. The Middle and Upper Palaeolithic points, scrapers, awls and possibly burins are made from chert.

ORISSA

South-west of Bengal, Orissa also has a deltaic region formed by the Baitarni, Brahmani and Mahanadi rivers. This alluvial salient is about 170 x 80 km; the large hilly area of Orissa occupies 85% of the state. These forested hills are called the Northern Circars. They rise to a maximum height of 1,500m and are composed mainly of Archaeans with an extensive development of Charnockites. The hills are sparsely populated today though many heavy industries are located here.

The Buharbalang valley in Mayurbhanj was explored by Bose and Sen and the Brahmani valley by Mohapatra (1962). Opinions vary as to the climatic inference to be drawn from the deposits, though broadly six phases have been demarcated. Stratified deposits are reported from the districts of Mayurbhanj, Keonjhar and Sundargarh; however, a complete sequence is not recorded at any site. The composite sequence is as follows:

TABLE 3.5 SHOWING STRATIGRAPHY IN ORISSA REGION

Geomorphological Unit	*Climatic Phase*	*Date*	*Artifacts*
I. Finer gravel	Wet	Upper Pleistocene	Middle Palaeoliths and burin industry
II. Weathered reddish silt	Dry	Middle Pleistocene	No tools
III. Pebbly gravel	Wet	Middle Pleistocene	Early Palaeoliths
IV. Clayey layer	Dry	Early Pleistocene	No tools
V. Primary laterites	Pluvial	Early Pleistocene	No tools

It is difficult to trace the evolution of Early Palaeolithic tools as most of them have been collected either from the secondary laterite or the pebbly gravel. The collection includes hand-axes, scrapers, points, cores, etc. The presence of small hand-axes indicates a late date for this collection. The Middle Palaeolithic industry is dominated by flakes (73%), though the true Levalloisean element is absent. Among the tools, scrapers form the largest element (71%) followed by points (21%); there are a few borers and burins. All the four burins are surface finds and may indicate an Upper Palaeolithic phase.

Recently, Subrata Chakrabarti (1990:13-21) has studied the prehistory of Khiching, Orissa. He reports that regardless of inadequate numerical representation of artefactual material in the region, there are distinct single unit and multi-unit occurrences. The former incorporates a homogenous tool group and the latter is composed of various tool groups. The single unit occurrences are represented by two Lower Palaeolithic and two Middle Palaeolithic sites. The multi-unit occurrences come from two sites of Lower/Middle Palaeolithic and one site each of Middle/Upper Palaeolithic and Middle/Upper Palaeolithic/Mesolithic.

Chakrabarti (1990) reports from Khiching (Orissa) that choppers and hand-axes form the major types in the Lower Palaeolithic. Scrapers, borers and points constitute the Middle Palaeolithic types. Although no "classic" tools of the Upper Palaeolithic were found or reported from the area, the presence of blades and flake-blades of Upper Palaeolithic type in two of the occurrences is, however, suggestive of this stage of lithic technology know-how. Microliths, especially backed bladelets of various forms and Microlithic waste, represent the Mesolithic industry. To sum up, the composite archaeological evidence from the single unit and multi- unit occurrences represents a kind of technological advance from Lower Palaeolithic to Mesolithic, albeit the data concerning the gradual evolution within the Palaeolithic or between the Palaeolithic and Mesolithic remain elusive.

He rightly claims that the Khiching plateau no longer remains *terra incognita* as far as Stone Age cultures are concerned. The Stone Age evidence collected from the 8 secondary context occurrences indicates a continuance of cultures from the Lower Palaeolithic to the Mesolithic. For the moment the possible development within the Palaeolithic tradition as well as the significance of a transitional stage, i.e., Upper Palaeolithic traits into the Middle Palaeolithic is a matter open for speculation. The Mesolithic material appears to share many of the characteristics of the Tel and the Indravati industries. This sort of similarity in artefact assemblages may reflect convergence rather than diffusion of cultures. From the few secondary context occurrences it is not possible to be certain about the cultural organisation of the hunter-gatherers in each successive stage (Chakrabarti 1990: 13-32).

In the coastal tract of the Rishikulya river basin in Orissa, a late Acheulian tool factory site has been found interbedded within an intensely lateritised basal conglomerate. The lateritised conglomerate is stratigraphically older and distinct from carbonate-cemented sandy beds containing the ca. 74.000-yr-BP ash bed. Both units contain laterite clasts. The extensively developed bedded secondary laterites from the alluvial basins close to the east coast of India represent the oldest Quaternary unit. This unit appears to include equivalents of both the ash-bearing sandstone and more oxidised older sediments and may range in age from 300,000 to 50,000 yr BP (Acharya & Basu 1993).

Assam Region

The region used to include the present states of Nagaland, Meghalaya, Arunachal, Mizoram, Manipur and Assam. This is an area of high rainfall (200-400 cm) and dense forests. The peninsular Archaean granites continue this far and are traversed by dolorite dykes, which were used by Palaeolithic man to make his tools. It is therefore obvious that even the dense forests did not deter early man so long as he got raw material to make his tools; in fact, up to 1970 this area was considered to be devoid of Palaeoliths. It is interesting to note that the Garos of this area still use primitive stone and bamboo tools for their daily chores and bark cloth to cover themselves. Of course, their stone tools are typologically unrelated to the Palaeoliths.

Goswamy and T.C. Sharma have been conducting investigations in Garo hills and Arunachal (IAR 1967-68:7-8; 1968-69: 2-3; 1969-70: 1-2). Garo hills is an extension of the Archean shield of the peninsula. The river-valleys with outcrops of dolerite dykes have revealed Palaeolithic remains. In the absence of flint, quartzite and other siliceous stones, dolerite was extensively used for manufacturing implements of all the phases of Stone Age. A thick crust of reddish patina (sometimes up to 3 mm thick), characterises the toolkit of the region. Palaeolithic implements have been reported from 10 localities (T.C. Sharma 1974).

The "cemented gravel" yields tools of both the hand-axe-cleaver and chopper-chopping traditions. At Waran, the yellow silt has yielded flake tools and a few belonging to Acheulean tradition. The assemblage is said to be of the Middle Palaeolithic vintage. However, the investigators confess that it is not possible "to trace the evolution of the lithic industries of the Garo hills based on stratigraphy" (Sharma 1974:5).

In the Lower Palaeolithic group choppers form an integral part of the dominant hand-axe-cleaver tradition. However, the Middle Palaeolithic people used dolerite as raw material for their tools. Typologically the tools are in the scraper-point tradition of the Indian Middle Palaeolithic. The well made scrapers and triangular points reveal Mousterian character, whereas, a few Aterian points have also been obtained. The Upper Palaeolithic phase is characterised by big and small blades (13 and 5 cm), with rare occurrence of burins. The leaf point is a specialised tool.

In 1970, a multidisciplinary expedition by the Geological, Archaeological, Botanical and Zoological Surveys, examined the 300 kilometre tract (lying between 27°45' & 28°15' N lat. and 96° & 97° E long.), in the Daphabum area of Lohit district to correlate the Western Himalayan glacial and glacio-fluvial phenomena with the formation of terraces and Stone Age industries with that of the eastern region. The hilly tract, in the vicinity of the surveyed river valleys of Lathi, Telly (Lohit) and Kamlong, belongs to the Archean system (IAR 1970:30). The altitude of the surveyed area lies between 180 and 3,350m above MSL, and the tool bearing deposits are located between 914.4 and 1,219.50 m. The artifacts include a chopper-chopping tool, a proto-hand-axe, ovates (2), cleavers (2), points on flake (2), side-scrapers on flake (5), flakes (4) and discoidal and cylindrical cores (2). The tools are made of dolerite, gneisses and schists (Bopardikar 1972:1-8).

PALAEOLITHIC CULTURES OF THE SOUTH

The southern states make up the Dravidian linguistic zone. On the eastern side is Andhra Pradesh comprising alluvial plains, the deltas of the rivers Godavari and Krishna, and the Eastern Ghats. The eastern coastal strip is much wider than the western coast. West of Andhra is Karnataka, mostly spread over the plateau. The southern tip of the plateau forms the north-western part of Tamil Nadu; the rest of Tamil Nadu is a wide coastal plain. The narrow south-western coastal strip forms Kerala, one of the most densely populated areas today.

We will briefly discuss here the Stone Age discoveries of Andhra Pradesh, Tamil Nadu and Karnataka, and also Sri Lanka. Recent work by Paddayya's group is very important as it has brought in new paradigms in Indian Stone Age research and therefore Karnataka will be dealt with in greater detail. Unfortunately for most of other areas one can only enumerate and describe tools.

ANDHRA PRADESH

The discovery of the first Palaeoliths in Andhra dates back to 1930 when Burkitt reported on Cammiade's collections from the Kurnool district. Since then several workers have extensively explored Andhra. This state is replete with Palaeolithic remains; practically all the districts have yielded Stone Age tools. The Eastern Ghats have some of the oldest rock formations on earth. Telengana is a region of pene- or pedi-plains intersected by broad graded valleys and littered with rock-boulders. Its poor sandy red soils are not fertile. Only the coastal and deltaic areas are a little more productive.

Quite often pebble tools form a sizeable proportion of the total assemblage; Isaac's collections (unpublished thesis 1960), for example, had 40% pebble tools. It is difficult to decide whether it is a concomitant of the hand-axe industry, or precedes it. The other types found are crude and fine hand-axes, cleavers and Clactonian flakes. Both in the Chittoor and Kurnool districts there have been several occurrences of Middle Palaeolithic tools represented by points, tanged and untanged, and a variety of scrapers. The Levalloisean technique was also in use. From these two districts one has also the best evidence for a separate Upper Palaeolithic industry.

Karnataka

The northern boundary of Karnataka (Mysore) is formed by the Deccan lava. The entire area consists of a basement of Archaean gneisses and granites, intersected by much metamorphosed Dharwarian sediments, mostly phyllites, schists, and slates, occupying the bottoms of tightly packed synclinoria. The plateau rises from 400m in the north to 1,000m in the south. The western region is called Malwad and is full of deciduous forests (sissoo, teak, sandalwood); but there is a 10-20 km wide strip consisting of evergreen trees. The eastern region is called Maidan (parkland) and has a diverse terrain. In the north are plains with blackish soil; in the east, high-lying red soils; the central portion consists of stony pasture land. Rainfall tends to become less from west to east; as a result, Chitaldurg in the east falls within the semi-arid belt.

The first Palaeolithic discoveries in this region were made more than a hundred years ago. Foote found Palaeoliths in the Shimoga district and also in the Malprabha basin. In recent years, Seshadri, Joshi, Pappu and Paddayya have discovered a large number of sites in this region. Seshadri reported a Palaeolithic site from Kibbanahalli, district Tumukur (Seshadri 1955). Since the industry is a mixture of Early and Middle Palaeolithic artifacts, Sankalia thinks that it may only be a redeposit. The Malprabha and Ghatprabha, the affluents of Krishna, have been extensively explored by Joshi (1955). Anagawadi and Bagalkot are the two richest sites on the Ghatprabha. At some sites, such as Mulanji, Alue, stratified sections are available. The sequence, starting at the top is black soil, fine gravel, fine sand and gravel, buff sand, gravel conglomerate, mottled clay and rock. Most of the tools have been found from the gravel conglomerate; the mottled clay is sterile.

Anagawadi has been studied more intensively. There is a perennial supply of water here, abundant raw material in the form of quartzite outcrops, and a forested area near at hand. Nittur is another important site in district Bellary, on the right bank of the Tungabhadra. Here the tools are made from dyke basalt and are marked by a high proportion of pebble tools, both unifacial and bifacial. This industry is associated with the fossils of *Bos namadicus*. On the other hand, in Ghatprabha basin, both the Abbevillian and the Acheulian hand-axes are found, the latter in large numbers. Pebble hand-axes here are few, but of special interest are chisel-edged and burin-type hand-axes. Another remarkable feature is that some of the hand-axes have a distinct tang for hafting which recalls the Belan examples from Uttar Pradesh. Though chert was available, only quartzite has been used for the Early Palaeolithic artifacts.

The Middle Palaeolithic industry is based on chert, though occasionally quartz and quartzite are also used. Many sites like Taminhal, Anagawadi, etc., are rich both in the Early and Middle Palaeolithic tools. The Gulbarga, Bellary and Bijapur districts have also provided many Middle Palaeolithic sites. At Taminhal borers (47.8%) dominate the industry, followed by scrapers (39.5%) and points (12.7%). The same types occur in the Anagawadi area. A large number of the Middle Palaeolithic sites in Gulbarga district are associated with the fossils of *Bos* and *Elephas*. Tools are stratified in a pebbly-cobbly gravel. The types are the same, scrapers, points and borers, though Paddayya thinks that a pyramidal or steep core technique marks the industry. Bangaitota (Bellery) has also provided a rich Middle Palaeolithic site with blade cores, parallel-sided flakes on quartzite and even heavier tools like hand-axes and choppers made on patinated basalt. There are Levallois flakes, points, as well as macrolunates in the upper levels, yet in the absence of slender blades and burins the industry cannot be termed Upper Palaeolithic.

Recently Paddayya has come out with very promising results for his long and extensive work in the Hunsgi and Baichbal valleys. In India only Misra's excavations at Bhimbetka rock shelter sites and Paddayya's work in Hunsgi area present a ray of hope for understanding the Stone Age settlements. We would therefore like to quote Paddayya group's work in the Hunsgi and Baichbal valleys in greater detail. It marks a welcome departure in Indian prehistoric studies (Paddayya 1973, 1975, 1991: 111-38, 2000: 751-52, in press; Paddayya *et al.* 1999-2000: 1-24).

Environmental Background

The Hunsgi and Baichbal valleys are located in the south-western corner of Gulbarga district of Karnataka state, forming a part of the semi-arid lower Deccan region. These valleys are separated from each other by a narrow shale-limestone plateau strip, but otherwise constitute a single erosional basin measuring about 500 sq. km. The basin is flanked by shale-limestone tablelands of 30-70m heights on the southern, western and northern sides. On the eastern side the basin is enclosed by low, dissected Archaean rocks. Buried underneath a shallow silt cover ranging from half a metre to a few metres in thickness, the valley floor is made up of granite gneiss and reefs or dykes of associated rocks like quartz, pegmagtite and dolerite, with occasional patches of sandstone, shale and limestone.

Kupi, Maralbhavi, Malnur and Isampur (Kamtahalla) (Pls. 3-3 and 3-4) nullahs drain the Hunsgi valley, joining together at the village of Hunsgi to form the Hunsgi stream. Sadab, Agni, Mudnur, Fatehpur and Kembhavi nullahs drain the Baichbal valley, coalescing near the village of Baichbal to form the Baichbal stream, which in turn joins the Hunsgi stream, eventually flowing into the Krishna river.

The valleys receive an average annual rainfall of 50 to 60cm during summers; the other months are dry. Perennial waterpools exist at bends and meanders in the nullah beds; the two basins also have several springs at several places. The local population makes use of these water bodies for various purposes. Extensive travertine deposits occur at Devapur, Kaldevanahalli and Mudnur; these sediments clearly prove that the phenomenon of spring activity antedates hominid occupation of the area.

The basin floor slopes gently towards east and south from an elevation of 460 to 470m above mean sea-level to a level of 400m in the east where the Baichbal and Hunsgi streams join together. Most of the Acheulian sites of the area occur on the rocky, gently rising sides of palaeodrainage tracts. This indicates that topographic features like the fluves and interfluves had already come into existence before the Acheulian occupation. Paddayya infers that before the commencement of agriculture on a regular scale the area supported a savanna woodland type of vegetation. Today it is only the rocky patches and stream banks which preserve a scrub jungle. Though the valleys now support only small fauna comprising fishes, amphibians, birds and animals like the hare, the jackal, the wild pig and the porcupine, the occurrence of fossilised bones of wild animals such as the cattle, the horse, the elephant and some cervid species on the Acheulian and other Stone Age sites proves that the area supported a rich animal life in the past.

Kankar conglomerates and travertine deposits are the oldest sediments formed on the basin floor. Since the Acheulian artefacts occur on the surface and not within these deposits it is reasonable to assume that both these antedate human occupation and belong to the Lower Pleistocene or even earlier periods. The basin floor is capped by brown silt deposits at Mudnur and Agtirth in the Baichbal valley (4 to 5m thick) and at Isampur (Pl. 3-5) in the Hunsgi valley (1 to 3m thick). Black silt (1 to 2m thick) is the most extensive sediment found on the basin floor as well as on the uplands. The sequence of Stone Age cultures in relation to sedimentary stratigraphy is given in Table 3.6.

TABLE 3.6 SEQUENCE IN THE HUNSGI VALLEY

Mesolithic	Top surface of black silt
Upper Palaeolithic	Upper portion of black silt
Middle Palaeolithic and Developed Acheulian	Brown silt
Early Acheulian	As a discrete level on weathered bedrock/ travertine/kankar conglomerate/fluviatile deposit

Apart from their distinctive positions in terms of sedimentary stratigraphy and their respective typo-technological features, these cultures are distinguished from one another even in the use of raw material. The Acheulian assemblages were largely made on limestone; cherts were employed by the Middle and Upper Palaeolithic and Mesolithic groups.

Reconstructions and Inferences: Paddayya *et al.* 's work in Hunsgi and Baichbal valleys assumes special importance in Indian Stone Age studies as perhaps for the first time it tries to give some bold, yet quite plausible, interpretations of their data. They have followed Binford's settlement system concepts, in preference to the settlement pattern which is only a descriptive concept. The settlement system concept seeks to discover functional interrelationships among various classes of sites and their articulation with the external environment so as to ensure the survival of the population group concerned. Paddayya explains that the application of the settlement system model of human adaptations hinges on two basic premises: a) humans are a component element of the ecosystem; and b) that human cultural mechanisms and their articulation with the biophysical and social environment produces a series of patterned relationships at the behavioural level, which in turn find their reflection in the archaeological record. Resource use schedule, site placement and demographic arrangement are the three crucial aspects of settlement systems.

Paddayya takes into account the effects of perturbations in the non-living part of the ecosystem on plant and animal communities and how these in turn influence the mode of life of human populations. He argues that it is the seasonality of climate, which was of overriding importance in the functioning of the Acheulian culture under study.

In these valleys the year consisted of a wet season and a dry season. Whatever limited ethnographic evidence pertaining to wild plant and animal food and water sources that could be gathered from the area shows marked differences between the two seasons, so much so that they could even be called 'economic' seasons - the wet season characterised by plentiful supply of wild plant foods, small fauna and ubiquity of surface water bodies; and the dry season showing considerable reduction in both these resources. Hence two major strategies governed the functioning of the Acheulian cultural system, viz., dry season aggregation and wet season dispersal.

Paddayya interprets the two major clusters of sites of the Hunsgi nullah and the Fatehpur nullahs as dry season aggregation sites because these two patches preserve perennial waterholes. Besides providing drinking water, these two nullahs could have supported gallery forests with edible plants like *Phoenix sylvestris, Balanites roxburghii*, etc., which also provided shade for camping purposes. During dry seasons both vegetation and animals would be scarce and therefore it seems reasonable to deduce that the Acheulian groups depended essentially on large game hunting, as indicated by the sites of Fatehpur IX, Yediyapur IV and Hunsgi XIV, which have yielded remains of wild cattle, wild horse and deer along with cultural remains. Quoting the examples of the Australian Aborigines and the Kung Bushmen! of Africa, Paddayya suggests such annual seasonal aggregations could serve several social, ideological and biological purposes such as exchange of information and materials, marriage brokering, and resolution of group conflicts by way of realignment of groups.

He suggests that the fragmentation of the population into individual bands or families and their spread all over the basin floor during the ensuing wet season would have been facilitated by several factors: abundant supply of water; plentiful vegetation; richer fauna comprising fishes, insects, amphibians, freshwater mussels, landsnails, crabs, etc. which would be available all over the area (Paddayya 1982:72-73). The dispersal of the population would also allow it to exploit more fully the resources of the surrounding plateau and hills. Paddayya cites examples of the extant hunter-gatherer populations of Australia, Africa and North America, to explain the process of seasonal fusion and fission of the Acheulian culture of the area under study. He also gives such examples from the Pleistocene archaeological records of the Olduvai Gorge and of the European Upper Palaeolithic sites such as Altamira, Laugerie-Haute. He however clarifies that the nomadism of his Acheulian settlement system was intra-regional, a 'water-tethered' nomadism. He decries the traditional system of Indian Stone Age research where the studies were confined to implementiferous fluviatile deposits like gravels and silts. He says that such a study would never have brought the Stone Age groups into the picture. The settlement system perspective employed by Paddayya (Paddayya *et al.* 1999-2000) marks a welcome improvement over the traditional vertical approach. Paddayya rightly claims that he has made a bold attempt to view a Palaeolithic culture as a system of interrelated units, exhibiting the organisational behaviour of a prehistoric group, as an aspect of the working of the ecosystem. Paddayya is conscious of his limitations and concedes that any refinements in his reconstruction of the palaeoenvironmental setting of the valleys will add to the existing knowledge of the Acheulian settlement system. Paddayya however admits that his study of the Acheulian culture of the area as a culture process is of the gross-level type and leaves many details unattended to.

Considerable attention has also been paid to the problem of secondary versus primary sites. At one end they have found true secondary sites yielding artifacts in fluviatile deposits. On the other, there are primary occurrences. Lying between these two extremes there are other contexts such as colluvial scree, washes and pediment fillings. There is considerable site variability: large and small sites yielding both finished tools and debitage; sites showing no evidence of on-the-spot chipping; sites with fossil fauna; sites, which may be called caches and food-processing spots.

To conclude this part, let us agree with Paddayya when he quotes Bertrand Russell's famous statement that scientific knowledge at any one time is "uncertainly certain" and then pool together their ideas and techniques to face the task of reading the mute archaeological record.

Chronology: The Acheulian culture of the two valleys perhaps can be assigned to a period covering between Middle Pleistocene to early Late Pleistocene. The fluorine-phosphate ratio values obtained on bone samples from the Acheulian sites are distinctly high and range from 8.39 to 5.06, whereas the values on bone samples from the Middle Palaeolithic to Neolithic sites in the same area vary from 5.28 to 0.22. Now there are three sets of $^{230}Th/^{234}U$ dates from Kaldevanhalli in the Hunsgi valley and four dates from Teggihalli, Sadab and Kudaigi, all lying in the Baichbal valley, given in Table 3.7.

TABLE 3.7 ^{230}TH/^{234}U DATES OF PENINSULAR REGION

Kaldevanhalli-I	^{230}Th/^{234}U Dates BP (all travertine samples)
Sample 1	(25 cm below surface) yielding Acheulian culture remains 35,000 + 2,500 - 2400
Sample 2	(1m below surface) without any cultural material 198,000+3,200 - 2500
Sample 3	(2 m below surface) without any cultural material 166,000 + 15,000 – 13,000
Sadab – I	Enamel Sample from molar of Elephas Sp. 290,000 + 21,000 -18,000.
Teggihalli-II	Enamel Sample from molar of Bos Sp. 288000 + 27,000 -22,000
Enamel Sample from molar of Elephas Sp.	350,000 (minimum age estimate)

The date for sample 1 at Kaldevanhalli and also the date for enamel sample from Kudalgi are unusually young and therefore anomalous.

Tamil Nadu

At the south-eastern extremity of the subcontinent is Tamil Nadu. It has physiographically diverse regions: the coastal plain; the Tamil Nadu hills; the Palar trough; the Coimbatore plateau; the Kaveri delta; and the dry south-east. Even though in some of these regions there are very diverse zones, yet culturally Tamil Nadu has great homogeneity. The rivers Palar, Penniyar and Kaveri drain the state. Between the Palar and the Kaveri there are prominent hills collectively known as the Tamil Nadu hills, and here the Shevaroys rise up to a height of 1,650 m.

Tamil Nadu is also rich in Palaeoliths. Though the first Palaeolith discovered in India by Foote in 1863 was from this region, not much subsequent work has been published yet. The general sequence of the lithostratigraphic units is (starting from the bottom): sterile primary laterite; implementiferous Boulder Conglomerate; and the Attirampakkam terrace. From the Boulder Conglomerate an Early Palaeolithic industry has been reported by Krishnaswamy (1947). On the basis of technology and patination this industry has been divided into three groups. The Attirampakkam terrace yields, along with older rolled forms, very advanced, elongated and thin Acheulian hand-axe types; and the top loam of this terrace contains Levalloisean flakes and cores. Banerjee excavated at Attirampakkam and Gudiyam. These excavations show a stratigraphic succession of the Acheulian and the Middle Palaeolithic flake-scraper industry. It is interesting to note that at 73 m, 45 m, 30 m, and 17m MSL peneplains can be observed today, presumably due to sea-level changes. The Early Palaeolithic artifacts are found in terraces 45 and 30m above sea-level; whereas the 17m peneplain yields only Middle Palaeolithic ones. The teri sites are associated with a mid-Holocene transgression of the sea. A large number of samples were radiocarbon-dated for the eastern coast so that a curve for sea-level changes could be worked out on an archaeological basis; the report is awaited. A Middle Palaeolithic industry comprising points, longish flake-blades and scrapers has been discovered from a stratified context at Gudiyam and Attirampakkam.

The characteristic tool-types, the hand-axe and the cleaver are made in the Acheulean tradition. Most of the hand-axes are made on core and only a few on flakes. In contrast, all the cleavers are made on flakes. The other noteworthy types are biface and pebble-scraper. Levallois element is 6.60%, and is represented by the flake-group only as there is no classical Levallois core. Gudiyam-3B is stratigraphically as well as techno-typologically later than the previous one. It is interesting to recollect that the excavator also noticed two types of Palaeolithic industries at Gudiyam. He calls one as Late Acheulean and the other belongs to a transitional stage between Late Acheulean and the Middle Palaeolithic.

The Kortalayar valley: The Kortalayar valley was explored by Banerjee in the 1960s and Vadamadurai is a well-known site of this valley. Vadamadurai-2 is the second implementiferous layer, which consists of 515 artefacts made on quartzite pebbles. Though not much rolled, the artefacts are heavily patinated. Though dominated by hand-axes made in Acheulean tradition, the industry also contains a considerable amount of chopper and chopping implements. The three varieties of cores namely prepared core with unprepared striking platform, prepared core with prepared striking platform and Levallois core, are represented by one specimen each. Blanks with unfaceted striking platform are predominant. Unprepared and faceted striking platform-types are almost in equal proportion; Levallois element is present in 4.8%, and the blades form 6% of the blank group. The occurrence of Levallois points is noteworthy. Mousterian technique of core preparation is also present in the form of bifacial discoidal cores. Jayaswal (1978) assigns the industry to at least "Middle Acheulian tradition". Fifty-five per cent of the total industry is converted into finished tool group (173). There are only seven cores (2.2%) and 195 blanks (62.3%). It is primarily a flake industry, whereas the industry was dominated by implements made on cores. A majority of cores in the industry are with prepared dorsal and prepared striking platform. Except the groups of unprepared and Levallois flakes, in which case the oval shape occurs more frequently, all others show a definite preference for elongated flakes. The blanks with unfaceted striking platform, which incidentally also have the widest angle-mean, far outnumber the other three, while the blanks with unprepared and faceted striking platforms are in equal proportion (16.9%). Jayaswal (1978) thinks that the two industries of Vadamadurai show that they primarily differ from each other only on a couple of techno-typological grounds. Firstly, the industry-3 is dominated by various types of side-scrapers, while they form only 8.50% of the finished tool group in industry-3. Probably because of this feature, the former shows a higher proportion of flake implements than those made on cores. Hand-axe, occupying predominating position in the industry-2, continues to be a major tool-type in the other as well. Pebble-tools (chopper and chopping-tools and scrapers on pebbles) are the other important tool-types of both the industries, although the percentage of the former is slightly higher in industry.

Recently extensive geoarchaeological investigations were undertaken by Shanti Pappu (Pappu *et al.* 1994; Pappu 1996, 1997, 1999, 2001 and references therein) in the Kortalayar basin (79°40'-79°56' E and 13°17'-13°10'N), which forms a part of the Palar basin. In fact, this area marks the southernmost distribution of Indian Lower and Middle Palaeolithic sites and is characterised by a high density of sites.

Two phases of Quaternary ferricretes are noted (Achyutan and Pappu 1997). Older ferricretes (1.5-2.5m thick), overlying bedrock, contain Acheulian to Middle Palaeolithic artefacts. Younger ferricretes contain Middle Palaeolithic artefacts and microliths. Pleistocene landforms were a result of weathering of pre-Quaternary deposits and their transport via colluvial, sheet and stream flood processes, followed by weathering of the profiles and ferricritisation. A total of 22 sites with a sample of 2,012 stone tools, belonging to the Lower and Middle Palaeolithic and the Mesolithic were studied. A study of site formation processes led to the categorisation of sites into several types based on their sedimentary context, artefact spatial distribution and morphology and degree of integrity. This work is the first of its kind in establishing a methodology for the study of Palaeolithic sites in ferricrete landscapes in India (Pappu 1999).

Pappu excavated the Palaeolithic site of Attirampakkam (13°13'50" N, 79°53'20"E; 33.56m AMSL) in 1999-2000 (Pappu *et al.* 2001). From the index trench (T3), excavated to a depth of 7.30 m, she found a total of 646 artefacts/natural clasts. The stratigraphy comprises two layers of ferricrete separated by sandy clays; and overlying a thick deposit of laminated clays (2.70-7.30m below surface). Possible Upper Palaeolithic artefacts were noted in Layer 2 (ferricrete: 1.15-1.80m. b.s.= metre below surface) and Middle Palaeolithic in Layer 5 (2.40-2.70m. b.s.). The most significant discovery of this excavation was the presence of 284 Acheulian artefacts in the clay deposit (Layer 6), occurring at depths of 2.7 to 6.90m below the surface, in what was previously termed the Sriperumbudur/Avadi series of Lower Cretaceous shales. Their occurrence in this deposit raises important questions related to the age of the clays and their environmental significance; and is a unique feature in the Indian Palaeolithic. She has found Acheulian artefacts on and within the laminated clays, though in a small area exposed. Three fossil teeth were also recovered from the site.

Her explorations have revealed that:

> In the case of sites located along the foothill zone and on hill slopes, e.g., Gudiyam, Nambakkam, Mettupalayam, Senrayanpalayam, Kirinayattam, and at Placepalayam artefacts are generally greater than 80 mm in size whereas at sites like Attirampakkam, Mailapur, Aryathur and Gunipalayam, located in sheet and stream flood deposits, exhibit a decrease in artefact sizes, which is in accordance with a decrease in the size of natural clasts available. At Attrampakkam a comparison of clast sizes and artefact sizes indicates that most tool > 80 mm and all tools > 160 mm have undergone preliminary off-site trimming and that raw material clasts were brought from elsewhere. In the case of sites located close to abundant raw material sources a relatively limited number of rock types were exploited. In the opposite situation, even coarse-grained quartzites have been used. No relationship between artefact types and rock types is seen, and locally available raw material was predominant.
>
> Most sites display little evidence of preliminary core trimming and the abundance of debitage in preference to cores points to considerable movement of partly trimmed cores and tools across the landscape. True quarry sites have yet to be discovered.
>
> At sites where raw material is easily available the size of debitage, in particular cortical debitage, tends to be larger. Cortical debitage has a chunkier or globular aspect as is also noted in other areas where quartzites are used (Jones 1994: 279). At almost all sites, equal percentages of 'late' stage to 'early' stage debitage predominates.
>
> Cores are few in number and never match the percentage of debitage (Table 1 in Pappu 2000). Flake cores grade into chopping tools, pounding tools and bifaces. On comparing bifaces with cores grading into bifaces, the latter are larger than the former, indicating some reduction in core volume. This is important when considering the fact that bifaces were possibly also a source of flakes (Jones 1994), and that no biface trimming flakes were found at these sites. At all sites the ratio of cores versus tools or cores versus debitage is very low. The highest number of cores is noted at sites further away from raw material sources. One reason for the small percentage of prepared cores could be attributed to clast size, where a smaller nodule size leads to the predominance of naturally backed pieces and lower frequency of the Levallois technique (Fish 1981: 379). Important to note is the existence of a possible gradation between Levallois and discoidal cores representative of stages in the reduction of Levallois cores. This is seen in West Asia (Bar Yosef & Meignen 1992; Rolland 1988: 163) at Bir Tarfawi (Close & Wendorf 1993) and in the Son valley sites (Sharma & Clark 1983).
>
> Only a few tool classes are seen at each site. In general, retouch is only along one edge and rarely does the same edge bear more than one type of retouch. Artefacts with more than one type of retouch along different edges are noted in small percentages at all sites. Retouch types are often dependent on the thickness of the tool/edge, with steep retouch in cases where the tool is thick. Retouch comprises steep abrupt, irregular scalar retouch with few cases of alternate or inverse retouch. Broken tools are few and re-use of older artefacts as indicated by differential patination is noted at some sites. At other sites broken/exhausted cores have been converted by re-chipping into core-scrapers. These

are most common at Attirampakkam and Aryathur, along with a high percentage of tools on debitage, pointing to intensive utilisation of such resources. Sites such as Nakalkona, Kirinayattam, Placepalayam, located on hillslopes, with low artefact densities, use of thermal fracture spalls and minimally retouched large tools, may point to short-term special-purpose sites.

Strategies linked to the preparation of raw material in anticipation of use, the importing and transport of cores/bifaces to areas where raw material is rare and the re-use of older/broken tools and debitage is seen at most sites in the region. Artefacts representative of Levallois, blade and biface technology are often associated with strategies representing higher degrees of mobility, but are however outnumbered by non-standardised tools.

In addition to resource structure, the repeated reoccupation of sites through time (from the Acheulian onwards), with the highest tool densities in sites located close to the river, could be tied to anticipation of re-usable raw materials, in particular in those areas where they are scarce. One possible strategy emerging is the seasonal movement of hominids between the river and the hills based on the availability of water and associated game.

Palaeolithic hominids in this region appear to have exploited locally available raw material sources (cobbles, pebbles, thermal fracture flakes) in an expedient manner, with minimal retouch and trimming. Most sites display little evidence of preliminary core trimming and the abundance of debitage in preference to cores points to considerable movement of partly trimmed cores and tools across the landscape. Reuse of older/broken artefacts was also noted. In addition to resource structure, the repeated reoccupation of sites through time (from the Acheulian onwards) with the highest tool densities in sites located close to the river, could be tied to anticipation of reusable raw materials, in particular in those areas where they are scarce. One possible strategy emerging is the seasonal movement of hominids between the river and the hills based on the availability of water and associated game. Ethnoarchaeological studies of the Irula hunter-gatherers inhabiting the study region and from other South Indian foragers, were also conducted (Pappu 2000 and references there in).

Gudiyam: Near the village Gudiyam, in the vicinity of the river Kortalayar, Locality-1 has revealed a post-Acheulean industry. Locality-2 has revealed two tool bearing deposits. The upper layer which is composed of loose brownish soil has yielded a mixed assemblage, according to the excavator, whereas, the underlying gravel contained industry belonging to the Lower Palaeolithic tradition. Gudiyam-2 industry comprises 787 specimens on quartzite. Hand-axe and cleaver group made in Acheulian tradition is the characteristic feature of the industry.

PALAEOLITHIC CHRONOLOGY OF SOUTH ASIA

In this section we summarise the main dating evidence for the Indian Pleistocene and the Palaeolithic cultures.

As an introduction to this section on chronology, we would like to give some extracts from a recent comprehensive review of the dating techniques and their applications to the Palaeolithic cultures of the world by Singhvi, who has pioneered the use of TL and other luminescence techniques in India (Singhvi *et al.* 1998: 71-73, and references therein). We give below a summary of the available dating techniques for dating archaeological and palaeoenvironmental events (given in Table 3.8).

Singhvi *et al.* (1998:71-73) state that in the Indian subcontinent, prospects of dating Palaeolithic artifact assemblages from the Neogene/Quaternary sediments in the Potwar region appear bright. In the 1980s, magnetic polarity statigtaphy of the Neogene sediments and tephrochronology of the interbedded tuffs (bentonites) of the Himalayan foreland basins resulted in the delineation of a structural evolution of the basins, tectonics and sedimentation. Fission-track chronology of the bentonites helped correlation of the magnetic polarity time scale with faunal and climatic changes (Opdyke *et al.* 1979; Agrawal *et al.* 1989). The Palaeolithic sites from

TABLE 3.8 PHYSICAL AND CHEMICAL METHODS OF DATING IN ARCHAEOLOGY
(After Singhvi *et al.* 1998)

Method	*Age Range(yrs)*	*Dated event*	*Materials*
Physical dating methods			
Potassium-Argon	$>10^4$	Rock and mineral formation, last	Volcanic ash falls, lava flows,feldspar, biotite heating event
Fission-track	$>10^3$	Rock and mineral formation, last heating event	Natural glass (obsidian, pumice), artificial glass, zircon, sphene, apatite
Alpha recoil tracks	10^3-10^6	Surface exposures	Rock varnish
Luminescence	10^2-10^5	Most recent heating, most recent burial, sedimentation, mineral formation	Heated pottery, slags, lava, flows, volcanic, ash, daylight bleached sediments, quartz, feldspars, flint, obsidian
Electron spin resonance	10^4-10^6	Mineral formation, mineral heating events	Silicates, carbonates, bones and other organic material
Uranium series	10^2-$4x10^5$	Calcium carbonate precipitation	Coral, bones, teeth, travertines, stalagmites
Radiocarbon	$<4x10^4$	Death of an organism	Wood, charcoal, seeds, nuts, peat, ivory, bones, shells
Other cosmic ray produced isotopes	10^3-10^6	Exposure of a surface to cosmic rays	Rock surface, sediments
Chemical dating methods			
Hydration	10^2-10^6	Fracturing	Obsidian
Fluorine-Uranium-Nitrogen tests	qualitative and large age differences	Death and subsequent burial	Bones, antler, teeth
Amino acid recemization	10^2-10^6	Death and subsequent burial	Bones, teeth, ivory
Cation ratio method	10^3-10^6		
Relative dating methods			
Palaeomagnetism	In principle unlimited $> 10^2$	Sedimentation, Volcanism	Sediments deposited under non-turbulent conditions, basalts

Riwat and Pabbi hills have acquired renewed significance, as they anticipate prospects of dating hominid expansion into South Asia to 2 Myr (Dennell *et al.* 1988a, 1988b; Rendell *et al.* 1989). In peninsular India, suspected Palaeolithic implements within a volcanic ash horizon at Bori (near Pune) in the Deccan Volcanic Province have been dated by the K-Ar method. A bulk sample K-Ar age was originally estimated to be 1.4 Myr (Korisettar *et al.* 1989). This was considered erroneous, as demonstrated by subsequent fission-track and K-Ar ages by Horn *et al.* (1993), who placed this age at 600 Kyr. Subsequent analysis using Ar-Ar methodology supported the age of 600 Kyr (Mishra *et al.* 1995). On the other hand, bulk geochemical analysis by Acharya and Basu (1993) and subsequent grain specific geochemical finger printing notched with the 75 Kyr youngest Toba tuff (Shane *et al.* 1995). The apparent inconsistencies in the stratigraphic reconstruction of the alluvial sequences in the Kukdi valley and the stratigraphic location of the Bori ash bed led to a currently unresolved situation. Most Acheulian occurrences in India have been placed using relative age estimates in the later phases of the Acheulian, most presumably dating to the second half of the Middle Pleistocene and to the Late Pleistocene. A set of uranium series dates places Acheulian sites comfortably to > 350 Kyr and to c.150 Kyr.

About China and South-east Asia, Singhvi *et al.* report:

> the Hominid bearing localities in Indonesia have been subject to K-Ar, fission-track and palaeomagnetic dating. The youngest Notoporo Formation has a fission-trick date bracket of 250-70 Kyr. Hominid remains recovered from the Kabuh Formation have been dated to 500 Kyr by the K-Ar method. Similarly, the older Pucangan Formation containing Jetis fauna has a K-Ar date of 1.9 ± 0.4 Myr. Based on the recent Ar/Ar dating of two hominid localities in Java, an early date for *Homo erectus* has been further advocated, with samples yielding weighted mean ages of .04 and 1.6 ± 0.04 Myr. The Indo-China region has recently produced dated Pleistocene sites, bridging gaps in our knowledge of hominid evolution and their movements in this north-south transact. The cave complex at Lang Tang in northern Vietnam has yielded a record of Pleistocene faunal remains in association with hominid fossils. Middle Pleistocene breccia samples, containing hominid dental remains, were ESP dated to 480 ± 2 Kyr.... In China, at least 400 Palaeolithic and hominid sites are known, many of which have been temporally placed based on biostratigraphy and palaeomagnetic correlation. The absence of volcanic ash beds has precluded the use of the fission-track and K-Ar methods. Dates exceeding 1 Myr have been advanced, but these are considered controversial or in need of further verification. The most reliable hominid and archaeological sites may be placed to > 780 Kyr by palaeomagnetism and biostratigraphic correlation.The Longgupo locality has recently placed hominid finds and artefacts to c. 1.9 to 1.7 Myr, although identifications and dates have not been roundly accepted. Most localities in China are clearly datable to the Middle Pleistocene. In the Zhoukoudian cave locality in China, sphene was separated from burnt ash deposits (in layers 4 and 10), and these were dated to 462 ± 45 and 306 ± 56 Kyr, respectively, suggesting that this site was inhabited for a duration of 156 Kyr. The majority of published dates are U series ages on fossil bones and teeth in which uranium is present in relatively high concentration. The closed system approximation, however, is rarely fulfilled. Nonetheless, the U series dating of the Chinese Palaeolithic has dated many localities to a range of 190-50 Kyr.
>
> Review of the Palaeolithic record reveals that a significant amount of chronometric and palaeoanthropological research has been carried out in Africa, followed by Europe. Although application of radiometric techniques is not as plentiful in Europe as in Africa, quaternary biostratigraphic and climatic records of the Middle Pleistocene are correlated to deep sea oxygen isotopic records, which aid the reconstruction of Palaeolithic chronology and environment. Unfortunately, similar investigations in the tropical South and Southeast Asia are generally lacking to this day; once these are conducted, further clues and perhaps surprises about colonisation are bound to emerge (Singhvi *et al.* 1998).

Coming back to South Asia, let us begin with Nepal which provides better chronological controls. Yoshida and Gautam (1988) have dated the deposits in Nepal using palaeomagnetic techniques. There the Lukundol Formation spans a long period: covering both Pliocene and the Pleistocene. The Members I and II cover the uppermost part of the Gauss chron (3-2.5 Myr); the Members III to VII span both Matuyama and Brunhes chrons. From Members II to IV (circa 2.9 to 1 Myr) were recovered *Elephas planifrons, Stegodon ganesa, Hexaprotodon sivalensis, Elephas hysudricus* and *Crocodylitis* sp. The Lukundol fauna corresponds to the Pinjor fauna of the Siwaliks and does not appear after Member IV, around 0.9 Myr. In the Siwaliks also such fauna does not occur after the Jaramillo sub-chron (0.9 Myr). Yoshida and Gautam (1988) place the Plio-Pleistocene boundary in the silt bed 25m below the base of Member V coinciding with the Olduvai sub-chron of the Matuyama chron. With this perspective of the fossil research in India, we are now set to explore the valley of Kashmir. Let us begin with the present fauna in the valley.

In Kashmir, besides geological techniques, a number of physical methods have been used to provide an absolute chronological framework to the intermontane valley-fill deposits. Palaeomagnetic measurements have been made at a minimum interval of 1m from all these exposed sections. According to our estimates, the Karewa deposits date back to 3.8 Myr (Cochiti sub-chron) and continue up to the Brunhes Chron. On the basis of the volcanic ash occurring towards the top of Remzone-5 and in Romzone-I, the two major sections have been inter-connected. The volcanic ash dates to 2.3 Myr (Kusumgar *et al.* 1985). The uppermost part of the sequence is covered by the normal polarity of the Brunhes chron. For the first time the Villafranchian fauna in the Karewas has been dated to be younger than 2.4 Myr, both on the basis of Palaeomagnetic measurements and fission track dating (Agrawal *et al.* 1989; Agrawal 1992).

The loess deposits have been dated using TL and radiocarbon techniques. Rendell *et al.* (1989) date the beginning of the loess as younger than 140,000 years BP.

Rendell *et al.* (1989: 202-6) have produced a chronology for the Potwar and Riwat region but it is not yet widely accepted. They claim that the only securely-dated material in northern Pakistan from this 600,000 year period are the three hand-axes and a few flakes from Dina and Jalalpur; and the hand-axe and disc core from the upper conglomerate at Riwat. They have dated the implementiferous level of Riwat to ca. 2.0 Myr. They recognise fully that "this is the most contentious part of our results, since this impinges directly upon prevailing views of human origins and Eurasian colonisation". They say, "There is no doubt in our minds that the lower conglomerate horizon is overlain by 70m of Upper Siwalik deposits, and we have shown that these must be between 0.9 and 2.47 Myr old on palaeomagnetic grounds. We also have no doubts that the section at Riwat is an integral part of the Sohan Syncline. The dating of that folding to 1.9 Myr is the result of the work of other investigators, but we see no reason to disbelieve their conclusion"(Rendell *et al.* (1989: 202-6). (For details see section on Palaeolithic cultures of the North.)

In a comprehensive review of Stone Age chronology of South Asia, Sheila Mishra (1992: 325-27) has remarked that it is only in Africa that the Acheulian has been dated to the Lower Pleistocene. She admits that in India a late age for the Acheulian has been generally accepted. In the last decade, $^{230}Th/^{234}U$ dates have been accumulating for Indian Quaternary deposits and the associated Acheulian artefacts. Mishra has argued that all the Acheulian sites dated by this method are beyond its limits of 350,000 years.

$^{230}Th/^{234}U$ dates for post-Acheulian deposits were first obtained by Baskaran *et al.* (1986) for a number of sites in Saurashtra. The dates of 190,000 years BP for the miliolite at Umrethi and 69,000 years BP for the miliolite at Adi Chadi Wao were the first indications that the Acheulian in India predated the Late Pleistocene.

TABLE: 3.9 TH230/U234 (Dates Years in BP) FOR THE ACHEULIAN CULTURE IN INDIA (after Mishra 1992 and references therein)

Site	*Material*	*Date*	*Context*	*Reference*
Umrethi	miliolite	190,000 + 29,000, -22,000	Overlying Acheulian artefacts in gravel	Baskaran *et al.* (1986)
Adi Chadi Wao	miliolite	69,000 + 3,800, -3,600	Overlying Acheulian artefacts in gravel	Baskaran *et al.* (1986)
Kadevanhalli	travertine	174,000 ± 35,000	Underlying rubble containing Acheulian artefacts	Szabo *et al.* (1990)
Sadab	Elephas molar	166,000 + 15,000, -13,000 290,405 + 20,999, -18,186	Associated with Acheulian artefacts	Szabo *et al.* (1990)
Teggihalli	Bos molar	287,731 + 27,169, -18,180	Associated with Acheulian artefacts	Szabo *et al.* (1990)
	Elephas molar	>350,000	Associated with Acheulian artefacts	Szabo *et al.* (1990)
Didwana (16R)	Calcrete	144,000 ± 12,000	Middle Paleolithic artefacts	Raghvan, Rajaguru and Misra (1989)
Didwana (16R)	Calcrete	150,000 ± 10,000	Middle Paleolithic artefacts	Raghvan, Rajaguru and Misra (1989)
Didwana (16R)	Calcrete	>390,000	Lower Paleolithic artefacts	Raghvan, Rajaguru and Misra (1989)
Yedurwadi	Calcrete	>350,000	Acheulian artefacts in gravel	Atkinson *et al.* (1990)
Nevasa	Calcrete	>350,000	Acheulian artefacts in gravel	Atkinson *et al.* (1990)

The work at Didwana carried out by Misra, Rajaguru, and others (Misra, Rajaguru, and Raghavan 1988) is very important for our understanding of the prehistory and the Quaternary of the Indian subcontinent. The excavation there of a 20-m dune section including detailed micromorphological, sedimentological, and archaeological studies is without parallel in India. From this section a series of uncorrected $^{230}Th/^{234}U$ dates range from 144,000 years BP to > 390,000 years BP. A thermoluminescence (TL) date of 163,000 ± 21,000 years BP (Raghvan, Rajaguru, and Misra 1989) was obtained from just below the level dated by $^{230}Th/^{234}U$ to 144,000 years BP. This level is characterised as Middle Palaeolithic. The level which is beyond the range of $^{230}Th/^{234}U$ dating is characterised as Lower Palaeolithic. The interesting result of this work is that here the Middle Palaeolithic is dated to the range of 150,000 years BP and the archaeological material below the Middle Palaeolithic is beyond the range of $^{230}Th/^{234}U$ dating.

Corvinus's work on the Chirki assemblage shows it to be Early Acheulian. Attempts at $^{230}Th/^{234}U$ dating of the calcrete containing Acheulian artefacts at Nevasa therefore has important archaeological implications. The date of > 350,000 years BP (Atkinson *et al.* 1990) places the Acheulian there beyond the dating range of the $^{230}Th/^{234}U$ method.

At Yedurwadi, on the Krishna river, the sequence begins with reddish clay with interlayered calcrete bands and occasional fine laterite-rich sands that have yielded one very small basalt flake. It ends with a gravel which has buried a number of trees preserved as root casts and which contains a number of crude trihedral hand-axes of the Acheulian tradition, polyhedrons, choppers, and flakes. The calcrete root dated by Th/U and the gravel which buried them could not have been separated by much time, and therefore the dating of these root casts to > 350,000 years BP (Atkinson *et al.* 1990) again places the Acheulian beyond the range of this dating method (Sheila Mishra 1992: 325-327).

During Ice Ages sea-levels fell by more than 100 metres. On the Saurashtra coast clear evidence of high sea-level up to 5 ± 3m is provided by inland oyster beds, coral reefs, coastal miliolites, high strand-lines, etc. The west coast of Maharashtra also shows these sea-level changes and a ^{14}C and $^{230}Th/^{234}U$ dated sea-level curve has been worked out (Agrawal *et al.* 1973: 3-17; Gupta & Amin 1974: 79-83). It shows that there were three marine transgressions at about 5,000, 35,000 and 130,000 BP. On Bhadar there is only one major aggradation cycle. If we equate it with the incursion of 120,000 BP, we can attribute this to an upper limit of the Early Palaeolithic in Saurashtra.

As discussed above (Karnataka section), Kaldevanhalli Acheulian site has produced five $^{230}Th/^{234}U$ dates ranging from 190 to 350 Kyr.

Rajaguru *et al.* have shown that the Middle Palaeolithic tools are found in an inset terrace cut into miliolite rocks. Near Junagadh, they have found Early Palaeolithic artifacts from a pre-miliolitic gravel. The miliolite rocks have been attributed different origins by different workers. One view holds that the miliolite is formed by foramanifera blown inland from the exposed continental shelf. It is not a reliable material for ^{14}C dating and the available dates range from 14,000-30,000 BP. The oyster shells from Badalpur and Hiran gave an age of about 22,000 ± 2,000 BP. These dates could represent the upper limits of the 30,000-35,000 BP marine transgression. The available evidence suggests that there are two miliolite formations, one formed after the 120,000 BP incursion and the other after the 35,000 BP rise in sea-level. This would give an upper date of 120,000 years to the Early Palaeolithic artifacts as they are pre-miliolite, and to the Middle Palaeolithic a post-35,000 BP date, as they are post-miliolite. These estimates are obviously based on tenuous arguments and need to be checked by more direct evidence.

As mentioned earlier, Acharya and Basu (1993: 10-19) have reported a late Acheulian tool factory site interbedded within an intensely lateritised basal conglomerate from the coastal tract of the Rishikulya river basin at Orissa. This unit appears to include equivalents of both the ash-bearing sandstone and more oxidised older sediments and may range in age from 300,000 to 50,000 yr BP.

Emphasising the importance of the Toba ash, Acharya and Basu (1993) state that the Youngest Toba ash (c. 74,000 yr BP) occurs extensively in the Indian subcontinent. The reworked ash samples are closely similar in their bulk chemical composition, REE signature, and bubble-wall shard morphology to those from the Toba cadera and deep-sea cores from the Bay of Bengal and Indian Ocean. The distal Toba ash is likely to have dispersed over a wider area. The Toba ash thus can be used as an event marker for regional and global Quaternary correlation. Quaternary correlation in the Indian subcontinent otherwise is very imprecise.

The Quaternary sediments in the central Narmada and middle Son basins contain well-exposed Late and Middle Pleistocene sediments containing rich mammalian and cultural records. Based on the presence of the c. 74,000 yr-BP ash bed marker and stratigraphy relations, it has been possible to correlate late Pleistocene sediments over wide areas in the Indian subcontinent, including areas in Bangladesh with those of Central India, as well as with deep-sea cores. This has resulted in recalibration and significant improvement in the correlation and dating of Quaternary alluvium of the subcontinent, and has led to the assignment of a Middle Pleistocene age to the formation containing the only remains of the hominid.

The Toba ash has a broadly north-westerly spread in the Indian Ocean and the subcontinent. The ash bed is significantly thicker in the Indian subcontinent, possibly because of reworking and contemporaneous redeposition. The ash units located close to the east coast often are very thick (2-5 m) and coarse-grained (maximum size 0.75-3 mm). Thus, the dispersal of ash might have been affected by rain flushing of the ash-laden cloud striking the Indian coast 2,500 km from the source (Acharya & Basu 1993: 10-19).

Mishra (1995) also suggests that the Early Acheulian contexts at Bori, Hungsi, Yedurwadi, Nevasa and Singi Talav are beyond the range of Th/U dating - i.e. > 400 Kyr. K/Ar dating of volcanic ash at Bori suggests that the Acheulian at Bori belongs to the Early Middle Pleistocene. From the Siwaliks in both Pakistan and Nepal, Acheulian artefacts have been found in comparably early contexts. The Riwat evidence is suggestive of man arriving in the subcontinent in the Early Pleistocene. The Middle Palaeolithic at the 16R dune near Didwana is associated with the last interglacial (125 Kyr) phase of dune stabilisation and a TL date of 126 Kyr. The levels below the Middle Palaeolithic horizon yielded Th/U dates > 166 Kyr, and a TL date of 166 Kyr. Th/U date from Jetpur in Gujarat places the Middle Palaeolithic around 50 Kyr. Many of the radiocarbon dates for the Upper Palaeolithic are >25 Kyr. The sites of Patne, Dharampuri and Bedaghat have been dated to more than 25 Kyr while the sites of Nagda, Chandresal and Mehtakheri date between 30 Kyr and 40 Kyr. The dates for Inamgaon (approx. 21 Kyr) are among the youngest for the Upper Palaeolithic phase in Western India. This would place the main Upper Palaeolithic phase to oxygen isotope stage 3 (Mishra 1995).

CONCLUSIONS

After this brief survey of Indian Stone Age, in a global perspective, we need to take stock of the scenario of the state of research, especially in India.

The Acheulian culture slowly developed into the Middle Palaeolithic by shedding some of the older tool types and by incorporating new forms and new techniques of making them. In western Europe, the Near East, north Africa and Central Asia the Middle Palaeolithic occupation sites are associated with the physical remains of *Homo sapiens neanderthalensis* or Neanderthal Man. Though no physical remains of Neanderthal man have been found in India, stone tools very similar to those found with this species in Europe and other areas are widespread in the subcontinent.

Mishra (1995) says that the Middle Palaeolithic culture developed during the Upper Pleistocene, a period of intense cold and glaciation in high altitudes and northern latitudes. Areas bordering glaciated regions experienced strong aridity. That is perhaps the reason why Middle Palaeolithic sites are comparatively sparse in western Rajasthan, the Mewar plateau and the Gujarat plain. In general, however, we may say that the Middle Palaeolithic populations occupied the same regions and habitats as the preceding Acheulian populations (Sankalia 1964). Middle Palaeolithic stone tool assemblages have been found in the Sanghao cave near Peshawar (Dani 1964), Sohan valley (de Terra and Paterson 1939; Salim 1986) and near Rawalpindi on the Potwar plateau (Rendell and Dennell 1987), all in Pakistan. In India, from Luni valley (Misra 1961), around Didwana (Misra 1987a; Misra and Rajaguru 1986), and around Budha Pushkar (Allchin *et al.* 1974, 1978), in western Rajasthan, at numerous sites in the valleys of the Chambal, Son and Narmada and their tributaries in Central India (Allchin 1959; Khatri 1958, 1962b; Ahmed 1966; Pant 1982; Sharma and Clark 1983; Misra 1985a; Pandey 1987), also from the Chota Nagpur plateau (Mohapatra 1962; Ghosh 1970), on the Deccan plateau (Sankalia 1956; Malik 1959; Paddayya 1968, 1974; Pappu 1974), and in the Eastern Ghats (Isaac 1960; Murty 1966; S.N. Rao

1966: K.T. Reddy 1968; V.R. Reddy 1968; V.V.M. Rao 1979; Nanda 1984; Mishra 1995 and all references therein).

During the Acheulian period Middle Palaeolithic occupations were located in open-air sites along perennial as well as seasonal streams, along hill slopes and on stable dune surfaces as in western Rajasthan (see Figs. 3-5 and 3-6), and in rock shelters as in Central India. Evidence from the site of Samnapur in Narsinghpur district, MP shows that in this case Middle Palaeolithic groups camped on high alluvial flats away from the river channel and close to the hills. This location provided protection from the floods and easy access to good quality chert in the Vindhyan hills (Mishra 1995).

Mishra (1995) describes the significant changes that took place in technology during this period. The use of bifaces (hand-axes and cleavers) as also of heavy core tools like choppers, polyhedrons and spheroids slowly disappeared. Instead, tools made on flakes and blades (parallel-sided thin flakes) became more common. Side scrapers of various types, end scrapers, denticulates, notches, points and borers are the most common tool types of this period. These were made by the application of retouch, that is, by finely trimming the edges of parent flakes by the removal of tiny thin flakes or chips. Many of the scraper forms are believed to have been used for manufacturing wooden tools and weapons and also for processing animal hides. Some of the points were perhaps hafted in wooden shafts for use as spears. Gradually the tools became smaller, thinner and lighter. Improved and economical techniques of removing flakes from cores such as the Levallois and discoid core techniques were used extensively. There was also a significant change in the choice of rocks for making tools. While quartz, quartzite and basalt continued to be used, in many areas they were supplanted in varying degrees by chert and jasper and other fine-grained siliceous rocks. Raw material for making tools was sometimes brought from considerable distances. At Samnapur, for example, while the chert used for making the bulk of the tools was available on the hill close to the site, other rocks like quartzite and basalt were brought as cobbles from hill slopes and seasonal stream beds several kilometres away. Factory sites with vast quantities of artefacts in various stages of manufacture occur on chert outcrops as at Choli Dongargaon near Maheshwar on the Narmada and at Sojat in Pali district of Rajasthan. The smaller size of the tools is probably due to the choice of the raw material (Mishra 1995). Mishra admits that our knowledge of the environment of this period is limited. The faunal remains from the Upper Group of the Narmada alluvium comprising *Equus namadicus, Bos namadicus, Hexaprotodon palaeindicus, Elephas hysudricus, Stegodon insignis*-ganesa and *Cervus* sp. suggest a savanna grassland environment interspersed with swamps and forests.

Most Indian Middle Palaeolithic sites display predominant use of locally available raw material, except at Samnapur (Misra *et al.* 1990) and the Son valley sites (Sharma & Clark 1983), and this pattern also emerges from the Kortallayar site complex. No relationship between artefact types and rock types is seen in the study region; and this is true for most Indian Middle Palaeolithic sites except Jamalpur (Jayswal & Pant 1977-78) and the Son valley sites (Sharma & Clark 1983). A shift in raw material from quartzites used during the Acheulian to siliceous rocks is noted only in those areas where such material was available. It has been noted that at Indian Middle Palaeolithic sites where quartzites predominate, tools have greater dissimilarities in shapes and less pronounced retouch (Alam 1990; Misra 1972), and this is a common feature in the Kortallayar basin sites. A continuation of Acheulian types is noted here as elsewhere and has been linked by Misra (1972) to the continued use of quartzites. The prepared core element (Jayswal 1978) is observed in the Kortallayar basin sites; and is linked to the use of quartzites, in contrast with the blade element predominant in areas with siliceous raw materials. As studied elsewhere in India (Sankalia 1974: 148), the size of tools in the Kortallayar basin is closely linked to the size of raw materials. Misra (1972) believes that during the Middle Palaeolithic there is a decrease in the size of tools and craftsmanship, and a decline in the percentage of Levallois flakes and an increase in tools on thin natural pieces with retouched margins. This is also seen over parts of Central, Western and Southern India (Sankalia 1974: 150; Joshi & Sali 1969), where natural nodules or pieces of stone were retouched into points and borers marked by a lack of symmetry and refinement. These observations hold good for the Kortallayar basin sites as well. Important to note is the unusual predominance of cores at the site of Lakhmapur (Petraglia *et al.* in preparation), in contrast to other Indian Middle Palaeolithic sites. In the present state of our knowledge, variability in lithic technology in the Indian Middle Palaeolithic appears to cross-cut geographic and environmental boundaries and to be largely conditioned by raw material constraints (Pappu 2000 and references therein).

There is no doubt that there are promising and excellent examples of work on primary sites from Bhimbetka (MP) and Hunsgi valley (Karnataka), but, we are afirad, they are exceptions rather than the rule. Elesewhere it is more a story of collecting loads of stone tools from secondary fluvial contexts, and describing them in great morphological detail, as if the humans who made them were of no relevance.

No surprise therefore that Varma (1997: 1-7) presents a gloomy picture of Stone Age research done during the post-Sankalia era (after 1990). "During the post-Sankalian era, unfortunately, most of the personalities who had taken a leading part in the pursuit of prehistoric studies gradually retired from the scene and were replaced by persons...who could not take sufficient interest.... The biggest casualty was the University of Allahabad which had an excellent team of scholars. It was followed by other Universities of Baroda, Banaras, Sagar and Vikram, to name only a few. Even the Deccan College could not keep up the old tempo for prehistory.... The Archaeological Survey of India, which had always taken a keen interest in all types of archaeological studies and had a tradition of producing eminent Directors and Director Generals has been reduced to a bureaucratic institution lacking vision and perspective. ...Presently the post of the Director General is simply an administrative one and it tackles problems only on a day-to-day basis. It has now ceased to play the role of leader in archaeological pursuits" (Varma 1997:1-7).

Somehow the Stone Age research has confined itself almost totally to collection and description of stone tools. We have hardly any time to look beyond the tools to the humans who made them. Though we have millions of stone artefacts today, we have no primary sites worth the name, or hominid remains (except the solitary exception of Narmada skull discovered by Sonakia).

Varma puts these lacunae of Stone Age research in a forceful manner. He says:

> It is important to note that most of the authentic publications that have come out during the preceding era are simply records of prehistoric tools gathered at the sites and a report on the geological formations from where they have been collected. In some of the reports and books detailed statistical analyses have also been provided, with the result that books on prehistory have become only inventories of artefacts. The discovery of sites, the classification of artefacts, the study of stratification and the evolving of a chronological framework are not the ultimate aim of an archaeologist. These are only the means to understand man's cultural achievements in their entire perspective. The question now arises as to what is the objective of prehistoric studies?.... What was the pattern of man's interaction with nature and his fellow beings?.... At the present stage of our knowledge we hardly know anything regarding the pattern of life, or about the men and women who fashioned the tools and artefacts that we carefully collect. It is important to note that although hundreds and thousands of Lower, Middle and Upper Palaeolithic sites have been located hardly a few primary sites have so far been excavated. The location and excavation of primary sites belonging to the Palaeolithic period is most important for the purpose of reconstructing environmental and social conditions, the

structure of society, settlement, etc. At present our entire knowledge regarding settlement patterns, economic and social structures have been reconstructed on European evidence" (Varma 1997:1-7).

We agree with Varma when he says that we should now try to concentrate on the excavation of primary sites of the Lower, Middle and Upper Palaeolithic and on that basis should try to understand and reconstruct the life pattern of Palaeolithic man in India. Hardly any effort has been made to interpret the evidence for reconstructing the pattern of life. We have however to happily note that Paddayya is still active in the Hunsgi valley, and the young scholars like Sheela Mishra, Richa Jhaldyal, Shanti Pappu, Ajit Prasad, Goudeller and many others are conscious of the lacunae and are trying to blaze new trails and, therefore, the future of Stone Age research in South Asia does not look bleak at all.

Finally, we would like to close this chapter with the optimistic remark of one of our most prolific anthropologists:

> South Asia is the next frontier of paleoanthropological discoveries, lying as it does at the geographical intersection of Africa and southern Asia and within oceanic waters confluent with those of Australasia. Today radiometric and other dating methods are widely used by archaeologists in south Asia. At the close of the twentieth century the groundwork in prehistoric archaeology, paleoecology and biological anthropology has been laid, but the true adventures lie ahead (Kennedy 2000: xvi).

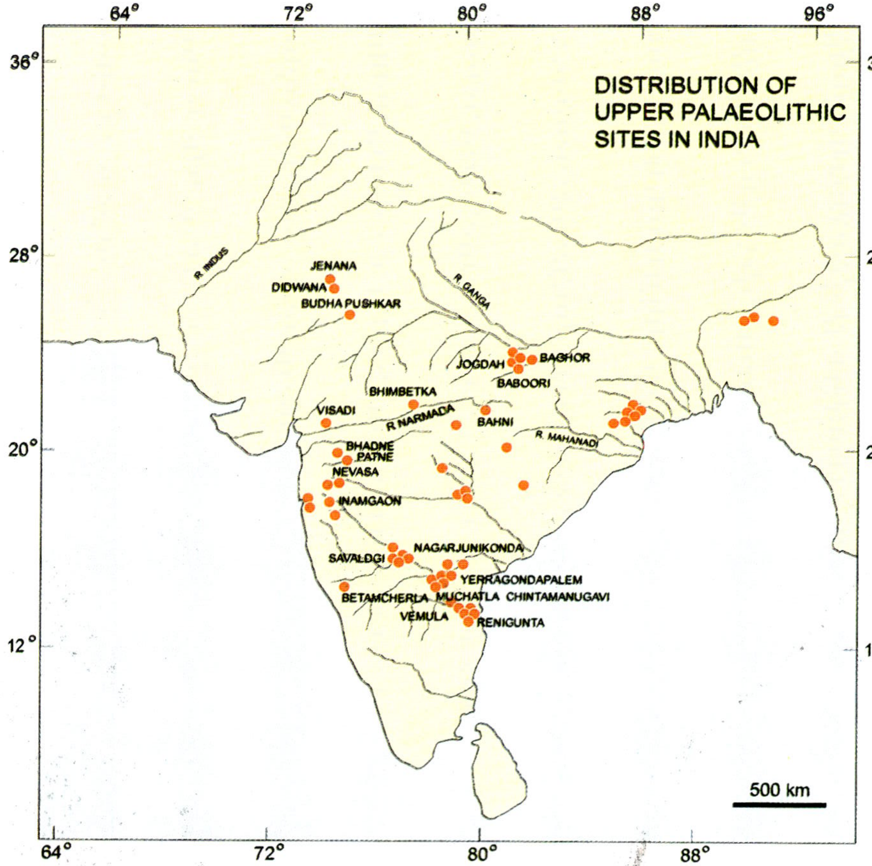

Map 4-1. Distribution map of Upper Palaeolithic sites (after Misra 1989)

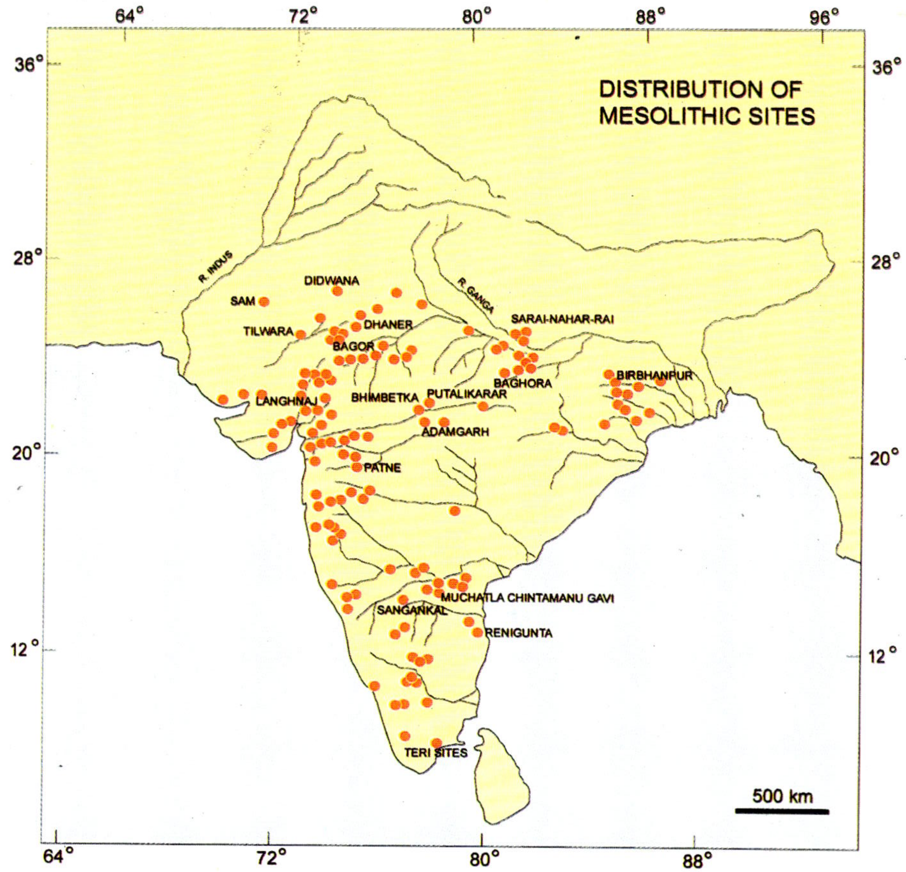

Map 4-2. Distribution map of Mesolithic sites (after Misra 1989)

Chapter 4

THE TRANSITIONAL CULTURES : UPPER PALAEOLITHIC AND MESOLITHIC

Contents :

- Upper Palaeolithic
- Mesolithic
- Post-Pleistocene Settlement Patterns
- Conclusions

In South Asia the Upper Palaeolithic phase of the South Asian prehistory is not well defined. On one end it is a continuation of the Palaeolithic cultures, and on the other end, it merges with the Mesolithic cultures. In fact, for some of the sites, we have described the Upper Palaeolithic phase in continuation of the earlier phases of the Palaeolithic in Chapter 3. In this chapter we propose to bring out the transitional nature of the Upper Palaeolithic and the Mesolithic phases of South Asian prehistory. The Mesolithic cultures merge with the early farming cultures, there being no sharp dividing line between the two.

UPPER PALAEOLITHIC

In a comprehensive survey, Raju (1988) lists the main Upper Palaeolithic sites of India (Figure 4-1). In Andhra Pradesh, these include the sites of Renigunta (Murty 1968, 1970), Erragondapalem and Vemula (Reddy 1970), Gundlakamma valley (Isaac 1960) and the limestone caves in the Kurnool district (Murty 1974, 1975, 1979; Murty and Reddy 1976), the Gambheeram valley in Visakhapatnam (Reddy and Prakash 1988), and the Paleru valley in the Prakasam district (Rao 1979). Sites in Karnataka include Shorapur Doab (Paddayya 1979) and Salvadgi (Seshadri 1962), and in Maharashtra, Inamgaon in Pune district (Sali 1974), Bhokar in Nanded district (Joshi and Pappu 1979), and Patne in Jalgaon district (Sali 1988). Other sites include Bhimbetka cave and rock shelter sites in the Raisen district of Madhya Pradesh (Misra *et al.* 1977), the Belan valley south of Allahabad in Uttar Pradesh (Sharma 1973), Singhbhum in Bihar (Ghosh 1970), and a few sand-dune sites in Gujarat and Rajasthan (Allchin, Goudie and Hegde 1978) (Map 4-1) (Raju 1988 and references quoted by him).

Murty and Reddy were the first to plead for a well defined place for the blade-and-burin industry in India. They said that these industries variously:

> referred to as Series III/flake-blade/blade-tool/blade-and-burin/Upper Palaeolithic or Upper Palaeolithic-like, having distribution in different parts of the country, warrant a taxonomical position

> for this phase in the Indian prehistory. Since these industries are typologically/stratigraphically intermediate between the Indian equivalents to the Middle Palaeolithic and Mesolithic of Europe, and they bear resemblances to the Upper Palaeolithic of the same region, the Indian industries could also be ascribed to the Upper Palaeolithic notwithstanding the fact that there are not as many Upper Palaeolithic subdivisions in the Indian subcontinent as in Europe. We are still a long way from understanding the extra-technological and suprasomatic preoccupations of the authors of these industries, as is true in other parts of the Old World. It is hoped that the investigations being conducted in the Kurnool caves and in the painted caves and rock shelters in Central India will unravel this problem (1976: 214-26).

Even today, one has to agree with Jayaswal (1978) when she said that the Upper Palaeolithic is the most controversial and least known phase of Indian prehistory. It has been frequently addressed by such names as 'blade-burin' or 'blade-flake' culture, etc. Compared to this, the European Upper Palaeolithic, particularly that of the western part of the continent, is the best studied phase of its prehistory. Geologically, its various cultures belong to middle and upper Wurm, a period lying between the different Mousterian cultures of the Middle Palaeolithic phase on one hand and the Maglemosian culture of the Mesolithic on the other. Culturally, it is characterised by a new lithic tradition of blades and burins, very rich bone industries the specimens of which are also at times decorated, and above all various forms of art activities including painting, engraving, terracotta, bone and stone sculpture. As compared to this, Jayaswal admits, the Upper Palaeolithic in India is neither geologically nor culturally well defined. There are only a few localities where the industries of this phase have been found in stratified deposits. Even in such cases the dates given to them are very approximate and hardly based upon any convincing scientific consideration (Jayaswal 1978).

In her book, *Palaeohistory of India*, Jayaswal (1978) has given a comprehensive summary of the Upper Palaeolithic of South Asia. After presenting the following discussion, mainly based on her book, we would go into some details of the important Upper Palaeolithic sites.

Regarding the chronology of the Upper Palaeolithic, Jayaswal admits that its very poorly dated. According to Rajaguru and Hegde, the associated Middle Pleistocene fauna with the Upper Palaeolithic blade tools in the peninsula could be taken as the late survivals of earlier species and could be dated to "Upper Pleistocene" (Rajaguru and Hegde 1972).

Giving the historical background of these discoveries, Jayaswal informs that the first indirect reference to the existence of "Upper Palaeolithic" in India was made by Foote. He claimed to have discovered a few bone implements from Billa Surgam caves in Kurnool and thought them to be comparable to Magdalenian of France (Foote 1916). In subsequent years Todd collected a "big flake assemblage in association with pebble tools and discoids from Dhok Pathan, a few miles away from Pindigheb in West Punjab" (Todd 1939). The investigations of de Terra and Paterson in the same region dated the assemblage to the fourth glaciation. This dating is based mainly upon the typological similarity of the assemblage with Late Soan industries which have already been assigned to the said period. There is also a possibility that the assemblage is even later than the 'Late Soan' industries (de Terra and Paterson 1939). Some similar collections were later made and named "Evolved Soan" by Movius. It is still a matter of controversy, whether these assemblages should be regarded as parts of the Upper Palaeolithic culture-complex of the subcontinent. Todd has also reported, one "Series III" assemblage from the stratified deposits at Kandivali (near Bombay), which is characterised by blades and burins (Todd 1939). This industry is said to be akin to the Aurignacian industries of Asia and similar other industries of Europe and Middle East. A passing reference to a similar industry is also made by Krishnaswami while he discusses the Palaeolithic phase of Kortalayar basin. Here the terrace which is 3m high seems to contain implements assignable to Upper Palaeolithic tradition

(Krishnaswami 1938). A few other stray finds have been reported by S.P. Gupta from Jabalpur region, by Malti Nagar from Ahmednagar, Maharashtra and by Raman from Madurai district of Tamil Nadu (IAR 1960-61). Besides the above-mentioned stray finds a few collections containing a good number of artifacts came from stratified deposits. To mention the important ones, Issac made a collection from Kurnool district (Issac 1960), A. K. Ghosh from Singhbhum district of Bihar (IAR 1965-66), G.R. Sharma from Belan basin (IAR 1968-69), M.L.K. Murthy from Chittoor district of Andhra Pradesh (Murthy 1966 and also 1968) and K. Paddayya from Shorapur Doab of the same state (Paddayya 1968). Almost all of these collections, except that from Singhbhum, were handled by the author personally (Jayaswal 1978 and references there in).

The five comparatively well-known Upper Palaeolithic groups are, from south to north, Chittoor, Kurnool, Shorapur Doab, Singhbhum and Belan. They are being discussed in detail in the following pages, mainly based on Jayaswal (1978).

Chittoor (Andhra Pradesh)

Murty (1970) has reported the implementiferous localities of blade and burin tradition, situated on the banks of the river Rallakalava. Vedullachervu has yielded the largest number of Upper Palaeolithic artefacts from a well stratified deposit. The artefacts of Vedullachervu industry are made of fine grained quartzite and are lightly patinated into grey and purple colours. The finished tool group is dominated by burins. Those made on cores far outnumber the other types. Points are the next dominant type. The occurrence of Levallois points is noteworthy. Thick elongated flakes in this case have been reworked on one of their sides at high angle to make them convex. The type seems to be similar to the Azilian point of Europe. The blunting of blades on the sides is also quite frequent. There are also a few blades with marginal retouch at low angle. Blanks have been first classified into three broad groups, viz., blade, flake and undetermined blank, thereafter the first two into various sub-types. The third group of undetermined blanks consists of 10 broken flakes and blades (6%) which cannot be definitely classified into either of the above two blank groups.

Prepared flakes overwhelmingly predominate in the group of flakes. Levallois element does not occur in very good percentage. If we leave aside the undetermined types, flakes with unfaceted striking platform are the most dominant type followed by faceted and unprepared types in the receding order. The size of the flakes ranges between 22 and 60 mm with a mean of 44 mm. The mean of the angle of prepared flakes is 115°, Levallois flakes 105° and Levallois points 95° only. Blade (97, 59%) is the most dominant type in the blank group. The general ratio between length and breadth of the blades is 2.2: 1 and that between length and thickness 4.6: 1. If these general ratios are any indication the blades of the industry are neither very thick nor very long (Jayaswal 1978).

Kurnool (Andhra Pradesh)

The first discovery of Upper Palaeolithic artefacts in the region was made by Burkitt and Cammiade from Giddalur and Nandipakkarn (Cammiade and Burkitt 1930). Thereafter Soundara Rajan discovered a few similar implements (Soundara Rajan 1952). The whole district was examined by Issac (1960) later on, who brought to light as many as 29 localities of this phase. Most of the artefacts of this phase either come from the surface of the fields or from the gravel deposits lying loose in the river-bed. All the 29 localities have been reported from two areas, viz., Erramaliay and Nallamalai: 8 of them are in Erramaliay, which have yielded 357 artefacts, only 13 out of which come from stratified deposits. The remaining 21 localities fall in Nallamalai area. Three hundred and seventy artefacts have been reported from this area among which only

63 were found in situ from the stratified deposits (Issac 1960).

As far as core types are concerned only two small Mousterian cores and a few blade cores were noticed. But the blank group comprises all the types of flakes and blades. Unprepared flakes and flakes with a little preparation are almost negligible. Prepared flakes are abundant, with a good proportion of Levallois element. Blades are very frequent in the industry. Faceting of the striking platform seems to be a very common feature of the industry. Micro and unfaceted striking platforms come next in the order. The length of the blades ranges between 40 and 90 mm, and their thickness between 6 and 25 mm. Jayaswal thinks that the assemblage does not seem to be very evolved and can probably be assigned to the early phase of the Upper Palaeolithic tradition.

In one of his early excavations, Sankalia (1969: 1-41) had tackled the pre-Mesolithic site to Mesolithic transition site of Sangankallu, in Bellary district. He concluded his observations in the following words:

> The Microlithic and pre-Microlithic industries from the excavations on the top of the hill (the terrace) and those found on the foot of the hill show conclusively that they are related stratigraphically, morphologically and typologically. But a good picture of both the industries can be had only from the excavations on the Nala.

However, the evidence from the terrace helps us in placing the Microlithic industry in a chronological (see Table 4.1).

TABLE 4.1 CULTURAL SEQUENCE AT SANGANKALLU

Period III (IV)	Megalithic
Period II b	Neolithic Terrace
Period II a	Neolithic
Period I (II)	Microlithic and Flake Blade (Levallois of Subba Rao) Terrace
Period II	Microlithic (Mesolithic) Terrace and Nala.
Period I	Flake and Prepared core Nala and Kupgal Mound Industry.

In view of this evidence we can now, without any hesitation, call the Microlithic industry as Mesolithic. For the preceding industry is, both stratigraphically and typologically and even in the raw material used, different from it.

Not only such an evidence is obtained for the first time in India, but as a comparison of the illustrations of tools will show at a glance that the Microlithic industry has probably developed from the earlier industry in quartz. In the latter we have incipient blade or fluted cores, flakes/blades as well as large thick lunates. These comparatively large tools were gradually replaced by smaller but regular fluted cores and lunates. This change in industrial equipment and consequent change in life of the people was probably due to the change in climate, and arrival of new influence which are evident all over India, but only adequately pinpointed in time at Sangankallu.

The climate at the time when the flake and blade makers lived in the region was probably drier, as opposed to or in contrast to the succeeding phase. For the reddish murrum is uniformly capped in this region by a thick layer of sticky reddish-brown soil. Chemical analysis of this soil profile as well as of the soil profile found at the base of the Kupgal ash-mound by Dr. G.G. Mujumdar tells us that this was formed under damper conditions. The Mesolithic man using microliths might have lived at this time or came upon the scene after this damp phase was over. Had he really lived when the wet phase was on, giving rise to a forested environment, it would be rather a new environmental feature for the Mesolithic people. For hitherto, it is generally assumed that the microlith using man preferred to live in dry, scrub, forest-country, which might be sandy as in northern Gujarat.

This is also suggested by the fact that no microliths of quartz, or any other material were found in the Kupgal ash-mound excavation. The absence of any tools on quartz, and the presence only of flakes, scrapers and choppers—though few—might suggest that we might have to postulate for a stage when the man-making quartz tools, albeit comparatively large, came and gradually displaced the dyke basalt man. Thus there will be two antecedent stages or periods before the Mesolithic Man appeared on the scene. This interpretation might be shown (see Table 4.2).

TABLE 4.2 CULTURAL SEQUENCE AT KUPGAL

V	Megalithic : Black—and-Red Ware with iron.
IV b	Neolithic B Polished Axe, Blade Industry, pale grey pottery, with painted B-&-R
IVa	Neolithic: a polished axe, Blade industry, pale-grey pottery.
III	Mesolithic microliths in quartz, agate, carnelian etc.
II	Pre-Mesolithic B Flake and Blade industry in quartz.
I	Pre-Mesolithic A Flake and Blade and prepared Core Industry in patinated dyke basalt.

Typologically pre-Mesolithic-A appears to be more advanced than the Scraper and borer or flake industry of the Middle Stone Age or the Middle Palaeolithic, if for nothing but the number of symmetrical flakes out of prepared cores. Still there is no trace of true blades or burins which are the hallmark of the Upper Palaeolithic in Europe and Western Asia. Considerable quantity of this has been found near Renigunta by Dr. M.L.K. Murty, on a silt terrace without any Middle Stone Age or Late Stone Age material. Typologically, therefore, the Sangankal pre-Mesolithic-A might be regarded as a facies of the Middle Palaeolithic of Andhra-Mysore (Sankalia 1969:1-41).

Murty (1974: 196-230) studied the Kurnool cave sites and suggested that the onset of the neothermal climate led to semi-aridity in this region in the Late Pleistocene. He says that the animals inhabiting the cave area to this day are the carnivores: *Felis chaus*, *Hyaena hyaena*, *Viverricula indica*, and *Herpestes edwardsi*; the rodents *Hystrix indica*, *Lepus nigricollis* and others belonging to the species of Golunda, Mus, Rattus and Bandicota; and *Manis crassicaudata*, whose survival would be unaffected by the changed ecology.

Murty (1974:196-230) describes the finds from the Kurnool caves and writes,

> The absence of occupation floors, charcoal, ashes, and accumulations of food refuse such as skeletal fragments indicates that the cave was neither a kill-site nor a permanent settlement. At the same time the incorporation of bone and lithic artefacts and the absence of accumulations resultant of human living further strengthen the belief that the cave under discussion must have been a ... transit site, probably during those months when the cave receives enough light. As a matter of fact the adjacent regions of the cave(s) are characterised by sporadic dispersal of artefacts and a few finished forms made of fine-grained rocks (jasper, chert, chalcedony) as well as of limestone. Also in the general area along the hilly slopes of valleys and in the plains, there are several places, again with few artefacts. The overall nature of such evidence is suggestive of a nomadic pattern probably in a restricted territory conditioned for plains-dwelling. The lithic industry extracted from the cave sediment, although it is short of finished forms, includes blades... along with Late Pleistocene fauna proves beyond doubt that the cave was frequented by prehistoric human groups in Late Pleistocene times. The great concentration of the finds in the bottom-most levels of the cave sediment (layer 3), resting directly on the floor, indicates that the period of greatest human activity in the cave was coeval with the initial commencement of cave-living. Why the cave was not made a permanent or semi-permanent

habitation can be understood if we take a few factors into consideration. First of all, the tropical climate with no sharp cold-to-warm climatic rhythms as in the temperate zones may not have forced the human groups to live in the caves. The Late Pleistocene faunal evidence and the general geomorphology of this area indicate a hilly and plateau terrain covered by vegetation, providing ample shade and plentiful game suited to open-air habitation. There was a low yield of artifacts charactersing the Indian (Upper Palaeolithic-like) blade-burin and blade-tool industries. If the contextual occurrence of lithic blade artifacts in association with bone tools (and Late Pleistocene fauna) signifies a terminal phase in the culture growth of the Palaeolithic, as elsewhere in the Old World, they have got to be ascribed to the Upper Palaeolithic. The blade element of this industry, in particular, resembles the unretouched blade-blanks of the blade-burin industries in the immediate neighbourhood at Yerragondapalem, Kurnool district and Renigunta, Chittoor district (Murty 1970:106-28), both sites situated further north, in the plain country broken up by the eastern hill ranges. Despite this basic analogy, the industry from the cave does not display equivalent typological characters, in that it lacks the backed-blade variants, several burin types and oilier retouched form on flake, which form a predominant attribute, of the Yerragondapalem and Renigunta industries. For that matter, even in the scattered sites in this general area, while there are typical blades made of chert, jasper, and limestone, backed tools appear to be rare. However, a few partially retouched blades are present in an industry at the foothills of Gollaglitta overlooking a high cave, and also a few burins are encountered in two other sites. The frequency of retouched tools either on flake or blade in the industries of this area including the cave under discussion is low, unlike that at Yerragondapalem and Renigunta. These industries also do not reveal the technological precision apparent in the Yerragondapalem and Renigunta industries and hence the former appears to be older than the latter. Thus considering the overall nature of the evidence in a broader framework, the lithic industry and the associated bone industry recovered from the cave sediment can provisionally be ascribed to an incipient facies of the Indian Upper Palaeolithic.

The knowledge of bone technology, a cultural attribute when viewed as one of the phenomena of culture, cannot be regarded as an isolated instance confined to the cave areas. It might have been spread over a wider geographical region and the non-availability of bone-artifactual evidence at the open air stations in the neighbouring zones, which had blade-component industries, might be due to disintegration under exposed conditions. The open air stations with no other evidence except the lithics, may also be regarded as of Late Pleistocene age on relative grounds, as the cave finds in association with Late Pleistocene fauna share the fundamental technological character (i.e., blade production technique) with that of the open air sites (Murty 1974: 196-230).

To sum up, the present study (1) on the one hand confirms the occurrence of bone implements along with Late Pleistocene fauna, as reported by Foote in the Billa Surgam caves, and on the other hand, provides additional data on the associated lithic evidence; (2) favours provisional ascription of the blade-burin and blade-tool yielding open air station, to a terminal phase of the Pleistocene; and (3) adds further weight to the view that several industries with a blade- and/or blade-tool component known from different parts of the country may represent a facies of the Indian Upper Palaeolithic (Murty 1974: 196-230).

More recently Raju (1988) has dealt with the Upper Palaeolithic of Andhra Pradesh. We give below a summary from *Stone Age Hunter-Gatherers: An Ethno-archaeology of Caddapah Region, South-east India*. He suggests that on the basis of radiocarbon dates from Nandipalli in the Cuddapah region, and other sites in the northern Deccan as also a TL date from the Kurnool caves, the age of this culture is ascribed to between c. 20,000 years and 10,000 years BP. The authors of this cultural phase are *Homo sapiens sapiens*.

The very large size of the sites (up to 2 sq. km) in the Gunjana valley and the high density of tools (5 to 67 per sq. m) suggest them to be home bases. The Gunjana industry is much advanced, comprising predominantly backed blade variants and scrapers which recall its counterparts in the blade and burin industries of Renigunta in Chittoor district. The only difference between the two is in poor representation of burins in the Gunjana industry. Raju thinks that the backed blade technology is very highly developed in the Gunjana industry and its products can be compared to those of the finest craftsmanship anywhere in the world. The various backed blade variants were probably used as composite tools—barbed arrow-heads, harpoons, knives, and inserts for fish hooks. Various types of scrapers are likely to have been used for processing wood, hide and bone and for making hunting, fishing and other tools. The predominance of backed points in the Upper Palaeolithic man's toolkit implies that bow and arrow and spear were principal hunting weapons (Raju 1988).

The excavation at Vodikalu yielded, along with flaked artefacts, 84 pieces of flat grinding stone slabs, 19 rubbers and 135 split pebbles suggesting processing of vegetal foods at the site. This evidence is in conformity with that found in surface context at Renigunta.

From the analysis of the artefactual assemblages from three base camps, Vodikalu, Beellu and Rallachenu and extension of these observations to other sites, Raju thinks that they reveal that there were two home bases in the Gunjana valley: (i) Venkatareddipalli in the upstream of Kodur with Mekalagunteru as the transient camp, and (ii) Vodikalu, downstream of Kodur with Beellu, Rallachenu, Gaddalarevupalli and Nagavaram as base camps and Nagavaram Voddipalli, Nagavaramcheruvu and Gollapalli as transient camps. These would represent two maximum bands, one at Venkatareddipalli and around, and the other at Vodikalu and towards north. Their toolkits do not show any appreciable variation in typology or technology. Since the distribution patterns of artefactual occurrences at Renigunta and Gunjana valley bear striking similarity, and occurrences with large quantities of artefacts spreading for several kilometres are not encountered elsewhere, it can be inferred that occupations by maximum bands of Upper Palaeolithic hunter-gatherers are unique to this geographical zone.

The Upper Palaeolithic camps in the Gunjana valley appear to be all season camps for the following reasons:

1. The camps are situated close to river banks and do not get inundated even during the height of monsoon when the river is in spate.
2. Raw material for tools is available as pebbles on the river-bed and chunks and nodules in the nearby Velikonda hills.
3. Central location with respect to food resources.
4. Absence of sites in the foothills and interior of the scrub jungle. The present day Yanadis also inhabit the same topographical settings and do not change their settlements seasonally.

The intra-site variability at Vodikalu, Beellu and Rallachenu indicates specific activity areas such as tool-making, butchering, wood working and food processing areas.

On the basis of ethnographic parallels, Raju suggests that there are several instances in the Yanadi life-style which can be taken to suggest the plausible modes of activities of the terminal late Pleistocene hunter-gatherers. Some of them are : use of bottle gourds for storage of water during hunting expeditions, use of various nets, traps and other hunting aids for hunting, fowling and bird catching, extraction of honey, collection of minor forest produce, foraging fruits, roots, tubers and green leaves, the use of digging sticks, hunting birds by pelting stones, catching fish with bare hands by diving into muddy waters and hitting fish with stones. Various scrapers and backed blades in the Upper Palaeolithic man's toolkit were probably used to make prototypes of nets and traps. While it is hazardous to correlate the Yanadi life-ways with the terminal Pleistocene hunter-gatherers, it does demonstrate the resource potential of the region and its carrying capacity to support considerable hunter-gatherer populations.

Taking clues from the food habits of the Yanadis, it is reasonable to predict that the Upper

Palaeolithic hunter-gatherers relied on aquatic food resources for their subsistence as much as on game and wild vegetal foods. All the Upper Palaeolithic sites are located close to perennial water sources. Further, consumption of roots and tubers must have been an important part of the Upper Palaeolithic diet as the Yanadis are known to have lived during seven years (1950-57) of continuous drought mainly on wild yams like *Dioscorea oppositifolia, Dioscorea bulbifera, Dioscorea pentaphylla* and *Dioscorea sylvatica* supplemented to some extent by roots, honey, fish and game. Such habits and practices possibly have a high antiquity and indicate the traditional subsistence patterns among the late Pleistocene hunter-gatherers (Raju 1988).

On the basis of the extant ethnographic populations, Raju estimates that Vodikalu supported 190 people divided into six minimum bands each comprising 5 to 6 nuclear families of 5 members each. Beellu would have supported two minimum bands consisting of six nuclear families (a total of 60 people) and Rallachenu would have supported 30 people - one minimum band with 6 nuclear families. Raju admits that these figures, however, are by their very nature highly speculative.

Raju makes an important point:

> Although Upper Palaeolithic sites are reported from many parts of India during the last three decades, to my knowledge the sites reported in this study and those of Renigunta appear to be some of the richest in the subcontinent and are very important for understanding the transition of hunting-gathering to agricultural and agro-pastoral economies. But unfortunately not a single habitation site has been subjected to large scale horizontal excavation in the entire southern Deccan (Raju 1988).

At some sites blade-and-burin industry occurs above the Mesolithic culture (e.g. Timayyagunta, Chundi) or with it (as at Nallagundha from where 6,000 blades and burins have been collected). A variety of burins, awls, etc., were also discovered. The material used is an olive green quartzite of fine quality. Later on, several other Upper Palaeolithic sites came to light from the Cuddapah and Prakasam districts. An important cave site, Muchchatla Chintamanu Gavi (Kurnool) was excavated by Murty (1970) and Sankalia. The bone industry at the site is 10 times the size of the blade-flake lithic industry and comprises scrapers, chisels, scoops, perforators, etc. The techniques of making bone tools resemble those of the European Upper Palaeolithic.

Murty has reported extensive faunal remains from the Upper Palaeolithic caves of the Kurnool district. From the presence of *antelope, gazellae, cervus, presbytis entellus* (langur), *Melurstis ursinus* and *Rhinoceros sp*, he infers a thicker forest cover and therefore more humid conditions. Chemical analyses of cave sediments have supported this inference. It is interesting to note the presence of *Ovis* (sheep) at this site from such early levels and may indicate a local domestication of this strain (Murty 1975). Soundar Rajan has also reported a blade and burin industry from Nagarjunakonda.

Shorapur Doab (Karnataka)

Sankalia and Paddayya have brought to light some stratified Upper Palaeolithic sites in the Shorapur Doab. In the Hunsgi nallah area they found a distinct brownish-black silt with blades and burins and points made from reddish chert. But the industry as a whole looks typologically more primitive than the Renigunta assemblage. Paddayya's work in the Shorapur Doab on the Early Palaeolithic has been discussed in detail in Chapter 3. Only two localities in Shorapur Doab have yielded Upper Palaeolithic or 'blade-burin' industries. They are Salvadgi and Meralbhavi. The first site was discovered by Sundara (IAR 1960-61: 64) and was revisited by Seshadri (Paddayya 1970). After a few years Paddayya undertook a small scale excavation at the same locality (Paddayya 1970). The other site Meralbhavi is the discovery of the latter investigator. Paddayya classifies the 225 implements into flakes (49) and blades (176).

The other locality, Meralbhavi, which is 3km south of the Salvadgi, is also said to have yielded a mixed assemblage of 'Middle Stone Age' and 'blade-burin' traditions. Four hundred and forty-six artefacts in this case were picked up from the surface of fields. The material available to the Paddayya consisted of only 43 specimens which were illustrated by the investigator in his doctoral dissertation. Finished tools as reported by Paddayya are 191, which have been reclassified as edged tools (137), non-edged tools (46) and multiedged tools (8). Jayaswal noticed 14 burins in this collection. Both the industries of the area are made of quartz minerals

From Mumbai (Bombay, Maharashtra) Todd published a sequence of lithic industries in and around Bombay area in 1939 (Todd, 1939). From the top of the 'upper gravel' he reported to have obtained a blade and burin industry which was regarded Upper Palaeolithic (or Series III). Thereafter, from the 'Upper clay' (which overlies the upper gravel) he discovered polyhydral, angle and parrot burins, which, according to him, belong to 'a more evolved class of blade and burin industry'. These industries consist of artefacts like steep-scrapers, burins, borers, blades, blade-cores, knives, etc. Malik also found an industry similar to what Todd had reported (Malik 1959). This group of tools, made of mineral of the quartz group, has been named as 'flake-blade-scraper' industry, which, according to Malik, comprises side-scrapers, end-scrapers, borers, blades, etc. Jayaswal does not seem to agree with the findings of Malik and Todd.

Singhbhum (Bihar)

The Upper Palaeolithic assemblages have been reported from four areas of the region under study. These are Chandil, Sini, Ghatsila and Gua in Singhbhum. The implements of this phase have been obtained from 'Upper Clay', the top of which marks the end of the Pleistocene and beginning of the Holocene period, and have been dated to 'Late or Upper Pleistocene' (Ghosh 1970). The industry comprises tools made of jasper, agate and various other similar minerals. This industry is comparatively much smaller than the 'chopper-biface' and 'flake' industries of this region. The largest number of tools was obtained from Chandil area (36.18%), followed by Sini (26.19%), Ghatsila (22.86%) and Gua (14.77%) areas in that order. The 'Flake-blade' industry is dominated by scrapers (53.32%). This group includes at least 11 types, i.e., side, end and steep scrapers on cores, flakes and blades, and also side-cum-end-and hollow scrapers. Many of them are made on Levallois flakes. The next dominant groups are finely worked out small choppers and points. But surprisingly the knives, borers and burins form very low percentage of the industry.

Jayaswal feels that the techno-typology of the Upper Palaeolithic or 'Flake-blade' phase of Singhbhum is somewhat similar to other such industries of the subcontinent. But the proportion of burins is lower in this region.

Belan Group (Uttar Pradesh)

Varma informs that no skeletal remains of Upper Palaeolithic man of the Vindhyan region have been found. However, on the basis of evidence from elsewhere, we know that *Homo sapiens-sapiens*, modern man, emerged with the dawn of the Upper Palaeolithic and with this increases the pace of cultural evolution. We have indirect evidence of *Homo sapiens sapiens* presence in the Belan valley. We have already seen that there was a gradual evolution in tool typology. The tools are now based completely on blades and a number of new types of tools emerge such as burins, awls, various types of scrapers, points, lunates, etc. This does indicate the emergence of a new type of society. The effective use of bows and arrows must have started from this time. Based on the principle of the concentration of energy, it was a weapon of great usefulness (Varma 1999: 175-204).

In the basin of the Belan and its tributary, the Seoti, the Upper Palaeolithic artefacts have been collected both from the old bank deposits and from the slopes of the adjoining foot-hills (IAR 1968-69: 33-34). The first group of artefacts, which have been found in situ from the section belong to three different layers, i.e., 5, 4 and 3. According to Sharma, layer 5 has yielded the implements of both Upper Palaeolithic and Middle Palaeolithic traditions. Layer 4, which is a 'cemented gravel III' deposit, has revealed a pure Upper Palaeolithic assemblage. Whereas, the layer 3, which is made of 'whitish clay', contains the Upper Palaeolithic tools with an aceramic non-geometric Microlithic industry. Jayaswal considers the said sequence to be fascinating, though it does not seem to be very convincing. The number of artefacts obtained in situ is also too small (less than 15) to support the above observation.

The other group of artefacts came from the factory sites, situated on the slopes of the adjoining hills. All the reported localities are on the southern slope of the Kaimur range (Sharma 1973). So far Mundva (Chandva) has yielded the largest number of tools. The artefacts of this industry are made of chert, and, are almost fresh. Jayaswal (1978) reports the following types:

TABLE 4.3 ARTEFACT TYPES FROM KAIMUR RANGE

Type	Number
Side scrapers	8
Backed blades	6
Big lunate	1
End scrapers	3
Burins	12
Borers	2
Scraper on core	4
Points	2
Round scrapers	3
Total	41

Burins are in high proportion and are made on flakes on cores and also on blades. The blank group had 22 flakes and 42 blades. The mean of the size of these specimens is 45.4 mm. In the group of blades eighteen out of forty-two are broken. The ratio between mean of the length and breadth is 2.6 : 1 and between mean of the length and thickness is 4.7 : 1. The blades of this region in general are longer and thinner than the similar specimens of the other regions.

Upper Son-Basin (Uttar Pradesh)

Jayaswal thinks that the stratigraphic position of these implements is not certain. A number of localities of this phase have been noticed by Nisar Ahmed and the artefacts from all of them have been studied together. On techno-typological grounds Jayaswal thinks that a few among them seem to belong to the Upper Palaeolithic phase. The artefacts are made on quartz. To a great extent the artefacts agree in size with 'blade-burin' industries of Chittoor district, rather than the Late Stone Age Microlithic industries. The size of the big blades of this collection is bigger than that of the Vedullachervu group, for the length of the blades ranges between 40 and 85 mm (mean = 64.5 mm), the breadth between 15 and 41 mm (mean = 25.0 mm) and thickness between 5 and 11 mm (mean = 9 mm). The means of the length, the breadth and the thickness of Vedullachervu blades are 42.0, 19.3 and 9 mm, respectively. But size factor only cannot be regarded as a determining criterion for an Upper Palaeolithic industry.

The other group of smaller blades has the following measurements :

Length range 15 to 36 mm
Breadth range 5 to 13 mm
Thickness range 2 to 7 mm

Possibly this group may be assigned to 'Late Stone Age', but the blades having above measurments may also occur in 'blade-burin' assemblages. The blades of smaller group are comparatively longer (length : breadth = 2.8 : 1) than those of the other group (length : breadth = 2.6 : 1), but the former are thicker than the latter (length : thickness 6 : 1 and 7.2 : 1 respectively).

Though nothing can be said with certainty at present yet there is a possibility of finding full-fledged Upper Palaeolithic industry in this region. The main raw material used was quartz, but Vedullachervu industry indicates that in some cases quartzite continued to be in use even in this phase. There is a general preference for blades. Implements made on blades also dominate all these industries. Retouching is mostly at a high angle. Compared to the European Upper Palaeolithic industries, here burins are in smaller proportion. The percentage of burins fluctuates in all the assemblages. A new type 'big lunate', which is to a great extent similar to the Azilian points of European Epi-Palaeolithic, makes its appearance. Jayaswal gives the following ratios between length and breadth mean in each industry (see table 4.4).

TABLE 4.4 LENGTH-BREADTH RATIO IN DIFFERENT INDUSTRIES

Industry	*Length: Breadth ratio*
Vedullachervu	2.2:1
Kurnool	2.1:1
Shorapur Doab	2.5:1
Upper Son	2.5:1
Belan	2.6:1

On the basis of the length-breadth proportion of the blades, the above industries may be divided into two broad groups. In case of the first, the blades are less than 2.5 times longer than the breadth, but in the other, the length-breadth ratio is 2.5 : 1 and more. It is indeed interesting to note that the specimens from Kurnool are the longest, if only the length is taken into consideration, and, on the other hand, in proportion to their breadth they are also the broadest (ratio 2.1 : 1). This shows that, at least in this respect, the Kurnool industry is the crudest among all.

Similarly to see the thickness of the blades Jayaswal has worked out the proportion between their length and thickness in each industry (see table 4.5).

TABLE 4.5 LENGTH-THICKNESS RATIO IN DIFFERENT INDUSTRIES

Vedullachervu	4.6 : 1
Kurnool	3.8 : 1
Shorapur Doab	4.1 : 1
Upper Son	7.2 : 1
Belan	4.7 : 1

The blades of Upper Son assemblage are very thin in proportion to their length, although they are the smallest among all, if only length is taken into account. The Kurnool industry, on the other hand, exhibits once more its crude technology (length-thickness ratio is 3.8 : 1). Thus, in respect of blade technology, the Upper Son and Belan are the most evolved industries, while the one from Kurnool proved to be the crudest (Jayaswal 1978).

Let us now turn to the Mesolithic cultures, though some of the sites will also be discussed with the early farming cultures.

MESOLITHIC CULTURES

With the passage of time there is a marked diminution in the size of stone tools, reaching its culmination in the Late Stone Age in the early Holocene. This period is labelled in India variously as Late Stone Age, Mesolithic or Microlithic period. Microliths with the length ranging from 1 to 8cm are the main industry of the period. It is obvious that such tools could have been used only as composite tools hafted in wood or bovine jaws, and not singly. We have evidence of such hafting from abroad but none so far from India. The first microliths were discovered by Carlleyle in 1867 from the Vindhyan rock shelters and this was followed by more discoveries by Cockburn and Rivet Carnac in the nineteenth century. In the first half of twentieth century, Cammiade, Todd, Hunter and Gordon reported microliths from different parts of the subcontinent.

The Mesolithic was generally the period when glaciers were withdrawing to higher latitudes in the north. In the rest of the country this period probably coincided with rise in temperature and precipitation. The pollen evidence from Rajasthan also shows that around 8000 BC (Phase II of Singh's sequence) precipitation was much higher than today.

Systematic and scientific work on the Mesolithic was heralded only by Sankalia's excavations at Langhnaj in Gujarat in the early 1940s. Zeuner, Allchin, Krishnaswamy, Subbarao and others explored and excavated many other sites. In recent years, Varma has excavated sites in Mirzapur district; Joshi and Khare in Madhya Pradesh; and Sankalia in Karnataka. V.N. Misra excavated sites in Rajasthan and Madhya Pradesh and has published a great deal on the Indian Mesolithic (Map 4-2). Some of the Microlithic cultures were perhaps Neolithic in the economic sense.

The Mesolithic cultures will be dealt with in four geographical zones: 1. Northern and Western; 2. Central; 3. Eastern; and 4. Southern. As microliths have been reported practically from all over the subcontinent, we will give emphasis only on the excavated sites.

I. Northern and Western Zone

In this zone are included Pakistan, North India—Rajasthan and Gujarat. From Jamal Garhi, near Peshawar, Gordon reported some microliths from a ploughed field. Misra, who examined this collection at Cambridge, says that it includes fluted cores, blunted back blades, lunates, angle burins and borers. Near Rawalpindi, from the Kalat and Quetta areas, and from the Tharro hills in Sind also, microliths are reported. At Sukkur and Rohri, the sites which provided chert for the ribbon flake blades of the Harappans, the Allchins have reported artifacts ranging from the Palaeolithic to the Indus times, though no Mesolithic horizon has yet been isolated.

The Aravalli hill ranges diagonally divide Rajasthan into two: the western region is more arid and less densely populated compared to the eastern zone which is greener and more thickly populated. The vegetation is sparse. The river Luni, which is now dry, had an integrated channel system in the past and indicates that conditions were wetter in the Late Pleistocene times. Singh's Phase II represents the onset of wetter conditions around 8000 BC and he attributes the origin of the lakes to this period which in due course of time turned saline due to progressive dessication.

The Mesolithic sites are known both from western and eastern Rajasthan.

Tilwara

Tilwara in west Rajasthan, a Microlithic site excavated by Misra is located on the eastern fringe of the desert in the Barmer district. It has a flimsy occupation of about 50 cm, divided into two phases. Phase I is marked by an abundance of microliths and a rarity of potsherds. The succeeding Phase II, on the other hand, has more pottery and a dwindling Microlithic industry; in this phase were also found bits of iron, glass beads and bangles of shell and glass.

Structural activity is denoted by stones arranged in a circular fashion with diametres up to 3 m. Hearths with charred bones and ash and stone querns and rubbers were found from these structures. Stone balls may have been used as missiles. Animal bones, not very abundant, represent mongoose, jackal/dog, humped cattle, goat, spotted deer (*Axis axis*), hog deer (*Axis percinus*) and pig - obviously a mixture of the domestic and wild varieties.

The stone industry was made from quartz, chert and rhyolite. It appears that they used a pressure technique to detach flakes out of cylindrical cores. Both geometric (trapezes, crescents, etc.) and non-geometric (points, etc.) microliths were found in association with scrapers and even burins.

Pottery is all wheel-made with squat vessels for cooking and dishes and lotas for eating and drinking. Misra thinks that this is related to the Rang Mahal culture of the first-second centuries AD.

Microliths were also found in the Pachpadra basin and the Sojat area but there are no substantial settlements available. This is an arid region with equally severe winters and summers. Despite late dates of Tilwara, the evidence suggests only a hunting-gathering economy with some degree of pastoralism. Periodic droughts result in considerable movements of population even today. Some amount of nomadism and contacts with more prosperous urban centres was a built-in feature of such Mesolithic communities.

Mewar, east of the Aravallis, presents a picture in contrast to the western region. Though more rocky, yet it has a greater rainfall and is vegetated with grass, shrubs and a savannah type of vegetation. Wild game is plentiful and a big depression on the Kothari river perhaps provided a perennial source of water. With such optimal conditions, no wonder that Mesolithic settlements should be more substantial in this region, than in the Marwar. A large number of Microlithic sites with hundreds of cores on rock eminences did suggest long periods of use, but actual settlements eluded the archaeologists (Mishra 1969, 1971).

Bagor

In 1967 V.N. Misra discovered the site of Bagor (lat. 25° 21' N, long. 74° 23' E) on the left bank of Kothari, a tributary of the Banas river at a distance of 25 km west of the town of Bhilwara in the same district. It is a large and prominent sand-dune covering an area of about 200m east-west and 150m north-south and rises to a height of about 6m above the surrounding plain. The site was excavated from 1967 to1970 by Prof. V.N. Misra, Deccan College, Pune. As we shall see in detail below, the settlements here have more substantial structures, stone-paved floors, more pottery and a rich stone industry. In the later phase metal and wheel-made pottery also occurs. To date, Bagor is the best studied Mesolithic site in the subcontinent and it will be worth going into some detail. A deposit of 1.5m at Bagor has been divided into three phases and five layers. The site reveals an uninterrupted settlement over a period of 5,000 years. The site represents basically a single culture undergoing evolution through time by the appearance of new material traits and decline or disappearance of others (Misra 1971: 237-90). On the basis of the material changes, the following three phases of the Bagor culture have been recognised.

Phase I (50-80cm deposit) is marked by extensive stone-paved floors and occasional circular alignments of stones probably to hold plastered reed walls. Numerous bones, many of them charred and split open, as also stone pebbles, used both to break the bones and to make microliths, were found in this phase. Querns and rubbers indicate use of plant food. Only one extended adult burial with head pointing west was found; the grave was inside the habitation and had no funerary appendage. Hunting-gathering economy with the possibility of domestication of sheep, goat and cattle is indicated.

Phase II (30-50cm deposit) shows contacts with the contemporary Chalcolithic cultures, indicated by the use of copper tools and beads. Other features of Phase I continue but a handmade pottery with incised and applied designs appears for the first time. Burials are more elaborate having pots and pans, copper tools and ornaments. The skeletons all in the habitation area were found interred in a flexed position. From one grave alone 36 stone and bone beads were discovered. One spearhead, three arrow-heads and one awl comprise the copper repertory—all found in burials.

Phase III (35-75cm deposit) was restricted to the central part of the mound. Microliths and animal bones become scarce. Iron tools, wheel made pottery, glass beads and brick structure form new traits. The excavator thinks that this phase might have continued up to the beginning of the Christian era.

A faunal analysis has shown that 72% bones were recovered from Phase I, 19% from Phase II, and 3% from Phase III. It clearly indicates a declining dependence on wild game. The animal remains are a mixture of wild (20%) and domestic (80%) varieties and comprise sheep/goat, buffalo, humped cattle, pig, blackbuck, chinkara (*Gazella gazella*), chital (*Axis axis*), sambhar (*Cervus unicolor*), hare, fox and mongoose; tortoise and fish bones were also found.

It is interesting to note that evidence of burials has come from all the phases of Bagor (Misra 1972: 58-65). In all five burials, one belonging to Phase I, three to Phase II and one to Phase III have been encountered. The last one, however, belongs to the Medieval phase. All the burials have been found within the area of settlement.

In the case of the earliest burial of Bagor, belonging to Phase I, the skeleton was found placed in an extended position with west-east orientation, the head lying to the west. The lower left arm rested partly over the trunk while the right one was placed along the body. No evidence of grave line was found. As regards the grave goods, no positive statement has been made, though the occurrence of a few animal bones found in the vicinity of the skeleton does not rule out the possibility of their having been offered as burial goods.

In the burials of Phase II, the individuals were placed in a flexed position, with arms and legs folded and oriented east-west, with the head lying in the east. Burial goods in the form of earthen pots, ornaments, metal objects and animal limbs were found in association with these burials. The number of pots placed in these burials vary from one to 8 and were kept near the head, side or feet. Among the copper objects, mention may be made of three arrow-heads, a spearhead and an antimony rod. A broken terracotta spindle-whorl and a necklace of 36 stone and bone beads were also found in the graves.

The method of disposal of dead varied from phase to phase at the site. If the earlier phase offers a case of extended burial, the later phase is marked by flexed burials. There had been directional change in the orientation as well from west-east to east-west. In the burial of Phase I, the position of offering goods could not be ascertained but in Phase II there is evidence for the same. Misra thinks that the inhabitants of Bagor in this phase had a more settled economy, which is reflected in their burial goods.

The excavations at Bagor have thrown some light on the vexed chronological problem of the Mesolithic age in India. On typo-technological consideration, the beginning of the culture may be placed in the geometric phase of Microlithic industries unassociated with pottery.

Subsequently, handmade pottery was added to the Microlithic and bone assemblage. In the absence of radiocarbon dates, this set of evidence would have provided only a relative chronology to the site, but five radiocarbon dates provide a firm chronlogy. For dates (uncalibrated, half-life of 5730 years; Misra 1973: 107-8) see Table 4.6.

TABLE 4.6 ^{14}C DATES (UNCALIBRATED) FOR BAGOR

Site	*No.*	*Dates on 5568*	*Calib. Dates*	*Culture Association*
Bagor	TF-786	6245± 200 BP	5232 cal.bc	Period I
Bagor	TF-1009	4585± 105 BP	3353 cal.bc	Period I/II, Bagor Ware
Bagor	TF-1005/6	3945± 90BP	2467 cal.bc	Period II
Bagor	TF-1011/2	5090±85 BP	3951,3842,3824	Period I
Bagor	TF-1007	5620±125 BP	4465 cal.bc	Period I

All the ^{14}C dates are on charred bones. In the absence of any radiocarbon date from the lowermost levels of Phase I (dates given in Table 4.6 are only from upper horizons), the excavator places the beginning of the culture around 5000 BC. The lower limit of Phase II can be placed in the middle of third millennium BC, i.e. contemporary to the Harappans, if not earlier. But for fixing the upper limit of the phase, no date is available. On the basis of the occurrence of iron arrow-heads, glass beads and wheel-thrown pottery in Phase III, the excavator extends the upper limit of Phase II to the middle of the first millennium BC or a little earlier (Misra 1973: 107-8).

Gujarat is mainly composed of alluvial or coastal plains. About 100 Microlithic sites have been reported from the alluvial plains of the rivers Tapti, Narmada, Mahi and Sabarmati. In many places there are sand-dunes and inter-dunal depressions which collect water from the surrounding area and retain it for almost three-fourths of a year. With 80cm of rainfall, Gujarat is one of the most fertile regions of the country.

Though Microlithic sites have been reported from the time of Bruce Foote onwards, it was only in 1941 that Sankalia undertook a major exploration of the area. He excavated Akhaj, Valasana and Langhnaj - all east of the river Sabarmati; the maximum information however comes from the last site. Further north, Subbarao and Malik explored and excavated several Microlithic sites which were marked by the absence of pottery, metal and geometric microliths-thus indicating that they represent the older cultures. Microlithic sites are reported from Pavagarh in the south and even from a coastal dune.

Langhnaj

The site of Langhnaj (lat. 23°27' N, long. 72°32' E) is situated at a distance of 59 km from Ahmedabad, almost to its north. The site has been excavated several times between 1942 and 1963 by the Deccan College, Poona and the University of Baroda, as a result of which a good number of microliths, 14 human skeletal remains, animal bones, etc. have been brought to light. Langhnaj has a sandy deposit of about 2 metres divisible into three phases. Phase I has produced microliths, burials, animal bones and an occasional potsherd. Though the nature of the site rendered it rather impossible to work out the stratigraphical details of various finds, the diggings of seven short seasons have given convincing evidence that the main Microlithic horizon lay between 90cm and 1.5 m. Out of the 14 skeletons exposed so far, 11 have been found between these depths (Sankalia 1963:12).

In the debris of the habitation were found the skeletal remains of men, women and children kept intentionally in a highly flexed posture. The nature of deposit did not permit to work out the details of grave-pits, if they were really dug out. The possibility of placing the dead bodies on the living floors and then covering the same with the surrounding soil cannot be ruled out. The 13 skeletons excavated earlier followed east-west orientation, the head being placed in the east. The bodies were not placed in supine position (Ehrhardt and Kennedy 1965:40); the head lay towards the right. On this point it would be pertinent to observe that the 14th skeleton of Langhnaj, excavated by Kennedy (1964: 44-57), offers some new features when compared with the earlier excavated skeletons. The position of this burial is 'dorsal extension while the others are in various attitudes of lateral flexure'. In contrast to the general orientation pattern of the other skeletons of the site, the 14th skeleton is west-east oriented, the head lying on the west. Significantly enough, the left hand of the individual was found placed on the left ilium and the face slightly turned to the north. Do these departures suggest that the buried person belonged to a different community following a different burial ritual?

In the light of the available evidence it is difficult to be precise about the burial goods found at Langhnaj. It is, however, not unlikely that microliths, animal bones and beads might have served as offering goods. If this hypothesis were correct, one has to assume that the animal bones at the time of offering would have been with flesh.

While discussing the burials, it may be pointed out that in some burials all the human bones were not found placed in their natural positions. In the cases of skeletons I, III, VII, IX, X and XII, only a few bones were available and that too not in an articulated position. It is not unlikely that in these the method of partial burial was resorted to (Ehrhardt and Kennedy 1965:41).

It has been suggested that some of the buried people at Langhnaj met violent death, as indicated by traces of blows on a few skulls. The said blows are supposed to have been administered from different sides to different individuals - front, back or side - with different types of weapons. In the cases of skeletons I, II, X, and XII, the weapons used are supposed to have been sharp. The employment of blunt weapons like big stones has not been ruled out in a few cases (Ehrhardt and Kennedy 1965:42). It is not clear whether this was due to some group fighting or invasion by another tribe or due to some custom. Kennedy, however, does not agree with the above interpretation. He asserts that these cracks in the skulls as well as in the post-cranial portions of the skeletons are the natural consequences of the weathering of the osseous tissues within the microenvironment of the mound. The cracks could have resulted from changes in temperature and humidity of the soil on the one hand, and pressure of overlying layers and ravages of small animals, vegetation, etc. on the other. Kennedy further claims to have observed many examples of this type of postmortem bone damage in American Indian cranial and post-cranial specimens where any hypothesis of untimely and violent death has been ruled out (Kennedy 1964:55).

The evidence of caries was found in the teeth of skeleton XII while that of healed fracture in the left ulna of skeleton V. Of the 14th skeletons of the site, the sex could be determined only in eight cases. Of these, five are male, one questionably male, one female and one questionably female (Ehrhardt and Kennedy 1965: 43 and 63). As regards the age, it ranges from 5-6 years (infantile) to mature senile. The average age index of the Langhnaj skeletons is considerably high.

Measurement of stature shows that the males (skeletons III, V and XIV) measure 167cm, 174cm and 166.52cm respectively, while the female (skeleton XII) measured 158 cm. According to the length-breadth index, the skulls are dolichocephalic (Ehrhardt and Kennedy 1965:43) with cranial capacity ranging from 1183 cc (skeleton I) to 1430 cc (skeleton IV). Thus on the one hand, some of them compare well with the Vedda skull, while the others with the average male skulls of Europe. The skeletons in question betray mixed features, the features of Mediterrianids on the one hand and those of the Veddid on the other. Thus it is significant to note that racial mixture in India had become an accomplished fact as early as the third millennium BC, if not earlier (Ehrhardt and Kennedy 1965:44).

The faunal remains recovered from the site are all of wild species comprising bovids, rhino, swamp deer (*Cervus duvaceli*), chital (*Axis axis*), hog deer (*Axis percinus*), Nilgai (*Boselaphus tragocamelus*), mongoose, and wolf. Besides these were found the bones of tortoise, fish, rodents and squirrels. Except those of rodents and mongoose, most of the bones were broken and charred, probably for eating.

The chronology of Langhnaj has also been a debatable topic. Besides microliths, animal bones and human skeletal remains, nothing datable was found from the site. On the basis of typo-technological consideration, Sankalia dated the Mesolithic phase—the phase associated with the burials - to a time going before 2500 BC (Sankalia 1965: 18). Following is only one ^{14}C date (based on half life = 5730 years; uncalibrated) for Phase II of the site:

TF - 744, 2040 ± 110 BC

II. Central Zone

Central India or Madhya Pradesh is a continuation of the rocky country of eastern Rajasthan. Rainfall varies from 80cm in the west to 140cm in the east. Vindhyas and Satpuras, the forested hills, provided rocks for microliths, game and wild plants for sustenance, springs for water and rock-shelters for protection against the elements. No wonder that prehistoric settlements throve in the area. In Bhimbetka hills alone, in an area of 10 sq. km, about 800 caves and rock shelters are located and most of them have habitational deposits from the Acheulian to the Mesolithic periods.

The Vindhyas continue into Uttar Pradesh in the form of the Kaimur range which is also full of Microlithic remains and rock paintings. Further north, in Allahabad and Pratapgarh districts of Uttar Pradesh, Microlithic sites have been reported.

The Ganga valley has a rainfall of more than100 cm and there are a number of oxbow lakes full of aquatic life in the Allahabad-Pratapgarh region. The area was forested until recent times, thus game and fish were abundant. In the absence of hills and the alluvium being very thick, rocks for stone tools were not available. Raw material for microliths was therefore obtained from the Kaimur hills and the Son valley in the south. Since raw material was brought from a distance, it has been used here with great economy, and as a result, we have the smallest Microliths in this region. The absence of raw material was a deterrent for the spread of Microlithic cultures in the doab. These sites have been discovered mostly in the last decade, and in fact, when the 10 author first reported microliths from the Agra district, the discovery was ignored in disbelief. Out of the 10 known sites in Allahabad-Pratapgarh area, only Sarai-Nahar-Rai was excavated. The surface collection from Kurha appears to be typologically the oldest, as it comprises scrapers, blunted-backed blades, which are larger in size than an average microlith, and there is a complete absence of geometric microliths.

Sarai-Nahar-Rai

Sarai-Nahar-Rai (lat. 25°48' N; long. 81°5' E), is situated at a distance of 15 km from Pratapgarh and measures about 1,800 sq. m. It was excavated by G.R. Sharma. The site overlooks a now dried-up lake and the settlement has an area of 2,000 sq. m. A floor, of 5 x 4 m was made of rammed, burnt clay lumps and four post-holes on the four corners suggesting a roof. Several hearths along with charred bones were found on this floor, indicating some sort of communal cooking. Bones represent sheep, buffalo, cattle, goat, elephant and tortoise. Most of these animals appear to be of a domesticated kind. This area is littered with microliths and contains hearths and burials. It seems that the dead were buried within the habitation area as there were hearths nearby. As many as 11 burials out of 13 were opened, which were placed in shallow oblong pits in extended posture, the head pointing west.

The grave was carefully prepared by laying a soil cushion 3-4cm thick. Microliths and a particular type of shells seem to have been placed as offerings. With the exception of one, all the graves of Sarai-Nahar-Rai contained single individual. In one grave as many as four skeletons were found. Size of grave on the one hand and the absence of subsequent disturbance on the other is the positive proof to demonstrate that the grave in question was originally prepared to receive multiple skeletons. From the careful placing of the bodies it is clear that all the four individuals were buried together. Of these, two belonged to male and the remaining two to female. It is of interest to note that the males were placed on the right, while the females on the left. There is no denying the fact that the symmetry of the grave pit, the orientation of body, the use of the material of hearths in the graves and the presence of burial goods presuppose that the burial ritual was fully developed and it had a long tradition amongst this tribe.

The excavated skeletons fall within the age group of 16 to 30 years with the exception of one, which may be of a person of more than 30 years of age at the time of death. The height of male measures 1.80m or slightly less than in the case of female. The bones of the individuals of both the sexes are sturdy and if the available skeletal remains are of any guidance, it may safely be said that the Mesolithic tribe of Sarai-Nahar-Rai was composed of tall and well-built individuals belonging to dolicocephalic race. Olecranon perforation was found only in a single skeleton. Evidence of caries was also observed in the same individual.

Sarai-Nahar-Rai appears to be aceramic. The presence of only triangles in the Microlithic assemblage also seems to point to its greater antiquity as triangles precede trapezes. ^{14}C dates (half-life=5,730 years; uncalibrated) for the site are:

TF - 1104: 8395 ± 110 BC
TF - 1356 & 1359: 990 ± 125 BC

TF-1104 is based on uncharred bones exposed to the elements and thus were more vulnerable to contamination but TF-1356 and 1359 are on charred bones and therefore more reliable. Both are based on inorganic fractions. The presence here of domesticated animals and diminutive geometric microliths also conforms to a c.1000 BC date.

Lekhahia

(lat. 24° 47' 30" N; long. 82° 8' 7"E): Lekhahia is situated in the vicinity of village Bhainsore in Mirzapur district. Microlithic sites as well as rock paintings were discovered in the Mirzapur district by Carlleyle more than a century ago. They have been rediscovered and excavated by recent workers. Varma exposed some Microlithic sites at Morhana Pahar in the Mirzapur district and Sharma (1965:77-78) excavated Lekhahia rock-shelters, both in the Kaimur range. The general sequence in this region starts with a non-geometric Microlithic and non-ceramic horizon at the lowest level; followed by geometric microliths and an ochreous pottery; finally topped by an iron (arrow-heads) using culture. The burials are extended, secondary and similar in finds to the Megalithic burials on the banks of the river Belan.

On the basis of stratification, superimposition and overlapping of graves, 14 out of 17 skeletons could be assigned to 8 burial phases at Lekhahia (Sharma 1965:77-78). Generally, the dead were buried in extended position. The bodies were laid supine. In a few cases the heads were placed left or right. In this connection it may be pointed out that skeleton IV offers a discordant note in the general burial practice at Lekhahia. This seems to have been a case of flexed burial. Except for two skeletons, XII and II, the remaining were oriented west-east with the head lying towards the west. The skeleton XII was oriented north-south, the head placed in the north; and in the case of skeleton II, the position was just the reverse, the head lying in the southern direction. Olecranon perforation was observed in the cases of four skeletons (IV, VII, IX and XVII). Deep caries in the left first molar of skeleton XIII was also noticed. Of these 10 seem to be male while three female or questionably female. There are 10 adults above the age of 20 years and two juveniles. We have only two ^{14}C dates processed on bone samples of skeletons VII and XVII. Both are based on inorganic fraction of uncharred bones and we have to keep in mind that bone samples are prone to contamination.

^{14}C dates (half-life = 5730 years; uncalibrated) for Lekhahia
TF - 417 1710 ± 110 BC
TF - 419 2410 ± 115 BC

Baghai-Khor

The Baghai-Khor rock-shelter (lat. 24° 48' 30" N, long. 82°5' E) is situated about 65 km south-west of Mirzapur. A human skeleton was found buried at depth of 30cm below the surface oriented west-east with the head lying to the west. No grave goods other than microliths were found from the grave. The skeleton was of a woman of 20 to 21 years of age with height of 152.68 cm.

Bhimbetka

Further south-west we come to the famous rock-shelter group of Bhimbetka, near Bhopal, on the Vindhyan hills. Bhimbetka (lat. 22°5' N, long. 77°57' E) is 40 km south of Bhopal, Madhya Pradesh. Bhimbetka complex extends over 13 km diametre and has more than 400 rock-shelters covering a long span of time from Lower Palaeolithic to the Medieval period (see Chapter 5). In fact many shelters show a continuity of occupation from the Acheulian culture onwards. The Bhimbetka hills are rich in forests, game and edible wild plants, which are exploited even today by the local tribes. The density of prehistoric settlements in the area does suggest optimal ecological conditions in the past too.

Out of 600, over four 400 shelters bear paintings or habitation deposit. Several primary and a few secondary human burials were found in this area too. Towards the close of the Palaeolithic period there is a diminution in the size of blades, leading to Microlithic technology. But the raw material used here, in Palaeolithic times was invariably quartzite, whereas the Mesolithic cultures used chalcedony. The general sequence of the Mesolithic cultures in Bhimbetka area begins with a geometric Microlithic horizon, devoid of pottery. The geometric types comprise blunted back blades, crescents, triangles and trapezes and scalene triangles, besides hammers, querns, rubbers and perforated discs made of basalt. From the top-most layer tiny sherds of plain red and grey wares have also been found. It is followed by a painted pottery using culture along with microliths and copper tools, obviously influenced by the contemporary Chalcolithic cultures. The top layers are marked by an iron using historical culture. Microliths, stone querns and mullers and red and yellow ochre pieces with rubbed facets occur in all levels. Bone tools and a beautiful tubular bone-ornament decorated with incised designs were also found. The burials appeared to be mostly fragmentary. V.N. Misra dug three primary burials in shelter IIB 33 and a secondary burial in shelter III F15. Apart from these Susan Haas and Wakankar also exposed several other similar burials in other shelters (IAR 1972-73, 1973-74, 1974-75, 1975-76, 1976-77). All these finds hint at the late Mesolithic character of the site.

Dorothy Deep and Jambudvipa rock-shelters (Hunter 1935:28-57) are situated at a distance of about 3.2 km west-north-west of Panchmarhi in the Mahadeo hills in Madhya Pradesh. In these rock-shelters Hunter found human burials in association with microliths. At Dorothy Deep, an extended burial was found with east-west orientation, the head being placed towards the east. Microliths were found in the graves but no potsherds. G.M. Morant placed the age of the individual between 13 and 17 years and height 150 cm.

The last important group of the Central Zone is at Adamgarh, near Hoshangabad, 30 km south of Bhimbetka. This area was mainly studied by Joshi and Khare (1966: 90-95). At Adamgarh also the sequence is similar to Bhimbetka. Microliths occur in the top 60cm of the deposit, which is also the richest in animal remains. Pottery occurs throughout the Microlithic level. The Microlithic industry is geometric and similar to Bhimbetka though a bit cruder in comparison. From the top layers were found iron and glass bangle fragments.

Both wild and domestic animal bones were found on the site. Dog, cattle, buffalo, sheep/ goat and pig are the domesticated varieties. Wild animals were represented by monitor lizard (*Varanus grisius*), porcupine, horse, spotted deer, sambhar (*Cervus unicolor*) and hare. The presence of domesticated animals, therefore, makes it obvious that despite the lack of polished stone tools, Adamgarh should be regarded as a Neolithic site. No plant remains have, however, been identified.

^{14}C dates (half-life =5,730 years; uncalibrated) for Adamgarh
TF - 116 895 ± 105 BC
TF - 120 5500 ± 130 BC

TF-116 is based on uncharred bones and TF-120 on shells and thus both are prone to contamination and these are therefore unsatisfactory dates.

Maharashtra has two regions: coastal Konkan and the inland plateau, Desh. The two regions are separated by the ghats. Coastal region and the ghats have a rainfall up to 400cm and the hills are thickly forested. The plateau is part of the Central massif and rainfall here varies from 60 to 100 cm.

Konkan is full of aquatic life and fowl (in the forests). Todd had reported a number of sites from Hog island, Kasu shoal, Janyira, Dabhalgo and Jalgarh. Later on he reported other stratified sites at Khandivalli, near Bombay while Yerangal Point and some other sites were explored by Malik. In recent years with Statira Guzder, the author explored some more Microlithic sites in this region. Interestingly, we did not find any microlithic sites between the sea-level and +5m height. It could be explained by the fact that sea level had gone up to +5m during mid-Holocene times.

Malik found blunted back blades, triangles, trapezes, rhomboids, borers, scrapers and burins at Yerangal. Here a variety of material was used for the tools, e.g., agate, chalcedony, carnelian and chert. Besides these microliths were discovered mace-heads, choppers and axes along with beads of stone and glass. From a small dig at Marve island Todd discovered microliths, a stone rubber and some potsherds. At Khandivalli, Todd found a river section giving a stratified sequence from a Clactonian industry to a Microlithic assemblage. The upper limit can be dated by the presence of glass beads, etc., to the Buddhist occupations from the third century BC onwards. The lower limit perhaps goes down to c. 5000 BC as the last Holocene rise of sea-level alone could wipe out the microliths from the zone of sea-level up to +5m.

The Deccan basaltic plateau has several microlithic sites, though none is excavated. From the Dhulia district Sali reported an industry comprising fluted cores, blades and scrapers made of chalcedony and agate. From the Poona district, Kosambi, and later on Sankalia, discovered microliths. Kosambi traced some prehistoric routes and ancient village deities associated with microliths. He may be right in suggesting Mesolithic origins of such routes and the tutelary deities. From Mahabaleshwar area on the Sahyadris Malik reported a few sites. Tools here include crescents, backed blades, triangles, borers and a variety of scrapers. Typologically this industry appears older than that of the Bombay area.

The main Mesolithic industry in the Vindhyan and the Ganga region, however, comprises microliths characterised by cores, flakes, debitage and finished tools. They used hammer stones, anvils, sharpeners, querns and mullers made of quartzite and sandstone to shape their tools. The Microlithic assemblage also has utilised, backed and truncated blades, points, percoir, scalene and isosceles triangles, trapeze, lunates, tranchet and scrapers. Nodules of semi-precious stones were dressed and blades/flakes were obtained from the resultant cores. At one or both the ends of the prismatic cores, striking platforms were prepared for detaching blades as blanks. These blanks were converted into different types of tools. For obtaining the blanks, the indirect percussion technique was resorted to. The working edges of microliths were retouched for making them sharper. These microliths could have been used as sickles, arrow-heads, etc., as composite tools.

III. Eastern Zone

We have included Bihar, Orissa, Bengal, Assam, etc. under this zone despite their geographical diversity. As very little work has been done in this zone, we need not treat each area separately. The main geographical divisions of the Eastern Zone are: the Chhota Nagpur plateau; the coastal plains of Orissa; the Gangetic plains of Bihar; the Bengal delta; the Brahmaputra valley; and the Shillong plateau. The only common factor in the whole zone is high rainfall ranging from 200 to 400 cm. Many areas in Chhota Nagpur and Shillong plateaus are inhabited by primitive tribes.

In the Eastern Zone greater emphasis was put on the Neolithic finds, and as a result less is known about the Microlithic sites, though the first discovery of microliths by Beaching in the Singhbhum district dates back to 1868. From the Chhota Nagpur plateau many surface collections are known which are marked by a developed blade technique and general absence of geometric forms. Though there is no clear stratigraphic evidence, it can be suggested that Microlithic industries here are both Neolithic-associated as also pre-Neolithic.

Surface collections have been made from quite a few sites in the districts of Mayurbhanj, Keonjhar and Sundergarh, in Orissa. The only excavated site of Orissa is Kuchai where microliths dissociated with pottery were found from the lower level and pottery with ground stone tools from the upper levels (see Chapter 6). Microliths include blades, pointed flakes, crescents and prismatic cores.

The only well-excavated Microlithic site of the Eastern Zone is Birbhanpur in the Burdwan district of West Bengal. The site is located on an old terrace of the river Damodar in a sal forest. The Microlithic deposit overlies a layer of silty sand mixed with laterite pellets. It has been suggested that this deposit is a product of lateritic weathering of the basal sandstone under a heavy rainfall regime. A sandy soil covers the Microlithic layer and it is said that this represents aeolian deposition under arid conditions. Exposed microliths occur in clusters of 1 to 10 sq.m and the industry is dominated by flakes and flake tools. Tool types comprise blades (37%), points (21 %), scrapers (15%), lunates (15%), borers (16%), and burins (4%). The main raw material is quartz though occasional use of chert and chalcedony is also indicated. There are no reported organic remains nor are there any ^{14}C dates, but the industry shows typologically archaic characters. There are other surface finds reported from the Burdwan and Purulia districts.

IV. SOUTHERN ZONE

The southern group of Mesolithic cultures occupies the Indian peninsula, an eastwardly tilted plateau, flanked by hills on east and west. Kerala, Tamil Nadu, Andhra and Karnataka are the present states of this peninsula. As all these states have produced Microlithic occurrences, it will not serve any purpose to describe individual surface collections. We will concentrate here only on important sites.

Of the surface explorations, Paddayya's work in Shorapur Doab, between Krishna and Bhima rivers, is very important. He recorded 25 Microlithic occurrences and analysed 10,000 artifacts. The microliths, mostly made from chert, are narrower and shorter than those found associated with the Neolithic cultures. The main types are blunted back blades, crescents, borers and burins; the assemblage is mainly non-geometric.

Sangankallu, situated on the western fringe of the Karnataka plateau, was excavated by Subbarao, and later by Sankalia. The excavations produced an industry based on trap and quartz. It comprised cores, flakes, chopping tools, discoids, points and crescents. The artifacts made from trap are predominant in the lower levels. Compared to the microliths, the flake industry here is large sized. At Kupgal, the trap industry is found below the ash-mound and from the top level of the Sangakallu mound the remains of a Neolithic culture have been reported. Since the beginning of the Southern Neolithic is assigned to c. 2500 BC on the basis of the ^{14}C dates, one can by inference date the quartz Microlithic assemblage to c. 3500 BC. It may however be noted that the Sangankallu industry has no blades, and except for crescents, no microliths at all.

From the Godavari delta Cammiade reported more than a hundred Microlithic sites. But here crescents, blades, triangles and scrapers are associated with polished adzes and gauge heads and may therefore have a Neolithic affiliation. In the Kurnool area of Andhra, Cammiade, and later Isaac, recorded a sequence of the Mesolithic industries topped by a non-geometric, archaic Microlithic industry. A variety of raw material was used: chert, jasper, indurated shale, quartz and quartzite. It is very likely that this Microlithic industry developed out of the preceding Upper Palaeolithic culture.

From Renigunta, in the Chittoor district, Murty has reported another Microlithic industry which also seems to have derived from an earlier blade and burin industry. This assemblage comprises points, backed blades, triangles, scrapers, and burins and thus bears an archaic character. The preceding blade and burin industry here was on quartzite, but in the Mesolithic assemblage only quartz was used.

A rich Microlithic industry is associated with the red sand-dune (teri) sites of the Tirunelveli district at the extreme end of the peninsula. Aiyappan, Zeuner, Allchin and Krishnaswamy explored many sites in this area.

Due to older transgressions of the sea, there are three terraces of sand-dunes, at 1.5 m, 6m and 15 m, quite inland from the present-day coast. The dunes obviously must have formed during arid conditions, but man occupied them only during wetter conditions as indicated by weathering of sand. Even the microliths are stained red by the hydrated ferric oxide, a product of weathering. Zeuner assigned the 6m terrace, from which most of the microliths derive, to c. 4000 BC. We have ^{14}C dated the +5m sea-level transgression for the western coast of India to c. 5000 BP. On the eastern board also a large number of samples were dated which confirm this date, but no report on the work has yet come out.

The teri microliths are made both from chert and quartz; the former is more dominant. Discoids, crescents and points are the main tool types. The pressure flaking used on some almond-shaped points and other tools has no parallels in India but only in Ceylon. In Ceylon,

Beli Lena Athula, a Mesolithic site has been dated to c. 6000 BC (TF-1094) and may indicate a similar age for the teri sites. From two teri sites chopping tools are also reported. Thus the teri assemblage is distinguished by a dominance of flake tools and discoids and a paucity of blades and almost an absence of geometric forms. Though the industry thus shows an archaic character, it cannot be dated beyond 6000 BC.

No sites of the mid-Holocene Microlithic industries have been encountered in the Gunjana valley. However, K.T. Reddy had reported four sites in the Sagileru basin. This again poses a problem. The question remains as to what happened to the late Pleistocene and early Holocene human groups. Swarnamukhi valley in the south and Kurnool and Ananthapur regions in the north and west of this study region have evidenced Mesolithic sites. Several sites also have been reported recently in the Vishakhapatnam coast by the Department of Anthoropology, Andhra University (Raju 1988).

To sum up the characteristic features of the southern Mesolithic in general, we may note that quartz was the main material used which allowed only a crude blade technique. Geometric element is either absent or very minor. In many sites, older elements like discoids and choppers persist along with the microliths. As most of the collections are from the surface and the few excavations that were attempted confined themselves exclusively to tool types, we do not know anything more about the Mesolithic culture except its tools.

TABLE 4.7 STONE AGE (MESOLITHIC): CALIBRATED DATES

All BP ages are based on 5568 yr half-life of radiocarbon. Calibrated ages are given in bc/ad (after Possehl 1994).

Site	*Sample No.*	*5568 Yrs.BP*	*Calib. Dates*	*Culture*	*Material*
Bhimbetka	PRL-317	2490±100 BP	762,678,662 627,600 cal.bc	Microliths	Charcoal
Bhimbetka	PRL-18	2650±125BP	813 cal.bc	Microliths	Charcoal
Chauldari	BS-617	1350±100BP	663 cal.ad	Shell Midden	Charred or Uncharred Marine Shells
Chennur	BS-79	>40,000 BP	None	Microliths?	Shell
Inamgaon	BS-146	11700±150BP	None	Microliths	Shell
Langhnaj	TF-744	3875±105BP	2452,2427, 2395,2374, 2366 cal.bc	Microliths	Bone Inorganic Fraction
Lekhahia	TF-342	180 ± 110BP	1673,1753, 1796,1944, 1950 cal.ad	Phase 4, Microliths and Pottery	Charcoal
Lekhahia	TF-417	3560±105BP	1908 cal.bc	Lekhahia I, Phase 3, Microliths and Pottery	Bone

Cont. Table 4.7

Cont. Table 4.7

Site	*Sample No.*	*5568 Yrs.BP*	*Calib. Dates*	*Culture*	*Material*
Lekhahia	TF-419	4240±110BP	2895 cal.bc	Lekhahia I, Phase 1, Microliths and Upper Palaeolithic	Bone
Mahadaha	BS-137	2880±250BP	1044 cal.bc	Mesolithic	Charred bone carbonate
Mahadaha	BS-138	3840±130BP	2315 cal.bc	Mesolithc	Charred bone carbonate
Mahadaha	BS-136	4010±120BP	2569,2538, 2503 cal.bc	Mesolithic	Charred bone carbonate
Mantai	BM-2341	3550±70BP	1895 cal.bc	Microliths	Charcoal
Mantai	BM-2340	3520±45BP	1883 cal.bc	Microliths	Charcoal
Nirgudsar	BS-43	39000±3200BP	None	Microliths	Wood
Oriyo Timbo	PRL-888/9	4720±160BP	3510,3396, 3388 cal.bc	Period I, Microlithc	Charcoal
Oriyo Timbo	PRL-886	4160±170BP	2870,2806, 2774,2720, 2702 cal.bc	Period I, Microliths	Charcoal
Oriyo Timbo	PRL-876	4080±160BP	2850,2845, 2652,2647, 2612 cal.bc	Period I, Microliths	Charcoal
Paisra	BS-675	7420±110BP	6223,6195, 6187 cal.bc	Microliths	Charcoal
Patiraja-Wela Site	PRL-107	4500±170 BP	3307,3235, 3177,3163, 3134,3112, 3110 cal.bc	Microliths	Shells
Sarai Nahar Rai	TF-1356/59	2860±120BP	1021 cal.bc	Microliths	Charred and Semi-charred bone
Sarai Nahar Rai	TF-1104	10050 ±110BP	None	Microliths	Human bone Inorganic

All BP ages are based on 5568 yr half-life of radiocarbon. Calibrated ages are given in BC/AD.

POST-PLEISTOCENE SETTLEMENT PATTERNS

In his unpublished thesis, *A Study of Subsistence and Settlement Patterns during the late Prehistory of North Central India*, Chattopadhyaya (1990) makes some valuable observations and lends life to the monotonous microliths!

He suggests that during the Holocene climatic amelioration there was an increase in forest cover, and hence an increase in size of the populations of the various species of deer. In that case, he predicts that the Mesolithic populations of the Vindhyas would have had a broad spectrum economy. According to Sharma *et al.* (1980), the intrasite residential pattern at Chopani-Mando, for example, suggests an egalitarian group structure for these Mesolithic populations; which is, again, in agreement with a nomadic-egalitarian characterisation of the hunter-gatherers of warm areas.

The available evidence from the Ganges valley thus tends to favour a semi-sedentary settlement pattern, as defined by Binford, rather than a fully sedentary one. In that case the archaeological evidence from the Ganges valley does not contradict the global prediction. But the question that still evades a solution is why the Ganges valley populations adopted this somewhat unexpected pattern of semi-sedentism, rather than the nomadic pattern which local environmental conditions should theoretically have favoured.

Let us try to follow Chattopadhyaya's argument on the basis of the evidence he cites.

The stratigraphic contexts have established the sequence of cultures now. From the earliest to the youngest it is: (1) the Epi-Palaeolithic, (2) the aceramic, non-geometric Microlithic, (3) the aceramic, geometric Microlithic and (4) the diminutive Microlithic with pottery. This sequence has been observed at a number of sites in the Vindhyas – Chopani-Mando, Lekhahia and Baghai-Khor. In contrast to the late Mesolithic phases at many Vindhyan sites, evidence of pottery from any of the Ganges valley sites is conspicuous by its absence. He however thinks (a) that categories like 'early' non-geometric and 'late' geometric phases are misleading, and (2) that if one discovers within a stratigraphic sequence a sudden shift from non-geometric to geometric forms, it is not necessarily because such a change was the result of 'evolution' in tool technology. Strata with geometric tools have, in general, produced a greater range of tool types, as at Chopani-Mando (see Sharma *et al.* 1980). So the possibility that these strata represent a wider range of activities than the preceding ones or even within-site craft specialisation cannot be ruled out.

Chattopadhyaya says that the evidence from both the Ganges valley and the Vindhyas suggests that, in spite of a possibly wide range of economic activities, these societies organised themselves at much simpler levels of technology and with less developed storage facilities than those of the higher latitudes. The relatively large sizes of the two sites (above 8,000 m^2 for Mahadaha and 8,750 m^2 for Damdama) do suggest a large population. Chattopadhyaya thinks that most, if not all, of the Mesolithic sites of the Ganges valley should perhaps be considered as part of a residentially stable settlement system, centring on more permanent home bases, near the lakes. He also suggests that whether the stones were procured through the mechanism of balanced reciprocity (barter) or generalised reciprocity (an open access system), the Ganges societies, in either case, were economically dependent upon resources from the Vindhyas. Without denying the possibility for an early rise of animal husbandry in the Vindhyas, Chattopadhyaya maintains that the archaeological importance of north-Central India does not rest on the antiquity of its agricultural developments, as has been so vigorously argued by Sharma (Sharma *et al.* 1980). The Vindhyas and the Ganges valley present, instead, an important example of the distinctive nature of the cultural adaptation, and the process of population diversification and cladogenetic mode of evolution experienced by the people of the subcontinent over the millennia (Chattopadhyaya 1990).

Being one of the rare breed of South Asian archaeologists who have a theoretical bent, Chattopadhyaya (2000a: 16-34) compares the two trajectories of post-Pleistocene adaptations: the Near-Eastern pathway and the temperate European pathway. He compares these pathways to the kind of response in warm regions like the Vindhyas and the Ganga valley.

> The response here in the early Holocene was not one of genetic domestication, as noted for the Near-East; it involved diversifying selection under cladogenetic mode of evolution. Residential stability here, as in temperate Europe, could be seen as an indirect outcome of various strategies towards meeting certain challenges, both environmental and social. As environmental conditions in temperate and tropical or sub-tropical zones are substantially different, the adaptive strategies might not have been the same. For example, technological sophistication and intensive resource management in temperate regions were directed towards developing proper storage facilities of food resources as a buffer-stock for unproductive months. In the Ganga valley a specialised technology on bone and antler did emerge, but there is no proper evidence either from the Ganga valley or from the Vindhyas for food storage. In other words, the response in the Vindhyas and the Ganga valley was 'different' from the said two trajectories (Chattopadhyaya 2000a: 16-34).

Chattopadhyaya, however, cautions:

> It is neither easy nor appropriate to compare phenomena under dissimilar units of analysis. Therefore, we have to adopt a broader unit where these phenomena could converge. One such unit of analysis constitutes a notion, comprising two interrelated variables - security and savings (through 'storage'). It is here that all kinds of peoples, be they hunter-gatherers, farmers or industrial communities, shed off their differences. Under this rubric, perhaps, it is more appropriate to understand the three trajectories of post-Pleistocene adaptation. The Pleistocene scenario is one, where hunting-gathering involves resources that are distributed in their natural state. They are equivalent to 'ecological' or natural storage; sedentism in this situation is an unlikely option. But when the level of security decreases for a variety of reasons - environmental, demographic, social, etc. - there is a possibility that 'ecological' storage might change to other, more secured forms of storage, which is what happened during post-Pleistocene times in many regions of the world. Sedentism can be a likely outcome. Now, genetic domestication of a mutually complementary set of species that developed in the Near-East can be understood, following Tim Ingold (1986), as the 'social' storage because certain wild resources had undergone a process of social control. It also involved sedentary settlements in most of the cases. Storage, again, has been the primary concern among the post-Pleistocene hunter-gatherers of temperate Europe, as their technological sophistication and intensive resource management hinged around it (Torrence 1983; Zvelebil 1986b). Their investment in large-scale storage facilities also promoted sedentism. However, groups in certain warm zones with environmental and topographic heterogeneity, the Vindhya-Ganga complex for example, seem to have invested in flexible 'social banks', comprising ecologically partitioned and occupationally specialised groups (often, lineal corporate groups) with their informal assurance of 'credit' during the time of need. According to Bailey, "Trade in foodstuffs may be seen as the spatial analogue of food storage, in that it represents the transfer of food from an area of surplus to an area of scarcity, as compared with the transfer of people from place to place, characteristic when food is absent" (1981: 8). This is also applicable to non-food resources, like stone raw materials or bone artefacts, which can compensate local scarcities. Resource partitioning strategy and ecological complementarity are some of the concepts underlying this mechanism of coping with resource stress and, therefore, constitute an efficient form of utilising and 'sharing' the total resource base by competing groups. This might or might not have resulted in the rise of sedentism (Chattopadhyaya 2000a: 16-34 and references therein).

CONCLUSIONS

We thus find that the Upper Palaeolithic cultures provided a link with the early Palaeolithic technologies, marking a distinct process of miniaturisation of artifacts, which reached its climax in the Microlithic industries of the Mesolithic phase. It led to the invention of composite tools and hafting to make sickles and knives, which played a crucial role in ushering in of agriculture. Somehow in South Asian archaeology ground stone axes are firmly associated with the Neolithic cultures, as if no farming was possible without such ground tools. As we will see in the next chapter on Early Farming, these Mesolithic cultures provided the initial stages, the substratum on which the agricultural revolution stood. We thus see that the Upper Palaeolithic cultures provided the transitional stage between the early Palaeolithic cultures and the Mesolithic stage, whereas the latter was a prelude to the Early Farming cultures.

Chapter 5

PREHISTORIC ROCK ART

Contents :

INTRODUCTION

There is considerable controversy regarding the meaning and significance of rock art. It is, however, generally believed that it is not something to fulfil the idle aesthetic urge to decorate one's living rooms. In fact, quite often it is preserved in some deep and inaccessible caves in Europe. Art for him was perhaps part of the hunting process as is evidenced by numerous hunting scenes depicted by Palaeolithic man all over the world. To emphasise this point, the famous art critic, Mulkraj Anand said,

> It is likely, however, that fashionable dilettantism will continue to consider these works as 'Art'. Nothing can be more disastrous than the misinterpretation of the decisive moments of these paintings through the imposition of modern attitude. These paintings are the heightened passion of man in search of food. They express the catharsis of fear, wonder and mystery, of the spell with which primitive man, in danger of extinction through the possible recoil of the beast in hunt, wanted to conquer his foe before the physical act of throwing the spear at his prey.

Palaeolithic art has some common universal denominators but the style was perhaps affected by local environmental conditions also. Where there was a glacial landscape, Palaeolithic man killed and froze his meat for the winters. But in tropical regions, like India, the kill had to be consumed immediately. Mulkraj Anand explains the difference in emphasis between the vitalism of Altamira and the silhouette of Bhimbetka on this basis.

From the simple Palaeolithic life, the Neolithic cultures ushered into a co-operative, collectivist society. Man's needs of plant-agriculture and domesticated animals made him aware of the contrasts of nature: good and bad weather, rain and sunshine, barrenness and fertility, which in due course led him to conceive malignant demons and benevolent spirits. This animism divided the world into a visible phenomenal world and an invisible world of spirits - it was a contrast to the monistic worldview of Palaeolithic magic. "Magic is sensualistic and holds fast to the concrete; animism is spiritualistic and inclines to abstraction ... that is the main reason why Palaeolithic art reproduced things true to life and reality, whilst Neolithic art opposes a

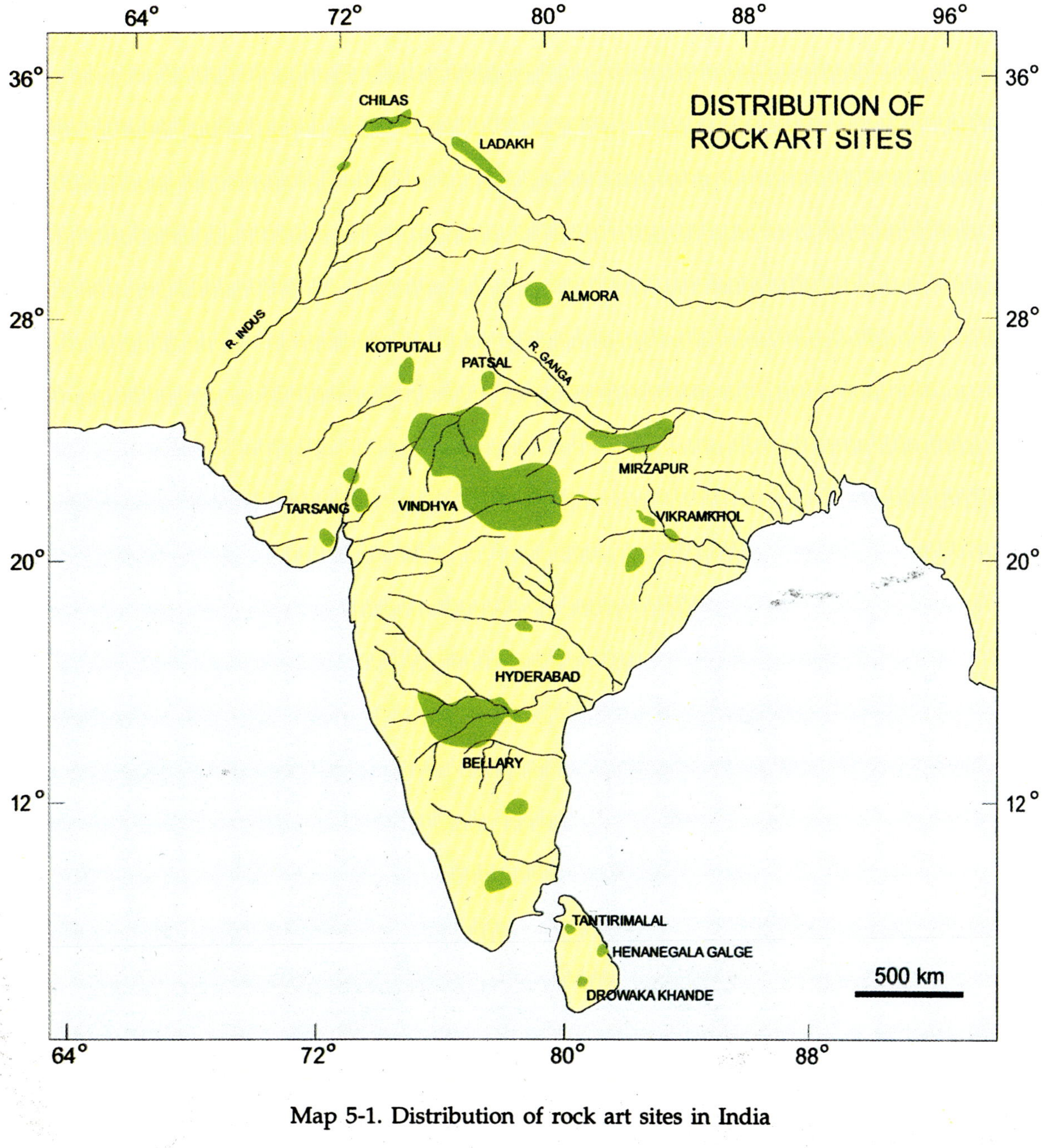

Map 5-1. Distribution of rock art sites in India

stylistic and idealised super world to ordinary empirical reality". To prove this contrast Hauser quotes two examples from contemporary tribes. The bushmen who economically still live in a Palaeolithic stage, with their individual search for food, have created naturalistic art 'surprisingly similar to Palaeolithic paintings'. In fact, a Red Indian complained of a research worker who had made several sketches, "I know this man has put many of our bisons into his book. I was there when he did it, and since then we have no bisons". This perhaps explains the conception of Palaeolithic man who considered art as a direct continuation of ordinary reality. On the other hand, the West African tribes practise agriculture and have produced an abstract, geometrically devised art. In Neolithic art, the bisons, the elephant and the boar, gave place to pregnant woman, the mother of fertility cults.

A Global Perspective

In this overview, we would try to survey the evidence of prehistoric rock art in the world and the various theories that have been propagated to explain it.

In the European rock art, one can observe some significant features. The animals depicted are naturalistic; often the paintings are in quite inaccessible locations. The animals depicted were hunted for food and at times they appear to be ritualistically killed on the painting itself. Perhaps such ritualistic killing was done to ensure success in the hunt. Thus we can see that for early man such paintings were, in fact, two-dimensional extension of the three-dimensional reality (Agrawal 1979: 7). Some scholars have made a topographical study of the rock art and have found evidence of the world-view of early man, others suggest that the expression through paintings heralded the advent of language.

Bronowski, who was a polymath but not an archaeologist, says about the European rock art,

> In these paintings the hunter was made familiar with dangers which he knew he had to face but to which he had not yet come. When the hunter was brought here into the secret dark and the light was suddenly flashed on the pictures, he saw the bison as he would have to face him, he saw the running deer, he saw the turning boar. And he felt alone with them as he would in the hunt; his spear-arm flexed with an experience which he would have and which he needed not to be afraid of. The painter had frozen the moment of fear... (Bronowski 1976: 54).

Altamira, meaning "high lookout", is located 5 km from the Cantabrian coast, in north Spain. Don Marcellion de Sautuola was the owner of this land. Only in 1868 he discovered some painted caves. Edouard Piette, the famous French prehistorian, instructed de Sautuola the cave exploration techniques. It was de Sautuola's daughter, Maria, who was the first to discover the low cave painted with bisons and horses in 1879. There were very few who believed in de Sautuola's discoveries; some even thought that he had faked them. Appalled by the scholar's reactions de Sautuola closed the cave. He died in 1888. It was other discoveries of La Mouthe and other sites in Dordogne area in 1895 which forced the prehistorians to accept the antiquity of these paintings. Once it was believed that the Upper Palaeolithic man did have the abilities for artistic expression, a lot of theories cropped up to explain this prehistoric art.

John Halvarson of the University of California suggested that the images are products of the "primal mind". "Palaeolithic representation is naturalistic because it is unmediated by cognitive reflection", he says. "At this early stage of mental development, precept and concept may have been undifferentiated". He does not ascribe any religious motivation to these paintings. It is true that the engravings and paintings do not represent scenes from Upper Palaeolithic life, but there is a pattern. Horse, bison and oxen count for 60% of the images. Carnivores are rare.

The early idea of art for art's sake was soon abandoned for the hypothesis of sympathetic magic. Reinach in 1903 argued that the paintings were part of magical and totemic rituals, as was evident from his studies of the aboriginal art of Australia. This view was developed and promoted vigorously by the Abbe Breuil during his long and dominating career. As a result, the majority of the archaeological establishment interpreted this art as hunting magic.

The Abbe Breuil died in 1961 and that was also the end of his all-encompassing hunting magic hypothesis. Where Breuil had seen chaos, Andre Leroi-Gourhan found order in them. Leroi-Gourhan was struck by the consistency of the Palaeolithic art. He said, "Palaeolithic artists repeatedly depict the same inventory of animals in comparable attitudes. Once this unity is recognised, it remains only for the student to see ways of arranging the art's temporal and spatial subdivisions in a systematic manner". According to him this art embodied ideas about Upper Palaeolithic society.

One problem with the hunting magic hypothesis was that the images depicted often did not reflect the diet indicated by fossil remains. Reindeer was the main component of diet but its paintings were rare. The reverse was true of the horse. Leroi-Gourhan recognised that horse, stag and ibex represented male-ness and the bison, the mammoth and the ox femaleness. He found that deer was mainly confined to the entrances of the main chambers. Horse, bison and ox were the predominant creatures of the main chambers. Carnivores were confined deep into the cave system. Thus there was a concentration on a diversity of meanings and a concern for the context of art, not so much what the images meant but rather what made them meaningful. Leroi-Gourhan died in 1986. It was followed by views which emphasised diversity. For example, Denis Vialou sees order in individual caves but not the global order of Leroi-Gourhan. He proposed that each cave should be viewed as a separate expression. Delporte is studying the differences between wall art and portable art. Conkey is focusing on the social context of the images.

The Upper Palaeolithic art covers 35,000 to 10,000 BP years, and coincides with that of the Ice Age. In Europe five periods have been identified, mainly based on technological changes (see Table 5.1).

TABLE 5.1 UPPER PALAEOLITHIC SEQUENCE OF EUROPE

1. Chatelperronean	35 to 33 kyr
2. Aurignacian	33 to 30 kyr.
3. Gravettian	30 to 22 kyr.
4. Solutrean	22 to 18 kyr.
5. Magdalenian	18 to 10 kyr.

There is no uniformity between the art of different periods. Eighty per cent of all Palaeolithic art comes from the Magdalenian. The Chatelperronean is marked by blade and burin industry, though not much of art is in evidence. During the Aurignacian there was no cave painting, though ivory beads and small human and animal sculptures are well represented. There are regularly spaced incisions which Marshack identified as systems of notation. A flute is also reported from this period. The Gravettian is marked by the so-called Venuses or female icons associated with fertility cult. It is only in the Solutrean period that painting in deep caves started appearing but much more impressive were the bas-reliefs, some of them standing out 15cm in relief. The era of deep cave painting starts really with the Magdalenian (e.g., Altamira and Lascaux), also carved and engraved ivory objects and a sudden burst of depiction of human faces. For instance, in the cave of La Marche there is a gallery of more than a hundred human faces engraved in limestone rocks.

These painted cave sites might have served as places for aggregation for renewing friendships, strengthening political alliances and arranging marriages, like they do in the tribal societies today. The real benefit of such aggregations would have been social and political, not economic.

The coincidence of geometric motifs with representational images is a puzzling aspect of this art. The Abbe Breuil saw in them traps, snares and even weapons, whereas Leroi Gourhan found structural duality in them. Dots and strokes were male signs; ovals, triangles, etc. were female's signs. On the other hand, Lewis-Williams in Central Africa identifies them with images created during the state of hallucination, a sure sign of shamanistic art. He derives grids, zigzags, dots, spirals, curls, etc. from the altered states of consciousness, no matter what their cultural background is. He draws parallels with the aboriginal San rock art. He finds all the three stages of hallucination depicted in Palaeolithic art. The therioanthropes perhaps represent shamans or hunters dressed in animal skins sometimes wearing horns. In short, these prehistoric art sites are imbued with meaning but we can not decipher it. In Richard Leakey's words, "The potency is palpable but we are culturally blind to its content".

Recent studies of South African rock art by Dowson show that,

> The rock art of southern Africa therefore is not exclusively ethnic art; rather, it came out of the crucible of southern Africa's all-encompassing past.... The depictions of animals, shamans, spiritual versions—are not just a historical scrap book. On the contrary, the rock art images point to and were implicated in the negotiation of changing social relations. Seen in this way, the art can contribute significantly to an understanding of the social processes that formed the past (Dowson 1994: 341-42).

On the other hand, discussing the rock art of Zimbabwe, Garlake says:

> The concept of an art of archetypes, established through attributes, and emblems, goes some way towards explaining the nature of art.... If the art was concerned primarily with the construction and formulation of archetypes, this necessarily implies that it was almost entirely symbolic... and the attributes of the emblems equally symbolic in content, establishing notions of archetypes and attributes is simply a step on the road to 'meaning' (Garlake 1994: 353-54).

Discussing the prehistoric art of the Coso Range of North America, Whitley tends to see the "depiction of changes in the subsistence pattern in this art, from a generalised foraging to more specialised seed-oriented subsistence because subsistence change requires larger cognitive adjustments..." (Whitley 1994: 370).

Europe

The paintings, engravings and bruisings on the ceilings of the caves and rock shelters of Europe came to light from the late 1870s. Sautuola was the first man to discover Stone Age paintings in 1879 from the caves of Altamira in Spain. However, at that time prehistorians first refused to accept the polychrome paintings of bison as being of Palaeolithic antiquity (Daniel 1962: 53). Only further discoveries of rock art sites in Dordogne area, for example, Chebot, La Mouthe and Pair-non-Pair caves around 1895 and Les Combarelles and Font-de Gaume by 1901, led to a gradual change in attitude. Since then, a large number of Pleistocene and post-Pleistocene rock art sites have been discovered in Europe. Breuil published some important paintings from Calapata in eastern Spain. This was followed by the discovery of paintings at El Castillo, Covalanas, La Haza and at Niaux in 1906. The caves of La Pasiega, Las Trois Freres, Tuc d'Audoubert and Lascaux were discovered before 1940. The Rouffignac cave in the Dordogne in the Franco-Cantabrian region was discovered in 1956. There are quite a few other well-known painting sites of the Spanish Levant which were discovered in the early years of this century, for example, Cogul in 1908, Alpera in 1910, Minateda in 1914, Morella la Vella and 15 rock shelters of Valltorta Gorge in 1917.

The European Palaeolithic rock art sites have been located in three main areas: the valley of Dordogne in France, in the Pyrenees, and in the Cantabrian mountains. However, other isolated groups are known from Sicily, Southern Russia and Eastern Siberia (Ucko and Rosenfeld 1967). A majority of post-Pleistocene rock art sites are known from Levant area of Spain (Beltran 1982). The post-Pleistocene rock art of Europe mainly consists of open engraving sites. The well-known areas for such art are Scandinavia, the Swiss/Italian Alps and the Spanish Levant. The common themes of this art are game animals, birds, warfare, dance, daily life, non-figurative motifs such as spirals, triangles, mazes, and sometimes agriculture and pastoralism (Beltran 1982: 72-75). The Palaeolithic cave paintings mostly include animals like bison, bull, mammoth, rhinoceros, horse, ibex, reindeer and boar and are characterised by a naturalism and dynamism, whereas the human figures are depicted only in a symbolic style, using only few lines. The Mesolithic paintings, dominated by hunting scenes, are smaller than the Upper Palaeolithic ones.

Though we do not know exactly how prehistoric man learnt the technique of making the colours and began painting, it has been suggested that there "was a long tradition of artistic expression on perishable material such as skin, bark, cloth and wood, before the first pictures appeared on the wall or ceiling in a dark cave" (Ucko and Rosenfeld 1967: 76).

Africa

In 1899, Molyneux was the first to publish a note on the paintings of Rhodesia (Neville 1949: 59). However, the first work on rock art of Africa was carried out by Flamand in 1921 (Alimen 1957: 359). In 1954, Breuil and Lhote published a detailed account of North African (Saharan) engravings. Paintings and engravings are known from the mountainous region of the Sahara in North Africa. Tassili is one of the well-known sites of this area from where more than 15,000 engravings have been recorded (Lhote 1961: 103). The earliest (Hunter period) portrayals depict naturalistic figures of elephants, rhinos, lions, large bovids and camels. The depiction of horses and chariots in later Saharan rock art is well documented in over 600 rock paintings and engravings. The introduction of camel is said to have coincided with the later phase. The rock art also documents a number of other changes including the introduction of pastoralism (Brandt and Carder 1987).

Apart from these, a large number of rock art sites in Zimbabwe, Mozambique, Botswana, Namibia, Tanzania, Lesotho and in South Africa have been recorded. The early art forms are characterised by a large number of animals including eland, antelope, elephant, rhino, hippopotamus, buffalo, and also human figures. Geometric designs and hand-prints also occur in some areas (Lewis-Williams 1983). Holm (1961: 153-203) has given a comprehensive analysis of the rock art of South Africa.

The South African rock art differs from the well-known Palaeolithic rock art of Western Europe. The European art is concealed in deep inaccessible underground caves, but the South African rock shelters are open, the sunrays often directly reaching the paintings. The paintings are generally smaller than the European ones (Lewis-Williams 1983). The earliest phase of rock art in this area is represented by painted stones found from excavations of different shelters. Their date goes back to 26,000 BP. The human figures are generally absent from this phase, but appear in the second phase. The third phase contains most of the shaded polychrome paintings of antelopes. The human figures are also drawn with equal skill. These paintings are associated with the San (Bushman) hunter-gatherers. In the last phase, human figures are depicted with their rifles, hats, garments and horses. Throughout these four phases, the eland has been increasingly depicted which suggests continuity of a single developing tradition of art (Lewis-Williams 1983).

Australia

From Australia, an enormously diverse and rich heritage of rock art is known, covering a period from some 20,000 years BP to the present (Gale and Jacobs 1987: 226). A number of rock painting sites were reported from North Australia by Worms (1955: 546-566). The areas such as W. Amhem Land, the Kimberley, the Pilbara, south-east Cape York, the Central Queensland highland and around Sydney have a vast concentration of rock art sites. The Koonalda cave, on the arid Nullarbor Plain, containing finger markings and incised lines on the soft parietal deposits, is the oldest well dated site. The pecked circles, dots, connecting lines and the bird tracks represent the early phase of Australian rock art. Rosenfeld *et al.* (1981: 85) have postulated that the engravings in Australia had begun prior to 13,000 BP.

The Central Australian art is characterised by geometric motifs, sand drawings, engravings and sacred paintings. In the Sydney basin, figurative motifs like fish, macropods, whales, humans, snakes and lizards have generally been engraved, which also reflect an environmental context. Rock art of Laura (south-east Cape York) includes figurative paintings of humans, macropods, flying foxes, dingoes, echnidas, fish, birds and reptiles. However, Western Amhem Land's paintings are distinguished by multi-coloured humans, macropods, birds, fish and reptiles with decorative X-ray style. Besides this, the 'Mini' art of small red naturalistic figures is significant for stylistic development.

The various discoveries of rock paintings from North Kimberley, Central-North Australia, Mungo, Miriwn, Kneiff, Clogg's and Koonalda are some of the well-known sites, which have provided a long sequence of Stone Age art in Australia. In recent years the Australian Institute of Aboriginal Studies has contributed a great deal to the study of rock art (Mulvaney 1975: 263). Chippindale *et al.* (2000) studied paintings and engravings in Wardaman area and have shown the importance of stratigraphy, Harris matrices method and relative dating of regional rock art despite use of absolute dating.

Lorblanchet (1991) has presented an important study of art forms as diverse as the cave art of the reindeer hunters of western Europe and the rock art of kangaroo hunters of Australia, which can complement each other. This study also reflects the comparative trend in historical research pointing out similarities as well as differences in time and space to further our understanding of the prehistoric past.

In order to assess the universality or diversity of the human mind in time and space, it is first crucial to know whether, at their two ends of the world, the reindeer and kangaroo hunters independently became creators of forms at the same moment, if they experienced the same First graphic infancy, and whether their arts then followed the same evolutionary paths.

Some art historians, like Rene Huyghes, no doubt unfamiliar with prehistoric art, have seen the Palaeolithic's evolution of styles as a transition from abstraction to naturalism with a final return to abstraction. The study of Palaeolithic and Australian art reveals that this conception is quite wrong. For a start, in both worlds, two fundamental tendencies of the spirit of *Homo sapiens* stand out; the trend towards geometric schematism and abstraction on the one hand, and, on the other, that towards naturalism. These two trends are parallel, antinomical and synchronous. As for the precise evolution of styles, it will soon benefit from in-depth regional studies that will call into question the current chronological systems.

The motivations of *Homo sapiens* artists are undoubtedly more or less always of the same kind everywhere, but these creators differ in their way of grasping aspects of nature. To reproduce the visible world, they often start out from the fundamental qualities of things, and their stereotyped symbols depict the essence of beings and objects, but they also strive to attain more superficial aspects such as volume, space, movement. We should note that, in this conquest of reality, the Australians took a different path.

They rejected volume, did not represent depth, and turned towards ornamentation. Hence, the constructed space of the Palaeolithic contrasts with the floating space of Australia which is an ornamental space par excellence. Perhaps the exuberant dynamism of certain Australian drawings is more of a simple playing with form, a simple means of obtaining new shapes by resorting to animation, than a faithful analysis of movement.

The reindeer hunters, on the other hand, achieved the third dimension. In so doing, they discovered almost all the graphic skills and knacks of European artists. The perspectivists of the Renaissance, all start in the Palaeolithic. It was also at this time that the search began for perfection of line through a constant purification and idealisation of form, later developed in Greek art and throughout the history of western art.

The same opposition between an art of surface and an art of volume blossoms in the treatment of the human figure. Some of the Magdalenian faces of La Marche are not only drawings in depth suggesting the third dimension, but also real portraits, that is, an exact transposition of nature. These images reveal the emergence of the individual within Magdalenian society following the process of "individuation" described by psychologists (Virel 1965), whereas the kangaroo hunters, interested in an abstract idea of man, geometrised his image. As shown by the faces of Cleland hill, probably contemporaneous with our Magdalenian, the first Antipodean artists played freely with human forms, considering them ornamental elements.

A wide range of insights can therefore be obtained from studies of prehistoric art, to their great advantage. Despite its dangers and limits, which are more obvious than ever, the internal analysis of evidence remains the basis of our research, but it can be illuminated by numerous data from outside.

The separation of analysis and hypothesis can now appear somewhat theoretical and illusory, because the latter does not always follow from the former, as Laming-Emperaire and Leroi-Gourhan wanted, nor does it necessarily precede it, as the New Archaeology's "hypothetico-deductive" method proposes. The art prehistorian entering a decorated cave cannot be compared to a "Martian entering a church".... He is not so neutral and foreign, but simply a man impregnated by cultural and thought processes of his time and his surroundings. Whatever his concern for objectivity, he inevitably applies his models, his ideas, his specific and implicit hypotheses to his study; this means that, fortunately, we never cease looking at prehistoric art in new ways.

In a symbiotic relationship, hypothesis and analysis back each other up, constantly growing in strength. "Exterior" models simply allow one to make the evidence undergo successive tests, multiple complementary verifications which, little by little, make its nature more precise and constantly expand its analysis.

Precise comparison, based on the ignoring of context and the assumption of a general, systematic analogy as practised at the turn of the century, must be abandoned today, although it was useful at one time. The "ethnographic present" starts with the appearance of Cro-Magnon man.

The ethnographic, archaeological and aesthetic comparison of these two independent but partly contemporaneous assemblages that constitute the kangaroo hunters' art and that of the reindeer hunters brings to the fore not laws but some general principles of human behaviour; it isolates not only universals, constants of artistic creation in hunting societies, but also significant differences. It is important to know about both of these, because in a sense Australian art also teaches us about the art of our own origins through its contrasts, and vice versa of course.

This approach is not limited to the study of prehistoric art, and the historians of the new French school have developed it splendidly. In the introduction to his magnificent last work, *The Identity of France* Fernand Braudel (1986: 15) defined his method by locating his subject in "the long term, the hexagon of territory, Europe, the world..." and declares: "France in retrospect presents itself like a laboratory for experiments, for 'interspatial and intertemporal' comparisons, that can restore to us the perspective of continuities, of rules and trends (I do not say laws), or repetitions that make this in-depth history into a retrospective sociology that is, moreover, indispensable to all human sciences". Perhaps the time has come for prehistory to leave its isolation, and to feel, in at least some of its endeavours, that it forms part of this vast current "of a comparative history, a history in search of similarities" - and, of differences - "the true condition of all social sciences" that the great historian has proposed and illustrated so brilliantly" (Lorblanchet 1991:34-35 and references therein).

America

The rock painting and engraving sites are also known from North and South America. The discovery of rock art sites in North America started as early as 1893 by Mullery. Subsequently, Grant (1967), Wellmann (1979), Heizer and Baumhoff (1962) studied a number of rock art sites of North America. The engravings of sheep and human figures are well-known from California. The beginning of rock engravings in California has been placed in the Late Pleistocene which continued into the historic period (Whitley and Dorn 1987).

Let us now examine the South Asian rock art with this global backdrop.

South Asia

In India, the first prehistoric rock paintings were found at Sohagighat, Mirzapur in Uttar Pradesh (Map 5-1) in the year 1867-68 by Carlleyle (referred to by Smith 1906). He was perhaps the first man in the world to associate these paintings with prehistoric stone-chippers whose cultural remains he had excavated in the floors of these shelters. Carlleyle had discovered painted rock shelters in India 12 years before they were discovered in Europe. However, the first scientific article on Indian rock painting was published by Cockburn (1883a,b). In 1881 he found fossilised bones of rhinoceros in the valley of river Ken and in 1883 he found a painting of rhinoceros hunt at Ghormangor near the Bijaygarh fort, south-east of Robertsganj in Mirzapur district (Cockburn 1883a,b). Even at this early stage, Carlleyle, the pioneer scholar, was able to establish the prehistoricity of these paintings. Cockburn published an account of all his discoveries made in the 1880s and 1890s and he compared the paintings of India with Australia, South Africa, North America and South America (Cockburn 1899: 91). Fawcett (1901) reported rock carvings from Edakal cave, in Kerala. A few years later a pictorial description of the rock paintings in Banda district (Silberrad 1907) and a painted shelter at Singanpur in Raigarh district of Madhya Pradesh (Anderson 1918) were published. In the history of Indian art, prehistoric rock art was included for the first time by Brown (1917: 14-41). These attempts were followed by the work of Ghosh, who brought to light the paintings of Adamgarh group near Hoshangabad in 1922. He carried out a study of the whole area, from Raigarh to Hoshangabad (Ghosh 1932). Thereafter the credit for discovering the paintings of Pachmarhi region goes to Gordon, who published many articles on rock art in Indian and foreign journals and summarised his views on Indian rock art (Gordon 1958). Varma (1964) studied the paintings of Mirzapur, shortly after which Gupta (1967) published a comprehensive study of rock paintings and engravings. Pandey (1969) has also thrown light on several prehistoric sites. Tiwari (1975) brought to notice the largest painted rock shelters in India and he also found many sites around Bhopal. In Ladakh a number of petroglyphs have been reported but from the Neolithic levels of Kashmir excavations we have only a flat rock engraved with a hunting scene (Fig. 5-1).

Wakankar did the most notable work in this field. He discovered several hundred painted

Fig. 5-1. A hunting scene in rock-bruisings, Burzahom, a Neolithic site of Kashmir

rock shelters in Central India. He attempted a broad survey of the rock art of the whole country and produced a chronology of paintings based on the style, context and superimposition (Wakankar 1975). In the following years, more painted shelters have been reported.

The efforts of these scholars brought to light over a thousand rock shelters with paintings at more than 150 sites in India. Central India is the richest zone of rock art in the country - and perhaps in the world - where 90% of the sites are situated in the Vindhyas, Mahadeo and Kaimur sandstone hills. They were thickly forested and were ecologically ideal for man's habitation during the prehistoric times. Between 1972 and 1977 extensive excavations were conducted by Vikram, Ujjain and Poona Universities in quite a few Central Indian caves ((Wakankar 1984). It was established by their excavations that right from the Lower Palaeolithic to Historic period man lived in the Central Indian caves. The excavations have helped to correlate the paintings with archaeological evidence.

The Mesolithic paintings are generally dominated by game animals, hunting scenes and other cultural activities. The drawings of post-Mesolithic or later period show domestic animals, chariots and bullock-carts, domesticated animals and fighting scenes. Now the painted areas have been found to extend from the Himalayas to Kerala and from Assam to Gujarat - almost 2,000 km from north to south and 2,000 km from east to west.

Sushila Pant (1999: 205-31) reports on the regional differences in rock art. She says:

> Thus, in Orissa and south Deccan, animals are not accompanied by humans. In Central India, on the other hand, animals and human beings appear together and practically in equal number. In Orissa and the Deccan, the animals are stouter compared to those in Central India. There is a difference between the human figures painted in the Deccan and those of the Vindhyan region. In the Vindhyan region, special effort has been made in depicting the eyes of the animals, whereas human beings are left without them. The Deccan, on the contrary, shows two legged men with very clear eyes. Such differences were not limited only to the broader groups. In Central India, there is a disharmony among the paintings of Raigarh and Mirzapur. Pachmarhi and Bhopal abound with representations of bow

and arrow whereas they are conspicuously missing at Raigarh. Thus, there is sub-regional variation also. The rock-paintings from Mirzapur very aptly tell the same story of variation. The art of this region of northern Vindhya is different from that of the western Vindhyan area.

Before we get down to a detailed discussion of South Asian rock art, we may note some critical remarks of Bednarik, a well-known rock art scholar. He says:

> No pre-writing rock art anywhere in Asia has been firmly dated, and even broad cultural attribution is often most tenuous. For instance, a Palaeolithic antiquity of Indian rock paintings (Wakankar 1983) is widely rejected by Indian scholars today. Wakankar's claim for the universal superimposition precedence of the green dynamic paintings of Central India has been negated by Tyagi (1988), whose findings I have been able to verify on various occasions. Having refuted the engravings on 44 ostrich eggshell fragments from Palaeolithic sites in India by demonstrating that they are natural markings (Bednarik 1991) and having also determined that the Upper Palaeolithic so-called 'mother goddess' of Lohanda Nala, Belan valley (Misra 1977), is in fact a damaged bone harpoon with four symmetrically arranged barbs (Bednarik 1990b), I have had to reject most evidence advanced in favour of Palaeolithic art in India; solid proof is limited to the engraved ostrich eggshell specimen from Patne and a few perforated disc beads (Bednarik 1991), and the Hunsgi evidence of the use of ochre crayons in the Acheulian" (Bednarik 1990c; Bednarik 1993b: 141-55 and references therein).

These are strong words but the dating of rock art is still on a weak footing. Though in Europe and Australia now AMS dating has provided absolute dates for their rock art, in South Asia no such attempts have been made so far. We will discuss this issue in the section on chronology towards the end of this chapter, as many scholars believe that the Indian rock art goes back to Palaeolithic times despite Bednarik's reservations (Sonawane 1997).

Now we will discuss South Asian rock art region-wise.

NORTHERN GROUP

In the Himalayan region we have as many as four different rock art regions such as Chilas (Gilgit-Karakorum area of Pakistan), Ladakh and Burzahom (Jammu and Kashmir), Attock (Indus region) and Almora and Chamoli (Uttaranchal). Barring Uttaranchal all these regions have generally evidence of engravings or bruisings. The German-Pakistani expedition (between 1979 and 1984) brought to light a variety of rock carving, which include naturalistic and sub-naturalistic and stylised animals, masks, chariot, stylised human figures, stupas, etc., from Gilgit-Karakorum region ranging between fifth millennium BC and second cent. AD. A few important sites are known as Chilas, Thalpan, Ziyarat, Hodar, Oshibat, Thor (Minar-Gah), Thor (north), Shatial Bridge, Balistan and others (Jettmar 1987). King (1940:65-68) found engravings on the boulders at least at four sites in Attock on the bank of Indus. At Burzahom, Kashmir, two stone slabs were found from Period III and one has an abstract design, which Pande (1971) identifies as a representation of a hut with a thatched domical roof. The hind portion of an animal and its tail can be seen clearly to the right. He compares it with the other Stone Age tectiforms. The other slab was also found from the same pit. The engraving covers about 48 x 27 cm area of the slab and depicts a stag (*Cervis elaphus*) being hunted. A human shoots an arrow from the front and one has already pierced the stag. The other human is attacking with a spear from behind. In the upper portion a dog and two suns possibly represent the day of successful hunt. The bow-man, the dog and the stag have all been depicted with enlarged genitals. The importance of these engravings lies in the fact that both are from well-dated Neolithic levels (c. 2000 BC) (Fig. 5-1).

Since the Kumauni rock art is least known in the pan-Indian context and we have carried out a detailed study in recent years, we will discuss this region in detail.

Kumauni Rock Art

The painted rock shelter areas are located close to the north and north-east of Almora town (29°37' N; 79°38' E, between 1,300 and 1,900m AMSL) in the Kumaun region (Fig. 7-3). The Almora-Pithoragarh and the Almora-Bageshwar roads lead to this area. The entire area comprises a series of ridges and steep mountain slopes descending from Kasardevi and Binsar. The Kasardevi hill is oriented north-west-south-east and a series of transverse and parallel mountain ridges bifurcate towards north-east, east and south-east. These mountain ranges meet the hills of the Binsar range descending in a southerly direction. Both the mountain ranges are visible from Almora town. The Binsar mountain range is covered by dense vegetation, which is dominated by *Quercus incana*, Rhododendron and coniferous trees of the Lesser Himalayan zone; however, the lower slopes are populated all along by *Pinus roxburghii*, and other species of this zone. The Kasardevi range also represents similar vegetation. In these hills, mostly on northern slopes, we find some species of wild fruits like kafal (*Myrica nagi*), kilmora (*Berbers asiatica*), and makhoie (*Solanica nigrum*). The lower slopes of these hills are sparsely populated, where the forest has been subjected to prolong and incessant tree-felling for timber and firewood. These hills also produce a large quantity of resin to run the plastics, turpentine and other industries in the Gangetic plains.

A perennial stream known as That gad or Binsar gad originates in the hills of Binsar and flows in a southerly direction through the Faurkanauli and Petshal area, where the rivulet Kakari, coming down from Narayankali, joins this stream. Further down it is known as Suyal and it joins the Koshi, south of Almora near Chausali village. However, the Suyal receives several other seasonal rivulets from the hills in its upper courses. Standing on the Kasardevi and Binsar hills, one gets a panoramic view of the countryside around and a stunning spectacle of the Himalayan ranges. For this reason the locality of Binsar attracts a large number of tourists and it is being developed as a sanctuary.

The area under study of rock art is located on the Almora nappe of the Lesser Himalaya, which is delimited by the North and South Almora Thrusts (Valdiya 1980: 94). Mica-granites, schists, gneiss, sandstone, quartzite, chlorite schist and slate are the rocks of this area, though mica-schist and slate rocks predominate. The outcrops of these rocks can be seen frequently on the hill slopes. The slate rock of this area generally bears layers of meta-quartz. The original colour of the slate rock is grey to medium grey to light grey. However, in course of geological time the slate rock has suffered extensive erosion due to sun, rain, wind, changes in temperature, acids percolating into the rocks with rain water and penetration of tree roots, resulting in the loosening and break-up of the rocks. As a result of weathering, the softer rocks slowly get removed in the form of small chips. This perhaps has led to the formation of several kinds of shape in the rocks. Different shapes and sizes of cavities have been noticed in these rocks. Most of the rock shelters of the area seem to have been formed by the enlargement of cavities through weathering.

D.P. Agrawal and M.P. Joshi (1978) were the first to report the Lakhiudyar site along with some more paintings nearby, initiating the rock art studies in the Kumaun region of the Himalayan foothills. The painted rock shelter at Dalband is located 18 km north-east of Almora town on the right bank of the Binsar gad. This is perhaps the biggest rock shelter of this region so far known. A huge pine tree has grown on the roof of this shelter. Pine grows long and thick roots, which may damage this shelter. Five years after this discovery, a painted rock shelter was found on the right bank of Alaknanda about 8 km north-west of Chamoli in Garhwal at an altitude of 2,000m AMSL (Saklani 1983: 217). This rock shelter is about 10m high and overlooks a deep valley towards the north-east. The paintings consist of stylised human and animal groups. The posture indicates movement of the figures. In this shelter, 18 human and seven animal

Pl. 5-1. Rock painting showing dancing figures in red from Lakhiudyar, district Almora, Uttaranchal

Pl. 5-2. Rock paintings from Matahwa/ Bhutahia, dist. Sonbhadra (Mirzapur), UP

Pl. 5-3. Lakhma rock shelter paintings, dist. Sonbhadra (Mirzapur),UP

Pl. 5-4. X-ray style paintings, Lakhma, dist. Sonbhadra (Mirzapur),UP

Pl. 5-5. Bison hunt scene. Kaua Khoh rock shelter, dist. Sonbhadra

Pl. 5-6. Rock paintings, Lakhama, Mirzapur

Pl. 5-7. A bull painted in red in X-ray style, Bhimbetka, MP

Pl. 5-8. Rock painting showing animals falling from a precipice, Bhimbetka, MP

Pl. 5-9. A hunting scene, Bhimbetka rock shelters, MP

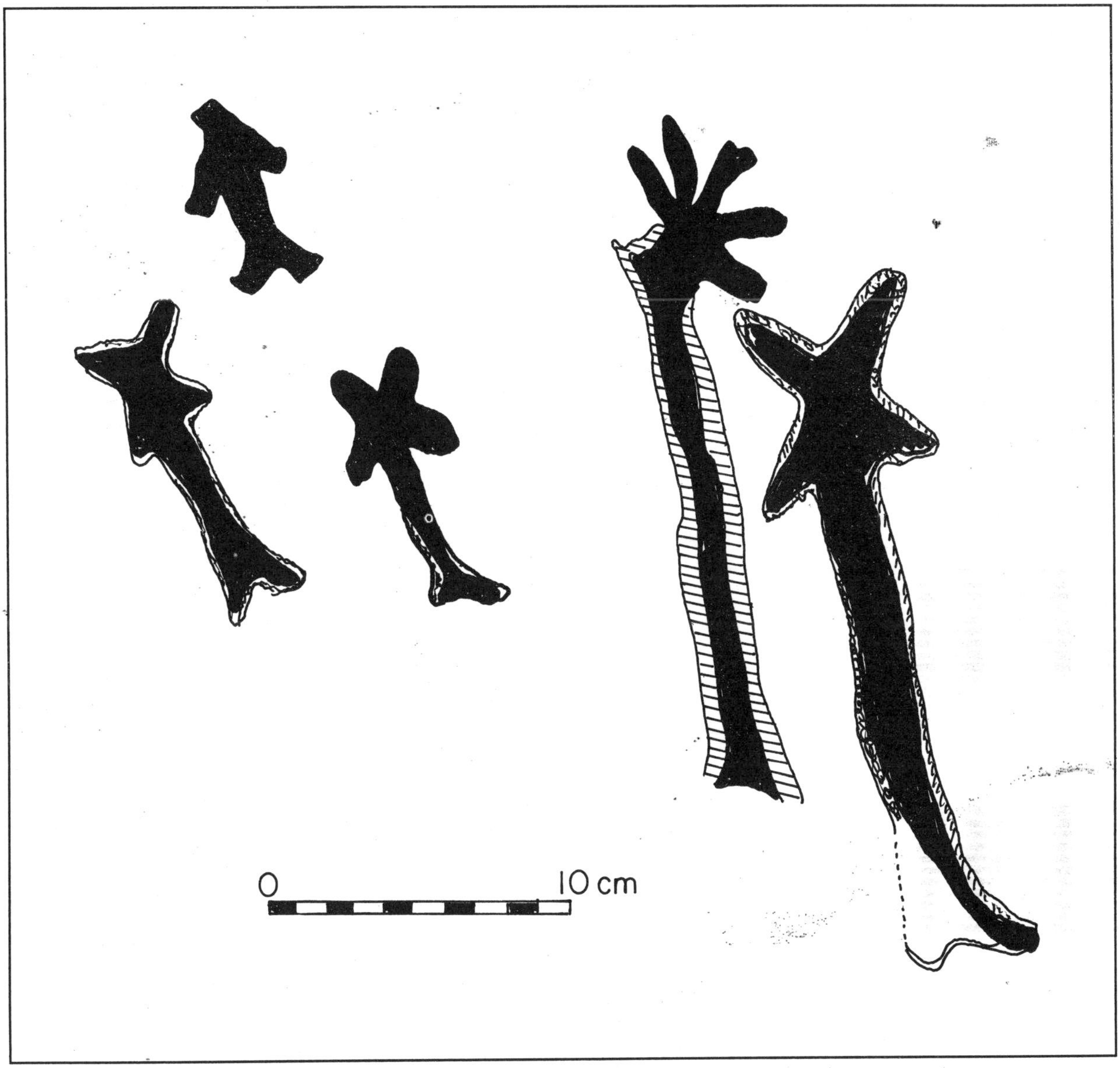

Fig. 5-2. Tree-like motifs in ochre red with a white outline and a human figure, Likhudyar rock shelter, Uttaranchal

figures were noticed in red ochre pigment. Among the human figures two are shown comparatively bigger in size. The animals represented look like stag and fox with long necks. The human figures in this shelter look as if they are out for hunting, though there are no weapons shown as such. Another evidence of rock shelter, having paintings, has been reported from the Kimni village on the Gwaldam-Almora road in Chamoli district. Here, a dagger-like object and some small animals are depicted. Some reptile-like creatures are executed in white colour. Nautiyal and Khanduri (1986: 82-83) assign these paintings to prehistoric period. Mathpal (1987) noticed some more painted rock shelters near Almroa.

To date over a dozen painted rock shelters are located in the Central Himalayan region, the concentration of which is near Almora town. The important sites are known as Lakhiuydar (LKDR), Likhudyar (LIKDR), Kafarkot (KFKT), Kasardevi (KDVI) and Falseema. There are several shelters at each site and they have been numbered with main site name, e.g., LKDR1,

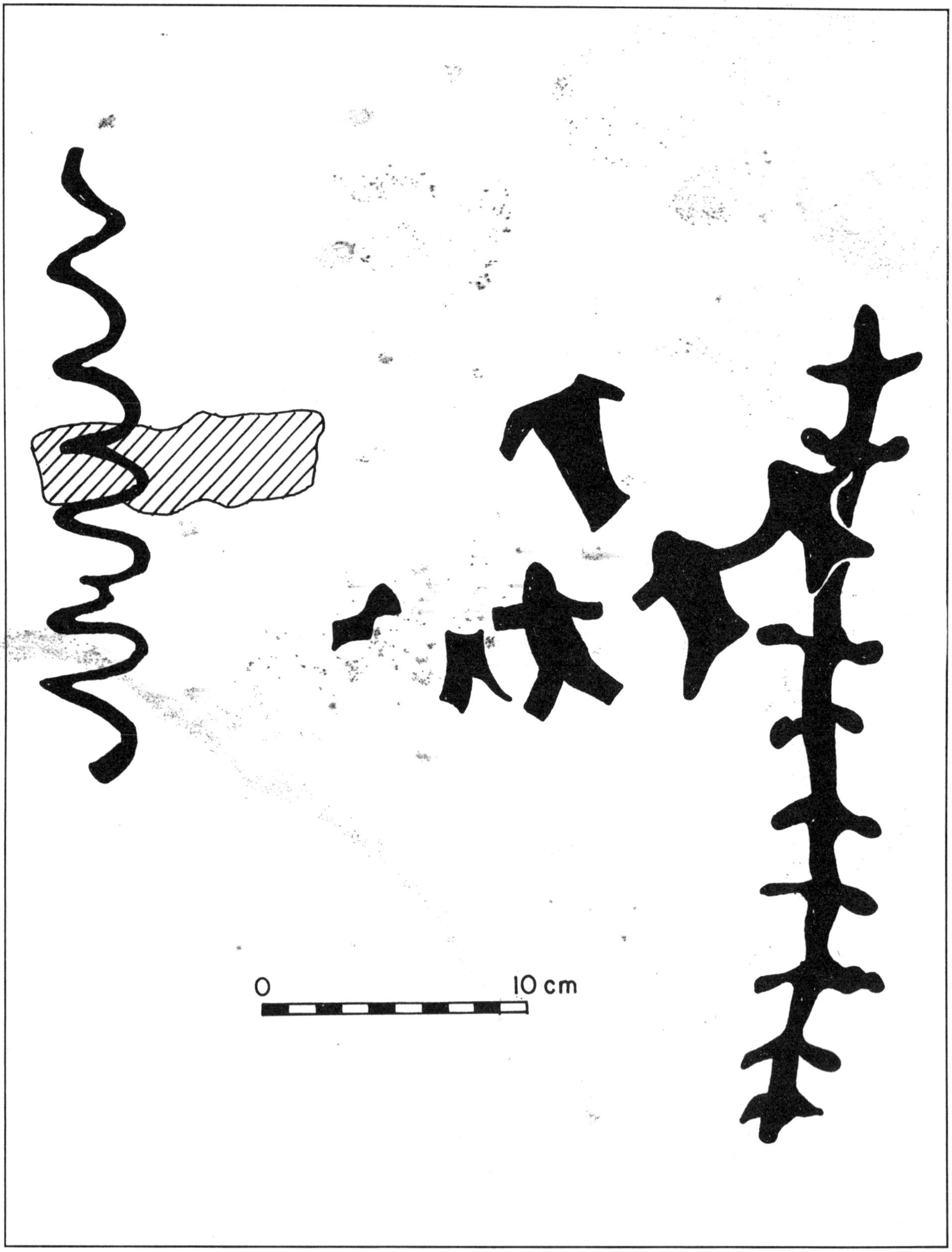

Fig. 5-3. Multi-legged lizard (?) with superimposed human figures, and a serpent-like motif. Lakhiudyar 1, Uttaranchal

Fig. 5-4. Animal and human figures. Lakhiudyar 1, Uttaranchal

LKDR 2 and so on. To find out the interrelationship, stratigraphy and chronology of these paintings, we have developed this nomenclature to make the study more convenient (see for details Agrawal and Kharakwal 1998 and Kharakwal 1993). We do hope that future researchers will use the same system so that different publications do not have different systems of reference. This will ensure that several terminologies and nomenclatures do not confuse the future researchers, as happened at some sites in Central India and other places.

Though some of these Kumauni painted shelters were earlier reported in a cursory manner, but in order to develop a better understanding of this regional art and to present an analytical study of the paintings, a total of 170 figures were copied. To copy them we applied the direct tracing method. We used highly transparent polythene sheet over the rock surface to trace the paintings. Subsequently the paintings were transferred on to drawing paper. Some of the drawings were coloured at the site. While tracing the paintings Munshell colour chart was also used to compare the tone of the colour. A few paintings were also photographed. Wherever tracing was not physically feasible, either due to the height of the drawing or faded condition of the painting, we had to copy them approximately. However, the paintings on the approachable height in the shelters were drawn by taking measurements. In several cases the paintings were much faded; to copy them the surface was moistened. The direct technique of tracing of the paintings has been found more precise than any other method, and it has been applied by several

Fig. 5-5. Dancing figures wearing head-dress. Lakhiudyar 1, Uttaranchal. (Not to scale)

scholars to study the prehistoric paintings (Cooke 1961: 61-65; Vinicombe 1966: 559-60).

We have classified the paintings under six major categories: 1. Male human figures; 2. Female human figures; 3. Child human figures; 4. Motifs; 5. Colour patches; and 6. Animal figures. The figure size in the Kumauni rock art is very small. The largest figure is represented by a set of small lines underlined by an 80 centimetre long line in shelter LIKDR 1. The bulky human figures, sometimes in head-dress and gown-like clothes, were identified as female figures. However, very small figures viz., less than 4cm in height were identified as child figures (Pl. 5-1, Figs. 5-2, 5-3, 5-4, 5-5, 5-6, 5-7).

Kumauni Themes: Prehistoric man generally depicted game animals in a very naturalistic form in the caves and semi-open rock shelters. The paintings of Mesolithic period and later depict hunting scenes. In the Indian context, though the human figures as well as other motifs seem to have been painted with equal skill; often they have drawn the human figures in stick-like and symbolic style. In Kumauni rock art we do not find a wide range of themes. It seems that the artists were greatly interested in drawing dancing figures, running bands, geometric and other decorative motifs. The paintings are dominated by human figures in different styles, i.e., stick-like, partially abstract, symbolic and so on. A total of 577 human figures were counted in all the shelters. They generally depict various social activities such as dancing, jumping, running, carrying objects, holding stick-like or small round objects and rarely hunting scenes. In comparison to males, female figures are very few—only 14. Barring four distinct women figures with breasts in the shelter of Kafarkot (KFKT 1) at Petshal, all other female figures have been identified by the bulky shape of their body, in contrast to the slim male human forms (Fig. 5-8, Pl. 5-2). The number of children is also very small—only 34.

The human figures are depicted in a variety of red pigments, though 20 figures are in black. Most of them have been portrayed by opaque technique in different forms. The human figures have been portrayed ranging from 4 to 25cm in height; those of smaller size of less than 4cm have been identified by us as children. The children are depicted in many shelters, for example, LKDR 1, LKDR 2, LIKDR 1, KFKT 1 and Falseema. They have been found in different forms such as sitting on shoulders, dancing, sitting on the shoulders of dancers and sitting on a

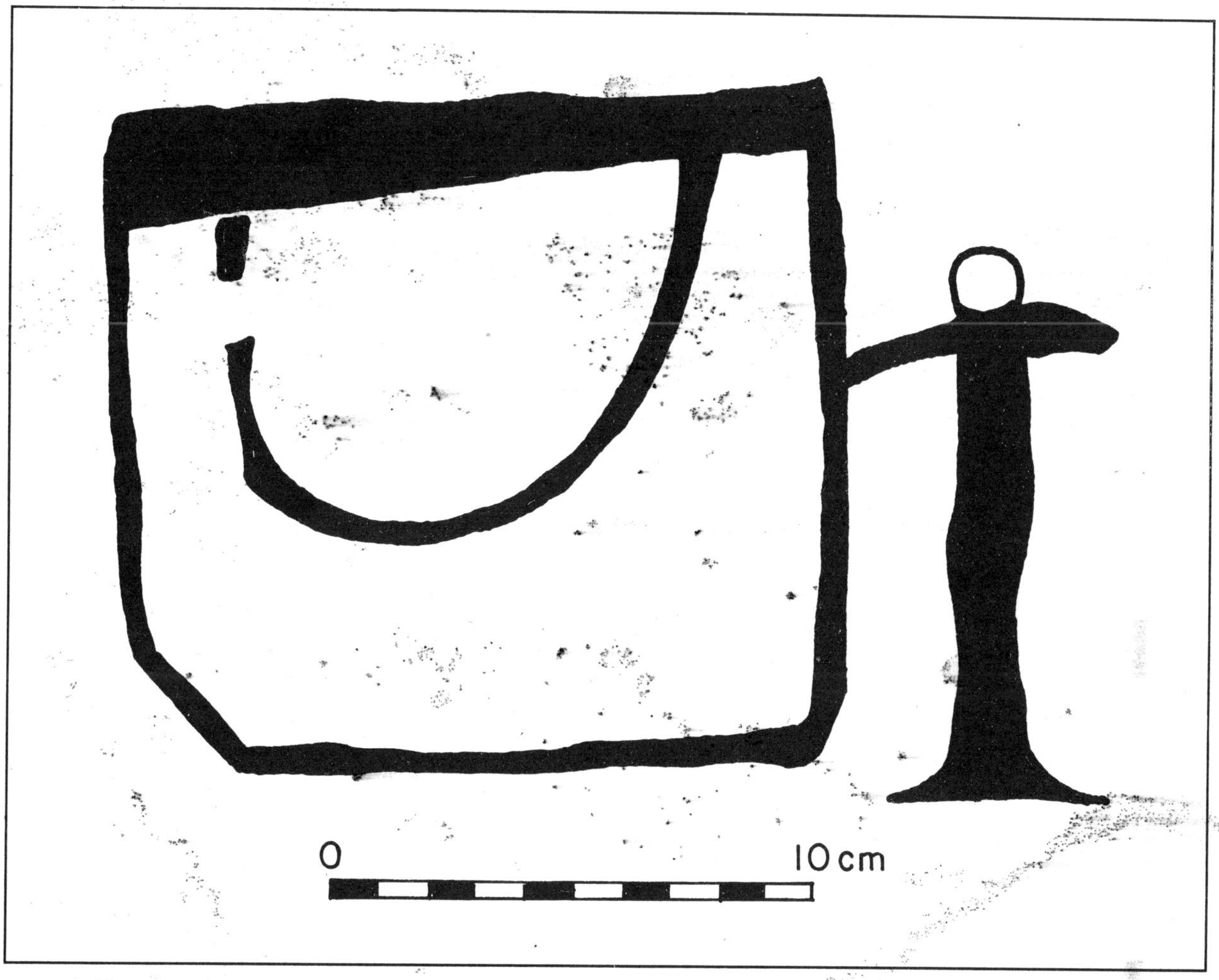

Fig. 5-6. A pentagonal motif (a trap?) and a human figure. Lakhiudyar 1, Uttaranchal

squarish structure. The human figures are generally depicted in rows and groups. However, sometimes they form part of a larger scene. In a few cases the human figures are shown either with head-dress or long skirt-like garments or a *langot*-like cloth hanging between their thighs.

The number of animal figures in the Kumauni rock art is very small. We have documented only nine animal figures, e.g., jackal, goat, horse, lizard, snake and deer-like animal.

There are no regular hunting scenes as such, though in LKDR 1 at least at four places the scenes seem to depict hunting. On the central right part of the shelter, a horse-like animal looks like falling down and an unidentified animal without head is also depicted; a man shown with raised hands, viewer of this scene, is perhaps excited. At one spot, two goats look frightened by the presence of a man; at another location a similar animal has been surrounded by human figures. On the left flank of the shelter, some human figures are depicted running after a small unidentified animal. In KFKT 1, a goat looks frightened and a jackal-like animal also gives a similar impression. The depiction of these animals suggests that they were wild and not domesticated.

A few other activities, perhaps related to daily life, have been depicted, for example, in LKDR 1 a man is shown in supine posture and two persons are shown each near its head and feet. At another spot, four people are carrying an unidentified object on their shoulders possibly approaching to the supine human figure.

In some cases, human figures are associated with motifs, for example, in LKDR 1 a man

Fig. 5-7. Dancing female figures and animals (cattle?). Kafarkot 1, Uttaranchal

is shown touching a pentagonal structure the meaning of which is not clear to us. Similarly, in LIKDR 2 a human figure is depicted inside a rectangular motif and another one is shown next to the motif. Besides these, in KFKT 1 several human figures are depicted in separate compartment-like conical structures joined with each other. At Falseema, a child is shown sitting in a squarish structure and two human figures are standing close to the motif. The associated motifs are probably only geometrical patterns.

In shelter LKDR 1, 76 dot-like motifs have been depicted in three groups on the ceiling of the shelter. Perhaps they represent some kind of symbols. The second shelter of this group bears two flower motifs; however, they are not associated with any other figures. Some of the paintings may be decorative motifs like the semicircular, wavy zigzag set of lines in LKDR 1, a half-diamond structure and the zig-zag lines in LKDR 2 and a similar structure in Falseema shelter. It is difficult to guess the motivation behind these paintings, unless they have some ritualistic significance. The paintings are generally made in monochrome, but in LIKDR 1, four dark red tree-like figures were outlined by white, perhaps at a later stage.

Chronology: In a recent paper (Agrawal & Kharakwal 1994) we have elaborated the steps to be taken to put Indian rock art firmly on an absolute chronological framework. This would entail a relative stratigraphy of paintings based on several independent parametres like the use of organic pigments, inorganic colours, binders, blood, honey, bees, wax, etc., in different periods

Fig. 5-8. Human figures, lizard and snake. Kafarkot 1, Uttaranchal

or styles of paintings. One can also use various laminae (sinter laminae, silica layers, oxalate layers, micro-erosion) and finally AMS dating to validate the chronologies based on other parametres. We have made some beginnings in this direction but till such definitive chronologies become available, we have to use the traditional techniques of superimposition. One of us (JK) has carried out the following analysis of the Kumauni rock art.

Most of the painted shelters of Kumaun are open and rarely semi-open, which bear close similarity to the other Indian rock art sites. Though the themes of the Kumauni rock art are confined to dancing, running, carrying objects, and hunting human figures and decorative motifs, they do give a glimpse of the prehistoric society in this Central Himalayan region. All the figures are micrographic, which again is a common character of Indian paintings. To execute human figures, stick-like, arrow-like and stylised styles were employed. Only one figure on the shelter KFKT 1 was made by executing only an outline. The abstract and arrow-like styles were employed right from the first to the fourth phases. However, stick-like human figures were mainly executed in the second phase. The fourth phase comprises both abstract as well as stylised human figures. Decorative motifs were found in all the five phases. The similarity of subject matter, colours and styles of younger figures vis-a-vis the older ones, state of preservation and location of paintings on the semi-open shelters suggest continuation of the art tradition and lend

inhabitants of the Central Himalayan region have generally been cited from different ancient literary sources (Atkinson 1980-81). If some of those cists belong to these Khasas, and as one of the Gagrigol cists has been dated to the early third millennium BC, some of the rock art may belong to them also. The present Raji-Raut people used to live in caves till the seventies of the twentieth century. They still worship celestial nymphs at the top of the hills. To worship them they paint a piece of rock in red pigment, which is prepared by a local grass called *ratpatti*. Thus tentatively it may be suggested that the ancestors of the present Raji-Raut people could be authors of these paintings.

CENTRAL GROUP

The rock painting sites are confined to five districts of Uttar Pradesh and 25 districts of Madhya Pradesh situated on the Vindhyan plateau, or the Satpura hills and in 8 districts of Rajasthan in the Aravalli hills. In fact, 90% of painting sites of South Asia are located in Vindhyan, Mahadev and Kaimur ranges of Central India. Gordon and Wakankar were the first to make a systematic survey of paintings in Vindhyan region. In recent years Tewari and Verma in Mirzapur region, Pandey, Mathpal, Neumayer and Pancholi in Vindhyan region and Murari Lal Sharma and Giriraj Kumar in Rajasthan have made important contributions. Sharma (1996, 1997) has discovered as many as 16 sites in Jaipur, Sikar and Alwar districts of north-eastern Rajasthan, the main subjects of which are human figures, decorative motifs and hand prints. We will discuss Mirzapur, Bhimbetka and Pachmarhi in more detail as they are better studied regions in Central India. The Vindhyan hills of Madhya Pradesh intrude into Uttar Pradesh in the form of Kaimur range. These hill ranges are full of Palaeolithic and Mesolithic remains and they are also full of forests, wild fruits, tubers and game. Natural rock shelters provided protection against the elements.

MIRZAPUR AREA

The Mirzapur district (23° 52' N; 82° 33' E) is the second largest rock art centre known in India. A. Carlleyle of the Archaeological Survey of India was the first to discover the rock paintings in the Mirzapur area (Carlleyle 1883). Cockburn discovered and published many more rock-painted shelters in this district (Cockburn 1883a: 56-64; 1883b:125-26; 1899: 89-97). Even today there is plenty of game like leopard, bear, deer, boar, etc. and a variety of flora, and water. Archaeological remains from the Palaeolithic, Mesolithic, Neolithic and subsequent cultures are abundant in this region. The area is mainly inhabited by tribes like the Baiga, Agariya, Gond, Kharwar, etc. In recent years many universities have explored the area. Our discussion of the Mirzapur area rock art is mainly based on the recently published comprehensive summary of rock art of this area by Tewari (1992:285-302, and references therein).

The painted rock shelters of Mirzapur are quite large. Paintings are usually executed on the inner walls and ceilings of the shelters, some of them at a considerable height. Paintings are often superimposed on the earlier ones. Weathering has adversely affected the paintings of open shelters. Besides black and white colours, different shades of ochre have been used. Tewari reports that the analysis shows that red and its shades were prepared from iron oxides like hematite, black from magnesium oxides, and white from limestone. Usually paintings are executed in one or two colours. The outlines of some of the paintings are depicted in white, yellow and dark thin or thick lines in ochre or black colours. The inner portion is filled with another colour. Sometimes only the outline of the figure is shown while in other instances they are partly or fully filled with colour (Pls. 5-3, 5-4, 5-5, 5-6). Polychrome paintings are rare.

Themes and Styles

The number of human figures is twice that of the figures of other living creatures. Tewari has identified 258 different types of human figures. They include dancers (33%), hunters (11%) and warriors (4%). They are also shown engaged in other activities such as fruit-gathering, tree-climbing, rowing, etc. About 213 styles of head-dresses made from feathers, leaves, horns and other materials have been shown. The hand prints include both negative and positive types. In some of the examples the outlines of the palms are shown. Most of the human and animal figures look like shadows, devoid of eyes, nose, fingers and hooves. The heads of the human figures of earlier groups are generally round or oval; they are square and triangular in the later group. In a few examples the mouth is shown open, resembling the open beak of a bird and the nose appears to be horned. Generally the human figures are shown in profile, nude. Warriors of the later paintings are shown with medieval costumes. X-ray style of depiction is very popular in the paintings of group one and early phases of group two. Tewari has classified them in six sub-groups. Dance is the most important social celebration depicted in the rock paintings. From Hathvani, they report a remarkable painting of weapon-wielding, hand-raised dancers. In a scene from Kauva-khoh rock shelter, every group of figures in this shelter seems to be engaged in dancing with harpoons, bows and other weapons. Tewari has identified many sub-types in the weapon repertoire, e.g., bows and arrows (13), harpoons (12), swords (14), shields (11), besides spears, sticks and barbed types.

Men with erect phalli are common. Paintings from Hathwani and Ghoramangar show homosexual activities. In a rare example from a later phase from Kauva-khoh two men, phalli erect, approach a woman lying between them.

Amongst animal figures, deer is the most common (42%). Others include one horned rhino, elephant, bison, leopard, wild boar, wild bull, nilgai, monkey, cattle, porcupine, horse, camel, dog and lizard (goh). A few depictions of birds, peacock, crane, water birds, ostrich, fish and snakes are also recorded. Two figures of fish-like creatures found in Lakhma rock shelter are interesting but could not be identified because of the highly stylised depiction. The figures of wild boar are less frequent in comparison with other animals. Except for a few depictions of leopard, the animals of the feline family are conspicuous by their absence. Figures of porcupine are found only in the Dhokawa Maharani and Matahwa rock shelters. The horse is restricted to the paintings of historical period. Camels are shown only in the Kauva-khoh rock shelter while the sole depiction of snake is recorded in Lakhma. Paintings of a long necked bird (ostrich?) have been recently discovered in the rock shelter of Jhandi Pahar.

Some later inscriptions in Brahmi, Sankha and Nagari scripts are also found in some shelters, ranging in dates from AD 400 to 1400. Tewari thinks that many circular, semicircular, triangular, square and irregular motifs in the paintings are comparable to the alphabets of Ashokan Brahmi and symbols of the punch-marked coins. He reports that the earliest among them are found in the lowermost layer of Phase I in the rock shelters of Matahwa and Ghoramangar. If it is so, it will make the dates of the paintings only early historic.

Tewari has recorded 70 hunting scenes of deer, rhino, bison, nilgai, wild bull, elephant, porcupine, iguana, fish and peacock. Sometimes it is a single hunter, and sometimes it is a group of hunters. Many illustrations of animals being hunted in herds are found in Central India, Europe and Africa, while Mirzapur has the maximum number of solitary animal hunt scenes. The muscular tension of the hunter's physique, while using spears or shooting arrows is vividly shown in the paintings. Sometimes angry and wounded animals - such as rhino and bison - are shown tossing a hunter in the air with their horns. The scenes of deer hunting are predominant. Mostly hunters are shown wearing various headgears decorated with feathers, horns, leaves, etc., probably as a camouflage against the wild animals. War or battle scenes are few in number and, except for the two assignable to the Mesolithic phase, all of them are of late phases. In other cases, scenes of fruit-gathering, tree-climbing, rowing and load-bearing are recorded.

Chronology

On the basis of superimposition, Varma (1986: 206-13) worked out four stages of the rock paintings of Mirzapur with three sub-divisions of stage II. He carried out excavations in some of the rock shelters and tried to correlate the excavated material with the rock paintings. Tewari, however, identifies 12 phases under three broad groups, such as:

Phases I to IV	Mesolithic
Phases V to VII	Neolithic/Chalcolithic
Phases VIII to XII	Historical

Phase I is represented by the naturalistic and small figures of archers, animals and fish in black, blood red and yellowish ochre colours. Vertical lines are found underlying these paintings in two examples. The figures of Phase II are generally monochrome and sometimes bichrome with a white or yellowish border. Hunting and dance scenes are very expressive and show a sense of action and rhythm. The weapons consist of harpoons and barbed arrows. The X-ray style of depiction of human and animal figures includes animals with foetus. Paintings of phases III and IV are found overlapping the preceding phases and almost of the same style as of Phase II. The bodies of some of the animal figures are decorated with a chequered pattern. Load-bearers, men in a row, dancers hand-in-hand, rowers, humped bulls and human figures with sexual overtones are the main themes of phase V. Weapons appear to be metallic. Sometimes men are shown with herds of animals. Hunting scenes are reduced in number. Phase VI consists of figures of carts, chariots, large-horned bulls and also load-bearers. Phase VII is represented by the white paintings of load-bearing men moving in a row and animals found overlapping the paintings of phase VI. Hunting scenes become rare. Phase VIII is distinguished by the symbols which resemble those of the Brahmi script and symbols found on the punch-marked coins of the Early Historic period. Human figures with triangular or round heads, X-shaped body sometimes shown with genital organs - belong to this phase. Phase IX (about AD 300 to 700) includes inscriptions of the Gupta Brahmi and Sankha scripts and the paintings associated with them are human figures (shown by an X shape), various *alpana* designs and long apron-type coats are also noticeable. Phase X (about AD 700 to 1000) consists mainly of war scenes, sword- and shield-holding warriors and archers are shown mounted on horses and elephants. Horse-riders in bright ochre and white paintings overlapping the paintings of phase X form phase XI (about AD 1000-1300). Objects like sitar, trident, human figures depicted in simple lines with their respective genital organs, positive hand prints and Nagari inscriptions belong to phase XII (AD 1300 onwards).

The presence of used hematite pieces in the Epi-palaeolithic or Mesolithic layers from Sohagi-ghat (Smith 1906: 187), Lahariya Dih and Lekhahiya (Varma 1987: 212), which might have been used to prepare colour, provides us the basis for dating. The ^{14}C date for this layer from Lekhahiya is about 2000 BC.

Vindhyan region

The Vindhyan hills are full of rock paintings; the main groups are located in the Adamgarh, Mahadeo and Bhimbetka hills. The last mentioned hills, located 45 km south of Bhopal, in an area of 10 sq. km, have about 800 rock shelters, more than 400 of which bear paintings (Pls. 5-7, 5-8, 5-9, 5-10, 5-11).

Several scholars have worked in Central India but here we have followed the periodisation worked out by Wakankar, who spent several years in surveying the inaccessible hills and jungles of Central India. On the basis of style, technique and superimposition, he has divided these paintings into seven periods: Period I Upper Palaeolithic; Period II, Mesolithic; and Period III, Chalcolithic. After Period III (c. 2500 BP) there are four successive historical periods. Though his entire periodisation may not be quite relevant to date, as some scholars like Tyagi and Bednarik have refuted his sequence, yet his first three periods are still acceptable.

The paintings of Period I are executed in green and dark red. The earliest paintings are of bisons, elephants, tigers, rhinos and boars. Generally they are large, some measuring 2/3 metres in length. A few are wash paintings but mostly they are filled with geometric patterns. But no hunters are associated with them. The green paintings are of dancers and the red ones of hunters.

Period II covers the Mesolithic paintings. In this period the themes multiply but the paintings are smaller in size. Hunting scenes predominate. The weapons of hunt are barbed spears, arrows and bows. Elephant, bison, tiger, boar, deer, antelope and at times birds are also depicted. On a rock is depicted a scene showing running animals falling down a cliff—perhaps as a result of a chase. Communal dances provide a common theme. Humans are sometimes depicted with masks. Though animals were painted in a naturalistic style, humans were depicted only in a stylistic manner. At times, humans have been adorned with ornaments and elaborate head-dresses. Females are painted both in the nude and with clothes. There are also a few engravings representing mainly animals.

Some repetitive scenes may signify a deeper meaning. For example, a massive boar is repeated on several rocks. Another scene which has been repeated thrice is of a bull, with an elephantine snout, chasing another animal and a human; a crab runs ahead of the human. Wakankar interprets this scene as a tribal war between three tribes represented by their animal totems. The most pathetic of the scenes is that of a child burial where parents are shown mourning over its death.

The Chalcolithic paintings of Period III depict a contact with the settled agricultural communities. There are many common motifs between the Chalcolithic ceramic motifs and the rock paintings, e.g., cross-hatched squares, lattices. Pottery and metal tools are also depicted. But the vividness and vitality of the earlier periods disappear from these paintings. Dating of these paintings is of course based only on circumstantial evidence.

Bhimbetka

Bhimbetka hill (22° 56' N: 77° 36' E): is located 45 km south-east of Bhopal in the Raisen district of Madhya Pradesh. There is a group of hills to the west of Bhimbetka. Wakankar defined all these into seven groups (I-VII) from east to west in order to recognise the rock art group. As many as 16 layers of paintings were found at Bhimbetka, which were grouped into three broad periods, e.g., Prehistoric, Transitional and Historic and nine chronological phases (A, B, C, D, E, F, O, H and I). The first five phases were assigned to the Prehistoric, the sixth phase to the Transitional or Chalcolithic period and the last to the Historic period (Misra and Mathpal 1979). The main subject of paintings is animals depicted in different postures. They are often shown in groups running in one direction and the hunting scenes are frequently depicted. Various animals like tiger, leopard, cheetah, bear, rhinoceros, wild buffalo, boar, sambar, swamp deer, muntjak, wolf, hyena, dog, horse, elephant, camel, squirrel, fish, crab, scorpion, frog, centipede, pea-fowl, jungle fowl and others were depicted. The size of each picture is generally small and their body was decorated with geometric or abstract pattern in the earliest phase. In subsequent phases the pictures are depicted full of motion, often highly artistic, simplified and decorated. There are hunting, fishing, dancing, men marching and various other kinds of scenes depicting social life. In the Transitional phase men are shown riding bull and the animals appear to be familiar to people. The paintings of Historical period were marked by the horse-riders, elephant riders, metal objects. Apart from these hand prints, dots, decorative figures and inscriptions in Ashokan and Gupta Brahmi and Sankha scripts are also recorded. These scripts form the uppermost layer of the painting.

Shyam Pandey (1992: 249-72), who worked on Central Indian rock art, has emphasised that though colour can never be a safe criterion for determining the chronology of the paintings, it can be of help in finalising the sequences. The superimposition of drawings of different colours can easily be worked out. This has helped in the formulation of various series in different rock shelters. In fact, the predominant colour in the paintings is red with its variant shades. The earliest paintings lying under the patination have a tan shade. Analysis has indicated it to be a mineral colour. Due to lime deposits and chemical reactions, the red ochre-colour changed into the dark tan shade. Wherever the early paintings are devoid of any patina, they look red. The successive groups are mostly in ochre red or bright orange colours. The earliest paintings at Pachmarhi and its adjoining areas were drawn in white or cream colour. Sometimes red lines were also added to give a bichrome effect. The white colour at other places was a slightly later introduction. At a later stage bichrome and polychrome paintings were also made, the examples of which are found at Bhimbetka, Bagbani, Hathitol and Satkunda.

On the basis of the green pigment recovered from the Upper Palaeolithic phase at Bhimbetka, Wakankar (1975) dated the green paintings as the earliest ones. The dynamic paintings of "S" twist style are drawn in green. Pandey, however, does not agree with Wakankar as the green paintings are always found under thin patina. At Ladi-ki-karar there are still a few groups, which underlay green paintings and are in tan colour. The vigour shown in the green paintings was a late product. Similar dynamic paintings in red colour can be seen in the same area. Other colours like black, yellow, blue, orange and pink are also found in the late series (Pandey 1992). It has been observed in this region that a thin or thick layer of lime ($CaCO_3$) is found deposited over the paintings of the early groups. This layer is transparent like a film and protects the paintings from weathering. This formation becomes more transparent when water is applied over it. The Historical group of paintings does not show any patination. A few early Chalcolithic groups, however, do have a certain amount of thin incrustation, though the Mesolithic paintings are invariably covered with thick or thin incrustation. Pandey infers that when Neolithic/Chalcolithic paintings were drawn, the Mesolithic paintings had already been covered with incrustation. This indicates a time gap between the two groups and the difference in climatic conditions. Pandey thus prefers to use patination as the main criterion to relatively date the paintings. He thinks that the paintings, which underlie the thick incrustation, are the earliest. Those under a thin layer of lime will naturally follow the earlier ones. Almost all the stick-shape drawings are in these two categories. From the Chalcolithic onwards there is no gap between the proto-historic and Historical groups. Sometimes they overlap each other as in the case of Kharwai and Satakunda. Thus the Mesolithic paintings can be separated from those of the proto-historic group. Pandey (1992) identified five painting styles:

Naturalistic
Stylised
Schematic
Conventionalised
Eclectic

The naturalistic style paintings have been drawn with thick brush. The colour is generally dark tan. This group underlies the rest or is drawn in a remote place without any superimposition.

Both human as well as animal figures are found in the group. The elongated body of the human figures is filled either with ladder-like decoration or with zigzag patterns. In the case of animal figures, only the herbivorous animals like elephants, bisons and antelopes are given a place in the depiction. These animals are drawn in silhouette, single outline or double outline only. The earliest animal paintings of this group are huge in size and sometimes cover the whole canvas; the later ones are smaller. The paintings of this group can be seen at Singanpur, Kabrapahar, Abchand, Adamgarh, Gupha Mandir, Bhimbetka, Firengi, Jaora and Sitakhardi.

In the second or stylised group human figures are either shown in linear forms termed as stick-shape or in "S" twist forms designated as dynamic figures; female figures are drawn in square shapes. The torso of these figures is filled with intricate patterns. Though the simplicity and naturalism of the animal figures were maintained, decoration with intricate patterns and linear designs was also introduced. The stick-shaped figures are symbolically presented in linear forms and look like a child's work. These figures do not show the skill, which characterises the animal figures. But these stick-shaped figures are capable of depicting the different human activities of Mesolithic men. The square-shaped figures according to Gordon are the earliest depictions of the human form and were classified by him in his first series, followed by stick-shaped figures. But Pandey does not agree with Gordon's observations. He says that both types coexisted simultaneously in almost all areas. The "S" twist figures follow the stick-shaped forms, but are always shown in a dancing posture. Change in the Stone Age was a slow process and switching over from simple stick shapes to decorated forms must have taken thousands of years. This is confirmed by the process of incrustation, which has been found over these paintings (Pandey 1992).

The schematic series represents the Transitional phase. The stick-shaped human figures continue in a modified and more decorated form. The unique mask-style of paintings, in monochrome as well as bichrome, was exclusively the creation of this period.

The conventional style brings a radical change as during this period, the stick-shaped figures were completely replaced by conventionalised forms decorated with head-dresses and garments. The paintings are in silhouette and no facial organs are shown. The animal drawings further deteriorated. The artist of this period was more inclined towards decoration than form. The designs include geometric patterns, horizontal, vertical and tapering lines like leaf-veins, and criss-cross patterns. The patterns and the animal drawings can be compared with those of the Chalcolithic paintings.

The painters of the eclectic series continued the tradition, but freely selected the earlier patterns as well. The multiple forms and designs, choice in colours and various human activities differentiate this group. The basic theme of this series is the warrior. Its outstanding features are horse-riders in their typical outfits, equipped with swords, shields and spears, engaged in battles (Pandey 1992). He divides the paintings into the following themes: a. Hunting-gathering (Mesolithic), b. Cattle rearing and food production (Neolithic/Chalcolithic), c. Domestication, d. War scenes (Historical), e. Religion (Historical), f. Entertainment. We will, however, confine ourselves only to the prehistoric group of paintings.

It is believed that the paintings of the first series (Mesolithic) can be related to magico-religious aspects (Pandey 1992). The shelters having these paintings might have served as places of worship. The second and third series represent the multifarious activities of the Mesolithic men. The stick-shaped human figures of this series wield bows and arrows or spears. To begin with they were static, but gradually started depicting movement of limbs. The dancers are often shown with musical instruments like drums, string instruments or flutes. Masked figures were added at a later stage. These masks generally represented bison heads. The superimposition of paintings make it very difficult to identify the different strata of the paintings. The situation further worsens when the same colour is used in different groups of paintings. Therefore Pandey admits that the studies of Indian rock art are at present in their preliminary stage of cataloguing and exploration only. It is observed that the Mesolithic paintings are generally drawn in a remote place, not easily approachable and are rarely superimposed. The subsequent artists of proto-historic and Historic periods did not hesitate to superimpose their paintings on those of earlier groups. He has identified three major groups of superimposition, e.g., (a) Group of intricate designs (Prehistoric), (b) Group of geometric designs (proto-historic) and (c) Group of decorative designs (Historic).

Sushila Pant (1999) reports important examples of floral depictions in the prehistoric art and writes, "The world of vegetation had equally mesmerised prehistoric man. It had both utilitarian and sacred value for him....Flora did not terrify struggling man, but still he bowed before their majestic forms. In Monteroza, we find a blooming tree being worshipped by four persons" (Pant 1999, Pl. 4, Fig. 4). Jagdish Gupta holds that it signifies some magico-religious belief or tree worship. We should however bear in mind that there cannot be one single reason for it. Adamgarh, on the contrary, exhibits an appealing picture, where an ochre-coloured man is holding a metal-tipped arrow and a bunch of flowers in the hands (Pant 1999, Pl. 4, Fig. 1). Perhaps it is a delineation of natural power as a deity. The deity of the forest appears to be represented here, giving the impression of the beginning of the personification of the deity.

Among the fauna depicted, there are certain animals and birds which are now extinct. Rhinoceros is now extinct in the area, but it existed in this part of the country as late as the Chalcolithic period. Similarly, paintings of huge birds looking like ostriches are also found. These existed during the proto-historic period but are now extinct.

Pandey found an adult extended human burial at Bhimbetka rock shelter. On the left side of the skeleton a stone slab and muller used for grinding colour were found. Red ochre colour is still visible on these stones. There is a possibility that this colour would have been applied to the dead body while performing the last rites. A piece of painted Malwa ware was also found in this level. The microliths are found in great numbers. The association of painted Malwa ware, coarse handmade black-and-red ware and the association of microliths clearly indicate that the burial belongs to the Chalcolithic period. The skeleton was radiocarbon-dated to 1300 BC (uncalibrated).

It has been reported that the paintings very vividly narrate that it was still a sexually uninhibited society. In Arden, intercourse is shown in the midst of other people and animals (Pant 1999, Pl. 3, Fig. 2). Some paintings possibly display scenes of molestation. Homosexual scenes and ithyphallic human figures have also been found depicted. Among such paintings, mention may be made of those at Javara and Kathautia (Pant 1999, Pl. 4, Fig. 3).

From Pachmarhi hills (22° 29' N; 78° 30' E) of Madhya Pradesh, a very well-known area of rock art in Central India, Dube (1991) has found depictions of severed heads in the rock paintings. There are a variety of scenes such as hunting, dancing, fighting, fishing, honey collection, deified animals, etc. mostly executed in red, white and yellow pigments in these hills. The paintings of severed head seems to be a new subject of painting in this region. Dube (1991) finds parallels of these paintings in the petroglyphs of Peru.

Dube writes (1991:83) that warring factions beheaded the vanquished enemy and carried away the heads as war trophies to show the folk who had stayed behind. There are scenes showing a man holding a human head in right hand and a sword-like weapon in the left, and they seems to be escaping/running (right to left in all cases) away and looking backwards, giving the impression that he is being chased by the enemy.

The rock shelters at Barkachar (locally called Swem Aam), Langi Nadi, Nagdwari, Rajat Prapat and others contain such scenes of head hunters at Pachmarhi. They bear bichromatic painting, in-filled with white and outlined in red. All the hunted heads have headgear, earrings and a necklace (?) similar to those of the head hunters, which are also shown wearing a loin-cloth. Hence Dube says that the head hunting clearly implies death of the enemy or annihilation of the group attacked and is a sign of proof of clear victory over the enemy. The rock paintings depicting these scenes are probably memorials to such events. On stylistic grounds she attempts to place these paintings in the Early Historic period (1991:83). She writes that:

> The tradition of human sacrifice to appease the gods and godessess has been documented amongst Indian tribes, particularly the Gonds and Korkus. Human sacrifice used to be performed by tribals in the Mahadeo hills till as late as the century. For example, in 1822 a European officer (Forsyth 1989: 180-84) witnessed the sacrifice of a visitor made at the Kal Bhairav shrine. Bhairav is one of the many names of Lord Shiva. In India shrines to Shiva are the oldest and most famous of all. Forsyth (1989: 179) also describes a scene where he witnessed devotees hurling themselves off a cliff, obviously offering their lives to Lord Shiva. The rock paintings provide further evidence of human sacrifice (Dube 1991:82 and references therein).

According to Wakankar (1987) the hill tribe communities in the Pachmarhi hills were hunters till the tenth century AD. It appears that they abandoned this practice due to the influence of Hindu sadhus (saints) who penetrated the deep forest to perform penance in the Pachmarhi hills. However, in her conclusion she informs that "The Nocte and Wanchu tribes in North Eastern India used to behead their enemies and display the skulls as war trophies in their clubs (locally called Morangs). Some of these tribals wear brass replicas of the head(s) as pendants, to indicate that their ancestors were warriors and hunted a specific number of the enemy. So that a person wearing two pendants meant that his ancestor had beheaded two enemies, thus exhibiting the deeds of valour of their forefathers (Gazetteer of Arunachal Pradesh)" (Dube 1991:85).

In recent years a large number of cupules, cup-like marks, dots have been noticed at a number of sites, e.g., shelter IIIF 24, and auditorium in Bhimbetka, Raisen, Kalapahar (near Kotputali), Daraki Chattan (Indragarh) in the Chambal valley and at several other sites. They have invariably been assigned to prehistoric period in Central India. However, one has to be very careful about their technique, degree of weathering, context and circumstantial evidence before accepting their antiquity. Such cupules have been found from various regions of India and rest of the world (Kharakwal 1993) and some of them, e.g., *okhali* (conical pit dug in rock for pounding grains) types of Kumaun and cupules of Karla and Bhaja associated with *gaichole* game in Maharasthra appear to be of a recent date (Kharakwal and Rane 1997).

SOUTHERN GROUP

Granite rocks of north Karnataka and Andhra provided suitable canvases to Neolithic man for his paintings and bruisings produced by pecking. Several sites are known: more famous among them are Kupgallu, Piklihal and Tekkalakota.

Allchin distinguished three types of paintings: a. white, b. red over a white background, and c. paintings in red. The paintings and bruisings have been divided into Late Historical, Early Historical and Neolithic periods and their dating is mainly based on the artefacts depicted. Tekkalakota produced a bowl depicting a peacock, two deers and a serpent executed in a punctured technique, which has been adduced by Sankalia as evidence for dating these paintings and bruisings. The subjects depicted are bulls, elephants, sambhar, gazelle, sheep, goat, horse, stylised humans, tridents, but rarely vegetal motifs. Quite often bull's horns are decorated with bow-like objects. Allchins (1968) quote local ceremonial tradition where bows were plucked from the horns of bulls. The Kupgallu group depicts a number of unique scenes where excited males with outsized organs are abducting females. Such scenes are almost absent from the rest of the painting sites of the country.

In recent years Mesolithic paintings have been identified from Karnataka, Andhra Pradesh and Tamil Nadu (Mathpal 1984; Venkatasubbaiah 1991; Chandramouli 1991) but they are not well-known. Chandramouli (1991) studied the painted shelters of Budagavi in Anantpur district of Andhra Pradesh and divided the paintings into three phases based on theme, style and circumstantial evidence. He has assigned the earliest paintings to the Mesolithic period and they are represented by two figures of deer and geometric drawings, identified on the grounds of stylistic and thematic similarities with the Kethavaram rock paintings. The red paintings, assigned phase two, belong to Neolithic phase whereas the white human figures superimposed on red paintings belong to third phase. He writes that none of the rock paintings can be dated to the Historical period when the site appears to have had a large human population, as seen from the extensive habitational deposit. He is of the view that most of these belong to early Neolithic phase and admits that style, as a parametre while considering the chronology for rock art, must be only tentative.

The humped bull figures are stylistically distinct at Budagavi. Such bull figures from other sites in Andhra Pradesh are shown with hefty bodies, long or short curved horns, a long and prominent penis and are executed in flat-wash (Chandramouli 1991 Fig. 11). He also does not find any similarity of the bruisings of humped bulls of Karnataka (with long bodies, almost a square-shaped hump, long and lyre-shaped horns and, in the majority of examples, face each other in a fighting posture) with the examples of Budagavi. Nevertheless he informs that the bruisings of two humped bulls from Velpumadugu, a Neolithic site about 10 km from Budagavi (Chandramouli 1991, Fig. 1) are similar to that of Piklihal and Sanganakallu.

NORTH-EASTERN GROUP

Like the northern group very little is known about the rock art of North-eastern region also. Our sketchy information is based on an unpublished report prepared a few years ago by Mutua Museum, Imphal. A large number of rock engravings and inscriptions have been found in Khoupum hill near Imphal, an important area of Megalithic monuments. The engravings include human figures, birds, horse-riders, foot-prints, *maun puan* (a local flower), swords, guns, game boards, circles, etc. Most of these figures may not be older than 300 years as is apparent from the subject too. Sometimes inscriptions (written in Manipuri language and Bengali script) have also been found associated with engravings, which indicate that every new generation added new picture on the same rock which was written or engraved by their forefathers (see Mutua Museum report).

CHRONOLOGY OF ROCK ART

In the Central Indian group of rock art, Wakankar suggested that the earliest paintings with green pigment are datable to the Upper Palaeolithic, but various scholars have refuted his chronology. Pandey concedes that Bhimbetka bears the physical remains of the Palaeolithic period. The chronological sequence of Bhimbetka, of course based on style and superimposition, developed by Misra and Mathpal appears to be more scientific. But Pandey finds it hard to place any of the rock paintings into the Palaeolithic phase. He found a green-coloured stone slab along with a skeleton from Bhimbetka ^{14}C dated to 1300 BC (uncalibrated). The concerned rock-shelter contains paintings in green colour. Obviously here the green paintings may belong to the Chalcolithic period. In fact, dating the rock art is the most controversial subject as we had noted Bedranik's strong comments. In the same text he further writes that the vast corpus of Indian rock paintings is attributed mostly to the Mesolithic and Chalcolithic periods, but it must be emphasised that not a single motif is actually dated, nor does the attribution seem to be based on objective and falsifiable reasoning or evidence (Bedranik 1993b: 141-55). He has however reported two petroglyphs from the excavated Auditorium rock shelter (III F-24). These consisted of a scooped out large circular cupule and a pecked meandering line running above it. Their stratigraphic position within the habitation deposit suggests that they were made during the Acheulian period. He considered them as the oldest known rock art in the world (Bednarik 1994:356-57). More recently, Giriraj Kumar has reported nearly 500 cupules at a place called Daraki-Chattan near Bhanpura in Chambal valley and assigned them to the Palaeolithic period based on the occurrence of the Acheulian and Middle Palaeolithic implements on the same cave floor (Kumar 1996: 38-46).

Sonawane has made some important observations despite Bednarik's reservations and he writes:

> Closer inspection of global rock art sites shows that pre-figurative rock art preceded figurative one in most cases. The pre-figurative art consists of a fairly restricted range of elements or form constants, which are found in numerous variants or which may be built into elaborate 'mazes' or geometric arrangements. The basic elements of all archaic rock art are dominated by curvilinear motifs, such as concentric circles, spirals and their variants and intermediate forms including geometric motifs (Bednarik 1994b). Indian rock art is no exception to this widely accepted phenomenon. The paintings consisting of geometric patterns or intricate designs form the most conspicuous stylistic feature of this earlier style (Neumayer 1993: 43). In several paintings these intricate designs often identified as 'Labyrinthian' or 'Phosphene' motifs, are composed of rhombic meanders and honeycomb patterns along with their multiple derivatives and cover large space of virgin surface of rock-shelters. None of these are superimposed on any of the earlier paintings (Tyagi 1992; 304-06; Sonawane 1997: 8-9, and references therein).

He refers to an example of pre-figurative rock art in the form of a solitary object found from Chandravati (Rajasthan) in the form of an engraved core. The design consists of a pair of parallel lines moving clockwise from the centre forming two intertwining spiraling arms. The design was engraved on the nodule prior to its use as a core. Identical designs have been found painted in earlier rock paintings at Mahadev hills, Bhimbetka, Kathotiya, etc. However, the Chandravati specimen is not actually dated, since it forms a part of the surface assemblage but it is in the Upper Palaeolithic tradition. Sonawane thinks that the rock paintings representing purely geometric patterns are pre-figurative or non-ionic, and succeeding figurative or iconic depictions painted either in red or green, animated human and animal figures need to be considered seriously as the earliest depictions belonging to the Upper Palaeolithic period.

As several ^{14}C dates are available for engraved ostrich eggshells discovered in different Indian sites ranging between 40,000 BC and 25,000 BC, Tewari suggests that "The dates of 40,000 BC to 15,000 BC (Wakankar 1984: 51), 12,000 BC (Varma 1986: 213), 18,000 BC (Pandey 1984: 223) and 6000 BC to 5000 BC (Tewari l982a: 12; 1986: 112; Mathpal 1984a: 60) and so on are the earliest dates available for rock art in India" (see all references in Tewari 1982). We should also bear in mind that the engravings on most of the eggshells are still doubtful. Realising the lack of definitive evidence, Tewari admits that the date of earliest rock paintings and a time-bracket of 8000-300 BP for all of them is logical at the present state of our knowledge (Tewari 1992 and references therein).

Pandey (1992) carried out study of selected shelters at Putalikarar. He prepared series of paintings based on styles and found that one shelter had superimpositions of all the styles. His results are as follows:

(a) In the shelter where paintings were under thick incrustation, the heavily patinated non-geometric microliths were found in the deposit.
(b) The shelter which had thin patinated drawings yielded geometric microliths.
(c) The shelter with proto-historic paintings contained Chalcolithic and other crude pottery in its deposit.
(d) In the shelter where the Historic group of paintings was to be seen, the deposit yielded NBP, black polished ware, and other Historical pottery including iron implements.
(e) The shelter having the series of paintings superimposed one on another, yielded each type of archaeological material in succession.

He writes that he confirmed his results further at Raisen, Khaywai, Shyamla hills, Bhopal, Shahad Karar, Bhimbetka and Pachmarhi (Pandey 1992).

As there are no absolute dates for rock art in South Asia, we have preferred to give all these opinions of leading workers in the field. However, rock art (paintings) have excellent potentialities for a variety of investigations today as there are techniques available to identify blood up to species level from just pinhead amount of a sample (nanograms). Wax, oxalate, carbonate layers covering the ancient paintings, organic pigments, etc. all provide excellent samples for AMS dating. Now the Institute of Physics at Bhubaneswar is starting an AMS facility; therefore, it should be possible to produce an absolute chronology of rock paintings in India. The final dating is possible only when we have a number of AMS dates from various regions; till then we can safely conclude that circumstantial evidence does point to an Upper Palaeolithic date for the beginning of South Asian rock art (see Table 5.2).

TABLE 5.2 CALIBRATED DATES OF MESOLITHIC SITES OF PENNINSULAR INDIA
All BP ages are based on 5568 yr half-life of radiocarbon. Calibrated ages are given in bc.

Site	*Sample No.*	*5568 Yrs.BP*	*Calib. Dates*	*Culture*	*Material*
Tenmalai	BS-646	4420±110BP	3040 cal.bc	Microliths and Paintings	Wood Charcoal
Tenmalai	BS-630	5210±110BP	4032,4026, 4001 cal.bc	Microliths and Paintings	Wood Charcoal
Tenmalai	BS-525	4971±115BP	3780,3731, 3728 cal.bc	Microliths and Paintings	Wood Charcoal

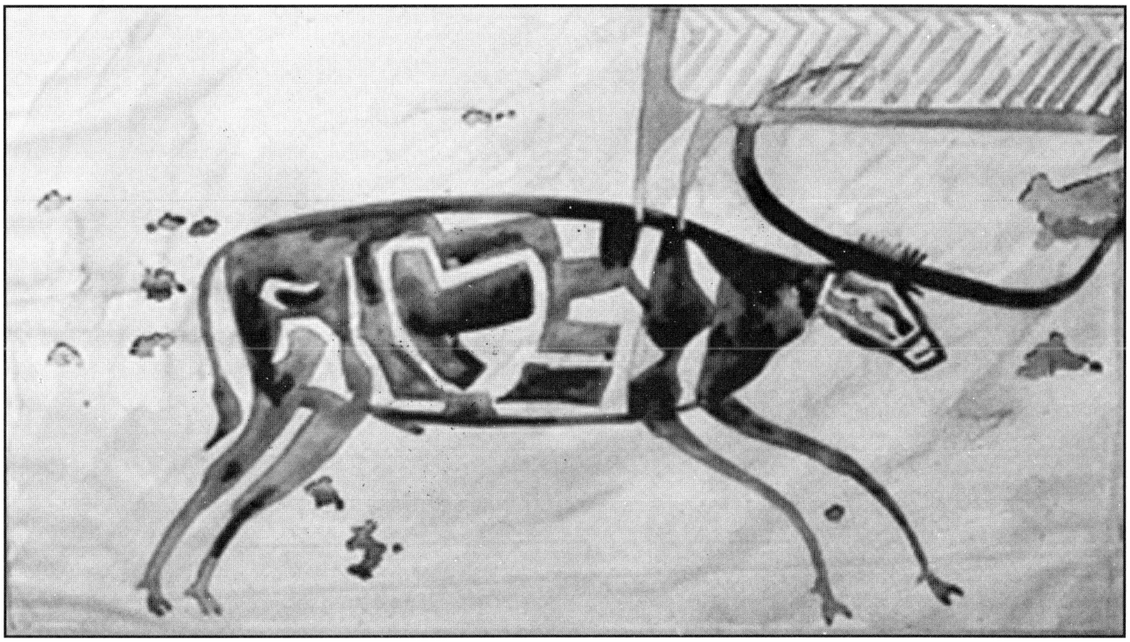

Pl. 5-10. Rock painting of bull done in X-ray style, Bhimbetka rock shelters, MP

Pl. 5-11. A mythical animal painted in red. This motif is repeated in several rock shelters at Bhimbetka, MP

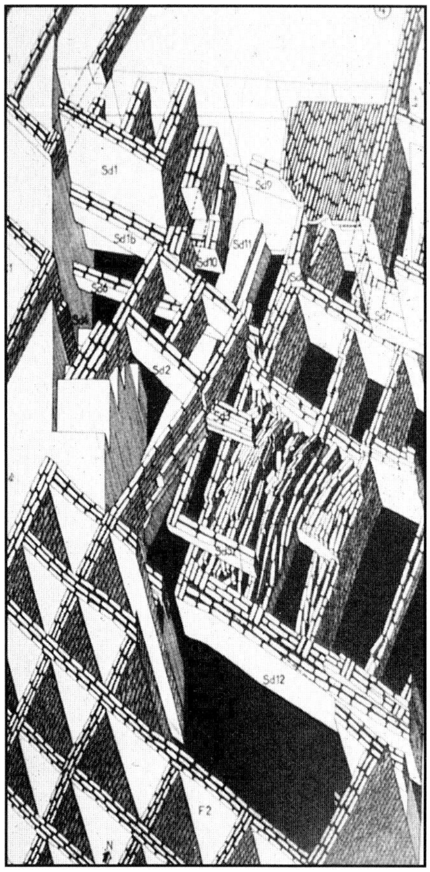

Pl. 6-1. Housing architecture, Period IIA, Mehrgarh

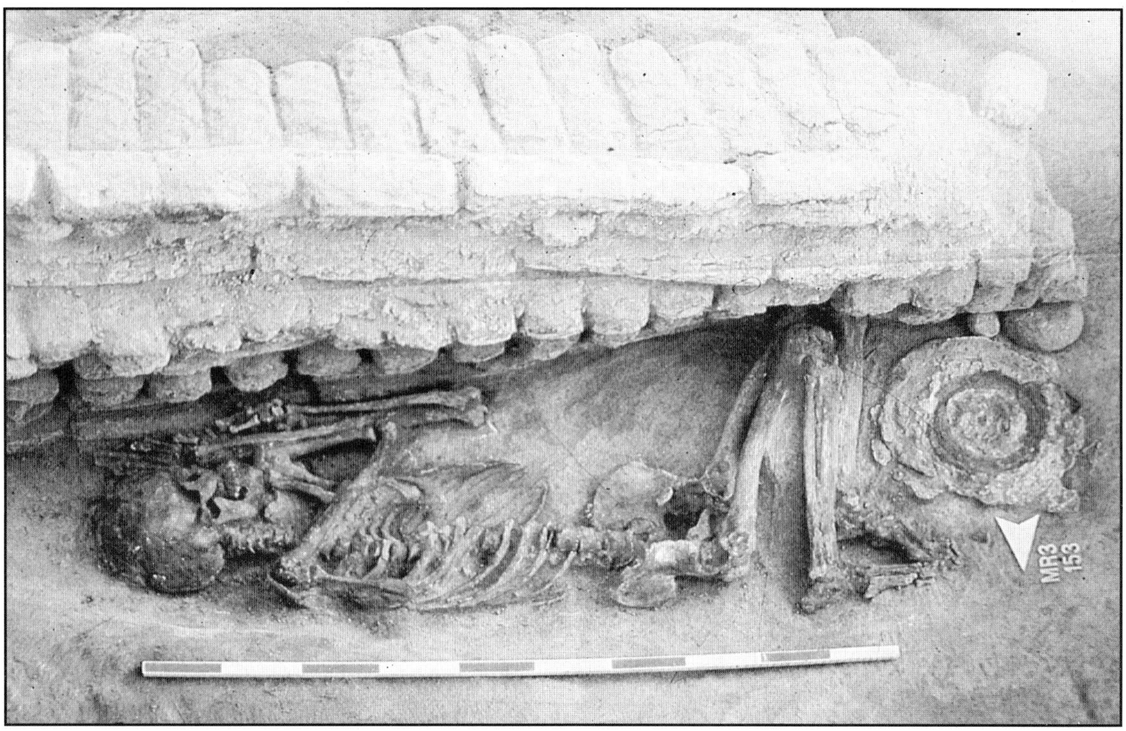

Pl. 6-2. Grave No. MR 3. 153, Period IB, Mehrgarh. Skeleton with folded knees and pots

Chapter 6

EARLY FARMING CULTURES

Contents :

- Introduction
- North-west
- Neolithic Cultures of Ganga Valley and Vindhyas
- Eastern Neolithic Cultures
- Southern Neolithic Cultures

INTRODUCTION

Let us have a look at the early agricultural revolution from the evolutionary point of view. Agriculture allowed us to sustain very large populations. About 100 Kyr ago the population was only about 10,000 and now very soon we will be crossing the 10 billion mark - a million-fold increase in just a few millennia! Though we generally regard hunting-gathering as a primitive stage and attribute civilisation to agricultural surplus, agriculture brought several problems with it. The easily digestible food of *Homo sapiens* gradually led to shrinking of the jaw. Our jaw now can accommodate only 28 teeth. The wisdom teeth create a variety of problems when they erupt. About 15% Europeans and 30% East Asians do not grow more than 30 teeth. During the last 10 Kyr *H. sapiens* is shrinking. From Cro-Magnon man's 6' height, it has come down to 5'8" today. Even our brains are shrinking. Molleson (1994: 60-65), who studied skeletons from Abu Hureyra (Syria) dating back to 11.5 -7.5 Kyr, found that daily grinding of grain for several hours resulted in damaged discs and crushed vertebrae. Maize cultivation, which started 8,000 years back by the American Indians, resulted in severalfold increase in tooth cavities, anaemia, TB, yaws, arthritis and syphilis. Almost 1/5th population died in infancy. Dense populations led to a variety of epidemics.

If agriculture brought such disasters then why did we opt for it? The answer is simple. Farming allowed a larger number of people to sustain themselves over a piece of land than would hunting-gathering. However, hunting-gathering life-style had its own advantages. The physical exertion of hunting kept us in good health (Stringer & McKie 1996). Possehl has made some interesting remarks in praise of hunting-gathering life-style. He says:

> The research on the Kung spawned a number of other investigations of hunter-gatherers, including some studies that claim to demonstrate, in theory at least, that their diet would be healthy, well balanced, with better protein than early farmers, who soon ended up with a diet based on large amounts of carbohydrate. The intensified "foraging" strategies of antiquity may have provided a very good, balanced, reliable food supply with relatively low labour inputs. All of which seems to suggest that the life of hunter-gatherer might have been quite good: ample leisure time, a balanced diet, and a reliable food supply. Things could have been worse! .... Since the surviving hunting and gathering

> groups in today's world are so few and therefore so special, it stands to reason that they may not be representative of hunters and gatherers from the eras preceding the Holocene, when all humans seem to have had this type of adaptation. The ethnoarcheology of modern hunter-gatherers should be used with some caution, mindful that all ethnographic analogy has its pitfalls. What seems to emerge from this research is that hunting and gathering could be a very productive livelihood, with dependable food supplies, a balanced diet and a very good quality of life. But, it is also apparent that this was not always the case. To conclude that hunting and gathering peoples represent the first "affluent society" may be true, but probably only for some, surely not all of them (Possehl 1999b: 401).

Agriculture and ceramic technology had a dramatic effect as porridge could now substitute the breast milk. Regular.breast-feeding suppresses ovulation and weaning of infants from breast milk led to more frequent pregnancies and an increase in population.

We should not forget that we still have Stone Age bodies and brains and perhaps behaviour. For example, if we look at the hair on our heads it shields our brains from dangerous fluctuations of solar radiation. Beards perhaps acted as visual devices to enlarge the face, to frighten the enemy or to impress females. The body shed most of its hairs though the pubic and armpit hair were left to allow hormones and scents to linger and disperse their intimate messages (Stringer & McKie 1996).

About 10 Kyr back, domestication of plant and animals started in several areas of the world. Wheat was cultivated in West Asia (Fig. 6-1), rice in China, millets, yam and sorghum in West Africa, and maize in South America.

To digress a little, it is interesting to note that origin of maize in India is quite controversial. Ashraf Jaweed (1994) observes that in contradiction to the established opinion, it is shown on the basis of a large diversity of primary sources that maize in India has an unbroken continuity on textual basis since the fifth century BC when it was gathered from virgin lands for use in *Yagya* rituals. Cultivation of maize in India can be taken back to second century BC on the basis of palm-leaf texts. This sacredness explains maize depiction in Hindu temple and Buddhist stupa sculptures during the second century BC and its later day transformation into a sacred motif known as Kirtimukha. It is further shown that from this religious role maize usage in ancient and medieval India diversified as it entered the category of garden fruits, medical pharmacopoeia of Ayurveda and Greco-Arab system of medicine and ultimately, during late medieval times, into agriculture. Maize in the Indian version of Greco-Arab system of medicine can be dated back to the fourteenth century while in Ayurveda it can be dated to second-fifth century. On the basis of Portuguese primary sources it is shown that during the early sixteenth century maize was exported from India. It is demonstrated that etymologically vernacular maize names *Mak(a)* / *Makh(a)* can be derived from its ancient Sanskrit name Markataka. This vernacular form of the name can be dated back to about the second century AD on the basis of its usage by Charaka. Based on the evidence cited above, it may be concluded that maize in India is not at all an introduction from outside. Maize in Indian culture is indigenous. European contributions during that last century are confined to process of commercialisation alone. There is botanical evidence to suggest that maize was experimentally cultivated by the Portuguese in Goa during the later part of the last century at a time when in British India it was commonly cultivated in the warmer regions of the subcontinent. Hence Portuguese involvement can be set aside. It is shown that de Condollo-Vavilonian theory of Centre of Origin of Cultivated Plants which assigns a special position to New World plants and designates them as obligate introductions everywhere in the Old World is not tenable due to basic methodological and subjective faults in data collection itself. Hence, it is concluded, that maize should be recognised as indigenous to India. The European contribution should not be exaggerated beyond commercialisation of a plant that was already under cultivation and export when the first Europeans arrived in India during the

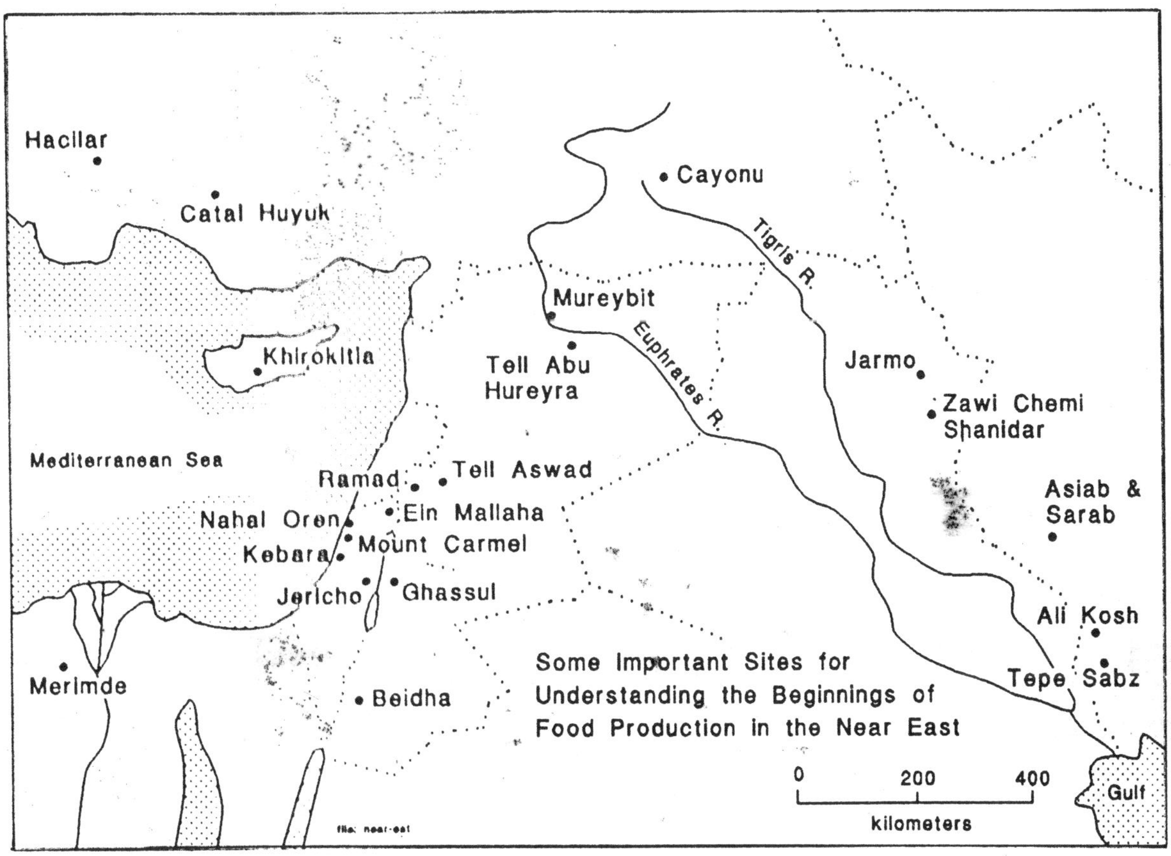

Fig. 6-1. Some important sites associated with the beginnings of agriculture in West Asia

fifteenth century. Ashraf does admit that well-known historians like Irfan Habib do believe that maize in India, as a representative of Latin American plants, is a post-sixteenth century Portuguese introduction. Ashraf continues:

> Present understanding that maize was introduced by the Portuguese during seventeenth century is based on the works of Gode (1960) for Maharashtra and S. Nurul Hasan *et al.* (1966) for Rajasthan showing that by later half of the seventeenth century maize in these regions was so significant an agricultural crop as to get recorded in village level revenue documents. These conclusions were later confirmed and taken back in time for Rajasthan but within the same century and on the same basis by Dilbagh Singh (1993) who put forward evidence for maize cultivation during the first half of the seventeenth century. These observations pushed the antiquity of maize in India back by a century. Earlier George Watt (1889) concluded that maize was introduced into India a century earlier viz. during the eighteenth century (Ashraf 1994: 6-26 and references therein).

Returning to the question of early agriculture, it may be worth noting warnings about dependence on agriculture that Possehl would like us to heed. He warns:

> There is a correlation between food producing subsistence systems and the use of domesticated plants and animals. With the full advent of the primary village farming community, and the evolution of pastoralism, human dependence on domesticated species was very great, almost total in some "mature " cases. As the system of farming and animal keeping developed into today's world, that dependence could be dangerous. Looking at the production of food on a world-wide scale there were six animals, or groups of animals that each produced over a million tons of meat per year: pigs, cattle, poultry, sheep, goats and buffalo (in that order), but of the 113 total metric tons just about 75% of

the productivity came from two animals, pigs and cattle. Plants are a bit different. The thirty or so principal plants yielded about 2360 million metric tons of produce. But the top seven producers (wheat, rice, corn, potato, barley, sweet potato, and cassava in that order) accounted for about 71% of the total yield. Thus, nine plants and animals constitute three-fourth of the world's food supply - this vulnerability is part of the legacy of the Neolithic Revolution.... There are, however, two sides to the issue. The legacy is good because these plants and animals have been brought to a point where they can provide food for the billions of people now living. It is bad because out of the millions of plants and animals species, we are dependent on so few. If something catastrophic should happen to just one or two of them, our extreme dependence could be turned into disaster for those same billions of people. There may be little resiliency in this subsistence regime (Possehl 1999b: 404).

We have however to note that there is no neat distinction between hunting-gathering and agriculture stages. Possehl remarks:

> The Higgs position suggests that the beginnings of both food production and domestication may be delicate and involve only slight modifications in human behaviour, animals and plants. Thus, a distinct threshold, or a "revolution" separating hunting and gathering from pastoralism and agriculture, might not exist at all, since they may be on a very slow continuum of change. Seen from this perspective, the food production relationship and domestication in some form may go back many millennia to the last glacial period. ...The interdependent questions of "when did it happen?" and especially "why did it happen when it happened?" remain unanswered. Why humans came to domesticate plants and animals at some particular point in history remains somewhat of a mystery. It seems to be a phenomenon that developed just after the opening of the Holocene in several regions of both the Old and New Worlds. Why it did not occur earlier is not known. The Higgsians, of course, hold that these special relationships were in place in the Pleistocene, and that the new development was the village farming community, not food production and domestication. Such are the unresolved conceptual debates (Possehl 1999b:412).

Lamberg-Karlovsky has made some very incisive observations in his introduction to *Hunters, Farmers and Civilisations* (1979). He writes:

> The definition of food production is in part dependent upon the ambiguous concept of domestication itself. Domestication is best seen as a continuum of relationships among human beings, plants, and animals. It is often difficult, if not impossible, to distinguish morphologically domesticated from wild plants. For some plants the essential factor in domestication is a shift in adaptation to new habitats that are modified or destroyed by people; the emphasis is on ecological rather than morphological change. Some domesticated plants like maize, dates, bananas, breadfruit are forever tied to people, having lost their independent power of seed dispersal and germination; others, even if controlled or manipulated by humans, revert to the original wild state if not constantly tended.... If it is difficult to determine the extent of domestication in past cultural systems on morphological or ecological bases, it follows that the agricultural status of a community is often ambiguous. There are degrees of food production, and the assignment must be an arbitrary one. Anthropologists and archaeologists can, however, agree on a working definition of domestication that posits, at a minimum, (1) a reasonably efficient level of food production entailing situations in which food acquired through direct production amounts to over half of the community's dietary needs for part of the year; and (2) both plant and animal domesticates are no longer bound to their natural habitat (Lamberg-Karlovsky 1979a: 85-89).

He differentiates the two processes of civilisation in the Old and the New Worlds as he further writes:

> The economic foundation for civilisation in the Old and New Worlds differed. The parallel and independent processes for development of civilisation in both hemispheres are distinctive in their subsistence pattern. Old World and New World civilisations developed essentially independently of

> each other and thus they provide opportunity for the comparative study of the rise of civilisations. The economic foundations on which Near Eastern civilisations were built depended upon wheat, barley, certain legumes (especially peas and lentils), domesticates. These subsistence resources are of remarkably different kind from those that established the economic foundation for the New World, and in their difference might be found a partial explanation for the distinctive paths that both hemispheres followed toward civilisation. In the New World the vegetable domesticates were principally beans and squash; the animal domesticates, the Lama of Peru and guinea-pig of Mesoamerica were far more limited geographically than those of the Old World.

He also remarks that the Near Eastern subsistence economy from earliest times supported two distinctive cultural patterns - the sedentary farmer and the nomadic herder. The relationship between these two provides one of the leitmotifs of Near Eastern civilisation. At times it was built upon animosity and suspicion, as over grazing rights and property ownership; at other times it provided important services and information between settled areas through which the nomads moved. This is an important aspect of the North-west Indian subcontinent too, as has been emphasised by Possehl (1999b).

The geographical area in which the manipulation of plants and animals began extends from the Anatolian plateau to the deserts of Central Asia and from the uplands of Palestine to the Caucasian range. In this large area several primary centres can be isolated where domestication of plants and animals was first accomplished. This occurred in the millennia following the stabilisation of our modern climate (after the last Ice Age); by 9000-8000 BC in the Syro-Palestinian Levant, the hilly flanks of the Zagros in Iraq and Iran, the south Anatolian plateau and eastern Elburz; in short, in the highland zones of the Near East. The presence at Nahal Oren, Israel, around 18,000 BC, of seeds of precisely those plants later domesticated indicates that already at such an early date particular plants were selected for exploitation.

Braidwood *et al.* (1981: 249-51) discerned two levels in the evolution of food production: an era of incipient cultivation and animal domestication and a later era of primary village farming. It is important to realise that these "levels" of socioeconomic evolution did not develop contemporaneously, nor did they inevitably succeed each other. Perhaps the mosaic of interdependence between village agriculturalists and nomads was never uniform over large geographical expanses.

Over the years there have been many explanations purporting to understand the causes that led to the Neolithic revolution. Flannery (1972) had proposed one of the most widely accepted theories. He suggested that pre-agricultural peoples adapted not to specific environments but to the exploitation of certain plants and animals that inhabited several environments. In order to successfully exploit these resources, populations had to be in specific areas at specific times; the procuring of foods required a scheduling of seasonal movement. The seasonal use of different environments is typical of both the Near East and Meso-America, enabling populations to schedule their exploitation of differing plants or animals in different seasons. Increasing populations would lead to new groups splitting off to exploit more marginal areas, where they would be forced to cultivate the plants they brought with them.

It has been shown that obsidian was utilised in most Neolithic communities, though it came from restricted geological deposits. The exploitation of this single resource, points to an exchange system that brought seemingly isolated Neolithic communities into contact. It is also true of the Neolithic cultures in India where raw material for tools was brought from long distances, probably through developed trade-networks.

It is interesting to note here that Meadow finds two early farming transformations in South Asia: one after the Indus Civilisation declined and the other in the Neolithic times. Meadow (1989: 1-16) says:

> One of the major unanswered questions of South Asian archaeology is the reason(s) for an apparent "de-urbanisation" of the Greater Indus valley beginning at about 1900 BC. This phenomenon took place together with the development of distinctly local manifestations of material culture that are particularly striking when compared to the extent of integration evident during the Harappan period. It is possible, even likely, that the degree of diminution in site size and amount of "localisation" that actually occurred is overestimated because of gaps in our knowledge and mistakes in our understanding of the archaeological record (e.g., Shaffer 1981, 1986). Yet one cannot escape the impression that significant shifts in settlement did take place if only in the abandonment of certain very large sites, including Mohenjodaro, and the establishment of many small sites throughout the region but particularly in East Punjab (Shaffer 1981, in press; Joshi, Bala & Ram 1984). Some abandonment and realignments can reasonably be attributed to changes in hydrological regimes in Punjab (e.g., Wilhelmy 1969; Mughal 1982; Agrawal and Sood 1984) and in Sindh (e.g., Flam 1981)....Yet there is increasing evidence that it was precisely at this time, in the beginning of the second millennium BC, that a new complex of cereal crops and domestic animals was becoming known in the region....When viewed on a broad basis, two distinct agricultural revolutions can be identified for the north-western region of South Asia during the pre- and proto-historic period. The first involved the establishment by the sixth millennium BC of a farming complex based principally on the rabi (winter sown, spring harvested) crops of wheat and barley and on certain domestic bovids including zebu cattle, sheep, and goats. The second saw the addition during the early second millennium BC of kharif (summer sown, fall harvested) cereals including sorghum, various millets, and rice along with new domestic animals including the camel, horse, and donkey.... The proposal explored in this essay is that new agricultural opportunities resulting from the introduction of the summer-sown cereal crops, when combined with the new means of animal-based traction, transport, and communication, facilitated widespread settlement in areas previously marginal to food production as well as realignment of settlement in already occupied areas of northwestern South Asia. This is by no means a new idea, having been proposed in part by Shaffer (1981:97) for East Punjab and Possehl (1986) for peninsular South Asia. What Shaffer did not emphasise was the importance of the differences in growing seasons (see Hutchinson 1977 and Costantini 1979, 1981), while Possehl did not stress the role that such a change could have played in the Greater Indus valley itself. Costantini (1979, 1981), Tosi (1983, but with a broader geographical scope), and Jarrige (1985a), have all underlined the significance of the new food production systems, and this essay can be seen as a distillation of ideas which we have explored together over a number of years.

In his concluding remarks Meadow observes:

> The new crops and animals that came to be widely used in South Asia during the early second millennium BC did not supplant but were exploited together with those that had formed the basis of agriculture for millennia in the Greater Indus valley. In terms of its subsistence base, the Harappan was very much a Middle Eastern civilisation, depending principally on wheat, barley, sheep, goats, and cattle although with significant distinguishing features including the overwhelming importance of cattle, which has continued to characterise South Asia to modern times. The claims of Fentress (1985: 367) that the risks and uncertainties of one-season agriculture led to double-cropping in Sindh during the Harappan period in order to "ensure a stable and regular food supply" are unconvincing, as present evidence indicates that the fruit of the date palm is the only significant food source used at that time in the Indus valley that matures in the summer or fall. Summer grown crops such as cotton and grapes were never vital to subsistence, although their cultivation may have developed expertise valuable to farmers who would later plant summer cereals (Meadow 1989: 1-16).

Summer (kharif) cultivation of the "millets" and rice appears to have begun in areas with significant monsoon rainfall east and south of the Indus valley where wild forms of some "millets" and rice are likely to have occurred. When and how this took place, however, is still obscure, although there is hope that palaeoethnobotanical investigations will clarify the matter in the not too distant a future. The presence of Harappan settlements in these areas may have provided the impetus necessary for local populations to begin to systematically plant seeds of grasses, which had previously been gathered to feed themselves or their animals (if the keeping of animals is truly earlier than crop-growing east and south of the Indus). The importation of sorghum probably from Arabia into Saurashtra at this time may also have played a role in developing the cultivation of similar grasses.

To date, the emphasis in discussing pre- and proto-historic South Asian subsistence has been placed on the major food crops and animals. As palaeoethnobotanical and archaeozoological studies have begun to show, however, other plants and animals played significant, if perhaps less critical, roles in the lives of the people of the region. Vishnu-Mittre (1985) has pointed to some directions worthy of investigation for plant materials, including consideration of those forms important for cultural and technological reasons and as animal fodder. The actual evidence for such practices will come from careful consideration of data gathered through flotation, wet sieving, and pollen analysis. As far as the animals are concerned, the processes of integration into the domestic economy of the water-buffalo, dog, cat, and chicken still require classification, as does also the spread of pastoralism into areas south and east of the Indus valley. The role of hunting, gathering, and foraging must also be evaluated in their relation to agricultural and pastoral practices and as the principal source of supply for particular resources. Finally, investigation of the climatic and environmental conditions prevailing on the local level during pre- and proto-historic times is essential to a better understanding of ancient settlement generally and of agriculture and animal husbandry in particular. To date, it has been extremely difficult to do more than to generally characterise the situation in the Greater Indus valley as a whole and to use analogy with modern conditions as a guide to the past.

With this preamble, we will now trace the origins and spread of agriculture and animal husbandry in South Asia in a pan-Asian perspective.

Here we may note that in India we have one more stage between Upper Palaeolithic and Neolithic, named Mesolithic, which is marked by the use of microliths. The Neolithic is marked by the use of ground stone tools. This is mainly because we have traditionally placed more importance on artefacts than on evidence of the domestication of animals and plants. As we will see below, even in Rajasthan we have evidence of clearance of vegetation and *Cerealia* type pollen from the lakes of Didwana etc., which may mark the beginning of agriculture in early Holocene but without any ground tool appendage. In the Vindhyas too use of pottery and domestication of plants and animals and permanent settlements mark the so-called Mesolithic. For us, therefore, the terminology of Mesolithic and Neolithic looks a bit contrived as it is based mainly on the presence or absence of ground stone tools. In fact, microliths are common to both. We have therefore taken them as stages of the same early farming. J.N. Pal (1986) seems to agree with this view and calls the Mesolithic proto-Neolithic.

It appears that there were four early centres of domestication of plants and animals: 1. North-west and West (includes Kachhi plains of Pakistan; Indian states of Kashmir, Rajasthan and Gujarat); 2. The Ganga valley and the Vindhyas; 3. East (the Indian states of Bihar, Assam, North-eastern states, Bengal, Orissa); and 4. Peninsular India. Out of these early centres the North-west and Western centre is very well documented mainly because of the extensive work of French teams. The Eastern centre is the least understood area. The Northern region mainly comprises the Ganga valley and the Vindhyas where some work has been done but much more is required. Peninsular India is less documented though we know a good deal about the Neolithic sites. There has also been a conceptual confusion as the Neolithic is generally identified with ground stone axe in South Asian archaeology.

Of the four nuclei, we have good documentation of the developmental stages in North-west as evidenced in Mehrgarh area. It should however be noted that an antecedent stage of hunting and gathering, preceding the appearance of the village farming community, has not been defined well in either India or Pakistan. There is a good chance that Afghanistan may provide the evidence for the origins of agriculture in this region. Possehl points out, the dates for the "Aceramic Neolithic" material from both Snake and Horse Caves compare well with dates from the Near East. At present, these dates and the archaeological materials themselves, can be seen as good indications that northern Afghanistan, probably the entire western Hindu Kush, should be taken seriously as a place where early, independent experiments with agriculture and animal husbandry may have taken place. There is more Aceramic Neolithic material in Pakistan which is clearly much nearer to the foundations on which the Indus Age rests (Possehl 1999c: 434).

No detailed work has been done in Rajasthan though the pollen evidence is suggestive. The lakes of Sambhar, Didwana and Lunkaransar are situated about 300 km apart from each other in Rajasthan, yet they show the presence of *Cerealia* type pollen accompanied by comminuted pieces of charcoal probably indicating clearance of vegetation for agricultural purposes. These levels are dated to c. 7500 BC (8300 cal BC) (G. Singh 1971: 185-86). There are no Neolithic sites though microliths are found from many sites. Baghor has given some evidence of early domestication of animals. Unfortunately, this palaeobotanical evidence has not been followed up archeologically. Pollen profiles also indicate that from c. 13,000 BC the monsoon had started strengthening though there were major fluctuations till the mid-Holocene when it was finally stabilised. The rainfall during this mid-Holocene period was probably twice than today. It is interesting to note that this climatic amelioration is coincident with the flourishing of pre-Harappan and Harappan cultures.

Traditionally Neolithic cultures are identified with ground stone axes in South Asia, though they are not at all necessary to begin farming. In fact, this presumed association of ground stone axes with the Neolithic is so strong that the evidence for domestication of plants and animals has been neglected. As a result, we know very little about early farming in Rajasthan and much of peninsular India.

The evidence from the Ganga valley and the Kaimur hills is also a bit confusing. To us it appears that rice cultivation could have come to South Asia much earlier than agriculture based on wheat and barley. This is because Koldihwa has given c. 7000BP dates for the levels, which have yielded rice husk on clay. Mahagara and Chopani Mando have also yielded similar evidence though there is considerable controversy both about chronology and proof of domestication. We would not be surprised if rice domestication goes back to early Holocene period in the Ganga valley. Below, we will discuss the evidence from the sites in more detail.

Wild rice grows in abundance in that area and could have been collected by these early people. However, some recent work from south-western China seems to make an early beginning of rice cultivation in the Ganga valley a distinct possibility. As we will see below, recent dates of rice domestication and ceramic technology go back to 15,000 BP. It has been shown by linguists that early rice technology travelled with Mon-Khmer speaking people. It seems that rice technology reached South-east Asia and the Brahmaputra valley with these people. There is some evidence of migration from the Brahmaputra valley to the Central Himalayas through Himalayan corridors. It is interesting to note that the Kumauni dialect has a strong residue of Mon-Khmer words. Of all the crops that are grown in Kumaun only rice agriculture is associated with a lot of rituals indicating its antiquity. It is quite probable that the Ganga valley received rice technology, and later on copper and iron technology, through the Central Himalayas (see Chapter 7).

In a recent study Weber (1998) has brought out the significance and origins of some important millets found in South Asia. Table 6.1 shows the name of the millet and the country of origin, as also the date.

TABLE 6.1 ORIGIN OF MILLETS IN SOUTH ASIA WITH DATES AND COUNTRIES OF ORIGIN (after Weber 1998)

Latin and Common Names	*Country (Area) of Origin*	*Earliest Finds in South Asia*
Setaria italica Foxtail millet	East Asia	2400 BC.
Panicum miliaceum broomcorn or common millet	East Asia	1900 BC.
Echinochloa colona sawa or barnyard millet	East Asia	1900 BC.
Panicum sumatrense little millet	South Asia	1000 BC.
Paspalum scrobuculatum Kodo millet	South Asia	1700 BC.
Eleusine coracana Ragi or finger millet	Africa	2500 BC.
Sorghum bicolor Jowar or large millet	Africa	2000 BC.
Pennisetum typhoides bajara or pearl millet, bullrush millet, spiked millet	Africa	1900 BC.

TABLE 6.2 CULTIVATED PLANTS FROM SOUTH ASIAN SITES OF THE 3rd AND 2nd MILLENNIA BC (after Weber 1998)

Plant Taxon	*Cropping Season*	*Region and Date BC.*		
		4000-2600	*2520-2000*	*2000-1700*
Cereals				
Wheat (*Triticum*)	W	R	R	R/K
Barley (*Hordeum*)	W	R	R/K	R/K
Rice (*Oryza*)	S		K	R/K
Millets	S	K	R/K	R/K
Pulses and vegetables				
Pea (*Pisum*)	W	R	R/K	R/K
Chick pea (*Cicer*)	W		R	R/K
Grass pea (*Lathyrus*)	W	R	R/K	R/K
Lentil (*Lens*)	W	R	R/K	R/K
Horse gram (*Dolichos*)	S		K	R/K
Bean (*Phaseolus*)	S		K	R/K

Cont. Table 6.2

Cont. Table 6.2

Plant Taxon	*Cropping Season*	*Region and Date BC.*		
		4000-2600	*2520-2000*	*2000-1700*
Vigna	S		R/K	R/K
Medicago	S		K	R/K
Oilseed and Fiber				
Lin (*Linum*)	W		R/K	R/K
Mustard (*Brassica)*	W		R/K	R/K
Sesame *(Sesamum*)	S		R/K	R/K
Cotton (*Gossypium)*	S	R (?)	R	R/K
Fruits				
Melon (*Cucumis*)	S		K	R/K
Date (*Phoenix)*	S	R	R	R
Jujube (*Zizyphus*)	W	R/K	R/K	R/K
Grape (*Vitis*)	W	R	R	R/K

Note: W = winter/spring-harvested; S = summer/fall-harvested; R = rabi areas, with winter rain; K = kharif areas, with summer rain.

With this backdrop, we can now go into more details about each centre. We begin with the north-west region.

NORTH-WEST

There is considerable controversy regarding the locales of the origins of wheat and barley. Possehl (1999c: 405) thinks that the Indo-Iranian borderlands may have played a significant role in the beginnings of agriculture. He remarks:

> The modern distribution of wild wheat and barley does not inform us of the distribution of these plants at the beginning of the Holocene. Thus, it is premature to insist that the Indo-Iranian borderlands were outside the distribution of wild wheat 10,000 years ago.... Even if wild wheat was not present on the Indo-Iranian Borderlands this region could still have played a key role in the domestication process. The genetic history of free threshing wheat, which was most useful to humans, involves genetic crosses with the genus Triticum and with a related plant, goat-face grass (*Aegilops squarrosa*), found all across the Iranian plateau. Richard H. Meadow has made the point that: "The necessary conditions for an emmer X ("and") Aegilops cross... could have been met anywhere the latter appeared as a weed in fields where emmer was cultivated. Therefore, *T. aestivum* could have originated as easily in the Pakistan area as in north-west Iran and, in fact, it seems quite likely that free threshing wheat of the west was *T. turgidum* cf. conv. durum and that of the east *T. aestivum* (Meadow 1993a: 301).

We have followed Possehl's chronological framework in discussing the early farming cultures of the North-west.

TABLE 6.3 PRE-HARAPPAN CULTURES (after Possehl 1999c)

Stage One:	
Kili Gul Mohammad (KGM) Phase	7000-5000 BC
Burj Basket-marked Phase	5000-4300 BC
Stage Two:	
Togau Phase	4300-3800BC
Kechi Beg Phase	3800-3200 BC
Hakra Wares Phase	3800-3200 BC

MEHRGARH

French and the American teams have worked for several years in the region of Mehrgarh. As a result we have quite a good documentation of early farming stages there. The following summary is based on the various reports (Jarrige, Meadow and Quivron 1995: 316; Costantini 1984; Meadow 1993: 301) of the French-Pakistani (French-Pak) team that have come out from time to time as also on Possehl's (1999c) encyclopaedic work, *The Indus Age.*

As the crow flies, Mehrgarh is situated at a distance of about a hundred kilometres from Kili Ghul Mohammed (KGM). The Bolan river cuts through the Kirthar Ranges and where the river debauches on the slopes are the Kachhi plains and it is here that Mehrgarh is located. Mehrgarh and the Kachhi plains are a difficult terrain to work in with no spectacular remains like those of the Harappan cities. Thanks to the extensive work of the French-Pakistani team for a dozen seasons, the area has yielded valuable information about early agriculture and animal husbandry. This work has also delineated the steps towards urbanisation, which eventually led to the efflorescence of the Harappan civilisation.

Mehrgarh I

The technology in this period was relatively simple. Some fragments of native copper were found. Flint sickle blades occasionally carried some sheen. A large number of ground stone tools like querns and grinding stones, two small limestone chisels, a small bowl, and a small mortar were also found (Jarrige, Meadow and Quivron 1995: 316). The baskets were lined with bitumen to make them waterproof. Some unbaked clay figurines were also found. The rich bone industry comprises awls, spatulas, a needle with an eye and two highly polished bone pendants with round perforation. Most of the bone tools were perhaps used in basket and cloth making. Some of the burials showed faint traces of textiles.

Beads:

Jarrige *et al.* report:

> .... Ornaments associated with the burial of the child show the quality of bead working at this early period. Tiny disc-shaped beads in black steatite, long barrel-shaped beads in calcite, and well polished bangles of conch shell reveal the existence at the beginning of the neolithic occupation of craft traditions that lasted for a long time in the region. The quality of the belt with its two flower shaped pendants in shell is especially worth noting (Jarrige, Meadow and Quivron 1995: 277).

Plants: The naked six-row barley (*Hordeum vulgare* subsp. *vulgare* var. nudum) is the main plant of Period I, comprising about 90% of the seeds and plant imprints. Also present is hulled six-row barley (*H. vulgare* subsp. *vulgare*), two-row barley (*H. vulgare*—both subsp. *spontaneum* and distichum), einkorn (*Triticum monococcum*), emmer (*T. turgidum*, subsp. dicoccum), and hard wheat (*T. turgidum* cf. conv. durum) were present though poorly represented. Other plant remains of the Period IB and IIB include the Indian jamun or jujube (*Zizyphus* sp.) and dates (*Phoenix dactylifera*) (Costantini 1984). Though the einkorn and emmer disappear from the region, the bread wheat and shot wheat continue as the eastern species of *Triticum*. The free thrashing wheat in the Near East was *Triticum turgidum* cf. conv. durum (hard wheat) and that of the east *Triticum aestivum*, bread or club wheat (Meadow 1993: 301).

Animals: Period IA is dominated by "...12 species of 'big game': gazelle (*Gazella dorcas*), swamp deer (*Cervus duvaucelii*), nilgai (*Boselaphus tragocamelus*), blackbuck (*Antelope cervicapra*), onager (*Equus hemionus*), chital or spotted deer (*Axis axis*), water-buffalo (*Bubalus bubalis*), wild sheep (*Ovis* [?] *orientalis*), wild goat (*Capra* [?] *aegagrus*), wild cattle (*Bos* [?] *namadicus*), wild pig (*Sus scrofa*) and elephant (*Elephas maximus*). This composition of the game indicates that the first inhabitants of aceramic Mehrgarh I exploited the Kachhi plain as also the nearby hills (Meadow 1984a: 35)". Fish and bird remains are poorly represented which may be the artefact of not screening of the deposits.

Regarding the subsistence economy of early Mehrgarh, Meadow observes:

1. Goats were kept from the time of the first occupation of the site.
2. Cattle and sheep are likely to have been domesticated from local wild stock during the course of the aceramic Neolithic.
3. Size diminution in goats was largely complete by Period IIA, and in sheep perhaps not until Period III.
4. The contribution of domestic or "pro-domestic" stock to the faunal assemblages came to surpass that of other animals early in the aceramic, but not in the earliest levels.
5. The development of animal keeping by the ancient inhabitants of Mehrgarh took place in the context of cereal crop cultivation, the building of substantial mud brick structures, and the existence of social differentiation and long distance trade networks as attested by the presence of marine shells, lapis lazuli, and turquoise in even the earliest graves (Meadow 1984a: 311).

Possehl thinks that at Mehrgarh there is evidence for local domestication of animals. To begin with, the sheep, goats and cattle were wild. Over time the potential domesticates come to look like domesticated animals showing a smaller size and other typical osteological features of domestication. They also come to dominate the animal resources used by the early inhabitants of Mehrgarh; something we would expect in the early-mature stage of food production. As stressed by Meadow, the local domestication of animals took place within the context of a fairly advanced cereal agriculture. Further east, it may be noted that the *Cerealia* pollen and early burning were noted by G. Singh in the lakes of Rajasthan, as early as 7500 BC (G. Singh 1971:185-86).

We may note here that Naik observes:

> In India only a beginning has been made on the study of the animal remains recovered from archaeological excavations. Further studies are needed to date them correctly so that the date of origin and distribution of domesticated cattle can be ascertained and compared with the rest of the animal species. The available archaeological and genetic evidence showed that the centre of origin of humped Zebu cattle is in India, and the Zebu cattle of Africa and southeast Asia showed a close genetic relationship with the Indian Zebu and therefore they might have a common origin. *Bos taurus*, on the other hand, revealed marked archaeological and genetic differences from *Bos Indicus* and thereby confirms their independent origin. Archaeological findings of humpless cattle only in the northern

part of India show that they were brought along with the people who came to India from the west and that they did not thrive in the tropical climate of India. The archaeological and genetic evidence on domesticated cattle and other species of animals with which man is supposed to have migrated to would throw light not only on the ancestral origin of cattle races and breeds but also actually on human history (1978: 23-30).

The long-distance interaction called for by the notion of an "expanded nuclear zone" in Middle Asia is documented by the trade network implied by the presence of marine shells, lapis lazuli (found in Afghanistan and Baluchistan) and turquoise (Iran and Central Asia), as noted by Meadow. The people of Mehrgarh IA were not isolated to the world to the north, south and west.

Possehl has suggested that there was a single "expanded nuclear zone" in Middle Asia within which food production and domestication took place within a single period of time: from about 11,000 to 5500 BC. In the Near East this would encompass the period beginning with the Natufians through pre-Pottery Neolithic B (PPNB). There is evidence that the people of Mehrgarh were participating in the early stages of the food producing/domestication revolution. Possehl thinks that there is evidence for local involvement in the shift of the animal economy from "hunting to herding". Their participation in interregional communication gives us good reason to believe that further work in the region around Mehrgarh will tend to support the hypothesis put forth here.

He also holds the view that over this period of time the peoples within the "expanded nuclear zone" were experimenting with their subsistence economy, seeking ways to better control the vagaries of production through husbanding of animals and management of plants. The communication within the "expanded nuclear zone" was generally rich. This was driven in many ways. Some of these would have been: 1) trade in material goods, raw materials and finished products; 2) the presence of marriage and other social network such as systems of exchange founded in reciprocity and ecological mechanism for spreading risk and forming alliances; and 3) the maturation implied by the emergence of food production and domestication. Possehl has emphasised the need for further work as the richness of this communication, and the diversity of these mechanisms of antiquity, are, of course, poorly documented today.

The French team has suggested that the association of the massive and remarkable piece of architecture with the impressive complex of compartmented buildings reveals a degree of planning probably related to well developed social and community organisation during the sixth millennium BC (Jarrige, Meadow and Quivron 1995:422). A significant amount of charred barley was found at the bottom of the completely excavated rooms in structure L 2. This tends to confirm that these were storage facilities. The fill in the rooms of this building had no indication of domestic debris. The cells or compartments are too small to have been inhabited. The absence of any fireplace or remains related to domestic activities on the floors of these buildings makes it difficult to believe that they could have been used as shelters even during the few cold weeks of the year. Moreover, there was an absence of doors between the small cellular compartments. "A connection with agricultural activities is shown by the discovery made in one of the compartments of two sickles composed of three blade-lets shafted slantwise in bitumen. These almost complete sickles, lacking only the now disintegrated wooden parts of their handles, are finds of exceptional interest for our understanding of the tools used for farming activities. The function of the building as a granary is also suggested by a large number of impressions of grains in the fill of the compartments" (Jarrige, Meadow and Quivron 1995:248). Possehl also says that there is good evidence showing that most of the buildings exposed in the context of Period IIA, mostly compartmented or cell-units buildings, must have been used as storage units and not as proper dwellings (Pl. 6-1).

Two copper artefacts (one bead and a ring) were found along with some slag. For shell working in Period II, conch shells (*Fascolaria trapezium* and *Turbinella pyrum*) imported from the Arabian Sea were used. A rectangular and a circular stone slabs were found covered with red ochre. A cylinder bead in terracotta was found in one of the compartmented building of Period II. When rolled out this bead produces an impression much like that of a cylinder seal. The motif is regular and portrays vegetation. Other finds include violin-shaped human figurines of unbaked clay coloured with red ochre, animal figurines, grinding stones, mortars, stone bowls, a broken mace head of alabaster, hundreds of chipped stone tools and drills. Most of the stone points had a lustrous polish that may suggest use in basketry or leather. That these tools were often found in association with red ochre is an interesting observation since ochre may be used for the tanning of hides. A well-preserved elephant tusk with three grooves cut to divide it into equal parts from Period II and a leg bone was found from Period I, which suggests that Sindh was a natural habitat for elephants (Jarrige, Meadow and Quivron 1995:422).

In another area the remains of a steatite workshop were found, with evidence for cutting the raw material and making beads. Flint drill and flakes were associated with 334 disc-shaped beads with diametres ranging between 3 and 4 mm including several broken ones. Associated with the steatite beads were a few cut dentalia, a few beads in white chalk (some coloured with red ochre), and wasters in black steatite. Near this workshop, six oblong-shaped cakes of red ochre were found. East of the building, an open space was covered with heaps of bones among which were about a hundred bone tools including awls and needles. About 50 more bone tools were found close by. This concentration would indicate that we have here an area where bone tools were used in connection with leather working. Associated with same building were collected several hundred charred seeds of cotton (*Gossypium sp*), indicating perhaps a ginning area.

Mehrgarh III

Three compartmented copper seals were found in Mehrgarh III along with unidentifiable fragments of the metal and one tubular gold bead is also associated with this period. Overall, copper is rare in Togau times and Mehrgarh is the only site where direct evidence for smelting, refining or melting the metal has been found. A surface survey of the Mehrgarh III settlement area, which is huge, about 70 hectares, preceded excavation there. This inspection revealed considerable evidence for craft activity involving the manipulation of lapis lazuli, carnelian, calcite, garnet, turquoise, shell and bitumen. The materials on the surface were clearly waste products from workshops in the area (Jarrige, Jarrige, Meadow and Quivron 1995: 213). One of areas had: "One micro-drill in phtanite, waster, and fragments of rattle-like objects, and a few bone awls. Several stone objects such as grinding stones, pestles and flint tools also were recorded. One more exceptional find is a polished stone axe..." (Jarrige, Jarrige, Meadow and Quivron 1995: 320).

Steatite "paste" was used for making beads at Mehrgarh at this time and the excavations have yielded an insight into how this material was handled. It was first heated to make it malleable. The craftsmen then squeezed it through a metal tube, slicing off a thin wafer bead (Samzun 1991: 68). A similar process for the manufacture of micro-beads was reconstructed from materials found at Zekhada, a site in north Gujarat (Hegde, Karanth and Sychanthavong 1982), although here the craftsmen used a true steatite paste of powder and water.

Agriculture and herding were well established by the beginning of Stage Two. Although it has not been possible to quantify food production, there is no reason to believe that subsistence surpluses were impossible. This does not imply that we can reconstruct the social stratigraphy that would be associated with an archaic state, but some internal differentiation of the Stage Two society is entirely possible, especially given the sophistication of craft production documented at Mehrgarh.

Togau Phase (human remains): The only Togau Phase site with human remains is Mehrgarh III where 125 human interments were found in an area reserved as a cemetrey (Samzun and Sellier 1985: 96); of these 99 were excavated. This burial ground is toward the centre of MR2. During this phase the density of human remains was high in some parts of the cemetery as two burial customs are noticed at Mehrgarh. Gone are the grave structures of Period IB (Pl. 6-2) and II and the practice of using red ochre in a lavish way was discontinued. There are also burials arranged in a way that suggests collective graves. These were aligned in an east-west orientation, with the head always to the east, lying on their side in a flexed position. Disarticulated, secondary inhumations were also found, some with the skull set on a brick.

Samzun and Sellier (1985: 116) discuss continuities and discontinuities between the funerary records of Stage One and Stage Two at Mehrgarh. This is summarised below:

Continuities:

Bodies placed in the same position
On the side
Flexed
Oriented east-west
Similar ornaments

Discontinuities:

Little red ochre in Stage Two interments
Wider variety of grave goods in Stage One interments
Stone vessels
Pottery
Bitumen baskets
Bone and stone tools
Animal offerings
Side-wall graves in Stage One, none in Stage Two

All age classes in the Stage One burials, not true for those of Stage Two
No collective sepulchre in Stage One

Coming at this theme of continuity and discontinuity from a slightly different data set, Hemphill *et al.* have also found evidence for something of a discontinuity between the Stage One and Stage Two inhabitants of Mehrgarh (Hemphill *et al.* 1991:172-74). The inhabitants of the later Stage of the site share important affinities with the individuals in Mature Harappan Cemetrey R-37 at Harappa, which taken together: "...bear close affinities to populations from the west, i.e., from the Iranian Plateau and the Near East (Hemphill *et al.* 1991: 174)". Lukacs feels that the Stage One population at Mehrgarh shared little with this western population, but had features pointing to a biological heritage to the east of the subcontinent.

These shifts are reflected in other parts of the funerary record as well as other evidence from Mehrgarh III, including the mass production of pottery, with more or less standardised shapes. So also a shift in the chipped stone tools industry away from true microliths to larger, bulkier types based on different technological principles (Lechevallier 1984) and rather massive signs of craft production including copper metallurgy and bead production that have already received much emphasis. These observations would tend to support the hypothesis that new ideas may have come to the site along with new people. The precise mechanisms of these changes are not understood. But the roaming of pastoral nomads, the travel of traders and craftsmen as well as the adventure of exploration have been historical constants.

There is continuity between Stage One (Periods I and II) and Stage Two (Period III) at Mehrgarh, and it should not be imagined that this theme is any weaker than the one just outlined. The architecture remains the same with two kinds of buildings, including the compartmented storage structures. The development of the Togau Ware repertory of ceramics, while new in itself, draws heavily on past ceramic technology and there is also continuity in the subsistence regime of the site.

One immediate observation that seems to flow from this insight is that it would argue against Colin Renfrew's hypothesis on the spread of the Indo-European languages. He proposed that these moved via their speakers who were farmers and herders migrating eastwards following the developments of the food production in the north-central region of the Near East (Renfrew 1987, 1989). He specifically notes that this would imply that the people of Mehrgarh Periods I and II spoke an Indo-European tongue (Renfrew 1987: 190).

The results of this research do not support Renfrew's Neolithic Aryan hypothesis. Rather than demonstrating biological continuity within the Indus valley from Neolithic time to the dawn of the Christian era, two discontinuities exist. The first occurs between 6000 and 4500 BC and is reflected by the strong separation between the two samples of Mehrgarh.

While this discontinuity stands in marked contrast to the archaeological interpretation of Jarrige (Jarrige 1981, 1985b; Jarrige and Lechevallier 1979) and others, it accords well with archaeological evidence for increasing craft specialisation, trade networks and ceramic similarities to the north-west with Kili Ghul Mohammed and Damb Sadaat (Jarrige 1982). This discontinuity also fits well with recent glottochronological studies, which place the entrance of the Dravidian languages into South Asia around the fourth millennium BC (Fairservis and Southworth 1989; Southworth 1979) as well as current linguistic research that not only ascribes a common origin to the Dravidian and Elamitic languages (McAlpin 1981), but also suggests that peoples of the Harappan civilisation were Dravidian language speakers (Fairservis 1983; Mallory 1989; Parpola 1984a, 1984b, 1986). The second biological discontinuity exists between the inhabitants of Harappa, Chalcolithic Mehrgarh, and post-Harappan Timargarh on the one hand and Sarai Khola on the other. This implies another discontinuity at some point after 800 BC but before 200 BC (Hamphill *et al.* 1991: 173-75) (see Possehl 1999c and references quoted therein).

A third theme within the context of the Stage of Developed Village Farming Communities and Pastoral Societies is the expansion of the geographical horizons of these farmers and herders. During the Togau phase, a settlement was established at Mundigak in southern Afghanistan within the drainage system of the Helmand river, but the most dramatic shift was eastwards into the drainage of the ancient, now dry, Sarasvati valley by the peoples of the Hakra wares. The old Sarasvati river is called the "Hakra" in Pakistan and the "Ghaggar" in India. The former princely state of Bahawalpur was a centre on the Hakra drainage, in the larger region also known as "Cholistan" or "Desert country" in the local vernacular.

Settlement of the Kechi Beg and Hakra Ware Phases: Kechi Beg is the largest site with an area about 21 hectares, although it is properly not as large as Dabar Kot at this time, which is the largest site of the stage. Mehrgarh III is said to cover 100 hectares (Jarrige, Jarrige, Meadow and Quivron 1995: 69). The ascendancy of barley over wheat also seems to take place during this period, and this grain will continue to be the predominant one through the Mature Harappan.

Hakra Wares and the Beginning of Regionalism: An illustration of some of this pottery is given in *Indus Age*: *The Beginnings* (Possehl 1999c: 534, Fig. 4.68). The field director at Harappa, J. Mark

Kenoyer has referred to this material as the "Ravi/Hakra Assemblage". This terminology expresses the sense that there is a general resemblance of the pottery to Mughal's Hakra wares, while recognising the fact that there are also fabrics, shapes and decorations unique to the Harappa assemblage.

Of the 103 Hakra ware sites, 54 can be classified as camps used by pastoralists, leaving 49 villages farming communities (Mughal 1994, 1997). Camp sites are represented by a light scatter of pottery without the build-up of an archaeological midden.

They also had an opportunity to play a role as traders, bringing product not indigenous to the Sarasvati drainage to peoples there. Given that this region was largely covered with sand, alluvium, grass and small trees, the list of such imported product could have been rather from long distance. The stability in such villages is not known; however it should not be assumed that everyone who lived there was a full time, year around resident.

Stage Two Food Grains: The study of plant remains from Mehrgarh III is incomplete but there is strong evidence for an expansion for farming activities. The Mehrgarh people continued to use four different varieties of wheat: einkorn, emmer, club wheat and shot wheat (*Triticum monococcum, T. dicoccum, T. cf. aestivum compactum, T. cf. aestivum sphaerococcum*), goat face grass (*Aegilops* sp.), oats (*Avena* sp.), and two rowed barley (*Hordeum spontaneum*) (Jarrige, Jarrige, Meadow and Quivron 1995: 250). The use of multiple varieties of wheat and barley is a reflection of the subsistence pattern that began during the Kili Gul Mohammad and Burj Basket-marked Phases at Mehrgarh, and doubtless other early village sites in the region. By the mature Harappan times this pattern changed and barley was the single predominant food grain. But, earlier peoples used verities of wheat that can be thought of as "eastern"; bread/club wheat (*Triticum aestivum/compactum*) and shot wheat (*Triticum sphaerococcum*). The durum wheat of the "west" was no longer used. This changeover seems to have adaptive value according to van Zeist and Bakker-Heeres: "*T. durum* is well adapted to the Mediterranean climate, whereas *T. aestivum* is a crop plant from more humid, temperate climatic conditions" (1969: 164). The Stage of the Developed Village Farming Community and Pastoral Societies seems to be the time when these changes began (Possehl 1999c).

Cotton: Probably *Gossypium herbaceum* is the wild ancestor of the Old World cottons. It is endemic to South Africa. The domesticated form is called *Gossypium arboreum*. There are weedy, "feral" varieties of *G. arboreum* also in South Asia. There is a wild species of cotton in Pakistan called *G. stocksii*, which yields short fibres. G. Willcox (1992:293) has suggested that this could have been the cotton used during the Indus Age. Sindh and Gujarat have ancient traditions as cotton growing areas (Hutchinson 1976:136). Santhanam and Hutchinson (1974) suggest that cotton may have been first brought under cultivation in this area.

Stage Two Domesticated Animals: The animal species exploited in the Stage of the Developed Village Farming Community and Pastoral Societies remain very much as in the preceding stage. An examination of the frequency graph showing the proportional use of species indicates that Mehrgarh Period III represents the beginning of stabilisation in the animal exploitation pattern at the site that lasts to the threshold of civilisation. This furthers the sense that Stage Two is a period of consolidation in the subsistence regime, and the maturation of the earlier food production into a more stable, less experimental subsistence system.

The ^{14}C dates of early agriculture sites of Pakistan are given in Table 6.4.

TABLE 6.4 NEOLITHIC DATES (EARLY AGRICULTURE: PAKISTAN)

All BP ages are based on 5568 yr half-life of radiocarbon. Calibrated ages are given in bc (after Possehl 1999c)

Site	*Sample No.*	*5568 Yrs.BP*	*Calib. Dates*	*Culture*	*Material*
Mehrgarh	BETA-2690	3590±60 BP	1997 cal.bc	Period IV	Unknown
Mehrgarh	BETA-1719	13340±125 BP	13994 cal.bc	Period IB	Unknown
Mehrgarh	BETA-1721	9385±120 BP	8416 cal.bc	Period IA	Unknown
Mehrgarh	LV-993	6110±90 BP	5040 cal.bc	Period IB	Unknown
Mehrgarh	BETA-2686	5860±70 BP	4727 cal.bc	Period IA	Unknown
Mehrgarh	BETA-2688	5490±70 BP	4350 cal.bc	Period IIA	Unknown
Mehrgarh	LY-1945	5360±310 BP	4235 cal.bc	Period IIB	charcoal
Mehrgarh	BETA-7315	5620±100 BP	4465 cal.bc	Period IIA	Unknown
Mehrgarh	BETA-2689	6500±78 BP	5474,5435, 5426 cal.bc	Period III	Unknown
Mehrgarh	LV-994	6290±70 BP	5238 cal.bc	Period IB	Unknown
Mehrgarh	LY-1946	33000±3000 BP	None	Period IB	Charcoal
Mehrgarh	BETA-1408	6925±80 BP	5737 cal.bc	Period IA	Unknown
Mehrgarh	BETA-1407	7115±290 BP	5961 cal.bc	Period IA	Unknown
Mehrgarh	BETA-1720	7115±120BP	5961 cal.bc	Period IIB	Unknown
Mehrgarh	LY-1950	8440±250BP	7490 cal.bc	Period IB	Unknown
Mehrgarh	LV-906	5950±65BP	4832 cal.bc	Period IB	Unknown
Mehrgarh	LV-907	6020±80BP	4917 cal.bc	Period IB	Unknown
Mehrgarh	LV-909	5940±55BP	4808 cal.bc	Period IB	Unknown
Mehrgarh	LY-1948	5720±730BP	4540 cal.bc	Period IA	Charcoal
Mehrgarh	LV-908	6090±70BP	4963 cal.bc	Period IB	Unknown
Mehrgarh	LY-1949	5530±180BP	4360 cal.bc	Period IA	Charcoal
Mehrgarh	BETA-7314	5400±90BP	4246 cal.bc	Period IIA	Unknown
Mehrgarh	LY-1947	5830±190BP	4716 cal.bc	Period IA	Charcoal
Mehrgarh	LY-1528	4190±140BP	2708 cal.bc	Period IV	Charcoal
Mehrgarh	LY-1529	3960±140BP	2470 cal.bc	Period VI	Charcoal
Mehrgarh	LV-910	5880±100BP	4775 cal.bc	Period IB	Unknown
Mehrgarh	LY-1527	3570±150BP	1923 cal.bc	Period VII	Charcoal
Mehrgarh	BETA-7316	5990±120BP	4901 cal.bc	Period IA	Unknown
Rehman Dheri	PRL-675	4400±110BP	3034 cal.bc	Period I, Kechi beg	Charcoal
Rehman Dheri	PRL-676	4520±110BP	3143 cal.bc	Period I, Kechi beg	Charcoal

Cont. Table 6.4

Cont. Table 6.4

Site Material	*Sample No.*	*5568 Yrs.BP*	*Calib. Dates*	*Culture*	
Rehman Dheri	WIS-1698	4190±70BP	2708 cal.bc	Period I, Kechi beg	Unknown
Rehman Dehri	WIS-1697	4300±70BP	2915 cal.bc	Period I, Kechi beg	Unknown
Said Qala	DIC-22	3620±220BP	1980 cal.bc	Occupation No.1 (Damb Sadaat III)	Charcoal
Said Qala	DIC-20	3710±90BP	2050 cal.bc	Occupation No.2 (Damb Sadaat III	Charcoal
Said Qala	DIC-18	3800±220BP	2209 cal.bc	Occupation No.3 (Damb Sadaat II)	Charcoal
Saraikhola	BM-1934R	4470±150BP	3102 cal.bc	Period I, Neolithic	Charcoal
Saraikhola	BM-1939R	4530±160BP	3148 cal.bc	Period I, Neolithic	Charcoal
Saraikhola	BM-1940R	4600±200BP	3360 cal.bc	Period I, Neolithic	Charcoal
Saraikhola	BM-1935R	4370±250BP	2928 cal.bc	Period I, Neolithic	Charcoal
Shahr-I Sokhta	P-2077	3950±60BP	2468 cal.bc	Shahr-I Sokhta II, Phase 5, protourban	Charcoal
Shahr-I Sokhta	R-627	4020+50BP	2506 cal.bc	Shahr-I Sokhta II, Phase 5-6, protourban	Charcoal
Shahr-I Sokhta	R-634	4050±50BP	2584 cal.bc	Shahr-I Sokhta-II, Phase 6, protourban	Charcoal
Shahr-I Sokhta	P-2542	3990±60BP	2495 cal.bc	Shahr-I Sokhta II, Phase 5-6, protourban	Charcoal
Shahr-I Sokhta	P-2543	4200±60BP	2782 cal.bc	Shahr-I Sokhta I, phase 9-10, archaic	Charcoal

Cont. Table 6.4

Site	*Sample No.*	*5568 Yrs.BP*	*Calib. Dates*	*Culture*	*Material*
Shahr-I Sokhta	TUNC-24	394370BP	2466 cal.bc	Shahr-I Sokhta III, phase 3-4 proto state	Charcoal
Shahr-I Sokhta	R-623	4050±50BP	2584 cal.bc	Shahr-I Sokhta II, phase 5-6, protourban	Charcoal
Shahr-I Sokhta	TUNC-27	3890±90BP	2405 cal.bc	Shahr-I Sokhta III, phase 3-4 protostate	Charcoal
Shahr-I Sokhta	R-405A	3960±50BP	2470 cal.bc	Shahr-I Sokhta II, phase 5-6 protourban	Charcoal
Shahr-I Sokhta	TUNC-22	3829±61BP	2298 cal.bc	Shahr-I Sokhta III, phase 3-4, protourban	Charcoal
Shahr-I Sokhta	R-629	4200±50BP	2782 cal.bc	Shahr-I Sokhta-I phase-8-9, Archaic	Charcoal
Shahr-I Sokhta	P-2081B	4150±70BP	2699 cal.bc	Shahr-I Sokhta II, phase 6, protourban	Charcoal
Shahr-I Sokhta	TUNC-26	4115±72BP	2625 cal.bc	Shahr-I Sokhta III, phase 3-4, protostate	Charcoal
Shahr-I Sokhta	P-2084	4110±60BP	2623 cal.bc	Shahr-I Sokhta II, phase 6, protourban	Charcoal
Shahr-I Sokhta	R-632	4100±50BP	2619 cal.bc	Shahr-I Sokhta II, phase 6, protourban	Charcoal

Cont. Table 6.4

Pl. 6-3. Burzahom excavations, Kashmir

Pl. 6-4. Neolithic stone tools, surface finds, Kashmir

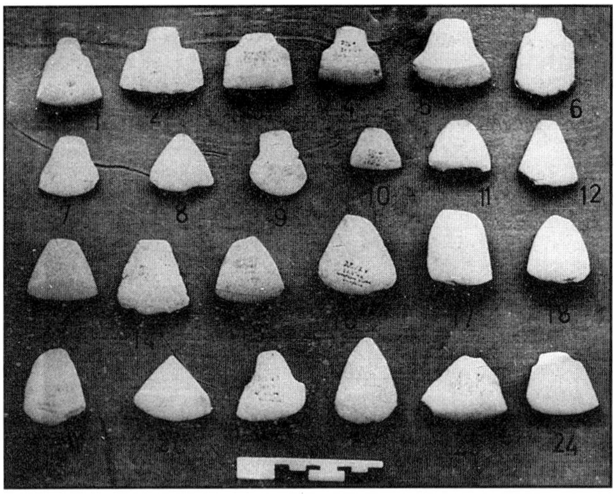

Pl. 6-5. Different types of celts from the excavation at Deojali Hading, North Kachar hills, Assam

Pl. 6-6. View of the ash-mound at Budihal, Gulbarga district, Karnataka

Pl. 6-7. View of the rubble embankment exposed in the trench, Budihal ash-mound, Gulbarga district, Karnataka

Pl. 6-8. View of Trench 4 showing a structure near the ash-mound at Budihal, Gulbarga district, Karnataka

Pl. 6-9. Part of the butchering floor in the habitation area around the ash-mound at Budihal, Gulbarga district, Karnataka

Pl. 6-10. Burnt clay impressions of wattle-and-daub houses, Tekkalkota, Karnataka

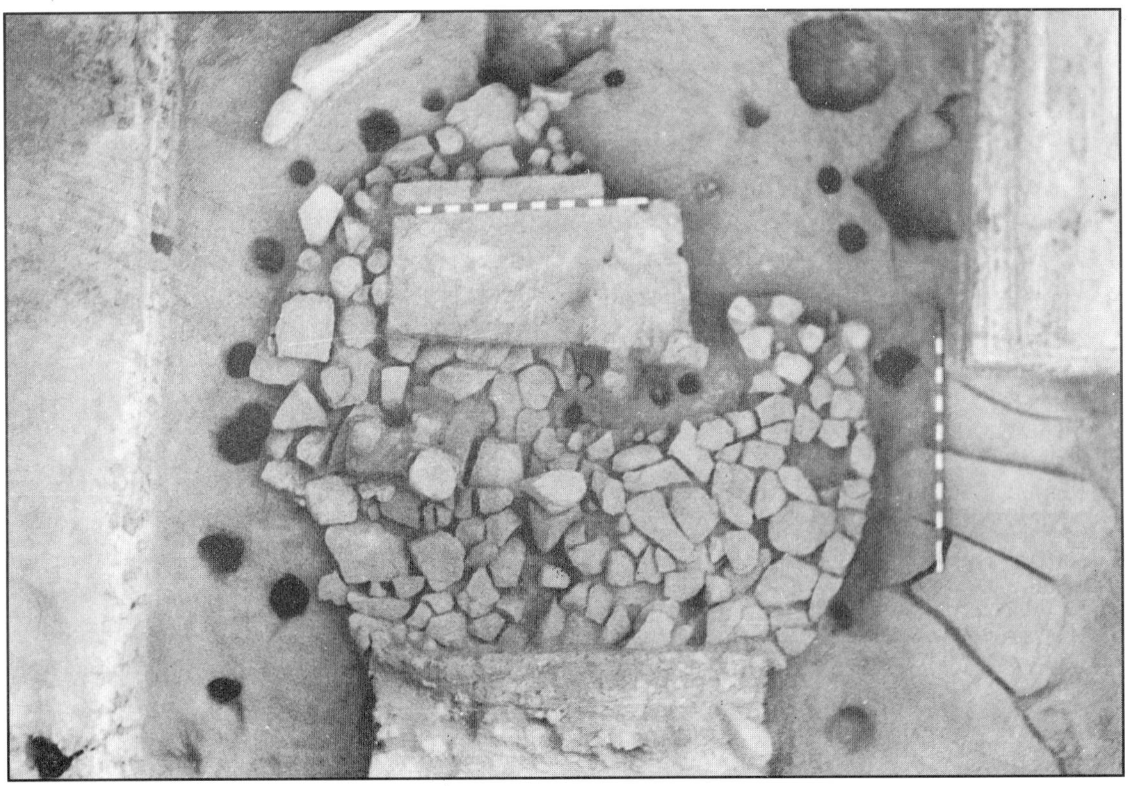

Pl. 6-11. Neolithic hut-floor from Sangankallu excavation from Karnataka

Pl. 6-12. A handmade pot from Tekkalkota, Karnataka

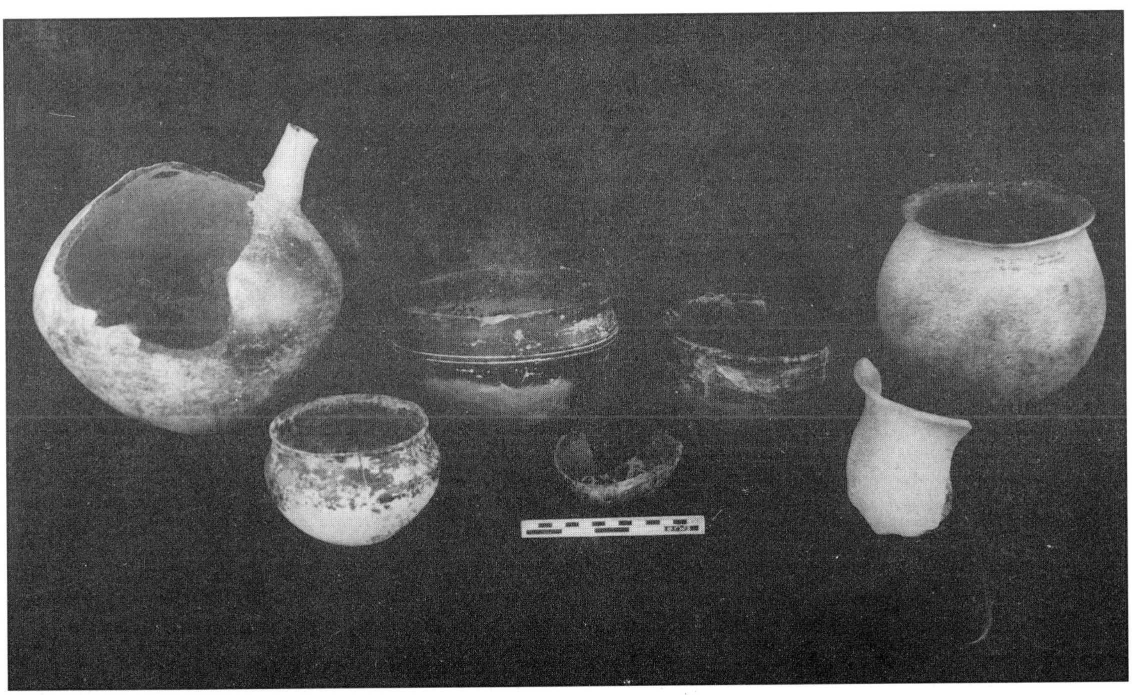

Pl. 6-13. Neolithic Gray Ware and Black-and-Red Ware pottery from Tekkalkota, Karnataka

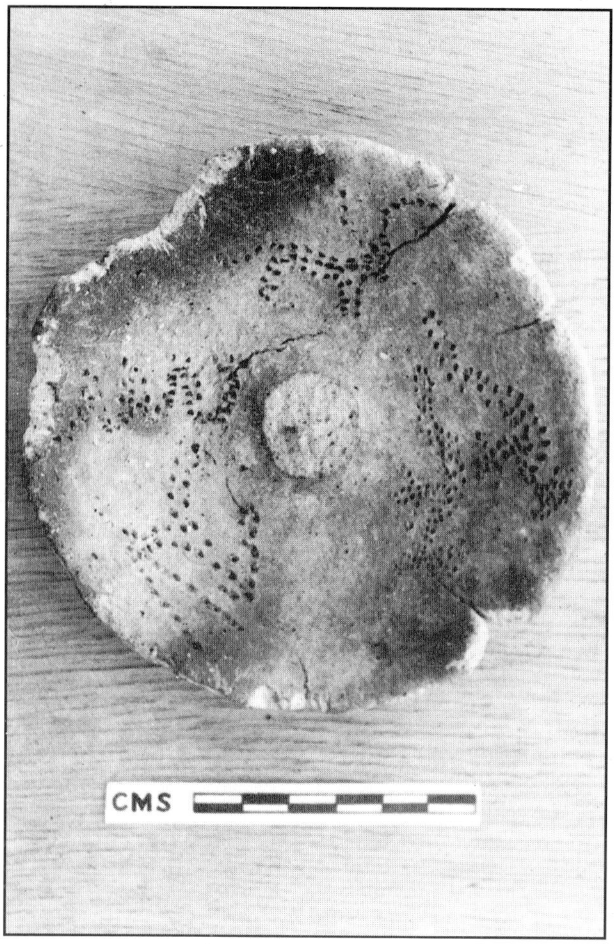

Pl. 6-14. Neolithic pottery lid showing punctured decorations of four animals - bull, peacock, antelope and snake, Takkalkota, Karnataka

Pl. 6-15. A copper axe from Tekkalkota, Karnataka

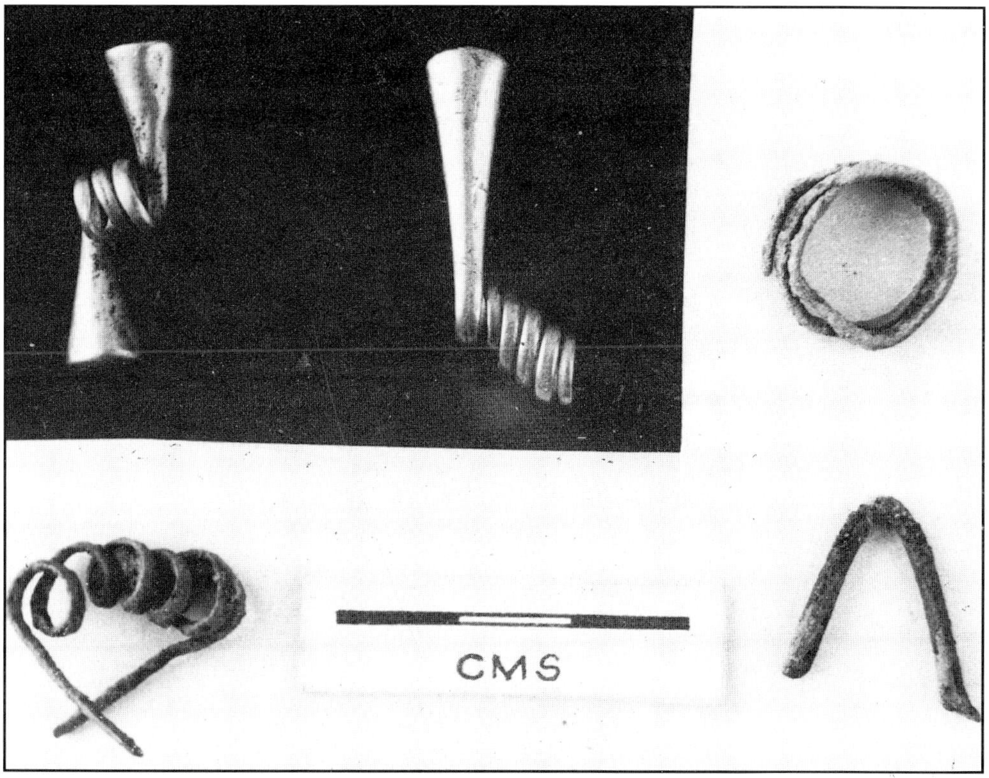

Pl. 6-16. Metal ornaments, with two gold pendants in the box, from Neolithic excavation at Tekkalkota, Karnataka

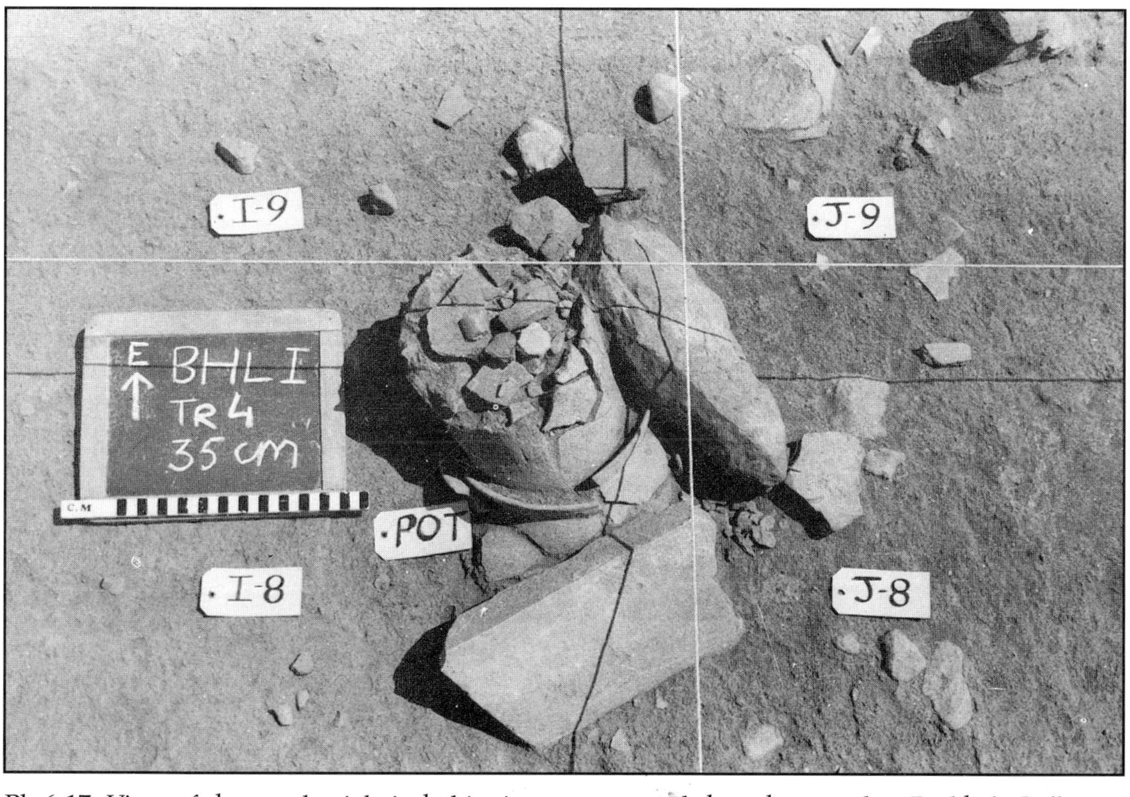

Pl. 6-17. View of the urn burials in habitation area around the ash-mound at Budihal, Gulbarga district, Karnataka

Pl. 6-18. Extended human burials from habitation area around the ash-mound at Budihal, Gulbarga district, Karnataka

Pl. 6-19. Kudatini ash-mound section, Bellari district, Karnataka

Cont. Table 6.4

Site	*Sample No.*	*5568 Yrs.BP*	*Calib. Dates*	*Culture*	*Material*
Shahr-I Sokhta	P-2071	3970±60BP	2483 cal.bc	Shahr-I Sokhta IV, phase 0, post-urban	Charcoal
Shahr-I Sokhta	TUNC-21	4065±65BP	2598 cal.bc	Shahr-I Sokhta III, phase 3-4, protostate	Charcoal

Let us now have a look at the northern-most early farming sites of Kashmir.

Kashmir

The Kashmir valley was a vast lake in the Pleistocene times, and it is estimated that around 85,000 BP, due to tectonic uplift, it was drained out, giving rise to the river Jhelum. The Neolithic settlers here occupied the commanding terraces of the Karewas, the remnants of the Pleistocene lake beds (Agrawal 1992). The Kashmir valley is full of deodar, walnut, pine, willow and birch. There are plenty of lakes around. The Neolithic folk thus had abundance of game, fish and fowl. Pollen profiles from Toshmaidan show a cold-warm-cold sequence and that deglaciation started here c. 15,000 BP. At Haigam, the pollen profile shows clearance of pine forest, which may have something to do with agricultural activity. But as there are no ^{14}C dates for this profile, one cannot hazard any guesses.

The Neolithic settlements in Kashmir are quite densely distributed as in the Jhelum valley alone, from Anantnag to Pampur, a number of sites were discovered, e.g., Begagund, Gufkral, Hariparigom, Jayadeviudar, Olchibag, Pampur, Panzgom, Sombur and Thajiwor. Other sites of the valley are Gurhoma Sangri, near the Wular lake and Damodara Karewa south-west of Srinagar (Fig. 6-2). In our recent explorations, we also could discover several Neolithic sites on the Pir Panjal side. The sites at Aripanthan near Magam and at Puthkah near Sangrama are noteworthy. Gandarbal in the Sindh valley and Baimlun on the Wangat nullah were discovered by Paterson.

Nearly three dozen sites represent the Neolithic culture in the Kashmir valley with its characteristic traits. All these sites are located on the elevated Karewas, overlooking rivers and lakes. Burzahom (Pl. 6-3) and Gufkral have been excavated out of these sites and both have yielded evidence of three distinct cultures - Neolithic, Megalithic and Historical.

In fact, Burzahom, situated 24km north-east of Srinagar in the Kashmir valley, is first Neolithic site discovered as early as 1935 by de Terra and Paterson in Kashmir. They also laid out some small trenches and thought that the site belongs to the Indus culture. It was Khazanchi of the Archaeological Survey who excavated the site from 1960 to 1974 (for nine seasons) and established its Neolithic character. The deposits at Burzahom can be divided into four periods, out of which the first two are Neolithic, the third Megalithic and the last, Early Historic. Here, we confine ourselves to the first three periods (Fig. 6-3).

Pit dwelling is the most distinctive trait of Period I. Both circular/oval and rectangular/squarish pits were used. Circular pits were bigger and deeper; a large pit had a mouth of 2.7m diametre expanding to 4.6m at the base with a depth of about 4 m. One can even see the marks of long celts left during digging. Post-holes around the mouth of these pits must have been used to cover it with a roof thatched with birch and hay whose charred remains have actually been found from such pits. Incidentally, Burzahom in Kashmiri language means the place of birch. Does the name carry the memory of birch-thatched roofs all over the place? Alcoves were dug into the walls of the pits; the walls were plastered with mud. In one case, an arched corridor connected two adjacent pits. Charcoal, ash, potsherds, etc., were found from these pits. From some of these pits irregularly dressed conical stones 1 to 1.5m long and 20 to 40cm wide were discovered, though their use is not clear. There were steps cut into the walls to go down into the dwelling pits.

The squarish pits were shallower, compared to the circular ones, with an average depth of 1 m. There were depressions running all around at the bottom of the pits with post-holes at the four corners. The stone ovens were made in the centre of such pits, as well as over ground. There were refuse pits on the surface. It is, therefore, obvious that they also lived on the surface whenever the climate was favourable. The number of the squarish pits is larger towards north of the megaliths and of the circular pits on the south. Deeper pits must have been used during winters when the valley becomes snowbound. The shallow pits could have been used during summers, as suggested by Rajnath Kaw (1979).

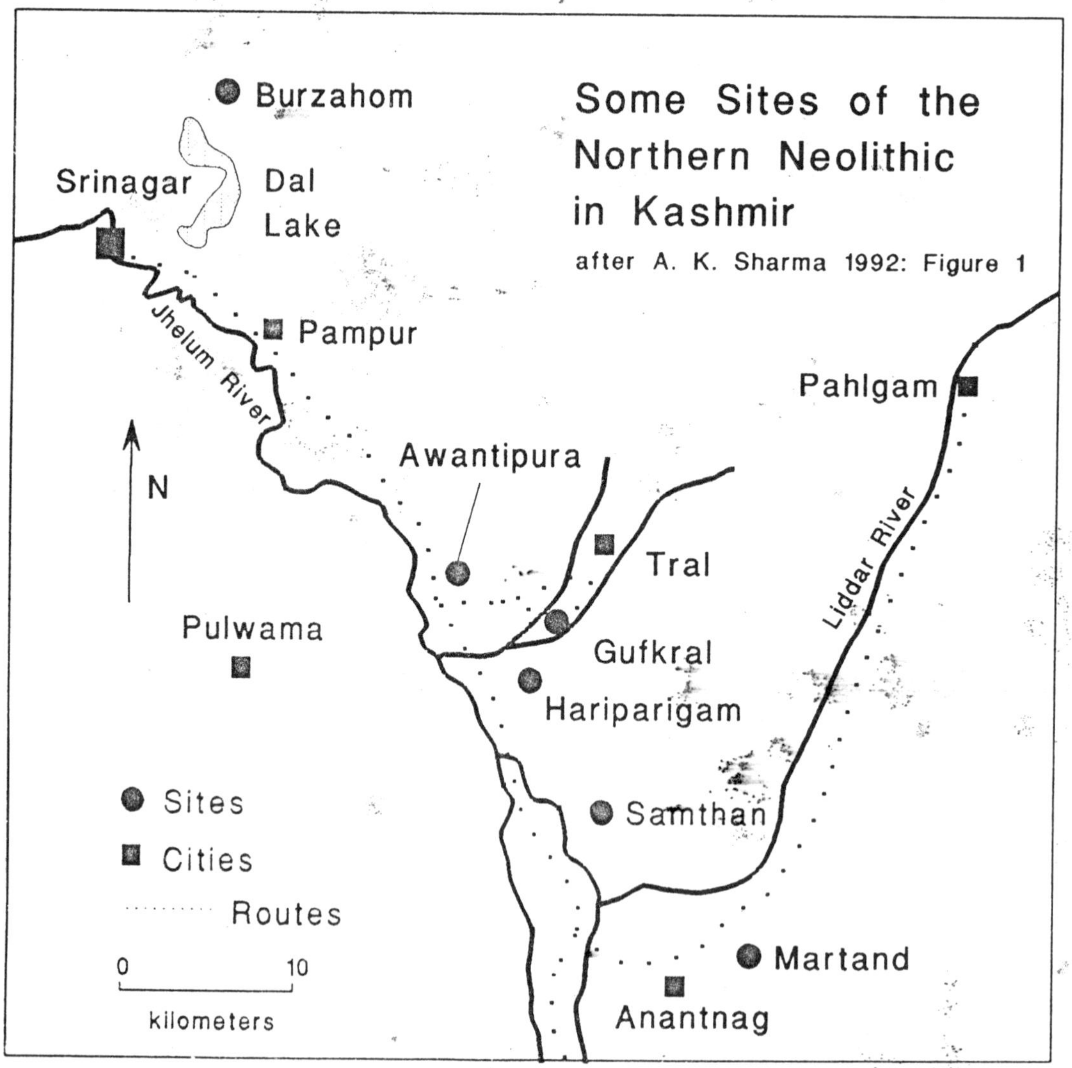

Fig. 6-2. Neolithic sites of Kashmir (after Possehl 1999)

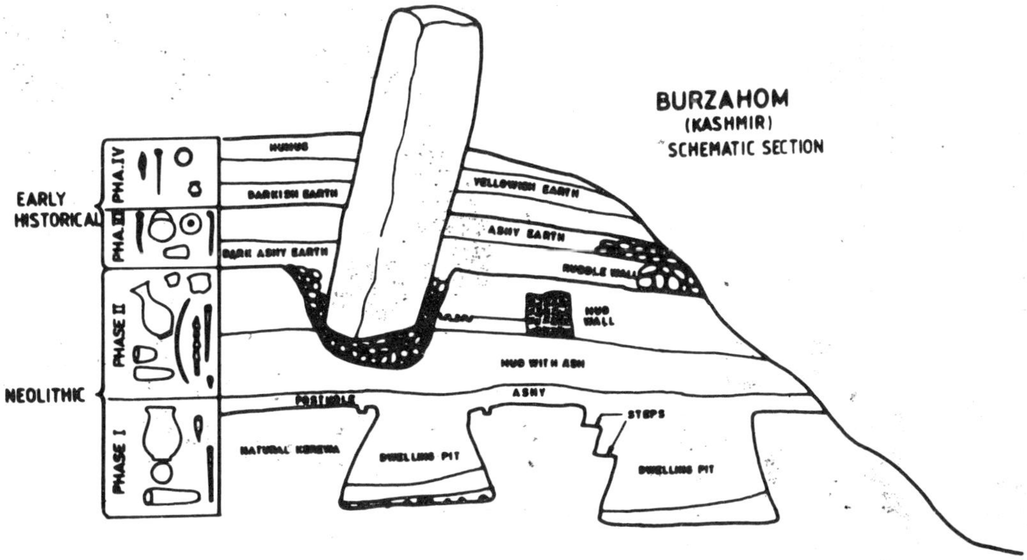

Fig. 6-3. Schematic section of Burzahom excavations, Kashmir, showing the cultural sequence

A variety of ground stone tools were used by these Neolithic people, e.g., polished axes, harvesters, pounders, polishers, chisels and mace-heads (Pl. 6-4). The harvesters are rectangular stone knives with two or more holes on the blunt side. This type is not found anywhere in India but only in the north Chinese Neolithic sites. Stone querns and grinders have also been reported. The bone tool industry of Burzahom is unique and most developed of all the Neolithic cultures of India (Fig. 6-4). It comprises harpoons, needles, awls, spear-points, arrow-heads, daggers and scrapers.

The Neolithic potters of Burzahom made graceful pots though they did not know the use of wheel. They were made by a coiling technique. Sixteen pots were made over mats, as is indicated by a variety of weaving patterns impressed on the bottoms of the pots, and were occasionally decorated with incised and notched designs. Colour-range varied from steel-grey to brown.

The earlier dwelling pits were given up in Period II. In fact, they were filled, rammed and sprinkled with red ochre and used as floors for their mud and mud-brick houses. Occasionally, rubble structures are also encountered. Mud platforms, with partitions in them, hearths and oval pits are found inside these homes. Ubiquitous post-holes suggest that they supported thatched roofs. In Period II, 45 well arranged postholes were seen in an area of 3.96 x 1.21m at a depth of 2.31m below the surface and probably it could be a community structure. Several successive floors were also noticed.

From one of the houses was found a rectangular structure made of upright stones and filled with sand. One of the stones from this structure bore a painting depicting a hunting scene. Another stone from the same house had a tectiform design. In stone and bone industries there is continuity from Period I, though now the tools are better finished and larger in number. A solitary copper arrow-head is reported from the upper levels.

Pottery is still handmade though new shapes and a burnished black ware make their appearance in Period II. Shapes comprise dishes with hollow stand, globular pots, jars, stems

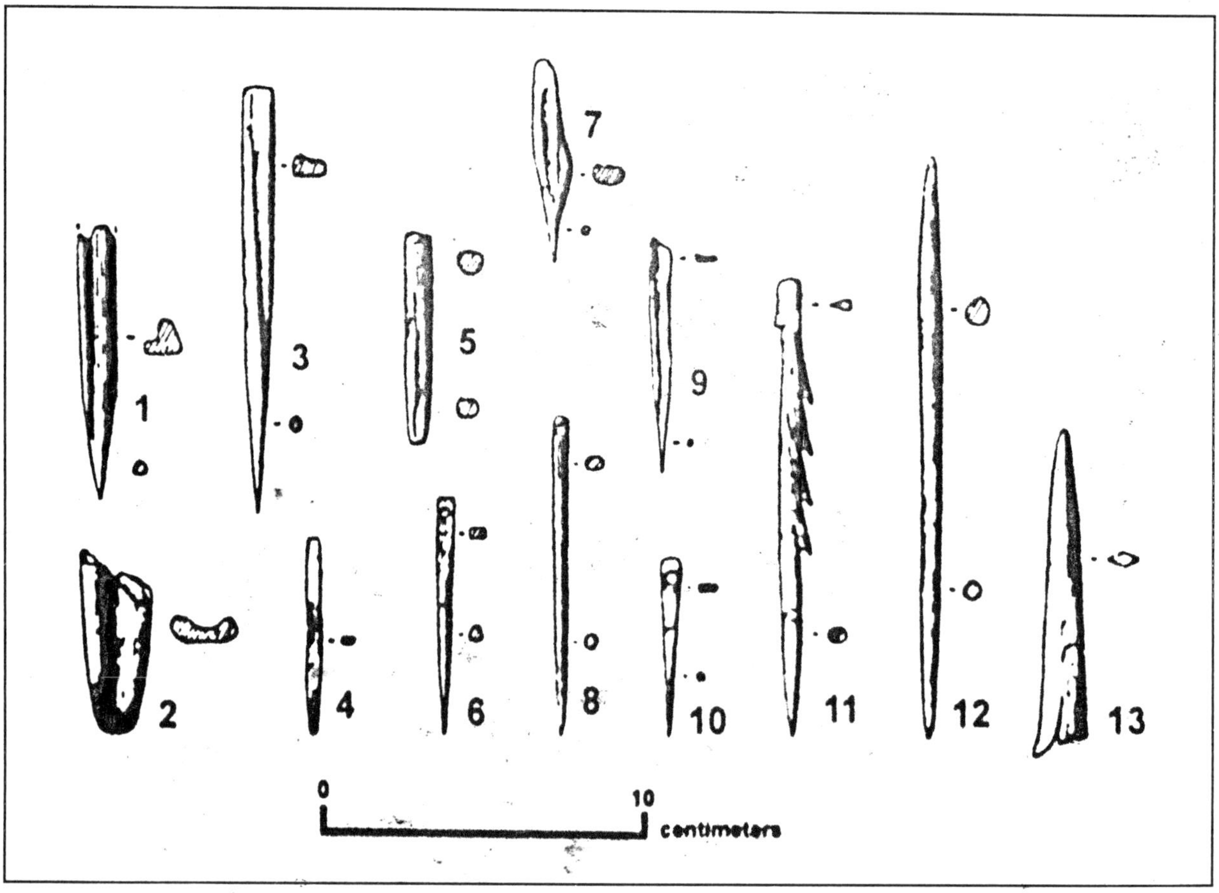

Fig. 6-4. Bone tools from Burzahom excavations, Kashmir

with triangular perforation and a funnel-shaped vase. In the burnished black ware a graceful type is a high-necked jar with a globular body. Towards the close of this period was found a wheel-made red-ware pot containing 950 beads of agate and carnelian. A few painted pots have also been discovered and are likely to be imports. More interesting is a globular pot with a horned deity painted on its shoulders (Fig. 6-5). It has almost an exact parallel in Kot Diji and also in Gumla. This indicates some contact with the Indus and the Baluchi cultures.

Burzahom Period IB yielded two broken stone pieces with engravings. One piece depicts a hunting scene in which a stag with antlers is being attacked both from the rear and front. The hunter from the rear is attacking the animal with a long spear while his counterpart in the front is attacking with an arrow. The upper portion of the slab depicts two circles with emanating rays and a dog-like animal. The circle may represent the sun. The engraving on the other slab, though incomplete, depicts a hut and the hind portion of an animal. It is interesting to note that both the pieces were obtained from one and the same structure.

Excavations at Burzahom have furnished interesting data regarding the burial practices prevalent in Phase II. These burials were found mostly within the settlement. Grave pits, oval in outline, were dug out either in the house floors or compounds. The sides of the adult graves were found plastered with lime. Both primary and secondary burials were practised, the former containing the skeletal remains in articulated position while in the latter only selected bones were buried. Red ochre has been found sprinkled over the human bones. In secondary burials, bones were excarnated by desiccation and interred, sometimes in a heap. In the primary burials, except for one solitary example, no red ochre treatment was given. Primary burials (flexed

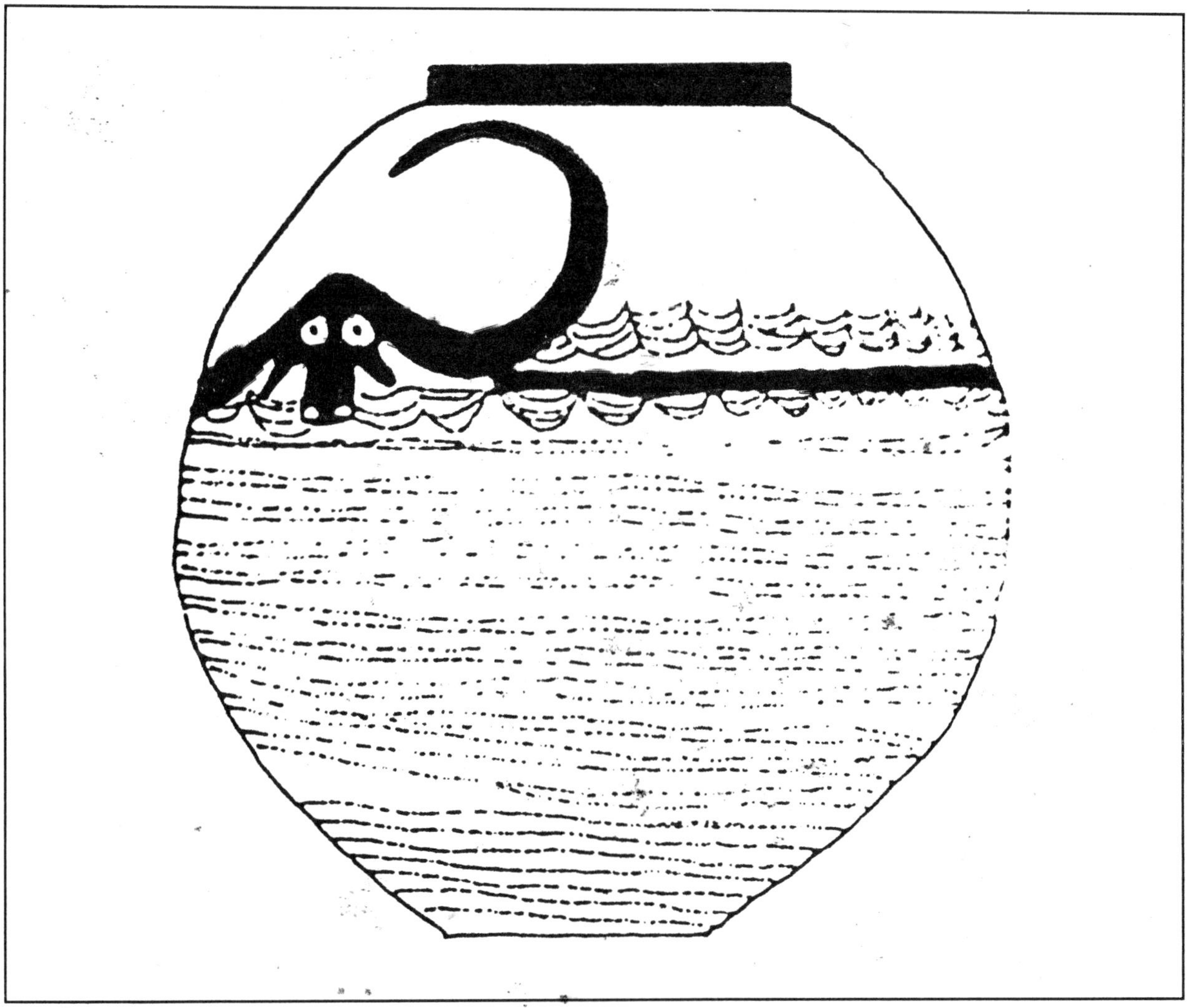

Fig. 6-5. A large red ware jar with a horned deity, painted in Kot Diji style, Burzahom, Kashmir

burials) of both children and adults were placed in a crouched, embryonic position. Skulls were placed either along a north-east or south-east direction. There were no grave goods, except for the occasional beads, which were worn by the dead. At times animal bones, generally of dogs, are also found in the graves, which may indicate a practice of burying the pets with their masters. In one skull, four finished and three unfinished holes show the practice of trepanning. A remarkable practice was that of providing regular burials to animals. In one case five dogs were buried with antler. The other animal graves are of ibex, wolf and dog.

Without any stratigraphic break, the Neolithic culture ushered in Period III. Many cultural traits continue from the previous periods. Wheel-made pottery and the use of copper and even iron are evidenced. The most remarkable feature of this period is the erection of half-a-dozen massive stones (menhirs) in a semicircular fashion. Though a burial has been found below one of the menhirs, they do not contain any regular sepulchres. Burial practices otherwise are similar to those of Period II. In one case five pots were placed with the skeleton. Many grave pits of Periods II and III were dug with a narrow mouth and a wider base, in the style of the dwelling pits. A few structures of mud, a rubble wall and post-holes depict their building activity.

Plant remains

Buth and Kaw (1985) report cereals like wheat and barley *(Hordeum vulgare)*, pulses *(Lens culinaris)* from Burzahom. Charred wood pieces of *Pinus, Betula utilis, Salix* and *Ulmus* have been found from the excavations. A variety of wild plants and weeds were also identified, e.g., *Lithospermum arvense, Medicago denticulata, Lotus corniculatus, Avenafatua* (wild oat), etc.

It is interesting to note that in the pollen profiles done by Dodia *et al.* (1985) for the Anchar lake they report pollen grains (*Cerealia* type and *Plantago*) from mid-Holocene levels, which is a good indication of domestication of plants and presence of humans at this time in the valley. The climatic conditions appear to be optimal and represent the hypsithermal warming of the valley. In the loess sequences also the last soil starts developing c. 5000 BP. It is therefore clear that the Neolithic in Kashmir also represents warming up of the climate from the cooler oscillation of the early Holocene.

Gufkral

Excavation at Gufkral has brought to light five periods of occupation right from aceramic Neolithic to Historical Period (A.K. Sharma 1982). There was an aceramic Neolithic period before pottery was introduced. As the earliest ^{14}C date for Period IB is 3980±120 BP, the aceramic Neolithic period at Gufkral is likely to go back by 400 to 500 years earlier. It is in this period that process of domestication of selected species of animals was attempted. People had also recognised the food value of various grains like wheat and barley and had started collecting them. Bone and stone tools were manufactured. People lived in open and in pits, i.e. hut with their bottom sunk into the loessic deposits, in order to protect themselves from freezing winds. They kept the floors tidy and beautiful by painting them with red ochre. Their main occupation however was hunting.

In Period IB handmade ceramic was introduced. The period witnessed the use of jars, bowls, basins, etc. in grey ware and rough dull red ware. There was a change in the settlement pattern. Pits were discarded and mud and rubble walls were constructed. Well-polished bone tools were made. There was a sudden spurt in the domestication of animals.

By Period IC the Neolithic culture had reached the mature stage. Sharma reports that Period IC at the site belongs to the mature phase of Neolithic period and is represented by a 70-80cm thick habitation. In the houses, thick whitish floors with chunam (lime) mixed earth were laid. There was now more variety in wares and in their decoration. A variety of well-polished bone tools were made in large number. People depended less on large stone objects. With the domestication of animals and agriculture fully achieved, hunting activities declined. People now got spare time to manufacture ornaments and also started weaving of woollen cloth. Of special significance is the recovery of a copper hairpin with flattened coiled head from upper levels of this period, similar to one found at Chanhudaro. It may point out to some foreign contacts.

Period II at Gufkral was marked by menhirs. With the menhir phase came to the site, wheel-made dull red ware, vessels with channelled spouts, copper objects, spindle whorls with medium sized holes, rice and millet. The bone tools industry declined but bone handles were manufactured. Period III represents the historical phase with the introduction of iron and wheel-made thin bright red ware having jars, bowls, cups-on-stand and lid-cum-bowls. Stamped designs and black-on-red paintings were introduced.

One season's limited dig at Gufkral has filled some of the gaps in the cultural sequence of Kashmir and has definitely pushed back the antiquity of the Neolithic culture in the valley. As the earliest ^{14}C date for Period IB is 1850 BC (calib.), the aceramic Neolithic period at Gufkral is likely to go back by 400 to 500 years earlier.

During the aceramic Phase I A, the subsistence economy of the Neolithic people appears to have been based on farming, stock-raising and hunting. Bones of red deer, ibex, bear, sheep, goat, cattle, wolf and Kashmir stag have been obtained. Of these, sheep and goat were domesticated; wheat, barley and lentils were cultivated. People lived in underground pits, circular or rectangular in plan. Oval or squarish pits were also occasionally met with. The natural loessic soil, locally known as karewa, was cut into for obtaining these pits. The floors of these pits were often painted in red ochre. Along the periphery of the mouths of these pits the presence of post-holes was noticed, suggesting that the pits used to be covered overhead. This was necessary for protecting the inhabitants from rain and winter storms. The non-occurrence of hearths inside the pits indicates that they were used only for living in. Evidence of plastered floors, hearths and shallower pits was also recorded in the close proximity of these pits. Of these, the shallower pits with floors painted in red ochre were probably used as storage bins.

The Neolithic people of Kashmir during the aceramic phase used tools and weapons fashioned on bone and stone. As these are found in various stages of manufacture, their local production is self-evident. Of the bone tools found from the sites mention may be made of points, needles, harpoons and scrapers. The stone tool assemblage made on Himalayan trap comprised axes, drills, picks, points, pestles, pounders, querns and rings tones (mace-heads?). The available evidence suggests that the bone tools were prepared out of the bones of goat, sheep and stag.

In sub-period IB also people used to live in artificial subterranean pits. Thick floors composed of clay mixed with chunam, storage pits and hearths were also recorded. This sub-period also saw the introduction of handmade pottery. The ceramic assemblage comprised three principal fabrics - thick coarse grey ware, fine grey ware, and gritty dull red ware, the first one being predominant. The main pottery types included globular jars, bowls and basins. Bowls and basins are characterised by ring or disc bases, often with a mat impression. The other decorative motifs included pinched designs in the neck and reed impressions.

The available evidence suggests that hunting still played an important role in their life and through it the Neolithic people augmented their food supply. Though sheep, goat and cattle were domesticated by now, the presence of wild variety is also indicated. Besides bones of fowl all the animals of Period IA were also hunted during this phase, indicating their use in the menu. A short-horned variety of cattle is also found in this phase. Presence of bones of dogs in appreciable number suggests that this animal was also domesticated during this period. Besides domesticating of animals, the people also cultivated wheat, barley, lentils and the common pea. In this connection, it may be pointed out that the common pea was a new item, which appears to have been introduced during this period.

From this period also a sizable number of bone and stone tools have been obtained. The bone tools repertoire included harpoons, needles (with or without eyes), awls, spears, and points, fashioned on antlers. The main stone tool comprised axes, chisels, adzes, pounders, and mace-heads (ring stones?), points and picks. A stone quern was also obtained.

The last phase of the Neolithic culture of Kashmir, IC (Pd. II of Khazanchi), exhibits both continuity and change. Underground pit and chamber dwelling was abandoned; overground dwelling units made of mud or brick or both are unearthed. Besides sheep, goat and cattle, bones of pig and fish have also been found. Domestication of pig during this phase adds a new element in the Neolithic economy of the Kashmir valley. Bones of horse, hedgehog, rodents, and beaver have also been obtained.

Among the cultivated grains pertaining to this period mention may be made of wheat, barley, lentils and common pea as in Period IB.

Stone objects, though less prolific in comparison with the preceding period, include celts, points, querns, pounders, balls, double-holed harvesters, spindle-whorls and stone engravers.

One of the double-holed harvesters was marked with incised decoration on one side. Potters for removing extra clay while finally shaping a pot used the stone engraver, according to A.K. Sharma (1982).

Bone tools, as in the other two phases, were still much in demand. These are, however, better finished than their counterparts of the earlier periods. Of the important tools, mention may be made of points, arrow-heads, awls, spatulas and harpoons. A bone object with four incised grooves was also obtained. Other finds of this period included terracotta bangles, cowry-shells and a comma-shaped pendant of light-green jade.

The ceramic assemblage of the period comprised grey ware, burnished grey ware, rough and thick dull red ware, along with the introduction of wheel thrown black burnished ware. A few examples of red gritty ware were also obtained. Besides the pottery types of the earlier period, long-necked jars and dishes-on-stand with triangular perforated designs on the stem region were the new types available in this period. The potters of the period thus exhibited their aesthetic sense on their pottery. Decoration comprised mat and cord-impressed bases, reed impressions to create the roughened surfaces of grey and dull red wares pinched designs and incised oblique designs on the neck region of the wheel-made black burnished ware. From this phase of Gufkral, a sherd bearing graffiti was also obtained. From the corresponding phase of Burzahom a few painted pots, probably imported, were also found. From the end of the Neolithic phase at Burzahom, a wheel-thrown red ware pot containing beads fashioned out of agate and carnelian, with excellent workmanship, was obtained. Another wheel-thrown red ware painted pot was found depicted with a horned figure. This pot might have been an import from the Kot-Diji phase of Sarai Khola. The beads of agate and carnelian are also out of context with the Neolithic phase. The occurrence of a few copper arrow-heads, a ring, bangles and a pin in this phase are also intrusive, as these do not fit in the Neolithic context in the Kashmir valley.

Burzahom and Gufkral both have furnished evidence of the Neolithic culture succeeded by the Iron Age culture. The aceramic phase of Gufkral was not found at Burzahom, therefore, Period IB of Gufkral should be bracketed with Period I of Burzahom and Period II with IB of Gufkral. For computing the chronology of the Neolithic culture of Kashmir, both the excavated sites have furnished a few ^{14}C dates, which are given in Table 6.5. According to Possehl and Rissman, the aceramic phase may be placed within the time-bracket of 2800 to 2520 BC and the IB phase of Gufkral and Period I of Burzahom within the time-bracket of 2520-2000 BC. The final phase of the Kashmir Neolithic, i.e., IC of Gufkral and Period II of Burzahom, are assigned to the 2000-1500 BC bracket.

TABLE 6.5 ^{14}C DATES OF NEOLITHIC SITES OF KASHMIR (after Possehl 1994)
All BP ages are based on 5568 yr half-life of radiocarbon. Calibrated ages are given in bc.

Site	*Sample No.*	*5568 Yrs.BP*	*Calib. Dates*	*Culture*	*Material*
Burzahom	TF-123	4055±110BP	2586 cal.bc	Period IA Neolithic	Charcoal
Burzahom	TF-13	3690±125BP	2130,2074, 2045 cal.bc	Period IA Neolithic	Charcoal
Burzahom	TF-127	3935±110BP	2465 cal.bc	Period IB Neolithic	Charcoal
Burzahom	TF-14	3860±340BP	2343 cal.bc	Neolithic	Charcoal
Burzahom	TF-129	3670±90BP	2114,2086, 2039 cal.bc	Neolithic	Charcoal

Cont. Table 6.5

Site	*Sample No.*	*5568 Yrs.BP*	*Calib. Dates*	*Culture*	*Material*
Burzahom	TF-15	3390±105BP	1730,1729, 1689 cal.bc	Period IB Neolithic	Burnt Organic Material
Burzahom	TF-10	2580±100BP	797 cal.bc	Neolithic	Charcoal
Burzahom	TF-128	4205±115BP	2881,2797, 2783 cal.bc	Period IB Neolithic	Charcoal
Gufkral	BS-359	3864±115BP	2347 cal.bc	Period IB Neolithic	Wood Charcoal
Gufkral	BS-356	3466±105BP	1860,1847, 1770 cal.bc	Period IB, Neolithic	Wood Charcoal
Gufkral	BS-370	2709±105BP	842 cal.bc	Period IC, Neolithic	Wood Charcoal
Gufkral	BS-371	3466±95BP	1860,1847, 1770 cal.bc	Period IC, Neolithic	Wood Charcoal
Gufkral	BS-358	3039±105BP	1313 cal.bc	Period IA, Aceramic Neolithic	Wood Charcoal
Gufkral	BS-360	3243±95BP	1519 cal.bc	Period IC, Neolithic	Wood Charcoal
Gufkral	BS-357	3369±105BP	1681 cal.bc	IB Period Neolithic	Wood Charcoal

Cultural Correlations

Burzahom has some affinities with Sarai Khola (near Taxila) and Ghalighai in the Swat valley. The handmade pottery, burnished wares, bone and stone artifacts recall parallels from Burzahom.

The Italian Archaeological Mission carried out excavations in the Swat valley from 1961to1968 under the leadership of G. Tucci. G. Stacul (1987) has worked out a general sequence of cultures in this valley, which was expressed in terms of Ghalighai periods. He finds close similarity in shapes and decoration of the handmade pottery of Ghalighai Period with Burzahom Period I. But at Ghalighai the stone tools are chipped and not polished like those of Burzahom. Stacul personally examined the wares from Burzahom and finds remarkable similarities in the burnished black wares of the Swat valley Period IV and Burzahom II. Polished stone tools also are common between the two periods.

Pande (1970) has pointed out that the tradition of dwelling pits is known from the Neolithic cultures of USSR, China and Japan. Particularly, the practice of burying dogs with their masters and the use of perforated stone knives are characteristic traits of the north Chinese Neolithic culture. The burial practices as also the tool repertoire of the Burzahom Neolithic are closer to north Chinese rather than to the other Neolithic cultures of India.

Ror, Baroli and Dehra Gopipur form a group of Neolithic sites in Kangra district of Himachal Pradesh. The industry comprises axes, chisels and ring stones made of soft shale. These are surface collections and are found mixed up with pebble choppers and flakes. Affinities of this group have been traced to the Burzahom Neolithic. But pebble tools are found in a Neolithic milieu only in Tajikistan where three types of Neolithic cultures flourished. In Keltminar culture pottery and stone tools were associated but it was a hunting economy. In Djetun culture agriculture was also known. But in Hissar culture 70% of the tools comprise the pebble industry and Gupta therefore compares the Kangra Neolithic with the Hissar culture (c. 7000-5000 BP) and states that the amount of parallelism that exists between the Hissar culture of the Tadjik depression (southern Tadjikistan) and the Kangra valley Neolithic culture is a clue to appreciate the characteristics of a Neolithic culture in one of the mountainous zones of this part of the world (1979:30).

Rajasthan

More than anything else, Rajasthan is famous for its Thar desert. In fact, the climatically arid region of Rajasthan extends into the present states of Gujarat and Punjab also. The antiquity and origin of the Thar desert and its lost rivers have attracted the attention of the scholars of different disciplines since last century (Oldham 1893). The old name for the desert, west of the Aravalli range is Marwar, meaning place of death. When there are consecutive drought years, it can turn into a place of death even today, though conditions here have not been as severe as in Sahara. For miles around, the area appears flat or gently undulating. The land surface varies from hard bedrock, to compact alluvium to sand sheets and dunes.

Holocene climatic changes in Rajasthan have been discussed in Chapter 2, in relation to the decline of the Harappa culture.

A large number of Mesolithic sites have been recorded by Misra and other scholars (see Chapter 4) from western and eastern Rajasthan particulary in the Berach-Banas basin (Misra 1967) and along the river Luni respectively. In fact, the sand-dunes of western Rajasthan are even dotted with Mesolithic sites. Few important ones like Bagor (lat. 25° 21' N. long. 74° 23' E), Tilwara, Didwana and others were excavated by Misra in 1970s and 1980s. Bagor is one of the important excavated Mesolithic sites by Misra in Bhilwara district. Bagor (Phase I) has yieldeda large number of animal bones and stone-paved floors, with a strong indication of domestication of sheep, goat and cattle. People perhaps lived on nicely built stone-paved floors protected by wattle-and-daub huts. Though the subsistence was by and large based on hunting-gathering yet this kind of change is very important for tracing the beginning of domestication and agriculture in Rajasthan. Phase II is marked by the introduction of copper/bronze tools and handmade pottery, though microliths continue but they are on decline. There is evidence of agriculture at this stage. In the Phase III microliths and animal bones become scarce and iron tools, wheel-made pottery, glass beads and brick structure appeared. The site represents basically a single culture undergoing evolution through time by the appearance of new material traits and decline or disappearance of others (Misra 1971: 237-90). The excavator thinks that the last phase might have continued up to the beginning of the Christian era. All these phases have revealed burials within the settlement. In the case of the earliest burials of Bagor nothing concrete has been stated about the offerings, but in the second phase earthen pots, ornaments, metal objects and animal limbs were found in association with the burials. The method of disposal of dead varied from phase to phase at the site. On the basis of available radiocarbon dates Bagor has been stated as a late Mesolithic site. The excavator brackets the entire deposit between the middle of third millennium BC and the middle of first millennium BC (Misra 1973:107-8) (see for details Chapter 4).

Gujarat

Like Rajasthan not much is known about the early farming Mesolithic–Neolithic cultures of Gujarat too. In recent years M.S. University, however, has carried out studies in northern Gujarat and other areas. A number of Mesolithic sites have been recorded particularly from north Gujarat, where they underlie the Anarta culture (Sonawane and Ajit Prasad 1994). In fact, the contribution of Chalcolithic cultures of Gujarat regarding the beginning of agriculture and domestication and in the civilisational process of Harappans in Gujarat has yet to be properly understood. Here at the moment we can only give a reference of Langhnaj, a well-known site, in northern Gujarat.

Langhnaj

The site of Langhnaj (lat. 23° 27" N, long. 72° 32"E) is situated at a distance of 59 km from Ahmedabad, almost to its north. The site yielded microliths, 14 human skeletal remains, animal bones and other cultural material (see for details Chapter 4). Varied patterns of disposal of the dead have been found at the site and we do not know if these departures suggest that the buried person belonged to a certain community following a different burial ritual. Male, female and child burials represent the human burials. In case of some burials all the human bones were not found placed in their natural positions and in some cases few bones were missing. The height of these skeletons was found ranging between 158 and 174cm. Some of them having dolichocephalic (Ehrhardt and Kennedy 1965:43) skull with cranial capacity ranging from 1183 cc. (skeleton I) to 1430 c. c. (skeleton IV) compare well with the Vedda skull whereas others with the average male skulls of Europe. Thus it is quite likely that racial mixture in India had become an accomplished fact as early as the third millennium BC, if not earlier (Ehrhardt and Kennedy 1965:44). Langhnaj has also been a debatable topic as far as the dates are concerned because really not much datable material was found. Sankalia dated the Mesolithic phase on the basis of typo-technological consideration prior to 2500 BC (Sankalia 1965: 18).

Paul Rissman (1986: 257-77) has made some very interesting observations on the pastoral mobility of the site Oriyo Timbo. We have included it here though he has discussed his findings in the Harappan context. He says that the site of Oriyo Timbo, displayed indications of temporary pastoral settlement in its lack of solid architecture, thin deposit, location in a non-agricultural zone, and abundance of animal bones, but other evidence complicated this interpretation. A seasonal determination of the deaths of archaeological zebu cattle was attempted via microscopic examination of annual rings in tooth cementum. Annular analysis revealed a clustered pattern of deaths during the dry season months of March to June. These data suggest that Oriyo was a dry season cattle camp associated with more sedentary occupations in nearby areas (Rissman 1986: 257-77).

Rissman states that in view of the erratic and scanty rainfall in Saurashtra, pastoral migration may have represented a major safety valve for Harappan cultivators. In years of poor rainfall cattle would be utilised as a mobile productive resource, the only one that could accompany a human population to more congenial surroundings until it could return to its land. One might further postulate that the importance of cattle as a mediator of agricultural risk meant that opportunities for nomadism were continually present in Harappan Gujarat. Cattle managers normally try to keep larger herds than is necessary for subsistence, partially to guard against disastrous losses from unforeseen calamities. Under these conditions herd size is prone to grow past the threshold at which all of the animals can be kept in the vicinity of a single settlement. The desire of the herd owner to personally manage his stock, combined with the need for large numbers of animals, can thus lead to increases in mobility, or nomadism.

Rissman thus concludes that seasonal aspects of man-cattle interaction can be identified in Bronze Age South Asia. He thinks that annular analysis is indispensable in this regard, and that migratory herding can be hypothesised to have great importance in the Harappan tradition in Gujarat. Annular analysis is not only useful in South Asian archaeology, but is widely applicable to pastoral sites in other regions and other times, as dental remains of herd animals are generally abundant at these types of settlements.

Now we will have a look at the early farming cultures of the Ganga valley and the Vindhyas.

NEOLITHIC CULTURES OF GANGA VALLEY AND VINDHYAS

We feel that the early stages of ceramic industry, plant and animal domestication in the Vindhyas and the Ganga valley have not received as much attention as they deserve, hence we have given it a more detailed treatment. We admit that the chronology requires a more thorough effort, so also detailed archaeobotanical and zooarchaeological investigations. We also feel that if there is some relationship between the origins of rice agriculture in North India and the spread of rice technology from south China, with the movement of Mon-Khmer speaking people, Ganga valley and the Vindhyas with their cord-impressed pottery do present the possibility of an appreciably early beginning of rice technology in this area. Unlike the North-west where wheat and barley were the main cereals, here in the Northern-Central India (mainly the Vindhyas and the Ganga valley), we have to trace the history of rice as that was the earliest cereal there.

Rice (*Oryza sativa*) is the most popular cereal in South Asia today. Wild rice, *Oryza rufipogon* is pan-tropical in distribution and found generally in the Ganga valley, Indus river system and in Gujarat. The archaeological record in India suggests that hunting and gathering peoples there used the wild form. When rice came under cultivation is not yet known for definite, though Possehl thinks that a date preceding the Mature Harappan cannot be supported given the present evidence. Domesticated rice often grows close to stands of the wild plant, offering abundant opportunities for hybridisation (Possehl 1999c:246).

Possehl (1999c: 246) reports that the earliest abundant use of domesticated rice in the subcontinent comes from Pirak, which begins c.1800BC. Rice at Mahagara and Koldihwa has been said to date to the seventh and sixth millennium BC (Sharma *et al.* 1980:23), but these dates are controversial. There are four calibrated radiocarbon determinations for the Mahagara Neolithic which range between c.1700-1200BC, concordant with the chronology of Pirak I. It should be noted that an uncalibrated ^{14}C date for the pre-Neolithic Mahagara is 8080+115 BC (Sharma *et al.* 1980:3). Possehl thinks that Koldihwa ^{14}C dates (PRL-100, PRL-101 and PRL-224) could be aberrations and it is more likely that they are indications of an earlier, unreported occupation at the site (Possehl 1999c). We, however, think that rice domestication in this area should go to early Holocene period.

Let us first have a look at the archaeozoological evidence.

Animal bones

We quote here the views of Thomas & Joglekar (1994:182-84) on the Mesolithic faunal remains. They observe that :

> The Mesolithic of India represents a cultural phase critical to our wider understanding of Holocene fauna. This phase is transitional between the 'hunting-gathering' and 'food production' patterns of subsistence. A large number of Mesolithic sites have been reported from several parts of India, where the Mesolithic folk inhabited previously colonised habitats as well as new areas (Misra 1989). However, there are only very few stratified Mesolithic sites such as Bagor and Tilwara (Rajasthan), Langhnaj (Gujarat), Adamgarh (Madhya Pradesh) and Damdama, Sarai-Nahar-Rai and Mahadaha (Uttar Pradesh). Only these have been considered in the following discussion. It is also to be remembered that the radiocarbon dates for the Mesolithic sites show a considerable variation, e.g. Chopani Mando has three dates 6570 ± 210, 5440 ± 240 and 4530 ± 185 BC (Misra 1989), while the youngest date from Langhnaj is 3875 ± 105 BP (Agrawal and Kusumgar 1968). Thus it is imperative that we understand that when considering Mesolithic fauna we are dealing with a period covering several thousands of years....The Mesolithic stage is also crucial from the point of view of the history of domestic animals, because it is in this period that most of them were domesticated....The Mesolithic sites in the Ganga valley like Damdama, Sarai-Nahar-Rai, Mahadaha, etc. have provided us with interesting, faunal material. Studies of this material reveal that a majority of these sites fall into the

hunting-gathering group (Thomas *et al.* in press). At these sites, Alur (1980) had identified bones of domestic animals. However, the fauna when re-analysed reveals not a single bone of any domestic animal among the thousands of bone fragments (Thomas *et al.* in press). Alur's identification (1980) of domestic species at these sites, e.g. Damdama and Sarai-Nahar-Rai is not convincing and therefore not included here....The fauna of these Ganga valley sites have revealed the presence of large mammals such as *Bos* sp. (perhaps wild cattle), gaur, wild buffalo, elephant and rhinoceros. Hippopotamus has also been identified at Sarai-Nahar-Rai by Alur (1980). In general the bones of these animals do not indicate that such large animals were actually hunted and perhaps the bones were collected for some other purpose (Thomas *et al.* in press). Mesolithic hunters are known to have exploited several species of deer (chital, sambar, barasingha), blackbuck, gaselle and nilgai. The range of wild mammals at these Ganga valley sites suggests a wide spectrum indicative of hunting-gathering groups exploiting all possible natural resources.

The sites of Bagor (Rajasthan) and Adamgarh (Madhya Pradesh), however, have provided evidence of domesticated animals (Thomas 1975). That the economy at Bagor was based on stock-rearing has been established beyond doubt, since at this site the faunal material was systematically collected and the radiocarbon dates are also reliable. At Adamgarh, the picture is very different. The radiocarbon dates from this site are insecure, the stratigraphy is unclear and the faunal material identified by Nath (1967) appears to be of a much later date than the Mesolithic period....Langhnaj in Gujarat has yielded very interesting evidence. This site had a hunting-gathering culture contemporary with sites of the Mature Harappan phase. The animals at Langhnaj include rhinoceros, pig, chital, hog deer, barasingha, nilgai, blackbuck, mongoose and wolf, of which the last two were not used for food (Clutton-Brock 1965). The list also includes an undetermined species of bovines, which may have been wild cattle. An estimate of the height of these animals at the withers is about 1.6 in and falls within the range of auroch measurements (Joglekar 1993-94), and the presence of wild cattle has now been established (Joglekar and Thomas 1992).... The fauna at Langhnaj is only of wild species and yet is of a relatively later date - 2550-2185 BC (calibrated: Misra 1989). On the other hand, in the contiguous states of Rajasthan and Madhya Pradesh sites have revealed full-fledged domestic faunal wealth much earlier than that of Langhnaj.

The period covering five or six millennia before the advent of the Harappan culture must have witnessed a slow but steady shift from the early hunting-gathering to animal domestication. However, an accurate picture of the fauna of this period is not available. Even if we consider the evidence of well dated rock art, the faunal picture of the Mesolithic period remains incomplete for want of a greater number of stratified sites with faunal assemblages (Thomas & Joglekar 1994:182-84 and references therein).

Indrani Chattopadhyaya (2000a) has also reported on the archaeozoological evidence:

Four classes (with the *Phylum Chordata*), namely Mammalia, Reptilia, Pieces and Aves are represented in the faunal assemblages of the excavated sites. All the species identified are wild. Besides, some invertebrates like Gastropods and Bivalvia are also present. The mammalian assemblages at Mahadaha and Warikalan-Damdama are dominated by the remains of deer, particularly swamp deer (*Cervus duvauceli*), hog deer (*Axis porcinus*) and spotted deer (*Axis axis*). The remains of *Cervus unicolor* and *Muntiacus muntjac* occur infrequently. Other taxa identified are *Rhinoceros unicornis, Elephas maximus, Equus* cf. *namadicus, Sus scrofa*, antelopes like *Boselaphus tragocamelus, Antelope cervicapra* and *Cazella gazelle*, large bovids, such as *Bos namadicus, Bos* (*bibos*) *gaurus* and *Bubulus arnee*, a few species of carnivores, and rodents. Some species of tortoise (*Chitra indicus, Trionyx gangeticus*, etc.), fish and birds complete the vertebrate assemblage. Figure 4 (in IC 2000A) presents the variation of Niche Width with Resource diversity at the three sites, which suggests a generalised or broad-spectrum economy for Mahadaha and Damdama, characteristic of a hunting society (see Christenson 1980 for details of the argument)....Absolute ageing of swamp deer and hog deer molars, using Klein's method (Klein and Cruz-Uribe 1984), helps not only in understanding the mortality profiles of these animals but also in addressing the problem of seasonality of site's occupation. The data analysis from Mahadaha shows that both these animals were killed year round, though the peak seasons of their respective cullinos were different (Fig. 5). The faunal evidence thus suggests residential stability, as opposed to residential mobility, at Mahadaha. This is further supported by the occurrence of rodent remains (*Batidicota bengalensis*) from both Mahadaha and Warikalan-Damdama (Chattopadhyaya 1990).

Despite the inadequacy of archaeozoological evidence, it is clear that the Ganga valley shows more of a hunting-gathering subsistence pattern than Rajasthan, and therefore an earlier phase.

V.D. Misra (1999b) has recently come out with a succinct summary of Mesolithic and Neolithic cultures of the Ganga valley and the Vindhyas. In fact, he and J.N. Pal have been associated with the excavations of these sites for several years now and we know a good deal about these cultures through their writings (V.D. Misra 1977, 1999b; Pal 1986). The following summary bases itself mainly on the reports of the Allahabad University group.

The research carried out by the University of Allahabad in the Belan and Son valleys of the south-eastern Vindhyan area covering parts of Uttar Pradesh and Madhya Pradesh, has placed these cultures in their geological sequence and chronological horizons. They suggest that Neolithic culture evolved out of the Mesolithic. In this respect, the archaeological evidence from Chopani Mando, Koldihwa and Mahagara is very significant.

The Vindhyas are dotted with Mesolithic sites as over 200 sites have been recorded and about the same number in the Ganga valley too. In the Vindhyas, microliths have been obtained either in open-air settlements or in rock shelters. The occurrence of microliths in the Ganga valley has been noticed on the old banks of the Ganga, the Bhagar, on or near horseshoe lakes. The wide distribution of Mesolithic sites both in the Vindhyas and the Ganga valley clearly indicates a substantial growth in human population, which indicates agricultural subsistence. In the Gangetic plains, the earliest evidence of man pertains to this period. The sites of Lekhahia, Baghai-Khor, Morhana Pahar (Mirzapur), Chopani Mando in Allahabad, Bhadaliwal (Varanasi) are located in the hilly tract of Uttar Pradesh. Sarai-Nahar-Rai, Mahadaha and Damdama are the excavated sites of the Ganga valley. Baghai-Khor, Morahana IV, Lekhahia I and II, Ghagharia and Bhimbetka are rock shelters; the others are open-air settlements.

Mesolithic deposits often exceed a metre in depth. For example, at Morahana it is 1.13 m; at Lekhahia 1.07m; at Chopani Mando 1.53m; at Mahadaha 0.6m; and at Warikalan-Damdama it is 1.5m.This clearly shows that sedentary life had started with the Mesolithic phase. Stone-paved floors and wattle-and-daub have been obtained from Baghor. At Bhimbetka (MP) floors made of flat stone slabs and a wall of stone boulders measuring 6m in length were found. Excavations at Chopani Mando, Baghor II in the Vindhyas and Sarai-Nahar-Rai and Warikalan-Damdama in the Ganga valley have also exposed some structures. At Chopani Mando, 20 huts were exposed: two belong to Phase II A, five to II B and the rest to Phase III and at Baghor II, three huts. The periphery of these huts was marked by post-holes while on the floors were found scattered large numbers of sandstone fragments, microliths, animal-bone fragments and burnt-clay lumps with reed impressions. At Warikalan-Damdama circular or semicircular burnt-plaster floors were exposed. Often these floors have multiple layers of burnt-plaster floors, which might have been used as living areas as well as for roasting animals, as is evident from the charred animal bones on such floors.

These floors also served as workshops as indicated by the microliths and bone objects found in different stages of manufacture. The Microlithic types are: scrapers, points, borers, blades, blunted backs, lunates, and, occasionally, triangles and trapezes, along with flakes, cores and debitage. They used quartz, chert, chalcedony, agate, carnelian, etc for their tools. From the excavations in this area the sequence can be delineated (see Table 6.6).

TABLE: 6.6 STAGES OF DEVELOPMENT OF MICROLITHIC CULTURES

Phase I:	Non-geometric, pre-pottery, locally patinated.
Phase II:	Geometric tools, triangle alone, without pottery.
Phase III:	Geometric tools, triangle and trapeze microliths with pottery.
Phase IV:	Geometric and diminutive tools with hand-made pottery.

Chopani Mando, Sarai-Nahar-Rai, Mahadaha and Warikalan-Damdama excavations exposed several pit-hearths divisible into two groups: simple, shallow pit-hearths and hearths with clay plaster on side walls or bottom or both. At Warikalan-Damdama as many as 32 hearths, circular or oblong in plan were opened. These contained charred and semi-charred animal bones, burnt clay lumps and blackish soil resembling ash. The available evidence from the hearths clearly indicates that Mesolithic folk used to roast meat before eating it. Adamgarh, Langhnaj, Baghor, Sarai-Nahar-Rai, Mahadaha and Warikalan-Damdama have yielded animal bones, which include *Bos indicus, Bos bubalus, Bos gaurus*, antelope, deer, pig, sheep, goat, *equus*, rhinoceros, etc. Bones of turtle, fish and birds were also found at the Mesolithic sites of the Ganga valley. Birds and fish were obviously hunted. The animal bones from Langhnaj, Sarai-Nahar-Rai, Mahadaha and Warikalan-Damdama belonged to the wild species, while from Adamgarh and Baghor domestication of animals is indicated. At Adamgarh, the domestic animals include dog, zebu, buffalo, goat, sheep and pig. At Baghor the domesticated bones comprise sheep, goat and cattle. This is the earliest evidence of domestication of animals in India and would suggest that the Mesolithic people at these sites were not only hunters but also practiced stock raising.

It seems that raw material for manufacturing microliths was brought often from distant places as at Baghor II, Medhauli and Banki in the Son valley and Mahadaha and Wari Kalan, Warikalan-Damdama in the Ganga valley. The Son valley sites are situated south of the Kaimur, which provided sandstone and quartzite. At the Mesolithic sites of Mahadaha and Warikalan-Damdama in the Ganga valley also sandstone and quartzite fragments are found in profusion which could have come from the Vindhyan area. These Mesolithic sites have yielded fragments of querns, mullers, hammer stones, anvils, anvil-cum-hammer stones, ring stones and sharpeners fashioned on sandstone or quartzite. The abundant occurrence of querns and mullers at these sites suggests that food gathering had a significant role. In this connection the finding of wild rice (*Oryza sativa*) from the late Mesolithic phase at Chopani Mando is of considerable importance (Possehl (1999c) however thinks that it was a different specie, *Oryza rufipogon*, as noted above).

Chopani-Mando is situated on Terrace T2 of the old channel of the river Belan, 77km from Allahabad, UP. The remains of charred or carbonised rice were found embedded in lumps of burnt clay. These remains have been dated to the ninth–eighth millennia BC. They probably represent wild variety of rice (Sharma *et al.* 1980: 23, 69). This occurrence of wild rice is important in the context of reported domesticated rice from the Neolithic levels at Koldihawa and Mahagara in the same region. Rice, jujube and bamboo are the main botanical remains. The remains comprised seeds without pericarp, impressions of caryopsis, stalk, glume and probably also spikelets and are found both as loose grains and also embedded in potsherds (Sharma *et al.* 1980:182). The remains have been identified as domesticated *Oryza sativa* (Sharma *et al.* 1980: 23).

The main Mesolithic industry however comprises microliths characterised by cores, flakes, debitage and finished tools. They used hammer stones, anvils, sharpeners, querns and mullers made of quartzite and sandstone to shape their tools (see Chapter 4). Ring stones have been reported from Langhnaj, Bhimbetka, Baghai-Khor, Chopani Mando, Baghor II, Banki and Medhauli. The Mesolithic sites of the Ganga valley have yielded bone arrow-heads, both long and small, but in the Vindhyas bone tools are rare.

The Mesolithic people made a variety of ornaments like beads, earrings and necklaces. Beads of semi-precious stones are reported from Adamgarh and Bhimbetka while Mahadaha and Warikalan-Damdama have yielded beads and earrings made of bone. Mahadaha has yielded valuable information regarding the process of manufacture of bone ornaments.

The rock-shelters in the hilly areas of Madhya Pradesh and southern Uttar Pradesh generally bear paintings on their walls or ceilings or both. The floors of these rock-shelters are often found littered with microliths and some have even yielded human burials. V.D. Misra (1999b) thinks that though the paintings in the rock-shelters cover a long duration of time, the majority have been executed by the Mesolithic people. A large number of scenes in these shelters depict food gathering activity (see Chapter 5).

Koldihwa (lat. 24°, 54', 30" N, long. 82°, 2' E) is a small village situated about 80 km to the south-east of Allahabad on the left bank of the river Belan. The excavations revealed that on the western mound occupation started in the Chalcolithic phase, while on the eastern and southern mounds it could be traced back to the Neolithic period. In the following pages an attempt is made to bring out the salient features of different cultures of Koldihwa, as gleaned from the excavations, of the three mounds.

The Neolithic deposit of Koldihwa was characterised by a corded ware of thick fabric, the plain red ware and the crude black-and-red ware - all handmade. Straw and rice husk were used as degraissant. The corded ware predominated the ceramic assemblage. The functional types are shallow or deep, straight sided and lipped bowls, basins, vases with broad mouth and carinated neck, deep troughs, storage jars and vessels with tubular spouts. The Neolithic pottery of the site is devoid of paintings. Decoration is limited to corded patterns and incisions. The incised motifs consist of criss-cross, zigzag, oblique, horizontal or vertical parallel lines.

The tool repertoire comprises rounded celts with flat sides and rectangular cross-sections and microliths. The microliths made of chert, chalcedony, agate, carnelian, jasper and quartz include cores, flakes and finished tools consisting of parallel-sided blades, blunted blades and scrapers. A few fragmentary animal bones were also found.

Rice husk has been found embedded in a number of potsherds. Vishnu-Mittre thought that these sherds contain imprints of rice of domesticated variety. Two uncalibrated dates PRL-100, 5440±240 BC and PRL-101, 4330±185 BC date the Neolithic horizon, though Possehl thinks that these dates are aberrations. Querns and mullers may also indicate that the people had started cultivating cereals. At the moment, however, typological evidence of pottery and stone tools is not definitive to date this site. Occurrence of burnt clay pieces with wattle and daub impressions was noticed. Mahagara excavations have brought to light the oval or circular huts.

The excavations at Koldihwa, specially of the western mound, have brought to light 33 circular or oblong pits of varying dimensions. Discarded material of day-to-day life was thrown in them. The diametres of the circular pits range from 1.26 to 4 m, and the depth varies from 50cm to 1.16 m. But stratigraphically these kitchen-middens have been ascribed to the Iron Age.

A comparative study of the Neolithic finds of Koldihwa and Chirand furnishes interesting reading. Microliths and rounded neoliths have been obtained from both the sites. Ill-fired black-and-red ware and types like vases and bowls are common to both the sites. Spouted vessels have also been found at both the places. However, comparison ends at this point; corded ware, an essential feature of the Neolithic Koldihwa, is absent at Chirand. The latter site has furnished evidence of post-firing painting in red ochre colour on grey, black-and-red and red wares, but the ceramic industry of the former site is devoid of painting. The excavations at Chirand have produced a corpus of bone and antler implements from the Neolithic strata, but from Koldihwa no bone implement was found. The terracottas of humped bull, bird and Nilgai figurines, which have been reported from Chirand, have no counterparts at Koldihwa. Viewed against the Neolithic Chirand, Koldihwa looks more archaic.

We may now refer to Chattopadhyaya's (1990:113) observations on subsistence and settlement patterns in the Vindhyas and the Ganges valley. He thinks that following the climatic change in the region from the cold and dry of the terminal Pleistocene to the warm and humid of the Holocene, the evidence for major environmental change is very strong. It is quite likely that the Holocene conditions favoured an increase in forest cover, and hence an increase in size of the populations of the various species of deer. In that case, the Mesolithic populations of the Vindhyas would have had a broad spectrum economy. Unless one finds adequate faunal samples from Mesolithic sites of the Vindhyas, any comparison between the economies of the two regions during the early/mid Holocene times would be premature. He says:

> The available evidence from the Ganges valley thus tends to favour a semi-sedentary settlement pattern, as defined by Binford, rather than a fully sedentary one. But the question that still evades a solution is why the Ganges valley populations adopted this somewhat unexpected pattern of semi-sedentism, rather than the nomadic pattern which local environmental conditions should theoretically have favoured.
>
> Chattopadhyaya gives the following sequence for this region: (1) the Epi-Palaeolithic, (2) the aceramic, non-geometric Microlithic, (3) the aceramic, geometric Microlithic and (4) the diminutive Microlithic with pottery. This sequence has been observed at a number of sites in the Vindhyas-Chopani-Mando, Lekhahia and Baghai-Khor, for example - in clear stratigraphic contexts. The four-fold developmental sequence of the Microlithic industry in the area under study has been understood by previous workers in a purely 'evolutionary' sense. In contrast to the late Mesolithic phases at many Vindhyan sites, evidence of pottery from any of the Ganges valley sites is conspicuous by its absence (Chattopadhyaya 1990).

He further observes that the evidence from both the Ganges valley and the Vindhyas suggests that, in spite of a possibly wide range of economic activities, these societies organised themselves at much simpler levels of technology and with less developed storage facilities than those of the higher latitudes.

On the basis of the fact that both scalene and isosceles triangles have more recently been found at Baghor I, a late Upper Palaeolithic site in the Son as also the fact that geometric forms, such as triangles and trapezes, are by no means numerous even at large excavated Mesolithic sites, Chattopadhyaya makes significant observations: (a) that categories like 'early' non-geometric and 'late' geometric phases are misleading and (2) that if one discovers within a stratigraphic sequence a sudden shift from non-geometric to geometric forms, it is not necessarily because such a change was the result of 'evolution' in tool technology. Strata with geometric tools have, in general, produced a greater range of tool types, as at Chopani-Mando (Sharma *et al.* 1980). So the possibility that these strata represent a wider range of activities than the preceding ones or even within-site craft specialisation cannot be ruled out.

Chattopadhyaya notes that the relatively large sizes of the two sites (above 8,000 sq. m for Mahadaha and 8,750 sqm for Warikalan-Damdama) do suggest a large population. The second phase of human occupation in the Ganges valley, the Mesolithic, includes the so-called non-geometric and geometric Microlithic sites. A total of 194 such sites are distributed within an area of 12,702 sq. km. Chattopadhyaya suggests that most of the Mesolithic sites of the Ganges valley should perhaps be considered as part of a residentially stable settlement system, centering on more permanent home bases, near the lakes.

Regarding the exchange he believes that perhaps stones were procured through the mechanism of balanced reciprocity (barter) or generalised reciprocity (an open access system). The Ganges societies, in either case, were economically dependent upon resources from the

Vindhyas. That the Vindhyan groups would have benefited materially and socially from such transactions, is perhaps also true. He also suggests that ecological complementarity would have enhanced the chances of survival of various kinds of traditional groups in India over the millennia.

Chattopadhyaya, however, suggests that the possibility for an early rise of animal husbandry in the Vindhyas cannot be denied, but maintains that the archaeological importance of North-Central India does not rest on the antiquity of its agricultural developments, as has been so vigorously argued (Sharma *et al.* 1980). The Vindhyas and the Ganges valley present, instead, an important example of the distinctive nature of the cultural adaptation, and the process of population diversification and cladogenetic mode of evolution experienced by the people of the subcontinent over the millennia (Chattopadhyaya 1990).

In the Indian subcontinent, the earliest human burials discovered so far, belong to the Mesolithic phase. Carlleyle (in V.A. Smith 1906: 187) had excavated several prehistoric grave-mounds in the Mirzapur district of Uttar Pradesh. It is interesting to note that Carlleyle did not find a single bit of metal either in the mounds or in the caves. The general description of Carlleyle gives the impression that the burials in question belonged to the Mesolithic phase, a point which has been confirmed by the excavations of Baghai-Khor (Varma 1965:73-74) and Lekhahia (G.R. Sharma 1980:77-78) rock-shelters where the human skeletons have been found along with microliths.

Indrani Chattopadhyaya (2000a) has drawn some interesting inferences from the Mesolithic burial data. As far as the ornamentation of the dead is concerned there are three categories of bone and antler ornaments: (i) pendants and necklaces, (ii) earrings and (iii) rings. The interesting thing to be noted here is that males are mostly associated with first two categories of ornaments while females are associated, if at all, with the third category. The ornamentation pattern indicates social asymmetry between and within sexes, on the one hand, and social position, social affiliation and possible ranking, on the other. In all the burials the body orientation shows a remarkably consistent west-east or east-west pattern (in all such descriptions, the direction given first suggests the direction of the head). Having said this, it has to be mentioned that there is a significant range of variation within this cardinal direction. The plausible basis for this pattern seems to be the direction of the sun (Tylor, 1871; Randsborg and Nybo 1 986:161-84). Over the centuries, due to gravitational perturbation, there is a variation of solar movement across the horizon between summer and winter solstices (*Astronomical Almanac*, 1988, preface). This range for Mahadaha (Latitude 25° 59' 10" N), for example, has been calculated to be 54° for the epoch ca. 8300 BC (the earliest date for the Mesolithic settlement in the region). For the epoch 6000 BC the range has been calculated to be 56° (Chattopadhyaya and Chattopadhyaya 1990). The present day range is 52°40'. This means that around 8300 BC sunrise during the summer and winter solstices would have occurred at angles of 63° and 117° from the azimuth, respectively. Similarly, sunset during the summer and winter solstices would have occurred at angles of 297°and 243°. At all the three excavated sites angles of grave orientation measured from the azimuth generally fall within the above range (Fig. 6). The conclusions we reached are: (a) Sarai-Nahar-Rai had a seasonal pattern of occupation in either the summer or the winter half, and (b) the normal distributions at Mahadaha and Warikalan-Damdama suggest a year-round pattern of occupation at the sites. This analysis further supports the faunal evidence for residential stability at Mahadaha. Population concentration was higher during autumn/ spring as greater number of graves are aligned close to solar paths around the equinoxes. Grave orientations in relation to solar variation suggest that the sites of Mahadaha and Warikalan-Damdama were logistically organised and residentially stable (Chattopadhyaya, 1991:111-12).

V.D. Misra (1977, 1999b) has given a summary of the evidence of Mesolithic burials. He reports that the Mesolithic people practised three modes of burials: extended, flexed and fractional. The practice of extended burials in shallow oblong graves was most common. The skeletons are generally found lying in a supine position. Extended burials are reported from Dorothy Deep, Jambudvipa, Baghai-Khor and Lekhahia rock-shelters, Baghor I, Sarai-Nahar-Rai, Mahadaha and Warikalan-Damdama. One burial at Langhnaj also falls into this category. The graves have generally yielded skeletal remains of single individuals, male, female, adult or child. The Mesolithic sites of the Ganga valley have graves with double or even multiple burials. At Sarai-Nahar-Rai one grave had two males and two females. Mahadaha and Warikalan-Damdama also had double, even triple burials.

Skeletons of bodies buried in a flexed position have been found at Langhnaj and Lekhahia RS-1. At Langhnaj, with one exception, all the skeletons were found in flexed position. At Lekhahia only skeleton IV furnished this type of evidence. Evidence of fractional burials has been obtained from Bhimbetka and Langhnaj. Langhnaj burials yield microliths, animal bones and beads. At Lekhahia RS-1, animal bones and mollusk shells have been reported. From burials at Mahadaha and Warikalan-Damdama bone arrow-heads, beads, pendants, etc. have been obtained from a number of graves. At Mahadaha one skeleton wears bone pendants and a necklace of boneheads. Erhardt found that the Langhnaj skeletons indicated traits characteristic of Mediterranids and Veddids, but also betrayed mixed features. The skeletons exposed at the Mesolithic sites of the Ganga valley represented dolicocephalic people who were fairly tall with sturdy and a well-built physique.

The Mesolithic burial practices thus show that the head was placed at a higher plane as found at Dorothy Deep Cave, Baghai-Khor and Lekhahia. The extended burials of Baghai-Khor, Lekhahia, Baghor and Sarai-Nahar-Rai, are oriented west-east, with the head to the west. But the flexed burials of Langhnaj and Baghor Phase II are east-west oriented with the head lying to the east which may indicate ethnic differences. Cases of partial or secondary burials have been found only at Langhnaj and Bhimbetka. It seems that a variety of objects were offered to the dead. All the burials without exception have been found in the area of settlement. The area of the dead and the area of the living were not demarcated. Olecranon perforation has been observed in the skeleton XIV of Langhnaj, skeleton X of Sarai-Nahar-Rai and in a number of cases in Lekhahia specimens. Evidence of caries comes forth from Langhnaj, Lekhahia and Sarai-Nahar-Rai. Longevity at Langhnaj is more pronounced.

Thus, it is quite likely that the burial practice of Neolithic period is more or less a continuation of Mesolithic trend. It will be quite interesting if we could point out identical characteristic features of the Mesolithic and Neolithic burials in respective regions.

Mesolithic-Neolithic Pottery from Vindhyas

About the pottery from the Mesolithic sites of southern Uttar Pradesh Morhana Pahar, Baghai-Khor, Lekhahia and Chopani Mando, Pal (1986: 159-69) notes that they have yielded handmade pottery in the late Mesolithic phase of their cultural deposit. The cultural assemblage of this phase indicates that the economy was based on hunting and food gathering. The use of querns and mullers demonstrates that grain formed a part of their diet. This inference is also supported by the remains of wild rice in the burnt clay lumps found at Chopani Mando. On the basis of the evidence of querns and mullers and pottery, tool technology, settlement pattern, floral and faunal remains (including wild grains), Pal thinks that the phase of Mesolithic culture at the above-mentioned sites may better be characterised as proto-Neolithic. Pal further notes that shallow and deep bowls and small-sized jars mark this ceramic industry. As there are no big storage vessels and cooking handis, he reasonably infers that the need of storing and cooking collected cereals was yet to arise. The pots are made of non-levigated clay, are ill fired and devoid of any surface treatment, though a few pots are decorated with incised and impressed designs.

Oblique lines making angles, horizontal or vertical lines, squares, criss-cross, irregular dot incision, etc., are the incised motifs. The impressed designs are divisible into two groups: (1) designs made by the impression of tortoise-shell and (2) designs made by impressing some engraved dabber. The first group of the impressed design is represented at almost all the excavated sites but the second group is confined only to Chopani Mando and Lekhahia. The decoration by impressing tortoise-shell is significant in as much as it continues into the succeeding Neolithic culture of the area as one of its characteristic marks. He thinks that all these primitive features mark the beginning of pottery tradition in the Vindhyan region.

It is worth notice that these Vindhyan Mesolithic sites with pottery present a stark contrast to the Mesolithic sites of the Ganga valley, which are marked by a total absence of pottery traditions. The non-pottery character of the Mesolithic cultures of the Ganga valley however does not necessarily establish their antiquity over the Vindhyan Mesolithic.

The Neolithic pottery, like that of the advanced Mesolithic, is handmade and consists of four wares: (1) cord impressed ware, (2) rusticated ware, (3) burnished red ware, and (4) burnished black ware. Rice husk, straw, chaff, etc., were used as tempering material. The pots are ill-fired, of coarse fabric with section varying from thick to medium. In case of the burnished red and burnished black wares cow-dung and husk of millet were used as tempering material. Shallow and deep bowls, platters or flat bowls, spouted bowls, basins, handis and jars are the functional pottery types. Basins and handis, sometimes with soot marks, are the cooking vessels. The Neolithic pottery continues the earlier Mesolithic tradition of incised decorations, applique designs and a total absence of painting.

The Neolithic ceramic industry, especially the Cord Impressed Ware, enjoys a wide distribution in the northern Vindhyan plateau. It has been obtained from Koldihwa, Mahagara and Pachoh in the Belan valley, Indari and Baraunha in the Adwa valley and Kunjhun and Lalnahia in the Son valley. This characteristic ware of the Vindhyan region is also found at Sohgaura, Lahuradewa, Chirand and Chechar Kutubpur in the middle Ganga valley. Not only the technique of manufacture but also the functional pottery types are common to the Neolithic phase of the Vindhyas and the middle Ganga valley. But the Neolithic pottery of the middle Ganga valley appears to be more advanced as compared to that of the Vindhyas, in view of a few turntable thrown pots and post-firing paintings in the pottery assemblage.

Everywhere in the early Neolithic cultures simple pottery types are found. It can be asserted that simple pottery types are so common that left alone they hardly constitute the regional personality of the Neolithic pottery. This is perhaps the reason why there is no significant regional variation in this respect. Though the cord impressed Ware has been found at Daojali Hading and Sarutaru in Assam, it differs in colour and in the range of decorative patterns from that of the Vindhyas. It is interesting to note that the shouldered celts mark Assam Neolithic assemblage, whereas the stone blade industry characterises the Vindhyan Neolithic.

It may be noted here that cord impressed pottery is reported very widely, from Siberia to Japan to Southeast Asia. In Japan the cord impressed pottery is associated with Jomon culture and has now been dated back to 12000 BP (Nakamura pers. comm), also from various parts of China and the island of Taiwan (Chang 1970), and from Southeast Asia at Spirit Cave (Gorman 1970a: 79-107) and Non-Nok-Tha (Bayard 1970: 109-43) in Thailand as early as sixth millennium BC.

Pal does note that the cord impressed pottery of the Vindhyan Neolithic culture seems to show an appreciable similarity in ornamentation and also in general technique of manufacture with that of the above-mentioned sites abroad. If this similarity is not due to the basic simplicity of Neolithic techniques of decoration and manufacture, we would suggest its worthwhile tracing its links with the movement of early rice technology and the Mon-Khmer speaking people. As mentioned in Chapter 7 (Agrawal 1999a), it is also found in the Central Himalayan region where early rice technology and a Mon-Khmer residue in the Kumauni dialects have been noticed by the linguists. Of course, Pal (1986) pleads for an indigenous origin of the Neolithic pottery in this region.

As noted by Pal, many pottery traits of the Neolithic phase survived in the Chalcolithic cultures of the area. There seems to be a cultural continuity from the Neolithic to the Chalcolithic cultures. The slip treatment on the red slipped and on the black slipped wares of the Chalcolithic period evolved out of the burnished red ware and burnished black ware of Neolithic period respectively. Rustication on the outer surface of red ware may also be treated as a survival of the Neolithic rusticated ware. Applique decoration is also a Neolithic trait, which continued in the Chalcolithic period. Many of the pottery shapes of Neolithic culture survived in the same or slightly modified form in the Chalcolithic period, though spouted vessels are conspicuous by their absence in the Chalcolithic period (Pal 1986).

TABLE 6.7 NEOLITHIC SITE OF GANGETIC DOAB

(Early Agriculture – Gangetic Doab and Eastern India) All BP ages are based on 5568 yr half-life of radiocarbon. Calibrated ages are given in bc/ad (after Possehl 1994).

Site	*Sample No.*	*5568 Yrs. BP*	*Calib. Dates*	*Culture*	*Material*
Chirand	TF-1032	3600±150BP	1961 cal.bc	Period I, Neolithic	Charcoal
Chirand	TF-446	1930±105BP	72 cal.ad	NBP	Charcoal
Chirand	TF-1035	3125±100BP	1418 cal.bc	Period I, Neolithic	Charcoal
Chirand	TF-1031	3525±135BP	1884 cal.bc	Period I,Neolithic	Charcoal
Chirand	TF-1126	2290±120BP	391 cal.bc	Period I, Neolithic	Charcoal
Chirand	TF-1125	3365±150BP	1679 cal.bc	Period I, Neolithic	Charcoal
Chirand	TF-1127	3230±95BP	1516 cal.bc	Period I, Neolithic	Charcoal
Chirand	TF-1034	3420±110BP	1740 cal.bc	Period I, Neolithic	Charcoal
Chirand	TF-1036	2485±120BP	761,681,659 596,633,577, 561 cal.bc	Period I, Neolithic	Charcoal
Chirand	TF-1033	3390±110BP	1730,1729, 1689 cal.bc	Period I, Neolithic	Charcoal
Chirand	TF-334	2715±120BP	890,845, cal.bc	Period I, Neolithic	Charcoal
Chopani Mando	BS-129	4540±110BP	3338,3213, 3203 cal.bc	Period III, Vindhyan Neolithic	Charcoal
Koldihwa	PRL-224	8280±210BP	None	Neolithic ?	Charcoal
Koldihwa	PRL-56	820±100BP	1225 cal.ad	Chalcolithic	Charcoal
Koldihwa	PRL-227	2050±110BP	92 cal.bc	Chalcolithic	Charcoal
Koldihwa	PRL-101	6295±180BP	5240 cal.bc	Neolithic ?	Charcoal

Cont. Table 6.7

Cont. Table 6.7

Site	*Sample No.*	*5568 Yrs. BP*	*Calib. Dates*	*Culture*	*Material*
Koldihwa	PRL-100	7180±230BP	6075,6059, 6043,6018, 6001 cal.bc	Neolithic	Charcoal
Koldihwa	PRL-102	2380±105BP	405 cal.bc	Chalcolithic ?	Charcoal
Koldihwa	PRL-99	2900±150BP	1092 cal.bc	Chalcolithic	Charcoal
Koldihwa	PRL-223	3300±120BP	1607,1554, 1544 cal.bc	Neolithic	Charcoal
Kunjhun River	BETA-6414	4010±110BP	2569,2538, 2503 cal.bc	Vindhyan Neolithic	Unknown
Kunjhun River	BETA-6415	4600±80BP	3360 cal.bc	Vindhyan Neolithic	Unknown
Kunjhun River	BETA-4879	3120±70BP	1414 cal.bc	Vindhyan Neolithic	Unknown
Mahagara	PRL-409	3260±150BP	1523 cal.bc	Neolithic	Charcoal
Mahagara	BS-128	3330±100BP	1628 cal.bc	Neolithic	Charcoal
Mahagara	PRL-407	3300±100BP	1607,1554, 1544 cal.bc	Neolithic	Charcoal

Now we can examine the early farming cultures further east.

EASTERN NEOLITHIC CULTURES

In this zone are included Assam (here the term Assam is used to mean undivided Assam, now divided into seven states, viz. Assam, Arunachal Pradesh, Meghalaya, Nagaland, Manipur, Mizoram and Tripura), Orissa, Bengal and Bihar (Fig. 6-6). There is little documentation of early domestication of plants and animals in this region, so the evidence is mostly confined to artifact types.

Assam

Affinities with East and Southeast Asia have been claimed among the faceted axe, the splayed axe and the shouldered celt found in this region. Assam seems to be ethnically, linguistically and also archaeologically related to Southeast Asia. Unfortunately none of these 'Neolithic' collections from eastern India is yet properly dated. One has to note that Neolithic artefacts found in stratified contexts, e.g., at Sonepur, Pandu Rajar Dhibi, Rajgir, etc., seem to occur in larger numbers only in historical levels. On the other hand, the types mentioned above and the cord impressed pottery connect these Neolithic cultures to Yangshao, Langshanoid of China and Hoabinhian of Thailand, thus pushing back the antiquity of such cultures to the early Holocene. We may also note here that A.K. Sharma has reported stone harvesters and celts of the Kashmir Neolithic type from Sikkim. Recent finds from Spirit Cave, Thailand and Formosa show that some sort of agriculture had started around 10,000 BP, which of course was based on roots, tubers and fruits. In north China, however, cereals received more emphasis and rice domestication seems to go back to 14,000 BP (Yasuda 1999a,b). Now for the earliest Jomon culture ceramics in Japan "the age of 16,500 BP is a calibrated age. The uncalibrated ^{14}C age is 13,780 ± 170 BP.

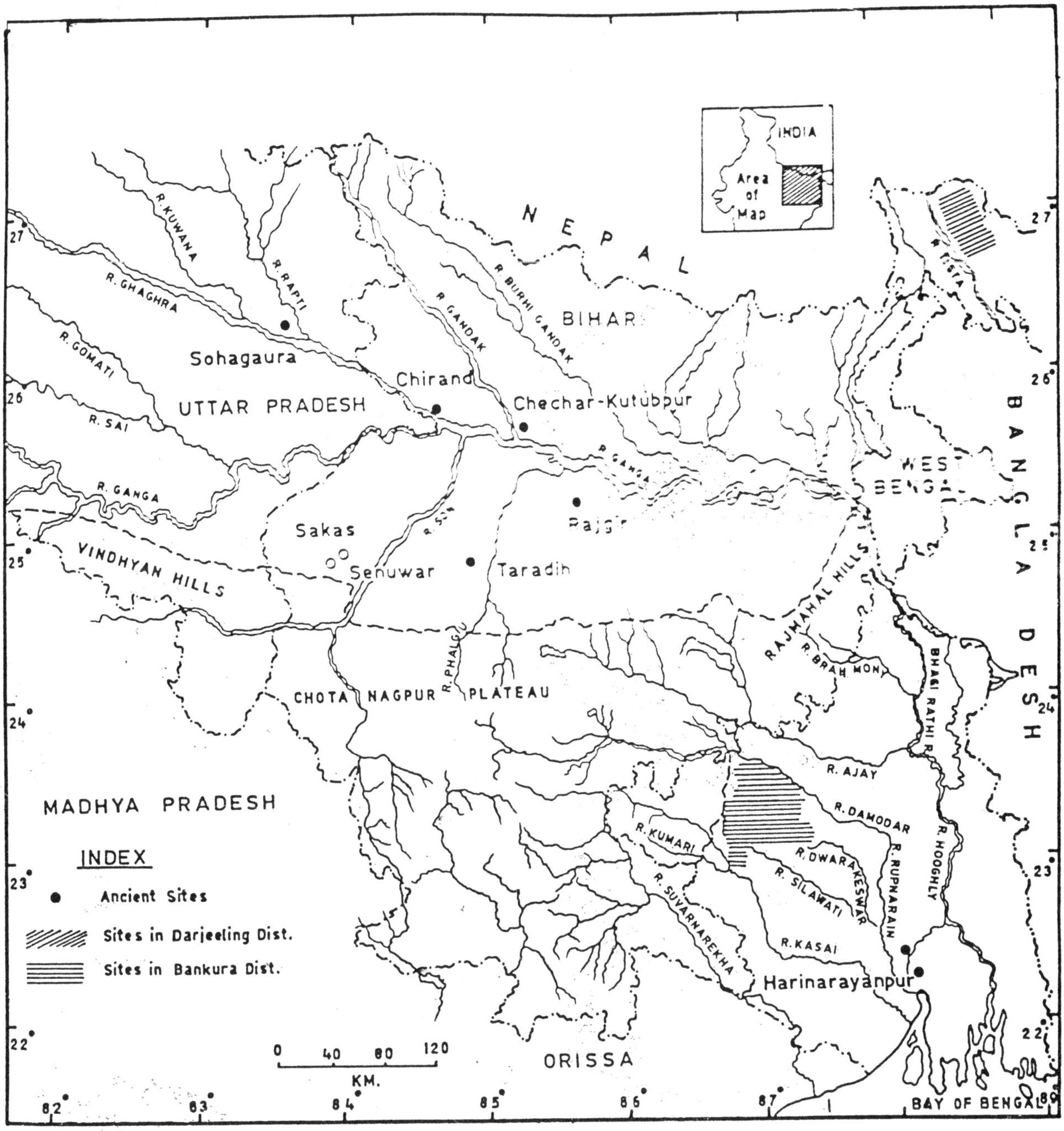

Fig. 6-6: Map showing the Neolithic and Chalcolithic sites in Eastern India

This is the oldest age I have measured on 5 ceramic fragments this time" (T. Nakamura, pers. comm. 1999).

The first jadeite Neolithic tool from upper Assam was reported by Lubbock in 1867. Since then quite a few army men and British tea planters have reported sporadic finds of Neolithic tools from this area; about 400 of these artifacts are now housed in the Pitt rivers Museum, Oxford. Mutton (quoted in Dani 1960) classified these neoliths into triangular, rectangular and shouldered celts, splayed-edged axes, round butt axes, wedges, grooved hammer stones and faceted tools. In Dani's classification (1960) he divided Assam into six divisions. Krishnaswami

(1962), however, held that two traditions could be discerned on a technological basis. The first used chipping and flaking techniques while the second used edge-grinding, polishing and even sawing. The second tradition, he thought, derived inspiration from Malaysia and Indochina. T.C. Sharma has done an exhaustive study of this problem and used several parametres in his analysis of the tool types. In the absence of excavation, the following account will have to be confined to discoveries of chance finds. T.C. Sharma (1966) groups them into the following regions.

Cachar Hills

The main types found in this area are flat, tanged and quadrangular celts, adzes, chisels, splayed-edged axes, querns, grinding stones and mullers.

Garo Hills

About 1,000 tools made on dyke-basalt were discovered from Ronogram, Tura, Rangchangiri, Chitra Abri, Ronchungra, Rombhagiri, Tura, Phalbariall located on the Arbela range at 600-750m altitude. There are two categories: only chipped and fully-ground tools.

Naga Hills

The tools from this area have been divided into three categories: (i) edge-ground tools; (ii) pecked and ground; and (iii) fully-ground ones. The main types are round-butt axe, wedge-shaped axe, tanged axe, quadrangular axe, rounded chisel and adze. River pebbles were usually used, though occasionally jadeite has also been employed which could have been an import from China/ Burma.

Rami Tetelia, Kamakhya, Loharghat, Sonapur, and Mumati are the main Neolithic sites of the Kamrup district, in the western part of the Brahmaputra valley. The material used was mainly mudstone and shale and occasionally phyllite. From Goalpara district of the same valley, a variety of artifacts have been discovered, e.g., adzes, celts, tanged celts, and rectangular axes. The last type has parallels in the 'Pan Shan Axe' of north-west China. In the northern Darang district of the Brahmaputra valley were found grooved hammer stones, grinding stones, axes, etc., made on slate or porphyrite. The Brahmaputra valley opens in the east into Burma. From Maharkotiya, Lohowal, Barkhamti and Gaon, in this district, were reported tanged and flat celts, chisels, quadrangular axes and some miniature celts made on jadeite.

The Khasi Hills

The Khasi hills form the eastern part of the Assam plateau. Quadrangular, triangular, and also shouldered celts of Southeast Asian type were found from these parts. Besides the stray finds from the Mizo hills and Manipur, Mushi and Abor hills area have produced 18 tools out of which six are made on jadeite and the rest on local rocks.

From a typological study, Worman suggested that the shouldered celt, the barchisel and the splayed-edged axe were intrusive types perhaps derived from China. But Dani has pointed out that in China the round-butted axe, which is common in India though not so common in Assam is associated with adze blades which are rare in India. Faceted axes on jadeite from the Ranchi district have been traced to Yunnan in China. Faceted tools made on local material, have also been reported from Santhal paragana of Bihar, Mayurbhanj in Orissa and Darjeeling in West Bengal. Shouldered axes have been discovered from several sites in Bihar, Orissa and Assam. Because of its wide distribution in Burma, it is considered an import into Assam. The bar-chisels, on the other hand, have resemblance with the Malaysian examples. The splayed-edged axes have a wider distribution and are reported from Burma, Yunnan and Malaysia.

Most of the collections in eastern India are from the surface and therefore cannot be dated. T.C. Sharma (1974), however, excavated Deojali Hading in North Cachar hills of Assam (Pl. 6-5). He has divided the deposits into - starting from below - Hoabinhian, early Neolithic, late Neolithic and Aneolithic.

Neolithic man here lived in mud-walled houses and made Cord-Impressed thick grey ware and thin walled, well-fired red wares. Stone artifacts discovered were small celts, adzes, chisels, shouldered celts, grinding stones, querns, troughs and mullers generally made on shale or sandstone. Previously it was thought that the shouldered axes were cut by wires, but now Sharma has shown that shale and sandstone can be cut by a shell piece or slivers of bamboo and therefore knowledge of metal need not be assumed. Even harder rock like quartzite could first be dressed by flaking. The cultural assemblage at the site has been compared with the late Bacsonian of Southeast Asia having significant influences from Szechwan and Yunnan.

The other site is Sarutaru, excavated by Rao (1977). The site is located on a hillock, 25 km south-east of Gauhati, on the Shillong plateau. This is a high rainfall (300 cm) zone. The site has hardly 40cm of deposit. Nine ground stone axes made on slate or sandstone were found, out of which seven are of a shouldered variety and two with rounded butts. A handmade ill-fired, quartz-mixed pottery was associated with the tools. The colour of the pottery varies from brown, buff to grey. The decoration is cord-impressed.

Marakdola, about a km away from Sarutaru was also excavated by Rao. It revealed a 1 metre thick deposit of Ambari culture marked by a fine, wheel-made kaolin ware. It is significant that terracotta models of stone axes were found from these levels. Ambari culture has been dated from c. AD 700 to 1200, but it may go back to the early centuries of the Christian era. Rao thinks that Ambari culture and Sarutaru Neolithic are contemporary and dates the latter to the beginning of the Christian era. Obviously such late dates for the Sarutaru Neolithic are a far cry from the early Holocene Neolithic dates of Thailand and Formosa.

The corded pottery from Jomon culture of Japan is now ^{14}C dated to 16,000 BC. From Ban Kao, Sorensen (1988) has reported a Neolithic culture dateable to c. 1800 BC. Thus the Southeast Asian evidence also suggests a very early date for the eastern Neolithic of India. But recent excavations by S.N. Rao at Sarutaru and Marakdola in the Shillong plateau show that the Neolithic there may not go beyond even the Christian era.

T.C. Sharma in his Presidential Address (in press) informs us that in 1990, Abdulla A. Ali excavated a very important prehistoric site at Parsi Parlo in Lower Subansiri district, Arunachal Pradesh and exposed (1) a pre-Neolithic Hoabinhian cultural layer without pottery; (2) a Neolithic layer with ground and polished stone tools and pottery; and (3) a ferro-Neolithic layer characterised by a Neolithic assemblage in association with iron.

Sharma further reports that O.K. Singh excavated four Neolithic sites at Napachik, Nongpok, Laimanai and Phunan, where stratified cultural layers yielding Neolithic celts along with microliths and pottery have been unearthed. He obtained a ^{14}C date 4460±120 BP for the Neolithic culture at Nongpok and a TL date 1450 BC for Napachik Neolithic site, thus giving us firm dates of the corded ware Neolithic culture of N.E. India which flourished between c. 2500 and 1500 BC (Singh 1997).

Bihar, Orissa and Bengal

Though the first discovery of a Neolithic tool from Singbhum (Bihar) by Captain Beaching goes back to 1868, to this day the area is not well explored and only a few excavations have been carried out. Surface explorations have indicated the presence of neoliths in the Ranchi district, at Rajor (Patna district) on the Sanjay basin in Manbhum area, and near Chakradharpur. In the hilly region of south Bihar, the Neolithic sites, thus, seem to be confined to high plateaus or terraces, much above the flood plains of the rivers. The Chhota Nagpur plateau extends into the western districts of Bankura, Birbhum, Midnapur and Purulia and forms the western zone of Bengal. The northern zone comprises essentially the hilly Kalimpong area of the Darjeeling district. The main tool types of Bengal are ring stones, shouldered celts, triangular axes and axes with rounded-butt and rectangular section.

Chirand, situated near the confluence of the rivers Ghagra and Ganga (district Saran, Bihar), is another Neolithic site with an identical cultural sequence, to that of Koldihwa, including the Neolithic, the Chalcolithic and the last pertaining to the Iron Age phase. Excavations have revealed a 3.5 metre thick Neolithic horizon. The small Neolithic celts, at least one with rectangular cross-section, hammer stones, balls, pestles and querns made on quartzite, basalt and granite were found. Microliths consisting of parallel sided blades, scrapers, arrow-heads, serrated points, notched blades, points, lunates, borers along with a few geometric shapes made on chalcedony, chert, agate and jasper are also reported. No crested-ridged specimen was obtained. A wide range of bone and antler tools including different types of celts, scrapers, chisels, hammers, needles, points, borers, daggers, shaft-straighteners, pins, styli, arrow-heads (both tanged and socketed) have also come to light.

The pottery is generally hand-made, although a few pots might have been made on turntable also. The wares include reed, grey, black, and black-and-red. Lustrous burnishing on the outer surfaces is also reported. The types consist of vases with broad-mouth and narrow-neck, spouted vases, bowls (lipped, perforated and footed as well), bowls with stands, footed cups, channel spouts and miniature pots. The pots with lower portions rusticated were also found. Decoration consisted of applique patterns and post-firing scratches. A single sherd of rust-impressed pottery is also reported. Post-firing painting in red ochre on grey and rarely on Red and black-and-red wares is another interesting feature of the Neolithic pottery of Chirand. Criss-cross in five lines, concentric semi-circles and wavy lines constitute the painted motifs.

Evidence of circular or semicircular huts has also been noticed. The occurrence of burnt chunks of clay bearing the impression of reed and bamboo indicate that the huts were provided with screen of reed and bamboo, often plastered with mud.

The authors of the Neolithic Chirand practised domestication and cultivation. Bones of ox and buffalo along with those of elephant, rhinoceros and deer have been found. Of these, the first two might have been domesticated. Among the cereals known to the people, mention may be made of rice, wheat, moong, masoor and barley.

From the Neolithic phase of Chirand, in all, nine radiocarbon dates are available so far, of which TF- 1030, -1031 and -1032 reading 1580±100, 1673±140 and 1755±155 BC respectively (Mandal 1972:204-6) are consistent. From the overlapping phase (Neolithic and Chalcolithic) a date reading 1050±90 has been obtained. The spread indicated by these dates is from 1800 to 1200 BC (Agrawal and Kusumgar 1974:71). But as of now no consistent date is available from the lowest horizon of the Neolithic phase, which was thought reasonable to trace back the beginning of the Neolithic culture at the site to around 2000 BC or even earlier (Varma 1987: 22).

Summarising the evidence, Singh (1999) says that a few specimens produced on turntable have been recovered from Chirand and Taradih while at Senuwar wheel-made pottery is much more common than the handmade varieties. Generally the clay is now well levigated but the pottery is ill-fired, has coarse and medium fabric whereas plain red ware and cord impressed pottery are generally found on all the four sites noted above. Burnished red ware and burnished grey ware are confined to the sites of south Bihar only (Taradih and Senuwar). In fact, black-and-red ware has been reported only from Chirand where a large number of shapes are recorded, but it is significantly absent at other three sites. With the onset of the Neolithic stage, prehistoric man settled at one place, the archaeological proof of which is manifested in the structural remains. There is evidence of a floor prepared below ground level at Chirand, which suggests the existence of some sort of pit dwellings. In the later phase (I-B) people started living in houses with mud-plastered reed walls on the ground floor. A circular, paved floor about 4m in diametre was exposed in the second phase. A semicircular hut with several oblong ovens, probably used for community cooking was also found. Outside this platform post-holes were located at regular intervals. A fairly large number of chunks of clay with reed and bamboo impressions that were found in these strata suggest that the houses perished in some conflagration. The remaining three excavated sites, have provided only indirect evidence of building activities, which comprises burnt clay lumps with reed marks and floors made of rammed earth, suggesting the existence of wattle-and-daub houses as excavated at Chirand. Evidence of hearths comes from Chirand and Taradih only. The discovery of several oblong hearths in a semicircular hut at Chirand has been noted above. An interesting feature of these hearths is that the soil around the hearths had become almost white in colour, indicating the presence of carbonates, calcium sulphates, salt or bone ash (calcium phosphate). From the white colour and the shape of ovens, it has been inferred that they were used for roasting animal flesh. A few hearths of different shapes and dimensions were also reported from Taradih but the details are not available. An insight into the technology of Neolithic people of Bihar can be had from their ground stone tools, blade and Microlithic industry and implements of bone and antler. The stone celts are exceedingly small in number and comparatively diminutive in size as well. Only four celts made of basalt come from Chirand. The triangular celts at Senuwar also made of basalt, generally of the small variety, are ground and polished all over the body. However, this inadequacy was more than made up by the discovery of a large number of ground stone objects presumably used for food processing (such as querns, pestles and rubbers), tool fabricators (hammer stones), fowling implements (sling balls) and other miscellaneous objects (discs). The use of microliths continued side by side, which falls in the category of Neolithic blade and Microlithic industry. At Chirand, these tools comprise micro-blades, notched blades, arrow-heads, points, lunates, borers and scrapers. In addition a few geometric microliths were also recovered from this site. All these tools are made of chalcedony, chert, agate and jasper and were manufactured from nodules probably collected from the bed of the Son river which flows not very far from the site and meets the Ganga at Harldi-Chapra, a few km south-east of Chirand. The lithic industry of Taradih comprises points, blades and cores and at Senuwar this industry includes blades, bladelets, flakes and cores. At the last-named site, these tools were also made of quartz and quartzite, along with those of chert, chalcedony and agate. An interesting feature of Bihar Neolithic is the occurrence of bone tools which have been recovered from all the four sites. Bone implements from Chechar-Kutubpur, Taradih and Senuwar generally comprise points and arrow-heads but at Chirand, which has yielded about 200 artifacts of this class, they have been grouped in 30 varieties. They are made either from antlers or from long bones of cattle or deer. Some of the types comprise wedge, chisel, bar celt, weeding tool, hammer, knife, hide cutting tool, needle, spearhead, bodkin, tanged arrow-head, drill and shaft-straightener (Singh 1999).

Orissa

Kuchai in Orissa was excavated by Thapar (1985) and he reported faceted hoes, chisels, pounders, mace-heads and grinding stones along with a brownish red ware tempered with coarse grit. Some sherds show incised decorations and a slip. From the surface explorations of Mayurbhanj district, Chandra discovered faceted and shouldered axes, bar chisels, rounded butt axes, wedges and hammer stones.

CRAFTS

The personal ornaments recovered from excavations are beads made of semi-precious stones like chalcedony, agate, jasper, marble and steatite. The discovery of a number of unfinished beads from Chirand and Taradih indicates that they were locally manufactured. Other ornaments include pendants, earrings and bangles made of bone (from Chirand). Chirand has also yielded a number of terracotta objects like human and animal figurines, bird figurines and other miscellaneous objects.

Plant remains

Paddy husk impressions on burnt clay as also some grains of charred rice from Chirand indicate the use of that cereal by the inhabitants in the Neolithic context. From layer 17 of CRD XI, the rice (*Oryza sp.*) remains have been analysed by Vishnu-Mittre. Thus it appears that in agriculture the "Neolithians" of Bihar had made significant advancement over their contemporaries from West Bengal. While rice was the main cereal content in the diet of Neolithic man in Bengal, at about the same time and even earlier agriculture based on two crops and even rotation of the crops had already been introduced in Bihar. Paddy husk impressions were noticed on some burnt clay pieces at Chirand, but apart from these, wheat, barley, lentil (moong, masoor), field pea (*Pisum arvense*) were also found. It is interesting to note that wheat, barley and field pea found here match the specimens found and recognised from Harappan and Chalcolithic sites in Western India (Vishnu-Mittre, 1974:18-22). Some leguminous weeds and wild fruits have also been found. These data from Chirand have been supplemented by that coming from Senuwar. It comprises rice (*Oryza sativa*), barley (*Hordeum vulgare*), field pea, lentil (*Lens culinaris*) and millets. In addition to this, the Neolithic deposit at Senuwar has also yielded dwarf-wheat (*Triticum sphaerococcum*), grass pea (*Lathyrus sativus*), kodon (*Paspalum scrobiculatum*) and seeds of vetch which grows as a weed in the winter-crop fields. Thus the variety of crops at Chirand and Senuwar suggests that agriculture was the main source of the subsistence economy and both kharif and rabi crops were raised by rotation. Food was also supplemented by hunting, fishing and fowling. Animal remains have been found at Chirand, Taradih and Senuwar. At Chirand a large number of bones of sheep/goat, cattle, buffalo, deer, pig, elephant, rhinoceros, dog, bird, tortoise, fish and shell have been found. Also a large number of charred animal bones with hewn marks were collected from Taradih and Senuwar but their zoological identification is not yet known.

Tools

A variety of artifacts, e.g., chisels, rounded butt-axes, wedges, perforated stones, hammer stones, faceted tools, splayed-edged axes and bar-chisels were reported from these sites. They employed chipping, pecking, grinding and polishing techniques to fabricate such artifacts. They used a variety of rocks such as phylite, epidorite, gneiss, sandstone, basalt, quartzite, slate and limestone.

CHRONOLOGY

There are 10 radiocarbon dates from Chirand of which the earliest date (TF-1032) goes to 1760 ± 155 BC, which after calibration falls between 2195 and 1750 BC. There are six other dates, which are progressively later than TF-1032; the latest in the series being TF-1035, which comes to 1270 ± 103 BC, which, after calibration, falls between 1575 and 1280 BC. Neolithic Chirand survived from circa 1800 to 1200 BC, with a margin of 100 years on both sides (Agrawal and Kusumgar,

1974:71). There is no ^{14}C date from Senuwar from the pure Neolithic phase (Period IA). Three ^{14}C dates 1770 ± 120 BC, 1660 ± 120 BC and 1500 ± 110 BC have come from the early phase of the Chalcolithic (Period IB) at this site (BP Singh, 1988-89:18). On the basis of these three dates, the beginning of Period IB, i.e. the Chalcolithic phase, has been dated to 1800 BC and hence the date of Period IA (pure Neolithic) will be definitely pre-1800 BC and its beginnings may as well go to the later half of the third millennium BC (P. Singh 1999).

Discussion

Singh (1999) summarising the survey of the Neolithic cultures of Eastern India, notes that Assam was a focal region of Eastern Indian Neolithic, while Bengal, Bihar and the eastern part of Uttar Pradesh seem to have been at the receiving end. As regards the basic tool types, there are two main traditions: the triangular axe with blunt butt end and the shouldered axe. While the shouldered axe tradition diffused along the coast into Orissa and north-eastern Andhra, the triangular axe with blunt butt-end tradition diffused eastwards into Bihar and Uttar Pradesh. The inhospitable natural conditions of the Brahmaputra valley and the adjoining region have made this region an area of relative isolation, mainly because the numerous hill ranges were covered with thick evergreen forest. The rainfall is heavy and the land available for cultivation is naturally very small. The slash-and-burn method of cultivation is practised even today. Food is also supplemented by collecting a variety of tubers from the forest. A similar life-style has been envisaged for Neolithic predecessors as well. As regards the genesis of this culture, it is supposed to have derived its inspiration from south China and South-east Asia. Recent discoveries made in Sikkim further demonstrate cultural links with south-west China and South-east Asia. The adzes, Honan knife, perforated celts and harvesters are typical of south Chinese Neolithic assemblage. A similar assemblage has also been reported from South-east Asia. However, the evidences present in the Belan valley seemingly point more towards indigenous development in the area.

The Cord Impressed Ware seems to provide a link, howsoever tenuous it may look, with the East Asian Neolithic cultures. Dr. Gautam Sengupta *et al.* (1991: xiii) in the editorial note of the book, *Archaeology of North-Eastern India*, makes an important observation,

> The relevance of the region in the subcontinental history and archaeology can hardly be overstated. A corridor region between South-east Asia and Gangetic India, North-Eastern India offers a series of problems and their probable answers having very significant bearing on the entire discipline of Archaeology.

Recent evidence from China

Before we discuss the linguistic evidence, let us have a look at the recent discoveries in China carried out by Yasuda and his collaborators. Yasuda reports:

> The Miaoyan site and the Tongliuzhou Dalong site in Guangxi Zhuangzu Ziziqu date back to 16,000 years BP (uncalibrated). Moreover, pottery dating back to 14,000-15,000 years BP (uncalibrated) was found at the Xianrendong and the Diaotonghuan sites in Wannianxian Jiangxi Province, and the Yuchanyan site in Hunan Province (Fig. 1; Yuan and Zhang, in this issue). The oldest pottery which I saw at the Cultural Relics and Archaeological Institute of Hunan Province was unearthed from the Yuchanyan site in Hunan Province. The pottery is greyish, pointed based and around 1cm in thickness. Pottery, which was as old as in the southern China, was also found at Shimomouchi site in Nagano Prefecture in Japan. It was ^{14}C dated to 16,000 years BP….. The people, who settled down in a forest and invented pottery, also started rice cultivation. Rice cultivation originated in the middle reaches of the Yangtze Basin. Some evidence of rice cultivation was found at Xianrendong,

> Diaotonghuan and Yuchanyan in Hubei Province and Bashidang and Pentoushan sites in Hunan Province. ^{14}C dating revealed that the Xianrendong and the Daiotonghuan sites dated to 14,000-12,000 years BP and Bashidang and the Pentoushan sites to 11,000-9,000 years BP. These are more than 5,000 years older than the Hemdu site in Zhejiang Province, which was dated to 7,000 years BP and considered to be the oldest rice cultivation site in China before 1991. The oldest pottery was also found at these oldest rice cultivation sites (1999b: 1-2).

About other Chinese sites Yasuda (2000:1-4) says:

> The Pengtoushan site, where archaeologists found husk dating back 9000 years is located about 2 km south-east from the Chengtoushan site. At the Bashidang archaeological site located about 20km north-east of the Chengtoushan site, rice husks date back more than 10,000 years. From these evidences, the Liyang plain is considered to be one of the earliest phases where rice cultivation was originated.

Makohonienko (2000:4) reports that according to archaeological evidence, two main agriculture systems based respectively on rice and millet cultivation appeared in prehistoric China. Neolithic cultures in the south, with a warm, humid climate, introduced the cultivation of rice. Recent progress in archaeobotanical studies has pointed to rice domestication in the middle reaches of the Yangtze river as early as 10,000 years BC. In contrast to the south, cultures of the north were substantially dependent on millet cultivation, which was suitable to the northern environmental conditions with a drier, temperate climate.

In view of these recent findings, and the early contacts of north-eastern states with China and Southeast regions, the linguistic data assumes importance. They seem to provide some evidence for possible contacts with South-east and East Asia as far as the early rice technology is concerned. Blust's (1996) linguistic arguments for the expansion of rice-cultivating, Mon-Khmer speaking societies down the Mekong from south-western China beginning by the late sixth millennium BC appears to be very significant. White (1997) also argues for a sixth millennium BC beginning of agriculture accompanied by the expansion of the Mon-Khmer family of languages. From Austric homeland a proto-AA speaker rice cultivating group began to move down the valleys of the Salween and Mekong (proto-Mon-Khmer), with pre-Munda speakers moving westward down the Brahmaputra (see for detail Chapter 7—The Role of Central Himalayas). Munda and Mon-Khmer dialects are two branches of the Austro-Asiatic family. There are many Austro-Asiatic aboriginal languages still spoken in Thailand (Bayard, pers. comm.; Bayard 1996) and they have a strong relationship with Austronesian languages as pointed out by Higham (1996). Bayard (1996) viusalises the westward expansion, under the stimulus of agriculture, of Austro-Asiatic (AA) language from Nanhailand through Viet Nam, Laos, Cambodia and Thailand to Burma and ultimately eastern India. Linguists have now reconstructed a number of terms related to agriculture in proto-Munda, and some of these (husked rice, rice-husking pestle) appear to go back to proto-Austro-Asiatic (AA) as well (see Chpt. 7). Therefore it is now very important for us to examine archaeological evidence and the beginning of rice agriculture in the north-east.

SOUTHERN NEOLITHIC CULTURES

In southern India the states of Andhra and Karnataka in particular are dotted with a large number of Neolithic sites. In recent years several of them have been excavated, e.g., Budihal, Kodekal, Utnur, Nagarjunakonda and Palavoy in Andhra Pradesh; Tekkalakota, Maski, Terdal, T. Narsipur, Sangankallu, Kupgal, Hallur, Brahmagiri and Hemmige in Karnataka; and Paiyampalli in Tamil Nadu. The ash-mounds are a peculier feature of the Neolithic culture of South India. Besides this, senior archaeologists, such as Paddayya (1973, 1975, 1993a,b, in press) and Sundara

(1985: 39-57) are still active in the field. We have, therefore, based our discussion of the peninsular Neolithic mainly on their writings, in general, and on Paddayya's work in the Shorapur Doab in particular. We have comprehensive information on these cultures, though minor variations do occur. These sites represent a fairly homogeneous group, therefore, a general survey of their cultural traits should suffice. The Neolithic occupations at most of the sites, e.g., at Tekkalakota, Sangankallu, Brahmagiri, Piklihal, Paiyampalli, T. Narsipur and Hallur are divisible into two phases. The use of distinctive ground stone tools, a blade industry, pottery, ornaments and art objects mark these occupations. At most of these sites there is evidence of animal husbandry and cereal cultivation, though hunting continued to supplement their diet.

Origins of Neolithic cultures

While Wheeler (1948: 295, 1960: 89) and Worman (1949: 199) postulated an eastern origin for the origins of the Neolithic culture, on the basis of the polished stone tool tradition, Allchin (1960: 139-42) derives the culture from Western Asia, relying on the similarities between the Neolithic pottery tradition and that of Shah Tepe and other Iranian sites. Allchin suggests that the culture originated in the wake of a migration to the southern Deccan of a group of tribes from the region of the Turkoman steppe and Elburz mountains. Allchin also holds them responsible for the introduction of the Dravidian family of languages.

Despite the weak points in Allchin's hypothesis, Paddayya accepts a Western Asiatic origin for the South Indian Neolithic. He, however, cautions that the culture as it is revealed to us today is not a wholesale transplantation from the North-west. On the contrary, the local hunting/fishing groups seem to have made a significant contribution towards its make-up. In this context we must keep in mind the following evidence. First, the single child skull from Brahmagiri is said to be of the autochthonous Australoid type (Sarkar 1960: 24), whereas in the skeletal remains from Tekkalakota (Nagaraja Rao and Malhotra 1965: 156-57) and T. Narsipur the intruding Mediterranean element has been found superimposed upon the proto-Australoid features. Secondly, there are several technological, typological and other considerations, which permit us to support Thapar's (1965: 93) view that the lithic blade industry of the Neolithic culture is essentially a continuation of the Late Stone Age traditions (Paddayya 1993a,b).

Shorapur Doab

Budihal

The village of Budihal (lat. 16° 22" N; long. 76° 23" E) is situated in Shorapur taluka, Gulbarga district, on the river Don, which is one of the tributaries of the river Krishna. The word 'Budihal' in the Kannada language means 'ashy ruins'. The Shorapur Doab is the area of the confluence of the Bhima with the river Krishna, where Budihal is located and forms part of the lower portion of the semi-arid Deccan. The average annual rainfall in this area is of the order of 500mm received during the summer monsoon. The vegetation of the area forms part of a complex called the Hardwickia-Anogeissus series. Owing to population pressure and the consequent reclamation of forest lands for agricultural purposes during the last three or four decades, and the more recent changes in the landscape introduced by irrigation, the original vegetation cover of the area is now more or less completely denuded. Only some isolated patches of scrub on the sandstone plateau close to the village of Budihal or in the area covered by granite hills indicate the nature of the original vegetation cover. The dominant trees include *Capparis aphylla, Prosopis spicigera* and *Acacia arabica*. Also noteworthy is the presence of some species of grasses, which provide pastures for the cattle.

Tremendous diversity is provided by the geological formations of the area around Budihal.

The Neolithic inhabitants made full use of all the locally available rock types. There is an extensive blade-manufacturing workshop at the site, the raw material for which was obtained from the chert found in limestone formations located 5 to 6 km north of the site. At some places limestone is capped by the Deccan trap, which marks the eastern limit of the basalt formations of the Maharashtra plateau. The area to the south of Budihal is composed of granite-gneiss formations which find their best expression in the Kodekal group of hills lying at a distance of 4 to 5 km from Budihal. The land surface here is strewn with boulders. The major traditional crops raised by the people are jowar and bajra. The limited agricultural potential of the land, coupled with the erratic and insufficient nature of rainfall, has forced the people to lay an equal emphasis on cattle and sheep/goat pastoralism. Practically every household keeps some cattle, which are the best insurance against the vagaries of climate. The Neolithic inhabitants relied heavily on cattle pastoralism because of the vast scope for grazing animal herds. On the other hand, only a low level of agricultural technology and a degraded environment was available to them.

The ash-mound site (Pl. 6-6) forms part of a fairly large tract of agricultural land which measures about 400m north-south and 300m east-west. The whole area is strewn with patches of Neolithic occupation deposit ranging from 15cm to 1 metre in thickness. Ash formations occur at two spots in the central part of this vast area (Pl. 6-7). These are designated as ash-mounds I and II. Ash-mound I is oval-shaped and measures 70m north-south and 45m east-west; it has a maximum height of about 3 metres. The ash-mound itself is located on the top of the plateau, about a kilometre north of the village. On its northern and eastern sides the site is defined by ravine-like gullies reaching depths of 15 to 20m below the plateau surface. Taking advantage of the springs present in these ravines, the villagers dig shallow pits to create perennial water pools which are used for drinking purposes both by people and their domestic animals. These water sources were probably a major attraction for the Neolithic occupants of the site (Pls. 6-8 and 6-9).

The ash-mound II, located about 100m north-west of mound I, is circular in plan and measures about 40m across. The area on the north-eastern side of ash-mound II is occupied by a deserted medieval settlement. A small portion of it is being used by villagers to quarry ancient soil for use as packing and cementing material in construction work. This digging has exposed the Neolithic deposit at the base. There is also a large dugout area on the eastern side of Ash-mound I from where the Neolithic deposit is being quarried. The calibrated ^{14}C dates place the Budihal sites between 2500 and 2000 BC (see Table 6.8).

TABLE 6.8 ^{14}C DATES FROM BUDIHAL (After Paddayya)

Lab. No.	*Layer & Depth (below grid surface)*	*Uncalibrated Dates B.P./B.C.*	*Calibrated Dates (B.C.) 68% probability*	*98% probability*
Budihal - I, Tr. 1 (Upper Ashmound)				
BM-2888	3(99 cm)	2380±60 B.P. (430 B.C.)	755 to 705 530 to 390	765 to 360
GrN-19661	6(80-85 cm)	3795±30 B.P. (1845 B.C.)	2278 to 2226 2208 to 2188 2164 to 3142	2312 to 2306 2294 to 3134 2070 to 2054

Cont. Table 6.8

Cont. Table 6.8

Lab. No.	*Layer & Depth (below grid surface)*	*Uncalibrated Dates B.P./B.C.*	*Calibrated Dates (B.C.) 68% probability*	*98% probability*
BM-2887	6(85-90 cm)	3880±60 B.P. (1930 B.C.)	2465 to 2295	2565 to 2540 2500 to 2195 2155 to 2145
GrN-19662	9(105-110 cm)	3805±5 B.P. (1855 B.C.)	2282 to 2192 2162 to 2146	2392 to 2384 2336 to 2136 2076 to 2054
GrN-19663	10(145-150 cm)	3795±40 B.P. (1845 B.C.)	2282 to 2216 2214 to 2186 2168 to 2140	2394 to 2384 2338 to 2130 2080 to 2046
BM-2886	10(210 cm)	3810±50 B.P. (1860 B.C.)	2450 to 2445 2395 to 2385 2350 to 2190 2160 to 2145	2450 to 2135
Budihal - I, Tr. 4 (Settlement Area)				
GrN-19978	2(28 cm)	3370±40 B. P. (1420 B.C.)	1734 to 1722 1688 to 1610 1552 to 1536	1740 to 1708 1700 to 1588 1582 to 1526
GrN-19979	2(35 cm)	3470±40 B.P. (1520 B.C.)	1874 to 1840 1814 to 1806 1780 to 1738	1880 to 1830 1826 to 1684 1714 to 1692
GrN-19980	2(40 cm)	3750±35 B.P. (1800 B.C.)	2196 to 2154 2152 to 2130 2080 to 2046	2278 to 2230 2206 to 2036
GrA-2502	2(20 cm)	3770±50 B.P. (1820 B.C.)	2278 to 2228 2206 to 2132 2078 to 2048	2390 to 2388 2334 to 2030 1998 to 1986
GrA-2506	2(28 cm)	3610±50 B.P. (1660 BC)	2030 to 1998 1984 to 1886 1842 to 1812	2130 to 2080 2044 to 1872 1808 to 1780
GrA-2504	2(30-35 cm)	3730±50 B.P. (1780 B.C.)	2194 to 2160 2146 to 2034	2280 to 2222 2210 to 1974
GrA-2503	2(30-35 cm)	3900±50 B.P. (1950 B.C.)	2460 to 2320	2482 to 2266 2264 to 2200
GrA-2484	2(37 cm)	3600±60 B.P. (1650 B.C.)	2032 to 1994 1988 to 1878 1834 to 1822 1794 to 1788	2132 to 2078 2048 to 1862 1850 to 1758

Cont. Table 6.8

Cont. Table 6.8

Lab. No.	*Layer & Depth (below grid surface)*	*Uncalibrated Dates B.P./B.C.*	*Calibrated Dates (B.C.) 68% probability*	*98% probability*
GrA-2486	3(40-45 cm)	3830±60 B.P. (1880 B.C.)	2398 to 2378 2346 to 2190 2162 to 2144	2458 to 2134 2074 to 2052
GrA-2487	3(40-45 cm)	3850±60 B.P. (1900 B.C.)	2450 to 2434 2402 to 2374 2264 to 2200	2464 to 2136 2354 to 2268
GrA-2488	2(25 cm)	3600±60 B.P. (1650 B.C.)	2032 to 1994 1988 to 1878 1834 to 1822 1794 to 1788	2132 to 2078 2048 to 1862 1850 to 1758
Budihal - I, Tr. 5(Animal Butchering Floor)				
GrN-1981	3(40 cm)	3820±45 B.P. (1870 B. C.)	2324 to 2192 2162 to 2146	2452 to 2430 2404 to 2368 2364 to 2136 2068 to 2056
GrA-2483	2(10 cm)	3770±60 B.P. (1820 B.C.)	2282 to 2216 2212 to 2128 2080 to 2044	2446 to 2440 2440 to 2376 2350 to 2022 2044 to 1978
GrA-2489	2(15-20 cm)	3810±50 B.P. (1860 B.C.)	2318 to 2186 2168 to 2140 2364 to 2130 2078 to 2046	2452 to 2430 2404 to 2368
Budihal - III (Trial Pit) (Settlement Area)				
GrN-19982	3(40 cm)	3810±80 B.P. (1860 B.C.)	2398 to 2378 2346 to 2134	2462 to 2030 1996 to 1986

Excavation at Kodekal

Paddayya (1993a,b) reports that the scraping exposed seven layers making up for a total thickness of about 3.3m at Kodekal. The base of the mound is made up of murum representing the residue of distinctive granite-gneiss. The even and compact make-up of its surface leaves no doubt that it was specially prepared. Then follows a layer of black-grey earth (Layer 6). That this layer represents a period of human occupation is fully borne out by the occurrence of pottery, stone artifacts and animal bones. There is no way of deciding whether the artificially arranged stones encountered in this layer belong to some form of structure. Above this there is a thin floor of powdery murum (Layer 5) and it is followed by a thick deposit of dark brownish soil (Layer 4). This layer produced large quantities of pottery, stone artifacts, animal bones, charcoal, etc., thereby proving another, and prolonged, period of human occupation. Over the levelled surface of this layer is a thick accumulation of vitrified ash (Layer 3). The absence of bands suggests that the ash resulted from a single enormous conflagration. This burning is followed by a third period of human occupation, as exemplified in Layer 2. The rarity of cultural debris, however, indicates that this occupation was of a short duration. The succeeding layer of vitrified ash (Layer 1), while proving another burning, represents the last of the prehistoric human activities at the mound.

The excavator observes that the repeated occurrence of ash layers at one and the same site is also a characteristic of the ash-mounds of other areas. There is evidence of as many as five burnings at Utnur. Like Kodekal, the mounds at Palavoy and Kupgal underwent two burnings. This phenomenon has also been observed at Kudatını and Gaudur. While the number of burnings seems to vary from region to region and from site to site, their cyclic nature is a feature common to all the ash-mounds.

The artefact repertoire from the site is typically of the Neolithic culture. Equally significant is the total absence of objects belonging to later periods. Admittedly the majority of the finds derive from Layers 4 and 6, but the occurrence of identical objects in the slag-rich layers (Layers 1 and 3) proves that the ash accumulations also belong to the Neolithic period. Thus the cultural evidence, supplemented by absolute dating afforded by the ^{14}C date, places the Neolithic age of the Kodekal site beyond doubt. From the unmistakably Neolithic character of the cultural material obtained from the surface of other mounds and the occurrence of ash lumps at Kupi, Kannekolur-1, etc. one can infer that the other ash-mounds found in the Doab also date from the Neolithic period. A comparison of the excavated pottery with that collected from the surface shows that the formation of these mounds covered the entire lifespan of the Neolithic culture. The beginning of the Iron Age is indicated by the reuse of ash for making circles around the dolmens at Dimanhal and Rajankolur, the presence of a stone alignment on top of the Shakapur ash-mound and of a stone circle on top of the Kodekal mound. The stratigraphical and cultural evidence suggests that these ash-mounds belong to the Neolithic period and the deposit of human occupation alternating with periods of cow-dung burning.

Thus Shorapur Doab has clear evidence of three occupation periods and two burnings of burnt cow-dung. Nevertheless, the presence of greyish soil as the bottom layer at Budihal and Tirth and the identification of three layers of ash at the latter site shows that the cyclic nature of the occupation periods and burnings observed at Kodekal holds good for the other ash-mounds also.

Settlement Pattern: Paddayya reports the predilection shown by the Neolithic folk towards granitoid hills and hillocks, which has already been commented upon by Foote (1916: 27-29) and other authors. This phenomenon also finds expression in the Shorapur Doab. In fact, a well-defined pattern presents itself in the geographical distribution of the sites occurring in this area as can be seen in the map reproduced (Paddayya 1993a,b). The sites appear to be clustered in the south-western belt, which is rather broken up by several hill ranges formed by the Peninsular Crystalline Complex. Budihal and Wadgiri are the only important sites, which lie outside the confines of this zone. True hill settlements like those found at Sanganakallu and Tekkalakota are unknown, but this feature is closely approached by the foothill sites of Kodekal, Mallur, Kakkera-1, Thanmandi Thanda, Bijapur and Benkanhalli. Apart from this favourable physiographic setting, four other factors must have guided the people in their selection of the Doab for settlement. These are: 1. the presence of pastures on and around the hills and in the valleys below, 2. the plentiful supply of raw materials in the dykes and veins already exposed on the surface, 3. the existence of perennial reserves of water in the form of large and small rivers and natural springs and 4. the presence of plentiful game.

Dwellings: People led a sedentary life in the open as proved by the thick accumulations of habitation debris. The evidence of bamboo-impressed clay clods (Paddayya 1993a: Fig. 22, Nos. 9 and 10) and the alignment of stones revealed in the ash-mound at Kodekal (Paddayya 1993a: Fig. 23, No. 2, PI. VIII) is insufficient for reconstructing the nature and types of structures raised by these people. We therefore have to turn to the evidence from other sites. At Tekkalakota (Pl. 6-10) (Nagaraja Rao and Malhotra 1965: 19, Fig. 6), Sanganakallu (Pl. 6-11) (Ansari and Nagaraja Rao 1969: 10, Figs. 6 and 7) and Hallur circular huts were brought to light through excavations. They have floors raised on stone chips and plastered with lime or clay. The walls consist of split-bamboo screens supported at regular intervals by wooden posts and daubed over with clay or cow-dung. The roofs are supposed to have been conical in shape. These structures have a striking ethnographic parallel in the circular huts of the Boyas and other communities belonging to the lower strata of the present-day society of the southern Deccan, which perhaps is a survival from the Neolithic period.

Evidence from the excavations at Hallur, Tekkalakota and Sangankallu, has indicated that generally huts were circular, of one room, with a low mud plinth, fortified by a split bamboo screen and a conical thatched roof. In rural India such houses are common even today. The Boya tribe, near Tekkalakota still uses exactly a similar type of house. Quite often granite boulders were used to define boundary of the house. At Sangankallu, a 5m wide circular house was made with 13 wooden posts. Storage jars and *chulhas* (hearths) were common finds in such houses. There is also evidence that they dug small pits for throwing rubbish. Sometimes floors were whitewashed with lime and at Hallur chips of schist were used to ram the floors.

Subsistence

a. *Animal Remains*: Foote (1916), Zeuner (1963) and others have already shown that great advances were made not only in the techniques of making tools but also in the domestication of animals during the Neolithic period. The more detailed studies are now available of the faunal remains from some of the sites, which show that the animal world was varied. Southern Neolithic sites have yielded evidence of domestic animals like cattle (*Bos indicus*), buffalo (*Bos bubalis*), sheep (*Ovis vignei*), goat (*Capra hircus*), dog (*Canis familiaris*), ass (*Equus asinus*), onager (*Equus hemionus*) and pig. And over a dozen wild animal species like elephant, barasingha (*Cervus duvaceli*), spotted deer (*Axis axis*), *Cervus unicolor*, black duck, nilgai, gazelle (*Gazella gazella*), rat, hare, tortoise, monitor lizard, varanus (*Varanus flavescens*), peacock, fowl (*Gallus*), bony fish and some aquatic animals (Paddayya 1975) have been identified, which also indicate hunting and fishing activities.

Paddayya has pointed out that some sites like Brahmagiri, Maski, Piklihal, Utnur, Tekkalakota, Nagarjunakonda, Hallur, Palavoy, Sanganakallu and T. Narsipur have not yielded remains of gazelle, fish, fowl and monitor lizard, but they are represented in the Shorapur assemblage. On the other hand, sheep, pig, elephant and horse (Alur 1971: 123) are not found in Shorapur Doab but they are represented at other sites. In all the excavated sites in the southern Deccan, cattle remains dominate, e.g., at Kodekal, no less than 57% (81 specimens) are cattle bones. The ash-mounds prove that the Neolithic people kept large herds of these animals. Cattle also provide the main subject of the rock bruisings found at Hebbal Buzurg. Cattle was also used for heavy draft work as indicated by the anchylosis of the hock joint, also found in the bones from Hallur and Utnur.

The studies carried out in recent years suggest that the economy was mainly based on cultivation, supplemented by animal husbandry as it is clear from the evidence at Kodekal and other places. The presence of marks of cutting, splitting and chopping and the evidence of charring demonstrate that these animals were eaten. People might even have learnt how to make use of cow's milk. We can therefore conclude that meat and presumably also other products, such as milk were regular items in the diet of these people. Dogs may either have been stray animals or were kept as watch-dogs. The presence of the remains of a variety of wild animals shows that the food produced by stock- and crop-raising was supplemented by hunting, trapping, fishing and collecting.

The presence of deer would imply that there was considerable vegetation with a wet climate. Mujumdar and Rajaguru (1965) who studied the fossil soil below the Neolithic deposits at Kupgal, have shown that at the time of the Neolithic occupation this region experienced more precipitation and possessed more vegetation with thorn and scrub forest interspersed with large areas of grassland.

The presence of the soil layer indicates that Shorapur Doab enjoyed a slightly wetter climate during the Neolithic occupation. This in turn implies that the region possessed more vegetation by way of thorn and scrub forest interspersed with large areas of grassland. This view is supported by the presence of fruits of teak (*Tectona grandis*) and other plant remains from Hallur. The present semi-aridity, which very often leads to drought conditions, seems to be due almost entirely to the 4,000 years of exploitation of the area through farming, animal grazing and timber cutting.

b. *Plant Remains:* It appears that the subsistence of the southern Neolithic cultures was considearbly supported by agricultural products as Tekkalakota (Sankalia 1974: 135), Hallur and other excavated sites have yielded remains of a variety of charred grains. Probably they used the terraces formed on the granitoid hills for agriculture.

The excavations in Shorapur Doab have yielded evidence of carbonised grains of barley (*Hordeum vulgare* and *Hordeum* sp.), horse gram (*Dolichos biflorus*), Indian bean/hyacinth bean (*Dolichos lablab*), graminaceous seeds (*Panicum* type, *Setaria* type) and Portulacaceae type of weed seeds. The uncarbonised (phosphatised?) plant remains include fruitstones of Indian jujube (*Zizyphus* sp.), Indian cherry (*Cordia* cf. myzta) and emblic myrobolan (*Phyllanthus* sp.). Kodekal (c. 2300 BC) has also provided the remains of Indian jujube (*Zizyphus jujuba*) whereas at Hallur, district Dharwar, Karnataka, wild and domestic finger millet (*Eleucine indica, Eleucine coracana*), ragi and *E. indica*, kodo millet? (*Paspalum scrobiculatum*), domestic rice (*Oryza sativa*) and fruitstones of teak (*Tectona grandis*) were found.

From the transitional zone between the Neolithic and Megalithic cultures were found carbonised grains of horse gram (*Dolichos biflorus*), Indian bean/hyacinth bean (*Dolichos* lablab), black gram/green gram {*Vigna mungo, Vigna radiata), Phaseolus aureus*} and Indian jujube (*Zizyphus* cf. jujuba). The evidence of legumes, date palm, *Acacia* sp and bajra (*Pennisetum typhoides*) is available at Hallur - but from the Neolithic-Megalithic phase. Similarly the site of Balijapalle has also yielded evidence for Abutilon type, indeterminate seeds (weed seeds) whereas Ramapuram (around c. 1000 BC) has given evidence of barley (*Hordeum* cf. vulgare), dehusked millet (wild grass type): Panicum sp., indet. Gramineae type, Cotyledons of horse gram (*Dolichos biflorus*), black gram type (*Vigna mungo*), green gram (*Vigna radiata*), Malvaceae type (*Abutilon* sp.), *Purslane* type (*Portulaca* sp.), Indian jujube (*Zizyphus jujuba*) and Umbelliferae type (*Coriandrum* type cf. sativa). Hence there is no doubt that the Neolithic folks cultivated cereals as well as pulses. Discovery of carbonised seeds of the *Zizuphus vulgaris* fruit indicate that such fruits were also exploited.

Tool Technology

The stone tool industry comprises tools made of coarse-grained rocks such as dolerite, sandstone and granite by flaking, pecking, grinding and polishing. The main artifact types are: a) edge-tools comprising axes, adzes, chisels, wedges and chopping tools, and b) non-edge-tools including hammer stones, rubber-stones and querns. The edge-tools seem to have been devised mainly for cutting wood. Paddayya suggests that the axes could be employed for clearing the plots selected for both habitation and cultivation. It is just possible that the damaged specimens were hafted adze-wise and used as hoes. The adzes, chisels and wedges may have been used for shaping hafts, handles and digging sticks and also for working up bamboo required for constructional purposes. The querns, hammer stones and rubber-stones, on the other hand, could be used for pounding and grinding cultivated grain as well as collected forest produce.

The other tool tradition is of the blade industry, which almost exclusively used chert. These tools were made on slender blanks, commonly referred to as blades. A vast majority of these blanks seem to have been put to use as they were struck from the cores. However, some show secondary working to make such types as the backed blades, saw-edged tools, points, lunates and trapezes. The blades as well as the fragments derived from them could be manipulated with the bare hand for cutting and slicing meat, fruits, vegetables and such other items of daily consumption. They could also be hafted in wood or bone to form sickles and knives; these composite tools could be used for reaping crops as well as wild grasses and for dismembering animal carcasses. The Microlithic types (lunates, trapezes, etc.) were almost certainly used for tipping and barbing arrows and harpoons. The borer group of artifacts would be eminently suitable for making perforations on edge-ground potsherds and beads of steatite, shell and bone. The existence of several extensive working centres makes the present industry the richest of its kind in the southern Deccan. Paddayya thinks that, apart from meeting local demands, these workshops turned out surplus products meant for delivery to regions further south, which were lacking in suitable raw materials.

Thus a variety of tools, e.g., axes, adzes, scrapers, wedges comprise toolkit of the early farmers. The edge of these tools was ground for use and the most common type is axe, which has a triangular shape, oval cross-section, round and pointed butt. Though one can find a variety of axes showing variation in technique of fabrication yet no evolutionary stages have been found. The adze is another important type though reported from a few sites like Maski, Brahmagiri and Nevasa. A variety of chisels have also been discovered but they are not common. Some pointed tools have often been labelled as picks or borers. Besides these types, there are hammer stones, sling balls, querns, etc. Paddayya emphasises that unlike Southeast Asia, in the peninsular India a lithic blade industry is always associated with the ground tools. At Sangankallu and Palavoy there is a Microlithic industry, which precedes the Neolithic one and the excavators claim that both stratigraphically and technologically the Neolithic blade industry is unconnected with the earlier one. The common types are parallel-sided blades, serrated blades and lunates. In the latter case they have been mostly used for agricultural activities and in the former for cutting, sharpening and shaving wood. Axes, chisels and points made of bone and shell have also been reported from these Neolithic sites.

Ceramics

Pottery is one of the most important Neolithic crafts. Except for the small number of sherds belonging to the Jorwe ware at some Neolithic sites, generally the ceramics, belonging to early stage, are handmade. The ceramics belong to the red and grey groups, each with its own sub-groups. There are three principal types of decoration: painted (both pre- and post-firing), incised and applique. The pottery repertoire has over 30 different shapes. It may safely be assumed that they served a wide range of domestic purposes - storing and carrying of liquids and possibly also grain, cooking and serving of foods, etc. The collections also include sophisticated shapes such as the footed bowls, lipped and spouted pots, bell-shaped jars and pots with high neck and collared rims; they were probably meant for some special (ceremonial?) use. The perforated bowl is yet another ingenious form devised by the craftsman; it was probably used for preparing a macaroni-like dish out of cereal paste and milk. It is evident that the Neolithic culture of the south had some contacts with the Jorwe culture of Maharashtra. Spouted dull red vessels, constricted necked jars, ovalish lamps are common between the Jorwe and the Neolithic cultures.

Pottery was handmade in Phase I (Pl. 6-12) and wheel-made variety appeared in Phase II. Perhaps, they made use of turntable also. Apparently firing was not controlled and resulted in a variety of colours: pale grey, grey, brown and buff. Some pots, after firing, were painted with red ochre. For decoration, perforations, the appliquè method and a limited range of painting was resorted to. Painted sherds were found only from the earliest levels of few sites such as Piklihal, Maskı and Brahmagiri and others. A purplish paint is used over a red burnished or buff surface. The motifs are few and comprise radiating triangles and wavy lines. A necked vase in this ware was perhaps adopted later on by the Jorwe culture where it is a common shape. Though the pots were handmade, yet some of the shapes are very elegant, e.g., the tea-kettle. Their pottery is made of well-levigated clay to which was added quartz powder or mica as tempering material. A variety of shapes occur in Phase I, e.g., bowls of various shapes; shallow dishes; lipped, lugged, spouted, channel spouted, handled and hollow-footed bowls; jars; dishes-on-stand; and perforated pots.

Pottery shows a remarkable change in Phase II. Now the clay does not contain mica but is gritty. Unburnished grey and brown wares disappear and even burnished grey ware dwindles. A dull red ware with paintings in black or violet and a black-and-red ware, occasionally painted, appear for the first time (Pl. 6-13). At Tekkalakota, bowls and dishes in black-and-red ware have been used exclusively in burials. The range of pottery shapes does indicate a sophisticated living. Special shapes like spouted lotas and channel-spouted pots could have been used for ritualistic purposes. A channel spouted copper vessel is used in yajna rituals to this day. Some terracotta human and bull figurines are also reported. The Black-and-Red Ware forms of the early Megalithic Phase at Brahmagiri are derived from the Neolithic shapes and in fact, the Black-and-Red Ware became the hallmark of the Megalithic culture. White painted Black-and-Red Ware is also found from several sites though in small numbers.

Other crafts

The mat-impressed potsherds from Kodekal indicate that mats were being made. Although no direct evidence is available as yet, we may also add the working of leather to our list. It has already been pointed out that the edge-ground bone object from Kodekal was probably used as a scraper for dressing animal skins. Some of the edge-ground potsherds could also be used for this work. Besides, there is evidence of large quantities of animal skeletal material. These varied data make it highly probable that the skins derived from the animals killed for food were dressed and worked, perhaps for preparing clothing, footwear, containers and the like.

It has been widely held that the use of copper and painted pottery reflects contacts of the Neolithic (Phase II) people with the Jorwe culture of the Deccan. But as mentioned above, some painted pottery occurs even in the earliest levels at Brahmagiri, Piklihal and Maski, so also copper. A copper celt was found at Tekkalakota from Phase I, and from Phase II a wire, a ring and couple of other objects (Pl. 6-15). But at Piklihal no copper is reported from Phase I, but Phase II yielded fragments of bowl and a chisel. Similarly, Hallur Phase I has produced two curious copper objects, besides a fishhook. Apart from these, a double-edged thin axe and a flat axe were also found but both are in miniature form. T. Narsipur yielded a bead. It is likely that they might have been made for ornamental or ritualistic purposes. Copper artifacts occur only at Maski, Pikhlihal, Brahmagiri, Tekkalakota, Hallur and T. Narsipur.

Art

Besides pottery decorations, we have the evidence of the rock paintings, bruisings and terracotta animal figurines. Most of the Neolithic sites are situated on granitoid terraces and hills. It appears that the Neolithic man made bruisings, peckings and paintings on them. Some paintings are white, done in limewash; others are in red with or without a white background. Sankalia found bruisings depicting a bull and a hand near Tekkalakota. Other motifs in paintings and bruisings are deer, gazelle, sheep, goat, horse, stylised humans and occasionally a trident. Evidence for a Neolithic date for these paintings comes from Tekkalakota, where a grey ware lid has a bull, a cobra and two antelopes depicted by puncturing shallow pits when the pot was in a leather-hard condition (Pl. 6-14).

Ornaments: The evidence is confined to the small number of beads and the solitary pendant from the sites of Kannekolur-1, Bijapur and Wadgiri. Copper ornaments, as has been mentioned above, including bangles, spirals and pins occur only at few sites, e.g., Brahmagiri and others. Tekkalakota has also yielded two pendants of gold (Pl. 6-16). People were using a variety of beads made also of gold, copper, terracotta, agate, steatite and carnelian. Many of these, e.g., steatite and others appear only in Phase II. Among the ornaments the gold objects of Tekkalakota with solid coils in the centre and a trumpet mouth are quite unique. Budihal has also yielded stone and bone objects (Fig. 6-7).

Burials

The southern Neolithic people had developed elaborate tradition of disposal of the dead. Though one may find minor variations between two regions or sometime within a region they dug shallow pits to bury their dead. Tekkalakota has produced the maximum amount of skeletal material and has the best-preserved evidence for all types of burials known so far. People were invariably buried within the precincts of the habitation area (Pl. 6-17), and in certain cases, within the houses themselves. Adults were laid in an extended fashion in pits dug specially for the purpose (Pl. 6-18). Less common was the practice of burying the bones collected after desiccation in pits or urns. Children were usually interred in one or two urns, placed horizontally face-to-face. At Piklihal, from the early levels, a child burial with head pointing south-east was unaccompanied by any grave goods. Often elaborate funerary goods consisting of pottery, stone tools, etc., were found in the burials. The Harappans made cemetreies away from their settlements, but the Neolithic folk buried their dead right below their house floors. Extended inhumation in a north-south direction, with some funerary goods was a common adult burial practice. Piklihal, however, also yielded two adult burials in shallow pits, one head facing north and the other south. At Tekkalakota the pits were dug about 45cm deep to bury and the graves were sealed with granite boulders. In one case at Tekkalakota, bones of three adults were found together from a burial.

In Phase II, however, there is some evidence of burying adults in multiple pots, e.g., at Tekkalakota a female was buried in multiple pots with the head pointing north. Seven pots were found towards its feet. Generally black-and-red pots were offered.

Variants of Neolithic Cultures

Paddayya has identified five variants of the southern Neolithic cultures. Although it cannot be disputed that certain aspects like the burial customs and the ground stone industry evince little or no change either in terms of space or in point of time, it would be preposterous to assume that the culture passed through identical stages of development in all parts of the area of occupation. His hypothesis is based on two premises: 1) It is argued that the culture was

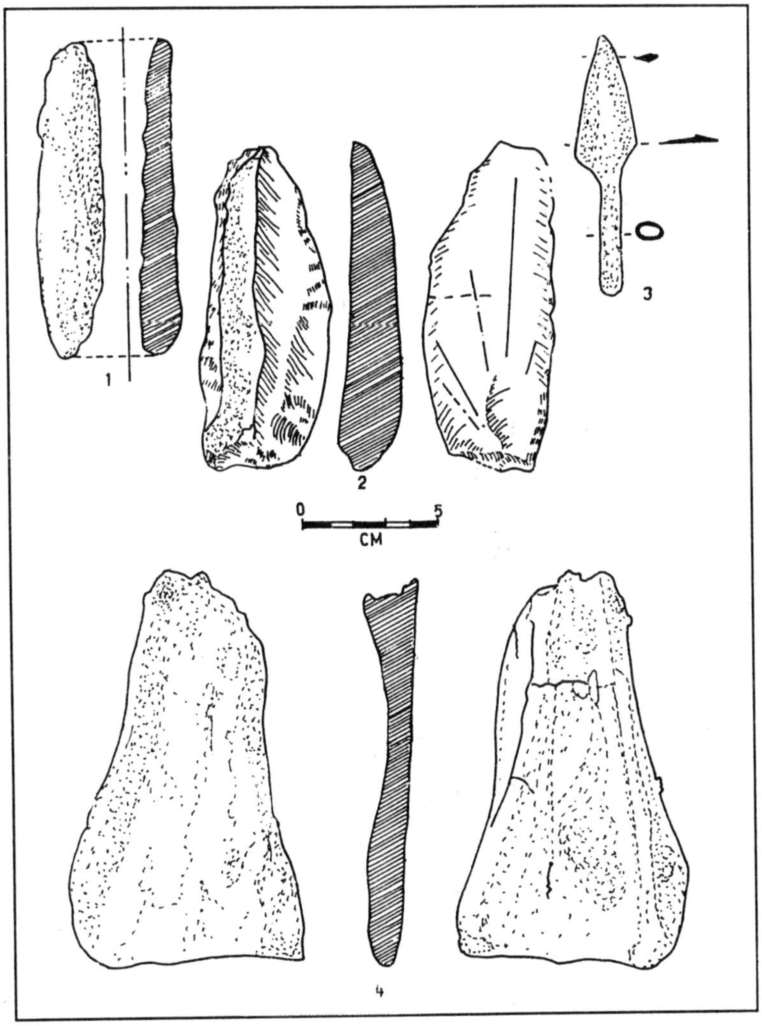

Fig. 6-7. Stone and bone artifacts from Budihal I (Nos. 1,2 and 4 from Tr. 4 and No. 3 from surface) No. 1, bone scraper; No. 2, chert knife; No. 3, bone axe on a shoulder blade of cattle; No. 4, arrowhead of iron found on surface (medieval)

restricted to a small area in the lower phase of development, which was dated between c. 2350 and 1900 BC. ^{14}C dates and the comparative evidence furnished by pottery and certain other items of the material culture suggest that the locale for these initial developments was formed by the hill country of the Bellary and Raichur districts. Hence the Shorapur Doab zone can be regarded as the nucleus or focal centre of the culture. 2) In addition to a continuous evolution in the nuclear area, the culture began to spread to the west, south and east in the upper phase commencing around 1900 BC (Paddayya 1971: 137). This diffusion was not merely a geographical expansion but involved the diversification of the culture ultimately leading to the growth of local variants or sub-cultures.

Variant 1: This variant, distributed over the nuclear area itself, comprises the developments following on the lower phase represented at Utnur (Periods I to IV), Piklihal (Lower Neolithic), Kodekal (Layers 4 to 6) and possibly also at Brahmagiri (sub-Phase IA). Stated in other words, it covers Piklihal's Upper Neolithic, Brahmagiri's sub-Phase IB, and the whole of the Neolithic occupation at Maski (Period I), Sanganakallu (sub-periods 1 and 2) of Phase II of Subbarao (1948) and phases 1 to 3 of Period III of Ansari and Nagaraja Rao (1969) and Tekkalakota (Periods 1 and 2) of Sankalia (1964) and phases I and II of Nagaraja Rao and Malhotra (1965).

Variant 2: This comprises a group of over 30 sites (including about 10 ash-mounds) explored by Sundara (1970: 7-12) in the upper Krishna basin. Grey pottery and polished stone and blade tools are common finds. A noteworthy feature pertains to the occurrence of a painted pottery in relatively high quantities at some of these sites, the number of sherds ranging between 80 and 450. There are clear signs of regional specialisation. Some of these sites also yielded small quantities of a kind of black-on-red pottery similar to the Kayatha fabric (Central India). Even more interesting is the fact that half a dozen other sites of this group have yielded a third painted pottery tradition (Sundara 1970: 11-12, Pls. III-V). This pottery is made on a fast wheel and the paintings are done in black, white or reddish brown on a red or grey background.

Variant 3: This group, representing the southern expansion of the culture, is formed by the sites investigated in the upper reaches of the Tungabhadra (Nagaraja Rao 1964) and Kaveri rivers. Among them Hallur, T. Narsipur and Hemmige (IAR 1963-64: 26-27) have been excavated. The sites explored by Foote (1916: 66-76) in the Mandya, Turnkur and Kolar districts of Mysore state as well as Paiyampalli (IAR 1964-65: 22-23) and other sites in the North Arcot district of Tamil Nadu may perhaps be included in this group. The ^{14}C dates available for Hallur, T. Narsipur and Paiyampalli reveal that the occupation continued for about 800 years, from c.1800 to 1000 BC. The importance of this variant lies in the characteristic physiographic setting of the sites. Spread as they are along the river courses, they testify to the fact that the Neolithic groups now adapted themselves to a riverine environment.

Variant 4: From the physiographic point of view, the territory covered by this variant, viz. the Anantapur district of Andhra Pradesh, is basically an extension of the hilly region of Bellary and Raichur to the west and north-west. Exploratory work at over 50 sites (including about 10 ash-mounds) and the small-scale excavation conducted at Palavoy give us an excellent picture of the Neolithic phase of the southern Deccan (Rami Reddy 1968; see also Foote 1916: 97-105). Paddayya feels that the features displayed by the cultural material from Nagarjunakonda are such that it is tempting to conjecture that this variant originally extended as far east as the lower Krishna valley. The single ^{14}C date from Palavoy is 1885 BC; it puts the lower end of this variant at c.1900 BC. The ceramic industry consists of two main fabrics: blotchy grey ware and dull red ware. As in case of the Variant 2, there is an emphasis on the painted pottery tradition. This pottery accounts for about 10% of the excavated assemblage from Palavoy. Finally, this region has produced a highly developed bone industry; certain types like the axe-shaped scrapers fashioned on the shoulder-blades of cattle are without parallels in other parts of the southern Deccan (Rami Reddy 1968: 302, Fig. 27, Nos. 3 and 4).

Variant 5: North-east of the Variant 4 zone is an interesting cluster of sites spread over the eastern part of the Kurnool district and the adjoining Cuddapah district. The famous "milk-bowl" of Foote (1916: 115, Pl. 26) comes from Patpad. This vessel is in the slipped red ware and fully painted over in black. Now about a dozen new sites yielding identical painted pottery have been located in the area. The most common shape is the bowl provided with a lip or short channel-spout. This shape also occurs in plain fabrics at T. Narsipur, Hemmige and numerous other sites. Other shapes include bowls with convex or tapering sides, high-necked jars, stemmed bowls, etc. Paddayya tentatively dates this variant to 1600-1400 BC.

Chronology (based on uncalibrated ^{14}C dates)

The pottery from Kodekal ash-mound Layers 4 and 6 is similar to that of Utnur and Piklihal, which has been firmly dated to the lower phase. Like the Utnur pottery, the assemblage from these layers is lacking in the perforated and surface rusticated varieties. Evolved forms like spouted and lipped pots are absent. This comparative evidence, supported by the ^{14}C date of

2335 BC from Layer 4, would place the Layers 4 to 6 in the lower phase. On the other hand, the surface pottery from the habitation sites, ash-mounds and the small collection from Layers 1 to 3 at Kodekal show all the above-mentioned features of the upper phase. No less important is the presence of shapes like the pots with high, cylindrical necks and bowls of T. 28. All these features are characteristic of the upper phase at Piklihal. The available calibrated ^{14}C dates show that the southern Neolithic time-spread is confined to (c. 2335-1350 BC).

Problem of Ash-mounds

Paddayya has done extensive work on the southern Neolithic in the late 1960s, early 1970s and again in the nineties (1975, 1993a,b). Apart from his excavations in northern Karnataka he also reported a large number of important ash-mound sites. The major ash-mound sites are Budihal, Kodekal, Kakkera, Mallur, Thanmandi Thanda, Shakapur and Gaudur, Wandalli and Eachanal in Raichur district and Kudatini in Bellary district (Pl. 6-19), all located in Karnataka; and Utnur in Mahbubnagar district and Palavoy in the Anantapur district of Andhra Pradesh. Several new ash-mounds were discovered in recent years in the Shorapur Doab of Gulbarga district. Bruce Foote (1916: 190-95) was the first to categorically assign these ash-mounds to the Neolithic cultures and confirmed that the ash-mounds are burnt remains of cow-dung. Sundara (1971, 1987) and Rami Reddy (1978, 1990) excavated Palavoy and Utnur and identified them as iron smelting sites. Allchin suggested that these ash-mounds were the cattle-pen/domestication centres. The ash-mounds of the southern Deccan had generated considerable controversy. Paddayya not only questioned Rami Reddy's identification (Rami Reddy 1976, 1990; Sundara 1971, 1987), which treated them as iron-smelting sites of the Iron Age but also doubted Allchins' suggestion.

Paddayya raises three fundamental questions. Do these mounds mark, as Allchin believes, the sites of cattle-pens? Is the cow-dung - the parent material of vitrified ash an in situ accumulation, or only a heaped up mass? And what were the reasons for its burning? While expressing his inability to support or reject any one of these interpretations, Paddayya admits that a clear understanding of the whole problem can only be brought about by horizontal excavation at about half a dozen selected sites in different parts of the southern Deccan. He has made the beginning and a significant contribution towards our understanding of the ash-mounds by excavating the important site of Budihal.

Now it is clear to us that the ash-mounds and the habitation deposits around them yielded pottery, stone tools and other cultural material typical of the southern Neolithic culture. He agrees with the views of Robert Bruce Foote (1916) and later workers who assigned these sites to the southern Neolithic culture, but doubts Allchins' identification. Giving due weight to the occurrence of occupation deposits around the mounds, he suggests that these ash-mounds should be called Neolithic pastoral settlements with ash deposits. The ash-mound sites were true pastoral settlements where the garbage accumulating from the nocturnal penning of cattle and other domestic animals was dumped along with household refuse at one or two convenient spots, in or close to the settlement, for periodically burning. It was done perhaps to keep the settlement clean, protect both the inhabitants and their domestic flocks from health hazards posed by vermin-infested dung heaps, and to scare away wild animals from settlements. The burning could have also formed part of rites meant for promoting the fertility of cattle. Taking into account the large size of some of the ash-mounds such as Budihal, Kakkera, Gaudur, Eachanal and Kudatini, he further argued that such sites could have served as local or regional centres where periodic congregations took place. Like the present-day *jatras* and cattle-fairs, these periodic congregations probably witnessed socio-economic and religious transactions of many types among people coming from fairly long distances.

Hence, some of the controversies have been resolved through controlled, systematic and multidisciplinary explorations and excavations in recent decades by Paddayya in the Hunsgi valley, northern Karnataka. For example, he has demarcated the areas used for cattle penning and cow-dung disposal, human settlements with burials, areas for animal butchering (see Pl. 6-9), chert workshop, etc. The identification of butchering area is certainly very important.

He used a landscape approach and his observations appear to be quite significant. He finds that the ash-mounds generally occur in the hilly tracts, close to perennial water sources, covered by Archaen granite-gneiss formations, which offer plentiful pasturage but contain soils of only sandy type, ill-suited for agricultural purposes. Large tracts of open land, suitable for human occupation, were available around the ash-mounds and most of the sites have thick and extensive habitation deposits. In fact, these sites were regular pastoral settlements. He dicovered as many as 13 human burials, which include both pits and urn burials. The skeletons belonged to sub-adult population.

His observations (Paddayya in press) can be summarised as follows:

1. These sites represent a characteristic mode of adaptation on the part of the Neolithic settlers to the ecological setting of the region. The area, which is covered with granite-gneiss hills of the Archaean age, offers limited scope for agricultural activities but has vast reserves of pasture ideally suited to pastoral activity. It is the latter alternative, which the Neolithic people specialised in cattle— and, to some extent, sheep/goat—pastoralism. Ash-mounds are an eloquent testimony to the overwhelmingly pastoral orientation of the Neolithic culture of southern Deccan.
2. These studies fully endorse Bruce Foote's views about the Neolithic age of the ash-mounds and their cow-dung origin. Paddayya however thinks that Allchin's division of the Neolithic sites of this region into habitation and cattle penning sites is untenable. It is now certain that ash-mounds are full-fledged pastoral settlements. Budihal excavations exposed various functionally specific activity areas within the site. In fact, Paddayya noticed (in January 1995) at Utnur (excavated by F.R. Allchin) a similar twofold division of the ash-mound into an upper mound representing cow-dung disposal and burning area and the lower portion where Allchin laid his trenches and obtained structural and other forms of evidence of cattle penning. Paddayya also noticed an extensive Neolithic habitation area on the eastern side of the ash-mound. The ash-mound at Hulikallu in Anantapur district also produced evidence of human occupation including burials around the ash deposit.
3. He noticed a definite gradation in the size of ash-mounds. Sites like Budihal are enormous in size and probably served as local/regional centres where periodic socio-economic congregations, similar to the present-day cattle fairs, were held. The extensive chert workshop found at Budihal must be exporting its blade products to other settlements.
4. In view of his extensive research, he suggests that evidence of cattle penning and resultant accumulation of cow-dung and ash deposits should also be expected at other Neolithic-Chalcolithic sites characterised by agro-pastoral economy. He notes that such deposits have been found at sites like Inamgaon (Dhavalikar *et al.* 1988:131) and other sites in northern Deccan and Balathal (Misra *et al.* 1995:74) in Rajasthan.
5. He suggests that ash-mounds do seem to hold clues for reconstructing even the sociological and ideological realms of Neolithic life. Recent attempts at redefining the 'Neolithic' concept in terms of human sentiments and motivations give rise to many possibilities of further work. There is tremendous scope too for additional geo- and bioarchaeological investigations.

Cultural and Trade Contacts

The nature of contacts between the southern Neolithic and the Chalcolithic and also with the Harappans has been discussed by scholars. Broadly speaking, all these cultures may be dated between the third millennium and the beginning of the first millennium BC. So it is not in the least surprising that contacts existed between them and the southern Neolithic culture. The working of metals and such ceramic items as the black-and-red ware, cream-slipped pottery and wheel-thrown pottery akin to the Jorwe ware reported from some of the Neolithic sites are attributed to influences from the Chalcolithic cultures. It is likely that manufacture of grey ware pottery and ground stone tools were perhaps copied by/from some of the Chalcolithic cultures of the southern Deccan.

There are certain elements present in the ceramic industry, which emphasise this cultural intercourse between the North and the South. Paddayya points out that: 1). Of particular importance are the pots with a high collared neck and the bowl- or dish-on-stand. So far, no comparable shapes have been found in other parts of the southern Deccan. On the other hand, the former shape calls to mind the two kuja-shaped vessels from Navdatoli, while the latter is common at many of the Chalcolithic sites. 2). The incised pottery reveals certain designs hitherto not recorded at the Neolithic sites. They comprise alternating herring-bone bands, short strokes or slashes, dot-like or large impressions, zigzags and fingernail impressions. All of these are found variously at Nevasa, Chandoli, Prakashe, Navdatoli and several other Chalcolithic sites. 3). The combed pottery, leaving aside a few sherds from T. Narsipur, this form of decoration may also be regarded as novel to the Neolithic pottery. It is regularly associated with the red wares of Period Ia at Ahar. A number of sherds treated in a similar fashion are also known from Navdatoli and Kayatha (Dhavalikar 1970a: 89, Fig. 2, Nos. 7-9). Further, an analogous form of decoration characterises one of the pre-Harappan fabrics (Fabric D) at Kalibangan (IAR 1962-63: 23, Fig. 7). Paddayya thinks that such decoration, the vessel shapes and incised patterns enumerated above were all copied by the Neolithic cultures from the Northern cultures.

The Jorwe culture is centred in the Godavari-Pravara basin and extends north up to the Tapti valley and in the south up to the Bhima valley. The excavations at Jorwe, Nasik, Nevasa, Daimabad, Bahal, Prakashe, Chandoli, Songaon and Inamgaon give us a well-documented picture of its various component elements. The ^{14}C dates from Nevasa, Chandoli, Songaon and Inamgaon indicate a time-spread of about 500 years, from c. 1500 to 1000 BC. It may be recalled that at Daimabad this culture succeeds the Malwa culture, the latter is preceded by the Neolithic phase distinguished by grey pottery and polished stone and blade industries (IAR 1958-59: 15-18). Songaon produced a comparable cultural sequence. We may therefore assume that the southern Neolithic culture once extended over a large part of Maharashtra. The ^{14}C date, TF-384, 1465 BC (uncalib.) from Songaon and the comparative evidence of pottery suggest that this northward expansion took place in the earlier part of the upper phase, i.e., between c. 1900 and 1600 BC. In fact Dhavlikar (1970b) has argued that the Jorwe culture is a product of the fusion of the southern Neolithic and Malwa cultures. Nagaraja Rao's comparative study has shown that close contacts existed between these two food-producing cultures. The evidence obtained from the Shorapur Doab and the adjoining Bijapur district places these contacts on a much firmer ground. This is revealed by the fact that they shared a number of features relating to pottery, burial customs, technology, etc.

The Bijapur Region

Over 80 proto-historic sites have been explored in the south-eastern and northern parts of this district (Sundara 1968). The sites occurring in the south-eastern part (Sundara's Group A) yield artefacts typical of the Neolithic culture. Those of the northern part occur on the Bhima proper or the tributary streams flowing into it. Sundara (1968: map in Fig. 1) classifies them into two groups: Group B and Group C. The sites in Group B roughly cover the Sindgi taluk which borders on the Shorapur Doab. Like Group A, they also belong to the Neolithic culture, but some of them produce small quantities of Jorwe ware and Black-and-Red pottery. The Group C sites yield both varieties of potteries in profuse quantities. Lying as they do in the middle reaches of the river Bhima, these sites are within a distance of 150 to 200 km only from the Jorwe culture sites of Songaon, Chandoli and Inamgaon, all located in the upper reaches of the same river. At Dhulkhed, Chanegaon, Anachi, Nagarhalli and Urchan small mounds are still present. Sundara suspects a distinct Jorwe phase at these places. The sites of this area provide indisputable evidence of the spread southwards of the Jorwe culture.

Paddayya observes that the influences exerted by the Jorwe culture extended further down into the Shorapur Doab as proved by three ceramic elements: 1. The evidence of Jorwe ware found at Bijapur and Kannekolur-1. This pottery shares all the technological characteristics of the black-on-red ware of the Jorwe culture. The available shapes - convex-sided bowl, bowl with concave sides and carinated base, wide-mouthed pot with short concave neck and jar with cylindrical neck - are all common at the northern Deccan sites. From its meagre presence at only two sites, it appears that this pottery was acquired by the Neolithic settlers through trade. 2. The Black-and-Red Ware occurring at Budihal and Kannekolur-1 forms another connecting link. Judging from the absence of burnish, it would seem that this pottery is different from the Iron Age Black-and-Red Ware. It is therefore justified to group it with the Black-and-Red/brown pottery found at Tekkalakota, Sanganakallu, Chandoli, Tekwada and other sites. 3. The evidence of the footed bowls and the bowl with squarish base also indicates contacts. As has already been noted, the former shape is paralleled at Chandoli and Songaon, while the latter - hitherto unknown to the Neolithic ceramic industry - has its analogues at Nevasa. These shapes were perhaps adopted by the Neolithic culture from its Chalcolithic counterpart.

The close relationship thus revealed between the two cultures is mainly due to their geographical contiguity. In this connection it is important to realise the peculiar geographical position which the Shorapur Doab and the Bijapur district occupy in the Deccan. They form part of a narrow belt of land running south-west-north-east between the Belgaum and Bidar districts. It is along this zone that the Deccan trap and granite-gneiss formations, each with its own physiographic peculiarities, meet each other. It is along this belt that the cultural traditions of Maharashtra - language, food habits, etc.- overlap with those of the Karnataka plateau. From both geographical and cultural points of view, this belt forms a transitional zone between the upper and lower parts of the Deccan peninsula. Spate *et al.* (1967) would describe it as a zone of "culture conflict". The evidence of cultural contacts presented above proves that this situation existed already in proto-historic times. Indeed, the area must have served as the meeting-ground for the two village-farming cultures. The river Bhima, rising as it does in the northern Deccan and debauching into the Krishna after flowing past the contact zone, must have acted as the communication line for this cultural traffic. The ^{14}C dates from Chandoli, Songaon and Inamgaon would place these developments between c. 1400 and 1000 BC (uncalib.). The site at Urchan may be very important to understand this phenomenon (The above account of the southern Neolithic is mainly based on Paddayya's reports) (see Table 6.9).

TABLE 6.9 NEOLITHIC (EARLY AGRICULTURE: PENNINSULAR INDIA)

All BP ages are based on 5568 yrs. half-life of radiocarbon. Calibrated ages are given in bc (after Possehl 1994).

Site	*Sample No.*	*5568 Yrs. (half life)*	*Calib. Dates*	*Culture*	*Material*
Gharluli	TF-1162	Modern	None	Late Neolithic?	Charcoal
Hallur	TF-576	3280±105BP	1570,1528, cal.bc	Period IB, Late Neolithic	Charcoal
Hallur	TF-580	3560±105BP	1908 cal.bc	Period IA, Early Neolithic	Charcoal
Hallur	TF-586	3055±95BP	1379,1343, 1319 cal.bc	Period IB, Late Neolithic	Charcoal
Hallur	TF-575	2895±100BP	1065 cal.bc	Period II, Neolithic/ Iron Age overlap	Charcoal
Marakadola	BS-42	660 ± 95BP	1287 cal.ad	Neolithic	Charcoal
Namphuk	PRL-539	19290±920BP	None	Neolithic	Charcoal
Paiyam Palli	TF-349	3340±100BP	1643 cal.bc	Neolithic/Megalithic transition	Charcoal
Paiyam Palli	TF-833	3215±210BP	1513 cal.bc	Late Southern Neolithic	Charcoal Charcoal
Paiyam Palli	TF-827	3570±105BP	1923 cal.bc	Neolithic/Megalithic transition	Charcoal
Palvoy	TF-700	3390±95BP	1730,1729, 1689 cal.bc	Neolithic/Megalithic transition	Charcoal
Palvoy	TF-701	3805±100BP	2281 cal.bc	Early Southern Neolithic	Charcoal
Polakonda	BS-98	3255±120BP	1522 cal.bc	Southern Neolithic	Wood
Polakonda	BS-97	2045±90BP	83 cal.bc	Megalithic Period	Wood Charcoal
Payatha Pattan	PRL-816	4190±140BP	2877,2800, 2780,2712, 2708 cal.bc	Aceramic Neolithic	Charcoal
Sangan-kallu	TF-354	3440±100BP	1746 cal.bc	Middle Southern Neolithic	Charcoal
Sangan-kallu	TF-359	3400±100BP	1733,1721, 1697 cal.bc	Middle Southern Neolithic	Charcoal
Sangan-kallu	TF-355	3435±100BP	1745 cal.bc	Late Southern Neolithic	Charcoal
Satanikota	BS-204	8960±120BP	None	Megalithic	Charcoal
Satanikota	BS-203	7520±140BP	6410 cal.bc	Megalithic	Charcoal
T. Narsipur	TF-412	3645±105BP	2033 cal.bc	Southern Neolithic	Charcoal

Cont. Table 6.9

Cont. Table 6.9

Site	*Sample No.*	*5568 Yrs. (half life)*	*Calib. Dates*	*Culture*	*Material*
T. Narsipur	TF-413	3345±105BP	1672 cal.bc	Southern Neolithic	Charcoal
Tekkala Kota	TF-237	3465±105BP	1859,1848, 1769 cal.bc	Neolithic Period	Charcoal
Tekkala Kota	TF-239	3395±105BP	1732,1725, 1692 cal.bc	Neolithic Period	Charcoal
Tekkala Kota	TF-266	3625±100BP	2023,1998, 1983 cal.bc	Neolithic Period	Charcoal
Tekkala Kota	TF-262	3460±135BP	1851,1850, 1761 cal.bc	Neolithic Period	Charcoal
Terdal	TF-684	3775±95BP	2200 cal.bc	Southern Neolithic	Charcoal
Terdal	TF-683	3615±120BP	2014,2016, 1976 cal.bc	Southern Neolithic	Charcoal
Utnur	TF-168	3875±110BP	2452,2427, 2395,2374, 2366 cal.bc	Period IIIA Neolithic	Charcoal
Utnur	BM-54	4120±150BP	2860,2817, 2693,2684, 2662,2633, 2626 cal.bc	Period I, Neolithic	Charcoal
Utnur	TF-167	3890±110BP	2455,2416, 2405 cal.bc	Period IIA, Neolithic	Charcoal

Chapter 7

THE ROLE OF CENTRAL HIMALAYAS IN THE ARCHAEOLOGY OF NORTH INDIA

Contents :

- Preamble
- Stone Age
- Rock Art
- Palaeoclimate
- Early Agriculture
- Genetic Data
- Archaeological Evidence
- Linguistic Data
- Metal Technology
- Conclusions

PREAMBLE

The new state of Uttaranchal in North India covers the Central Himalayas (Fig. 7-1), comprising the major divisions of Almora, Nainital, Garhwal and Pithoragarh (Fig. 7-2). Recent years have seen fairly extensive archaeological research in this region, thanks to the efforts of the Kumaun and Garhwal universities and the Uttar Pradesh State Department of Archaeology.

The Central Himalayas provide a mini-example for understanding the Indian civilisational processes. Through the millennia different tribes and people - protoaustroloids, Mundas, Kiratas, Mongoloids, Indo-Aryans, Khasas, Sakas and others—have been pouring into this cultural melting pot and leaving their signatures and producing a mosaic of cultures, which got integrated in the course of time. For long years this region of Central Himalayas was considered a cul-de-sac. But now it is becoming clear that this region has provided a corridor for cultural interactions. We have briefly indicated the role of the Central Himalayas in the introduction of agriculture in Chapter 6 and the same will be done for copper and iron technology and the urbanisation processes of the Ganga valley in a separate volume. Hence this requires a paradigm shift in our thinking.

It is very interesting to note that in this region the local deities are more powerful than the Brahmanical/classical gods. The antiquity of such deities goes back to prehistoric times. Even Badrinath, which has been regarded a Vaishnav deity is, in fact, a local god. Nanda is essentially a local goddess but later on appropriated as a consort of Siva. In the Central Himalayas one can also study how people create deities (and not vice versa!). Often historical personages have been deified as powerful gods like Goll Devata. He was in fact a court judge of the local kings less

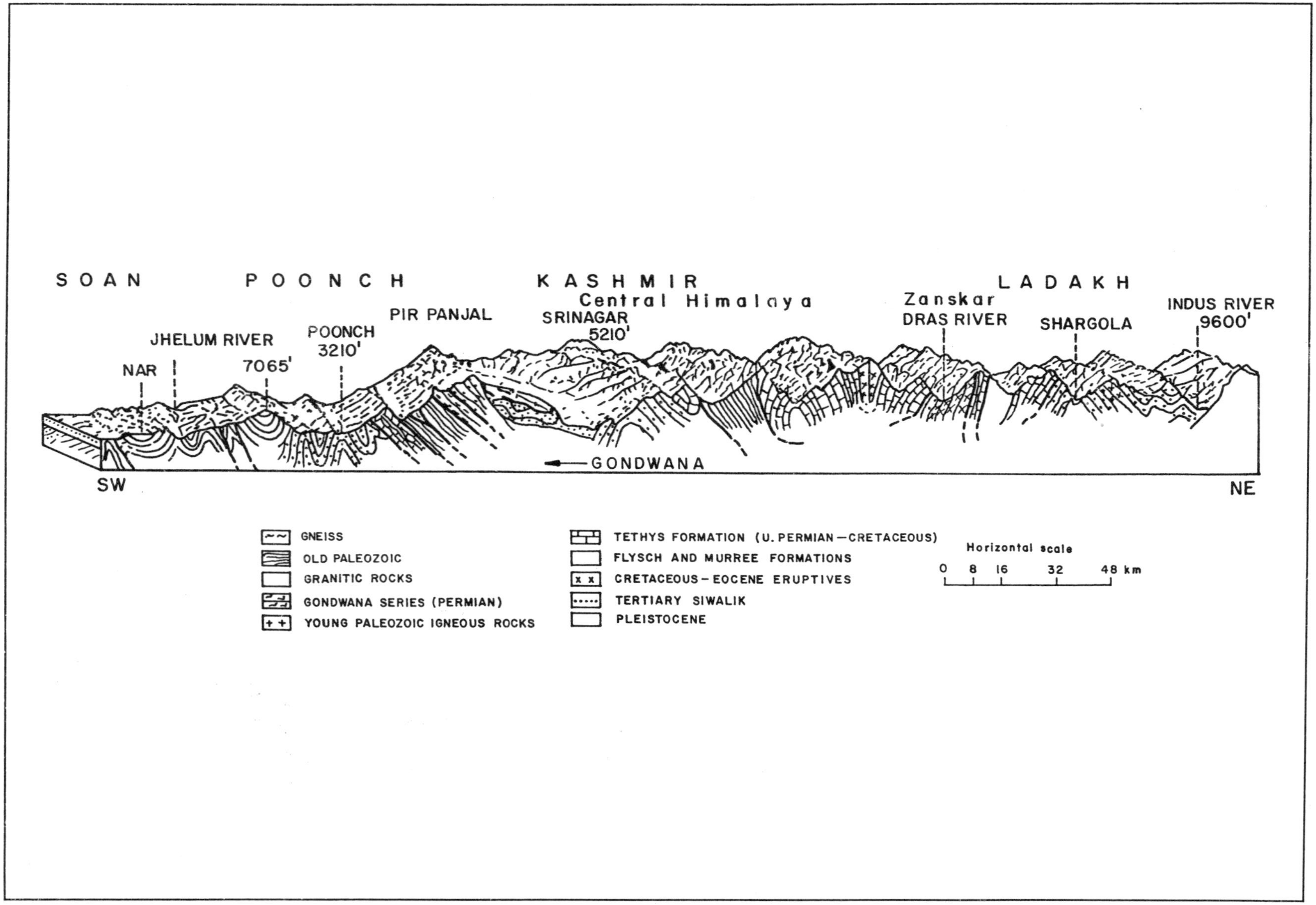

Fig. 7-1. Block diagrammatical sketch of the North-western Himalayas

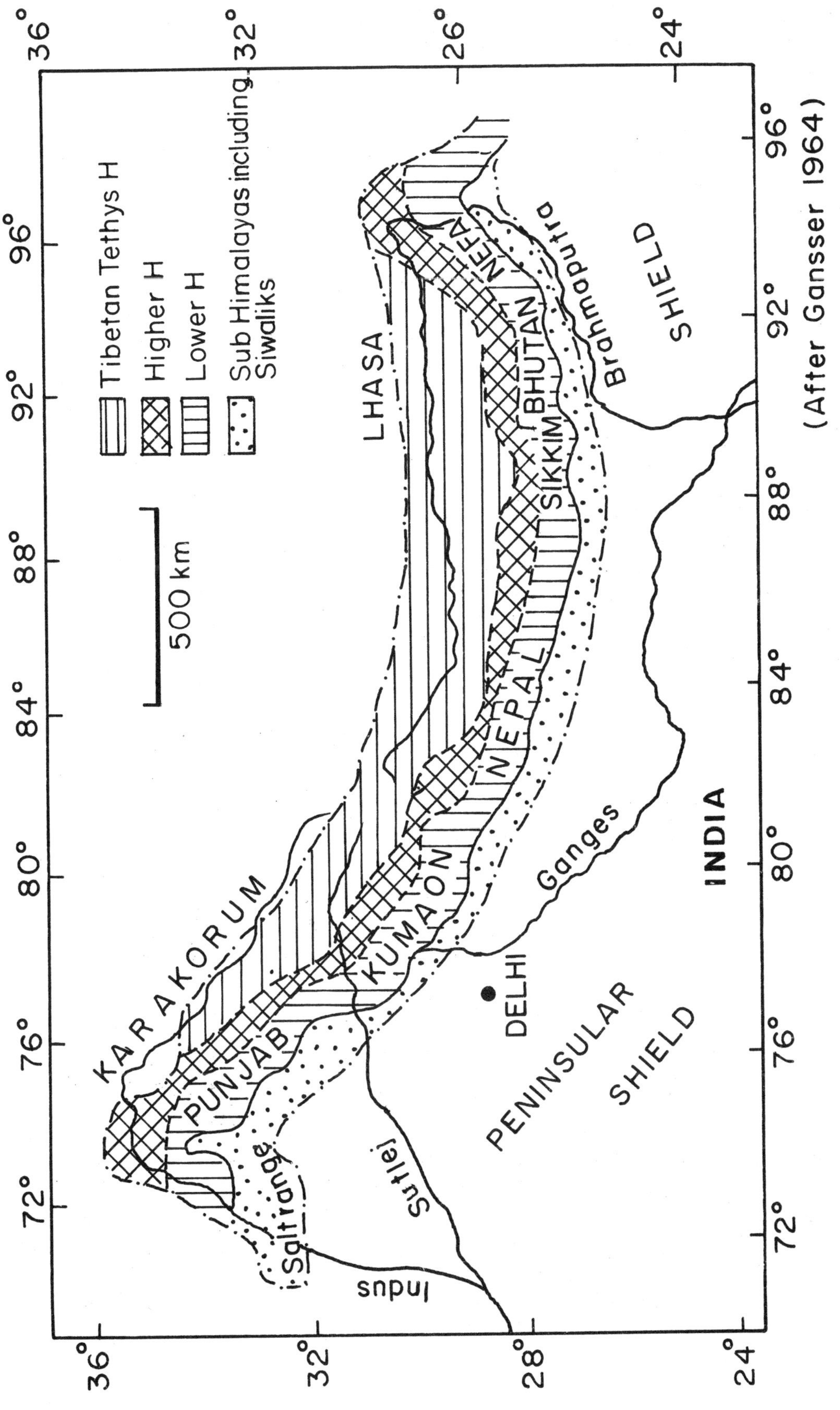

Fig. 7-2. Map of Himalayas showing higher, lower and sub-Himalayas, and Tibetan Tethys Himalayas

than a thousand years back. There are several shrines in this region devoted to him. Thus we see that the process of apotheosis of making gods of historical persons can be seen in a very concrete form here. Brijendra Lal Shah ('Lala') has brought out a small book on Goll Devata, which is in fact a piece of historical writing though written in verse form.

The Central Himalayas also provide excellent opportunities for studying traditional knowledge systems as they are better preserved here than in the plains. These systems of knowledge need to be studied, documented and preserved for the benefit of humankind. To appreciate its relevance to the North Indian archaeology, let us have a closer look at the past of Kumaun, starting chronologically from the Stone Age onwards.

STONE AGE

During the early 1990s we made some concerted efforts to look for Stone Age artifacts in different parts of Kumaun (Agrawal & Kharakwal 1998). At many sites we found bifacial choppers, scrapers, and even some cleavers. But unless one gets a workshop where one can find the flakes and the cores from which they were struck, caution demands that we do not make a claim of finding Stone Age tools in this region. We have also noticed that the floors of several painted rock shelters are littered with quartz chips and flakes but could not find definitive tools. Nevertheless we are not ruling out the possibility of their presence in the region as Nepal, Himachal and Kashmir have yielded Palaeoliths. We are also aware of the claims made by some scholars about their Stone Age finds from Kumaun as well as Garhwal regions. Scientific rigour demands that we look for factory sites; only then the world will believe the occurrence of Stone Age artifacts.

ROCK ART

In early 1970s, along with M.P. Joshi, we (D.P. Agrawal) reported the rock art site of Lakhiudyar at Dalband. As we did not find any evidence of metal tools or agriculture in the paintings we assigned them to prehistoric period (Agrawal & Joshi 1978) (see Chapter 5).

Subsequently, many such sites have been discovered in the Central Himalayan area (Fig. 7-3). Apart from paintings a variety of engravings and cupules have also been found from this region. Though on stylistic grounds some paintings are similar to the Central Indian examples (see Chapter 5) yet most of the figures tend to form a regional style or tradition. The rock art (paintings) has excellent potentiality for a variety of investigations as now techniques are available to identify blood up to species level from just a pinhead amount of sample (nanograms).

PALAEOCLIMATE

Unlike Kashmir, where the Indian monsoon could not reach since 2.5 Myr, Central Himalayas are on its route and thus provide excellent sediment profiles for studying the changes in monsoon system vis-à-vis the pulsed uplift of the Tibetan plateau (Agrawal & Yadava 1998:55-59). There are many excellent sites, which can provide us clues to the changes in climate during the last 2 million years. Now it is established that during the last 2 million years there had been several cycles of cooling and warming. The glacial phases had lasted 100 thousand years but the inter-glacial phases lasted only 10-12 thousand years. Kumaun University (Kotlia *et al.* 1997) has also made some notable efforts in this direction. In Bhimtal area we had also made such investigations (Agrawal *et al.* 1988, 1989, 1994). For the Kashmir valley, we have produced a consistent sequence of climatic change during the last 4 million years based on a variety of parametres (Agrawal 1992).

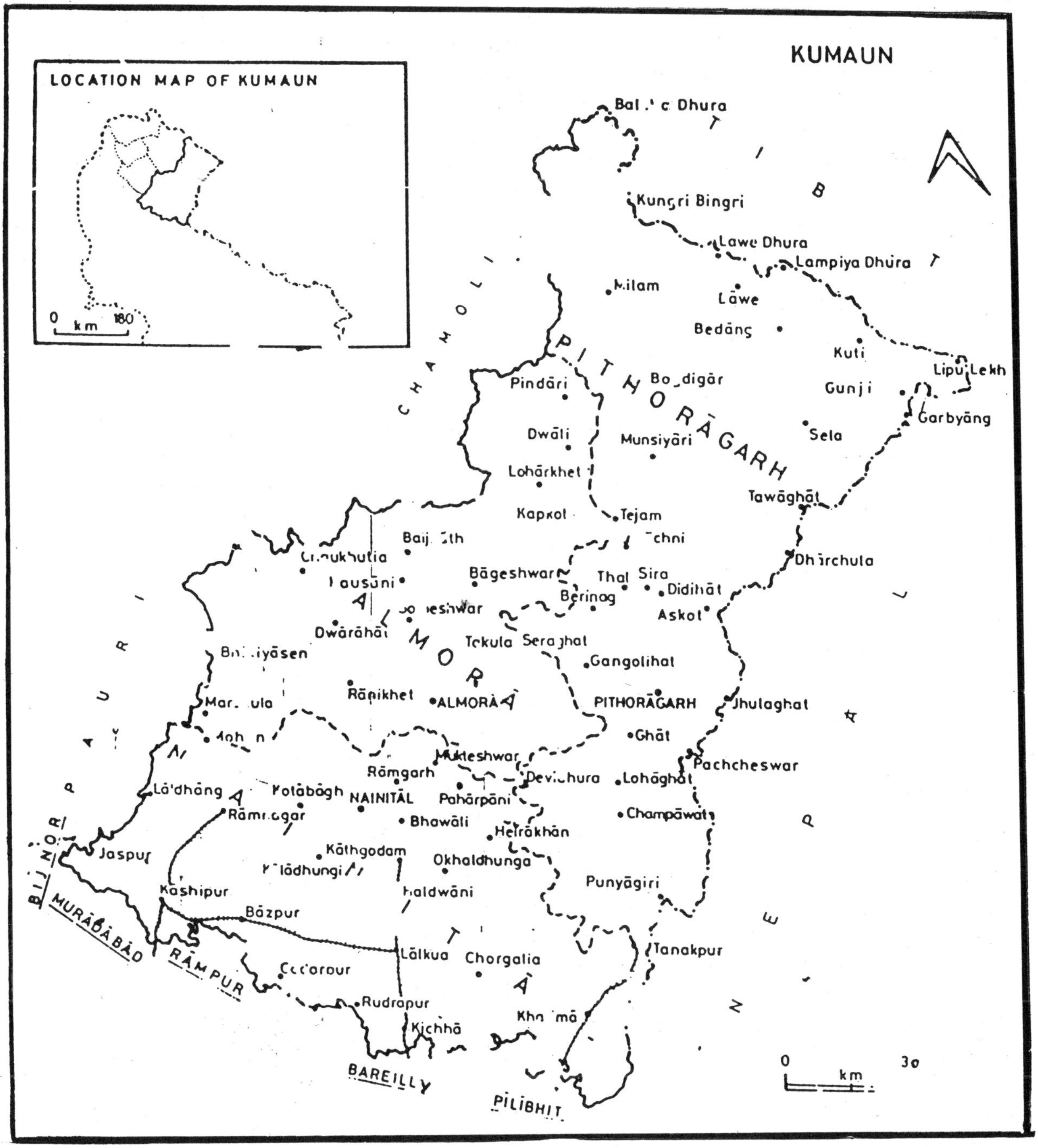

Fig. 7-3. Map of Kumaun showing main sites

EARLY AGRICULTURE

We have to look at the problem of the origins of early agriculture in a pan-Asian perspective.

With the recent work of Yasuda (2000:1-4) and Gordon (1999 Field Report), the dates of earliest domesticated rice in south China have been pushed back considerably. Recent progress in archaeobotanical studies have pointed to rice domestication in the middle reaches of the Yangtze to 10,000 years BC and beyond (see chapter 6). We have discussed in the earlier chapter that the early rice growing communities of China, Japan and South-east Asia were using cord ware. This kind of pottery has been also found from many sites in north-eastern India, Ganga valley and Central Himalaya. Barring the last region it has generally been found associated with the evidence of rice in other areas. Unlike other crops, rice cultivation in the Central Himalaya, is associated with a lot of rituals, which is a sure indication of its antiquity. Recent archaeological and linguistic research has shown that rice domestication in south China goes back to 15-16 thousand years. There is evidence that early agriculture spread to South-east Asia and to Brahmaputra valley, as also along the Himalayan corridors. We will not be surprised if the antiquity of rice goes back to thousands of years in this region. Linguistic evidence also sheds some new light on the problem.

Rice (*Oryza*) is unique among cereals in being an aquatic crop, which can vary between a perennial and annual according to water conditions. The wild *Oryza rufipogon* has both perennial and annual types. Perennials have lower seed productivity, lower self-pollination, long anther length and greater height. Annuals tend to have high seed productivity, self-pollination, short anther length and lesser stature. Annuals adapt to more heavily disturbed conditions like pond edges and drought conditions, making them the likely domestic rice ancestor.

GENETIC DATA

A significant proportion of the South-east Asian human populations possess the 9-bp 'non-deletion' allele on Ddel (10394)-Alul (10397) +/+ or +/-backgrounds. In fact, the two classes of haplo-types observed in South-east Asian populations, one of which is completely absent in Indian populations, leads one to believe that South-east Asian populations were derived from two sources: one from India and the other possibly from central or southern China. It may be noted that the 9-bp deletion is present in high frequencies among Tharus and Japanese - populations that are postulated to have arisen from human migrations originating from southern China (Roychoudhury *et al.* 2000:1182-1192). Tharus now live in the foothills of the Central Himalayas. Another tribe, called Raji-Raut, is also suspected to be original speakers of Mon-Khmer language. It may be essential to determine if there is genetic evidence also of the south China populations having come through the Central Himalayas corridors.

Chinese wild rice *japonica* carries specific isozyme alleles and neucleo- and cyto-types at high frequency. Carrying this further, DNA analyst Sato (1996) showed *indica* and *japonica* differentiated before domestication. As the main domesticated rice in China is *japonica,* we should look for circumstances surrounding its transition from wild *rufipogon*. The same should be studied for the Indian varieties also. This transition can be estimated with multivariate analysis of wild verses domesticated rice phytoliths, but important environmental data may be found using pollen and insects from the same samples.

ARCHAEOLOGICAL EVIDENCE

In the Ganga valley several sites have yielded rice impressions on clay, e.g., Koldihwa, Mahagara, Chapani Mando and others. Though abundant use of domesticated rice in the subcontinent comes from Pirak, which begins around c. 1800BC whereas in the Ganga valley sites it has been assigned to seventh-sixth millennium BC (Sharma *et al.* 1980:23). There are four radiocarbon determinations for the Mahagara Neolithic phase with calibrated dates ranging between c.1700 and 1200BC, concordant with the chronology of Pirak I. It should be noted that an uncalibrated ^{14}C date for the pre-Neolithic Mahagara is 8080+115 BC (Sharma *et al.* 1980:3). We, however, think that rice domestication in this area should go to early Holocene period. Though some of the dates go back to 7000BP, there is considerable controversy both about chronology and proof of domestication. Rice (*Oryza sativa*) is the most popular cereal in South Asia today. Wild rice, *Oryza rufipogon* is pan-tropical in distribution and found generally in the Ganga valley, Indus river system and in Gujarat. The archaeological record in India suggests that hunting and gathering communities used the wild form. We have, however, yet to make some serious effort to find out when exactly rice came under cultivation in the Ganga valley and in Central Himalayas. We thus see that rice technology has a high probability to reach Central Himalayas and then on to Ganga valley from south China. But this has to be confirmed through a multidisciplinary study as suggested above.

LINGUISTIC DATA

Grierson (1967-68) in his linguistic survey of the Himalayas had identified some residue of Mon-Khmer words in the Kumauni dialects. Mon-Khmer is part of the Austro-Asiatic language group (Bayard 1996). With the new ^{14}C AMS dates from Thailand, the copper metallurgy there can be pushed back to second-third millennia BC. White (1997) reports, "The earliest evidence of bronze at Ban Chiang appears by Early Period II/III in both burial and non-burial contexts. The calibrated results...indicate an early second millennium BC date for this part of the sequence". White further says, "The 3KUM dating and pollen evidence is broadly consistent with Blust's (1996) linguistic arguments for the expansion of rice-cultivating, Mon-Khmer speaking societies down the Mekong from south-western China beginning by the late 6th millennium BC". The dates quoted by White from 3 KUM come from a sediment core. The evidence is consistent with land clearance in the early fifth millennium BC. Such a date seems to accord well with the linguistic argument of Blust (1996). Our experience from the Rajasthan lakes has also been similar: the advent of *Cerealia* type pollen is accompanied (c. 7000 BP) by finely comminuted charcoal, which has been interpreted as clearance for agriculture (Singh *et al.* 1990: 351-58). White argues for a 6th millennium BC beginning of agriculture accompanied by the expansion of the Mon-Khmer family of languages, as argued by Blust (1996); and a substantial time gap between the advent of agriculture and metallurgy. Higham, on the other hand, thinks that this gap could be only a few hundred years.

Unfortunately in India the North-east is still archaeologically a *terra incognita*. It will be interesting to define the gap between the advent of agriculture and copper metallurgy through the Himalayan corridor. The movement of Munda speaking people along the Himalayan corridor, however, is generally agreed upon.

Now let see how this evidence is relevant to the Central Himalayas. In Kumaun, the *shilpkars*, earlier called Doms, are supposed to be Kols, speakers of Munda dialects (D.D. Sharma 1988). Munda and Mon-Khmer dialects are two branches of the Austro-Asiatic family. There are many Austro-Asiatic aboriginal languages still spoken in Thailand (Bayard pers. comm.; Bayard 1996). Elsewhere we have discussed (Agrawal & Kharakwal, 1998) that the Kols are said to be the first ethnic people of Kumaun, which had descended from the Munda speaking group, which is related to the Austro-Asiatic sub-group. They represent the aborigines of Kumaun. Doms (*shilpkars*) are perhaps the modern representatives of the Kols (Atkinson 1980-81: 370), who today occupy the lowest rung in the hierarchical status in Kumauni society and are now included among the Scheduled Castes. They also claim to have been in Kumaun before either the Khasiya or the immigrants from the plains arrived. The Doms are the traditional smiths in Kumaun.

Higham (1996) discusses the relationship between the Austro-Asiatic and Austronesian languages and whether they belong to a common ancestral Austric phylum and its implications for archaeology. In view of the recent work by Reid (1993, in Higham 1996) and Blust (1993, in Higham 1996), Higham tends to agree with the Austric hypothesis as it would require only one Neolithic expansion and spread of rice cultivation which, according to him, is better supported by archaeological evidence. He describes the South-east Asian rivers as being like spokes in a wheel, "with the hub in the eastern foothills of the Himalayas.... In a westward direction, ancestors of the Munda moved, perhaps down the Brahmaputra into eastern India. (Higham 1996:115) Obviously, the movement did not stop there but went further westward to the Central Himalayas. This type of South East and Westward movements probably explain better the expansion first of the rice cultivation and later on of metallurgy.

Synthesising the archaeo-linguistic evidence Bayard (1996) agrees, "It is very tempting to correlate this with the westward expansion, under the stimulus of agriculture, of Austro-Asiatic (AA) language from Nanhailand through Viet Nam, Laos, Cambodia and Thailand to Burma and ultimately eastern India. Linguists have reconstructed a number of terms related to agriculture in proto-Munda, and some of these (husked rice, rice husking pestle) appear to go back to proto-AA as well. It has been generally agreed for some time now that the prehistoric and early historic inhabitants of Thailand and Burma spoke languages in the Mon-Khmer branch of AA. Such an expansion would account neatly - in a general sense for the distribution of the AA languages". Bayard further says:

> Based on morphological evidence such as that presented by Reid (1988: 31-32, in Bayard 1996), Blust is convinced that Schmidt's Austric hypothesis is correct and postulates an Austric homeland in the eastern Himalayan foothills in the area of the converging valleys of the Salween, Mekong, and Yangtze rivers. From this homeland, one group of rice cultivating people moved down into the middle Yangtze valley to give rise to the AT superfamily of languages ca. 6500-6000 BC. Somewhat later the now proto-AA speakers remaining in the homeland began to move down the valleys of the Salween and Mekong (proto-Mon-Khmer), with pre-Munda speakers moving westward down the Brahmaputra....

We admit that considerable miscegenation has been going on in the Central Himalayas for several millennia now and the concept of race is now defunct. Yet in the relative isolation (compared to the Ganga Doab) of Central Himalayas one can still observe that the Brahmins and Kshatriyas have sharp features and fair complexion. The Bhotiyas and the descendants of the Kiratas bear unmistakable Mongoloid features. The Doms, who practise blacksmithy as a traditional craft, are typically short statured, dark complexioned and answer to Austro-Asiatic features.

METAL TECHNOLOGY

Let us briefly look at the possibility of contacts between Central Himalayas and Ganga valley in early metal technology and metals.

The copper hoards of the Ganga valley are by and large made of arsenical copper, the source of which was perhaps Central Himalayas (Agrawal 2000). In recent years copper hoards have also been found from many sites in the Central Himalayan region, which are technologically crude compared to the Doab examples. It is quite likely that they preceded the Gangetic specimens. There has been a strong tradition of ancient copper and iron mining and smelting in Kumaun region as discovery of a large number of such sites would suggest. We have also found that iron smelting goes back in this region as early as first millennium BC and the cist burials, similar to ones found in Swat, appear to be equally old (Agrawal and Kharakwal 1998).

Cist burials were exposed at Malari, in higher Himalaya and in the valley of western Ramganga by Garhwal University and in the Gomati valley by Archaeological Survey in early 1990s. The Garhwal University group has, however, termed the painted pottery found from Sanana-Baseri as proto-painted grey ware (PGW) type, though PGW is also found in the remote hills of the Central Himalayas. The cists at Bechandhar (Chaukhutia), Ladyura and Gagrigol all have black-and-grey ware pottery. Some of these burials have also yielded evidence of iron too. It has been discussed elsewhere that the Central Himalayan region was perhaps a prime source of iron for PGW culture (Agrawal *et al.* 1995; Agrawal and Kharakwal 1998; Kharakwal and Harbola 1996; Kharakwal *et al.* 1993). Thus it seems that the Central Himalayan region played a vital role in the diffusion of metal technologies and agriculture.

CONCLUSIONS

The Central Himalayas, in recent years, have thus produced some important new evidence. The North-east still largely remains *terra incognita*. It is time we explored the Himalayan corridors and looked east. This will require a paradigm shift in our archaeological thinking - no less.

From what we have argued above, it seems that in Central Himalayas the human occupation is as old as any other region of the subcontinent despite its rugged terrain. In fact, this region, endowed with scenic beauty, may not have been a closed cul-de-sac but involved in the dynamics of technological diffusion as the evidence of large number of archeaometallurgical sites as well as rich folklore also indicate. The folklore even marks different human immigrations. It seems that the Himalayan corridors played very important role in trade and agriculture of this region. One can fortunately visualise the dynamics of trade across the Himalayas as now Gunji, an important corridor, is opened in mid-June of 2001. These considerations justify the inclusion of this small chapter in the archaeology of North India.

Chapter 8

CONCLUSIONS

Traversing millions of years and thousands of kilometres of the South Asian subcontinent's past, we have reached the end of our journey. It is time to summarise what we discussed in the previous chapters; point to the gaps in our knowledge; and indicate the new directions towards which we need to move. We have also to counter attempts of fundamentalists, both in Pakistan and India, to push us back to the Dark Ages by glorifying such pseudo-sciences as astrology, and also the jingoist attempts to Aryanise all our past.

South Asian archaeology is still obsessed with only artefacts and material remains, without any serious efforts to look beyond to the humans and their society, which created them. When the French Annales schools (Braudel 1972; Bintliff 1991) are providing new ideas and insights for archaeological reconstructions, we in South Asia seem to have stuck up most of the time with artefact descriptions. Recently we came across the book *The Archaeology of Society in the Holy Land* (Levy 1998). The very title emphasises that it is archaeology of society, not merely of artefacts. There are excellent reconstructions in the book, but they are not flights of fancy - but logical inferences based on multidisciplinary data.

We have done some interdisciplinary studies to reconstruct the past environment. The most exhaustive studies have been done in Kashmir, Rajasthan and Gujarat. In other areas, the evidence is still sketchy. In marginal areas, like Rajasthan and Kashmir, a little change in precipitation or temperature forces the humans to seek out greener pastures. The mid-Holocene climatic amelioration is a global phenomenon and it has had its impact on the Neolithic and Bronze Age cultures. It was followed by severe aridity at the turn of the second millennium BC, which had a marked impact on the decline of the Harappans; and at the beginning of first millennium BC on the Chalcolithic cultures of the Deccan. We have quoted a long passage from Diamond's *Guns, Germs and Steel* in Chapter 2 to emphasise that the environmental changes do affect humans, both in the past as well as today. We need to study the human cultures in a holistic perspective, which takes into account resources, technology and environmental change. This is one of the directions in which we have to move. In Chapter 2, we discussed the evidence of environmental change, and what needs to be done. We began Chapter 3 on Palaeolithic cultures with a survey of early hominid finds. There is so much excitement in these early hominid discoveries. Humans are no more to be defined as the toolmakers; there are other human relatives like chimps who also make tools. Even birds make probes to ferret out insects from the tree crevices. Moreover, planning - or manipulation of time - is no more the sole monopoly of humans. Humans have language but other animals too have their communication systems. The evidence of an efflorescence around 40 Kyr is too sudden, and perhaps attributable to the command of language that humans got by this time. Of course, there are other competing causes postulated too.

Here too our strategies seem to have gone wrong: we have millions of tools but no humans to speak of, the single exception being the hominid skull cap from the Narmada valley. A few decades back, Sankalia and Krishnaswami and their numerous students, filled the map of South Asia with Palaeolithic sites. In this, the contributions of de Terra and Paterson (1939) in the 1930s played an epochal role to initiate and inspire such studies. Of course, today their studies seem quite out of date and many of their conclusions erroneous (Rendell *et al.* 1989). But that is the way of all science and knowledge. There is no absolute truth that one can discover, which will hold good for all time to come.

There are so few primary Palaeolithic sites, which have been studied. V.N. Misra in Central India and Paddayya in the peninsular India have provided some excellent examples of contextual Palaeolithic studies; so many others however have been going on merrily describing the millions of artefacts that have been discovered. So far both the dating and environmental interpretations were based on the occurrence of artefacts in secondary and tertiary fluvial contexts. With the availability of physical techniques of dating, we now need to collect the right type of samples and date them. Many of such technologies are now available in South Asia (Singhvi *et al.* 1998).

At this point it may be interesting to recall a comment by Flannery (1998: xvii-xx) in his stimulating Introduction to *The Archaeology of Society in the Holy Land* (Levy 1998). It reflects how sick he had become of endless morphological descriptions of artefacts. He says, "I am often asked why, after 10 happy years in the Near East, I left to work fulltime in Mesoamerica. It began with a terrifying dream. In that dream I was arrested, strapped to a chair in a Near Eastern dungeon, and tortured for 10 hours. The first five hours of torture consisted of lectures on Palaeolithic tool typology, accompanied by 1000 slides of microburins, *pieces esquillees*, and informative debitage. The next five hours consisted of lectures on prehistoric pottery, accompanied by 1000 slides of Halaf bukrania, 'Ubaid black-on-buffs, and Uruk glockentopfe. Worst of all, I woke from the dream to realise that I had actually enjoyed both lectures. That's when I knew it was time to go...."

The transitional cultures (Upper Palaeolithic and Mesolithic) were briefly discussed in Chapter 4. Elsewhere the Upper Palaeolithic heralds major revolutionary changes, but here this phase of the Palaeolithic culture is little understood or documented. Mesolithic is an enigma. It is marked by the use of tiny tools (microliths), quite often with signs of pottery making, incipient agriculture and animal husbandry. We feel that it is better to merge both the so-called Neolithic cultures and the Mesolithic in one category of Early Farming cultures.

We had also pointed out in Chapter 6, on Early Farming, that in South Asia ground stone tools and the Neolithic have become synonymous; they need not be. We have suggested that in Rajasthan some of the so-called Mesolithic cultures might have ushered in early agriculture. The evidence of *Cerealia* type pollen and comminuted pieces of charcoal from the lakes of Didwana, Lunkaransar and Sambhar, may indicate forest clearance and beginning of cultigens.

Chapter 5 deals with the rock art. It needs to be emphasised that India has some of the world's richest rock art areas, like the Bhimbetka and Pachmarhi groups of rock shelters. They have been thoroughly studied by competent scholars, but their dating is based on stylistic considerations. With a variety of dating techniques available now, e.g., AMS dating, micro-erosion studies, TL dating of silica layers, etc., we can use them to provide an absolute chronology of the rock art.

The beginnings of farming and animal husbandry are discussed in Chapter 6. We have traced the sources of wheat, millets and rice from where they possibly reached South Asia. Some millet has been traced to Africa. Maize, unlike the general conceptions, seems to be a local product. We have suggested that possible rice technology reached North India through the

Himalayan corridors from south China. These new ideas have been discussed in Chapter 7 on the role of Himalayas.

We have however to admit that in this phase of South Asian prehistory also tools have dominated the studies. Little efforts have been made to recover and study the agricultural remains from various sites. No definite criteria for identifying domestication of various animals have been scientifically standardised. One glaring example is of horse bones. Though there are large collections of bones from various sites like Kalibangan, Banawali, Dholavira, etc., they have not been systematically studied to solve this problem of horse in the Harappan sites. What it needs is to study some rich collections from a place like British Museum and establish the diagnostic criteria. Of course, there are some honourable exceptions. Deccan College and Birbal Sahni Institute have done some pioneering studies in these fields, but they can't cover the whole of the continent.

A higher level of study would be on the effects of agriculture on population growth and health of people. As explained in our discussions in Chapter 6, agriculture has not been an unmitigated boon to humanity. No doubt it made it possible to sustain large populations on smaller patches of land, than permitted by the hunting-gathering mode of life. But agriculture also brought a host of diseases in its train. We need to develop techniques of calculating population densities and also find evidence of various diseases in the agricultural populations. Such studies are at a very nascent stage despite brave attempts by younger archaeologists like U.C. Chattopadhyaya.

Agricultural surplus and new metal technologies led to urbanisation of the Bronze Age.

We traced the evolutionary steps from hunting-gathering mode of subsistence to full-fledged urbanisation of the Indus civilisation in Chapter 6. At Mehrgarh, in the Kacchi plains of Pakistan, one can see a decrease in wild animals and corresponding increase in domesticates with time. Thanks to decades of the painstaking and meticulous work of the French team in Mehrgarh and Nausharo area, led by Catherine and J.F. Jarrige, and with no less significant contributions from Richard Meadow, we can now trace a continuous history of humans - from the late Stone Age to the flowering of the great Indus Civilisation. Their researches have finally demonstrated that the Indus Civilisation, a glorious chapter of South Asian history, was first written in Baluchistan, and not in the Sarasvati valley, as some scholars have claimed. Their work also finally settles the controversy whether the Indus Civilisation was a West Asian implant. It has turned out to be purely a flowering of the South Asian genius.

Chapter 7 is a bit of a digression, though very relevant and necessary. So far, we have traced the route of cultural diffusion from West Asia to South Asia, be it Palaeolithic cultures, or the urban processes, or the metallurgical know-how. With new evidence - from archaeology, linguistics, and also genetics - it seems likely that rice technology came from south China, via South-east Asia, Brahmaputra valley and the Himalayan corridors to North India. The Mon-Khmer speaking people were responsible perhaps for bringing rice technology with them. This requires a paradigm shift in our thinking, hence the need of interpolating this chapter, which deals with the role of the Central Himalayas in the archaeology of North India. We have tried to demonstrate that the Central Himalayas were not *cul-de-sacs* as is often assumed but responsible for diffusion of technology and metal trade - from rice, to copper to iron.

The great Indus Civilisation tradition heralds the onset of Bronze Age in South Asia. We close our story at this point. The story of South Asian Bronze and Iron Ages requires a book on its own right, which we hope to take up some other time.

BIBLIOGRAPHY

Acharya, S.K. and P.K. Basu. 1993. Toba Ash on the Indian Subcontinent and its implications for correlation of Late Pleistocene alluvium. *Quaternary Research* 40: 10-19.

Achyutan, Hema and Shanti Pappu. 1997. Observations on the geomorphology and archaeology of Erumaivettipalayam, Red Hills, Tamil Nadu. *Man and Environment* 22(1): 87-90.

Agrawal, D.P. 1979. The relevance of archaeology today. *Society and Science* 2(1): 1-15.

Agrawal, D.P. 1982. *The Archaeology of India*. London: Curzon Press.

Agrawal D.P. 1984. Metal technology of the Harappans. In *Frontiers of Indus Civilization* (Eds.) B.B. Lal and S.P. Gupta. New Delhi: Books & Books. Pp. 163-168.

Agrawal, D.P. 1987. Environmental changes in India during last 4 million years. *Journal of the Palaeontological Society of India* 32: 1-4.

Agrawal, D.P. 1992. *Man and Environment in India through Ages*. Delhi: Books & Books.

Agrawal. D.P. 1999a. The role of Central Himalayas in Indian archaeometallurgy. In *Metals in Antiquity* (Eds.) Young, Suzanne, M.M, P. Budd, A.M. Pollard, and Rob Ixer. Oxford: Archaeopress. Pp. 193-199.

Agrawal, D.P. 1999b. Early Indian iron technology, Himalayan contacts and Gangetic urbanisation. In Proc. *Fourth International Conference on the beginning of the use on Metals and Alloys (BUMA–IV)*. Matsue, Japan: The Japan Institute of Metals. Pp. 53-58.

Agrawal. D.P. 2000. *Ancient Metal Technology & Archaeology of South Asia*. Delhi: Aryan Books International.

Agrawal, D.P., R.K. Avasia and S. Guzder. 1973. A multidisciplinary approach to the Quaternary problems in Maharastra. In *Radiocabon and Indian Archaeology* (Eds.) D.P. Agrawal and A. Ghosh. Bombay : TIFR. Pp. 3-17.

Agrawal, D.P. and D.K. Chakrabarti. (Eds.) 1979. *Essays in Indian Protohistory*. New Delhi: B.R.Publishers.

Agrawal, D.P., R. Dodia, B.S. Kotlia, H. Razdan, and A. Sahni. 1989. The Plio-Pleistocene and climatic records of the Kashmir Valley. *Palaeogeography, Palaeoclimatology and Palaeoecology* 73: 266-286.

Agrawal D.P., Rekha Dodia and Mala Seth 1990. South Asian climate and environment at c.18000 BP. In *The World at 18000 BP*, Vol. II (Eds.) O. Soffer and Clive Gamble. London: Unwin and Hyman. Pp. 231-235.

Agrawal, D.P., P.S. Dutta, Z. Hussain, R.V. Krishnamurthy, V.N. Misra, S.N. Rajaguru, and P.K. Thomas. 1980. Palaeoclimate, stratigraphy and prehistory in North and West Rajasthan. *Proceedings of the Indian Academy of Science* 89 (1): 51-66.

Agrawal, D.P. and A. Ghosh (Eds.). 1973. *Radiocarbon and Indian Archaeology*. Bombay: Tata Inst. of Fundamental Research.

Agrawal, D.P., S.K. Gupta and P. Sharma (Eds.) 1988. *Palaeoclimatic and Palaeoenvironmental Changes in Asia*. New Delhi: Indian National Science Academy.

Agrawal D.P. and S. Guzder, 1972. Quaternary studies on the Western Coast of India: preliminary observations. *Palaeobotanist* 21(2): 216-222.

Agrawal D.P. and M.P. Joshi. 1978. Rock paintings in Kumaun. *Man and Environment* 2: 76.

Agrawal, D.P. and J.S. Kharakwal. 1994. Use of scientific techniques in Indian rock art studies. *Purakala* 5(1-2): 67-69.

Agrawal, D.P. and J.S. Kharakwal. 1998. *Central Himalayas: An Archaeological, Linguistic and Cultural Synthesis.* Delhi: Aryan Books International.

Agrawal, D.P. and J.S. Kharakwal. In press. Jodhpura-Ganeshwar Complex, Meluhha and sociology of metallurgy. Paper presented at the *Annual Congress of Indian Society for Prehistoric and Quaternary Studies*, held at Deccan College, Pune 27th to 30th December, 1999.

Agrawal D.P., J.S. Kharakwal, Sheela Kusumgar and M.G. Yadava.1995. Cist burials of the Kumaun Himalayas. *Antiquity* 69 (264): 550-554.

Agrawal D.P., B.S. Kotlia, P. Sharma, and S.K. Gupta. 1988. Environmental magnetism of lake sedimentation in Kumaon Himalayas. *Proceedings of Indian National Science Academy* 54(4): 595-604.

Agrawal, D.P., R.V. Krishnamurthy and S. Kusumgar (Eds.). 1985. *Climate and Geology of Kashmir and Central India: the Last 4 Million Years.* New Delhi: T.T. Publishers.

Agrawal, D.P. and S. Kusumgar. 1974. *Prehistoric Chronology and Radiocarbon Dating in India.* New Delhi: Munshiram Manoharlal.

Agrawal, D.P., S. Kusumgar, R.D. Deshpande, R. Ramesh, C. Sharma and M.G. Yadava. 1994. A comparative study of monsoon and non-monsoon Himalayan lakes, India. Presented at *15th International Radicarbon Conference held at Glasgow*, August 15-19.

Agrawal D.P., S. Kusumgar and P. Sharma. 1989. Radiocarbon chronology and magnetic susceptibility variation in Kumaon lake sediments. *Radiocarbon* 31(3): 957-964.

Agrawal, D.P. and B.M. Pande (Eds.). 1977. *Ecology and Archaeology of Western India.* New Delhi: Concept Publishers.

Agrawal, D.P., H.M. Rendell, R.A.M. Gardner and N. Juyal. 1989. Chronology and stratigraphy of Kashmir loess. *Z.Geomorph. Suppl. Bd.* 76: 213-223.

Agrawal, D.P. and R.K. Sood. 1982. Ecological factors and the Harappan Civilization. In *Harappan Civilizaion* (Ed.) G.L. Possehl. New Delhi: Oxford and IBH Publishing Co.

Agrawal, D.P. and M.G. Yadava. 1995. *Dating the Human Past.* Poona: Indian Society for Prehistoric and Quaternary Studies.

Agrawal, D.P. and M.G. Yadava. 1998. A comparison of proxy climatic data from Tibet and Kashmir. *Himalayan Geology* 19(2): 55-59.

Ahasan, S.M.K. 1993. *A Study of Palaeolithic Site Formation Processes in Sub-humid Environment of Central India with Special reference to Samnapur Palaeolithic Site (Madhya Pradesh).* Ph.D. Dissertation. Pune: University of Poona (unpublished).

Akazawa, Takeru. 1982. Cultural change in Prehistoric Japan: receptivity to rice agriculture in the Japanese archipelago. In *Advances in World Archaeology* Vol 1 (Eds.) Fred Wendorf and Angela C. Close. New York: Academic Press. Pp. 151-211.

Alimen, H. 1957. *The Prehistory of Africa.* London: Hutchinson.

Allchin, B. 1973. Blade and burin industries of West Pakistan and Western India. In *South Asian Archaeology* (Ed.) N. Hammond. London: Duckworth. Pp. 39-50.

Allchin, B. 1976. Palaeolithic sites in the plains of Sind and their geographical implications. *The Geographical Journal* 142/3: 471-489.

Allchin, B. and Allchin, F.R. 1968. *The Birth of Indian Civilization.* Harmondsworth: Pelican.

Allchin, B. and Allchin, R. 1982. *The Rise of Civilization in India and Pakistan.* Cambridge: Cambridge University Press.

Allchin, B. and Goudie, A. 1974. Pushkar: prehistory and climatic change in western India. *World Archaeology* 5 (3): 358-368.

Allchin, B., A. Goudie and K.T.M. Hegde. 1978. *Prehistory and Palaeogeography of the Great Indian Desert.* London: Academic Press.

Allchin, F.R. 1960. *Piklihal Excavations.* Hyderabad: Govt. of Andhra Pradesh.

Allchin, F.R. 1963. *Neolithic Cattle-Keepers of South India: A Study of the Deccan Ashmounds.* Cambridge: Cambridge University Press.

Alur, K.R. 1971. *Animal Remains from Bagor.* Unpublished Report. Pune: Deccan College.

Amphan, Kijngam. 1984. Excavations at Ban Na Di, north-east Thailand. In *Southeast Asian Archaeology at the XV Pacific Science Congress* (Ed.) Donn T. Bayard. University of Otago Studies in Prehistoric Anthropology. Dunedin: University of Otago 16 : 38-41.

An, Zimin. 1982. The Neolithic Archaeology of China. *Early China* 5: 35-45.

An, Zhisheng and Ho Chuan Kun. 1989. New magnetostratigraphic dates of Lantian *Homo erectus*. *Quaternary Research* 32:213-221.

Anderson C.W. 1918. Rock paintings in Singanpur. *Journal of Bihar & Orissa Research Society* 4 (2): 298-306.

Ansari, Z.D., and M.S. Nagaraja Rao. 1969. *Excavation at Sanganakallu: 1964-65*. Poona: Deccan College.

Armand, J. 1985. Emergence of the handaxe tradition in Asia with special reference to India. In *Recent Advances in Indo-Pacific Prehistory* (Eds.) V.N. Misra and Peter Bellwood. Delhi: Oxford & IBH Publishing Co. Pp. 1-8.

Ashraf, Jaweed. 1994. Maize (*Zea mays* L.) in India: introduction or indigenous? *Annals of the National Association of Geographers India*. 14 (2): 6-26.

Asthana, Shashi. 1985. *Pre-Harappan Cultures of India and the Borderlands*. New Delhi: Books and Books.

Atkinson, E.T. 1980-81. *The Himalayan Gazetteer*. Vols.1,2,3. New Delhi: Cosmo Publication. (First published in 1884).

Atkinson, T.C.P., J. Rowe, N.J. Powar and V.S. Kale. 1990. *Unpublished Report Submitted to the Natural Environmental Research Council*. United Kingdom.

Badam, G.L. 1984. Pleistocene Faunal Succession in India. In *The Evolution of the East Asian Environment Vol. II. Palaeobotany, Palaeogeology and Palaeoanthropology* (Ed.) R.O. Whyte. Hong Kong: University of Hong Kong Press. Pp. 746-775.

Bag, A.K. (Ed.). 1997. *History of Technology in India* Vol. I. New Delhi: Indian National Science Academy.

Bajpai, K.D. (Ed.). 1975. *Prachya Pratibha*. Vol. 1-2. Bhopal: Prachya Niketan. Birla Museum.

Ball, V. 1881. *A Manual of the Geology of India Part III, Economic Geology*. Calcutta: Geological Survey of India.

Ban-Kao. 1967. *Archaeological Excavations in Thailand* Vol. II, Neolithic Settlements with Cemeteries in the Kanchnaburi Province. Copenhagen (Denmark): Munksgaard.

Ban-Kao. 1969. *Archaeological Excavations in Thailand* Vol. III, Neolithic Cemeteries in the Kanchnaburi Province. Copenhagen (Denmark): Munksgaard.

Baskaran, M., A.R. Marathe, S.N. Rajaguru and B.L.K. Somayajulu. 1986. Geochronology of Palaeolithic Cultures in Hiran Valley, Saurashtra. *Journal of Archaeological Science* 41: 505-514.

Bayard, D.T. 1970. Excavation at Non Nok Tha, north-eastern Thailand. *Asian Perspectives* 13:110-143.

Bayard, D.T. 1975. North China, South China, Southeast Asia or simply Far East? *Journal of the Hong Kong Archaeological Society* 6:71-79.

Bayard, D.T. 1984. A checklist of Vietnamese radiocarbon dates. In *Studies in Prehistoric Anthropology* (Ed.) D. Bayard. Dunedin (New Zealand): University of Otago. 16: 305-322.

Bayard, D.T. 1996. Linguistics, archaeologists and Austronesian origins: comparative and socio-linguistic aspects of the Meacham-Bellwood debate. *Bulletin of Indo-Pacific Prehistory Association* 15(2): 71-86.

Bayard D.T., P. Charoenwongsa, and S. Rutnin. 1986. Excavations at Non Chai, northeastern Thailand. *Asian Prespectives* 25(1):13-62.

Bayard, D.T. in press. *Non-Nok Tha Excavation Report*. Otago: University of Otago.

Beck, L. 1891-1901. Die Geschichte des Eisens in technischer und kulturgeschichtlicher *Beziehung* 1:1-5

Bednarik, R.G. 1992. The Palaeolithic Art of Asia. In *Ancient Images, Ancient Thought: the Archaeology of Ideology* (Eds.) S. Goldsmith, S. Garvie, D. Selin and J. Smith (Proceedings of the 23rd Annual Chacmool Conference). Calgary: University of Calgary. Pp. 383-390.

Bednarik, R.G. 1993a. Palaeolithic Art in India. *Man and Environment* 18(2): 33-40.

Bednarik, R. G. 1993b. Developments in rock art dating. *Acta Archaeologica* 63: 141-155.

Bednarik, R.G. 1994. Art origins. *Anthropos* 89: 169-180.

Beltran, A. 1982. *Rock art of Spanish Levant*. London: Cambridge University Press.

Bhattacharya, S.C., V.D. Misra, J.N. Pandey, and J.N. Pal (Eds.). 2000. *Peeping Through the Past*. Allahabad: University of Allahabad.

Binford, L. 1968. Post-Pleistocene adaptations. In *New Perspectives in Archeology* (Eds.) S.R. and L.R. Binford. Chicago: Aldine. Pp. 313-341.

Bintliff, J. (Ed.) 1991. *The Annales School and Archaeology*. London: Leicestor University Press.

Blust, R. 1996. Beyond the Austronesian homeland: the Austric hypothesis and its implications for archaeology. In *Prehistoric Settlement of the Pacific. (Transactions of the American Philosophical Society)* (Ed.) W. Goodenough: Philadelphia. 86(5): 117-140.

Bopardikar, B.P. 1972. Prehistoric investigations in Daphabum. In *Archaeological Congress and Seminar Papers* (Ed.) S.B. Deo. Nagpur: Univerity of Nagpur. Pp. 1-8.

Bose, N.K. and D. Sen. 1948. *Excavations in Mayurbhanj*. Calcutta: University of Calcutta.

Braidwood, R.J., H. Cambel and W. Schirmer, 1981. Beginnings of village-farming communities in southeastern Turkey: Cayenu Tepesi, 1978 and 1979. *Journal of Field Archaeology* 8: 249-258.

Brandt, S.A. and N. Carder. 1987. Pastoral rock art in the horn of Africa: making sense of udder chaos. *World Archaeology* 19 (2): 194-213.

Braudel, F. 1972. *The Mediterranean and the Mediterranean World in the Age of Phillip II*. London: Collins.

Brock, J.C. 1965. *The Fauna: Excavations at Langhnaj: 1944-63*. Part II. Poona: Deccan College.

Bronowsky, J. 1976. *The Ascent of Man*. London: BBC.

Bronger, A., R.K. Pant and A.K. Shinghvi. 1987. Pleistocene climatic changes and landscape evolution in the Kashmir basin, India, palaeopedological and chronostratigraphic studies. *Quarternary Researches* 27:167.

Brown, M. 1990. *The Search For Eve*. Harper Collins: New York.

Brown, P. 1917. *Indian Paintings*. Calcutta: Y.M.C.A. Publication.

Brumfiel, E.M. 1995. Heterarchy and the analysis of complex societies: comments. In *Heterarchy and the Analysis of Complex Societies*. (Eds.) R.M. Ehrenreich, C.L. Crumley, and J.E. Levy. Archaeological Papers of the American Anthropological Association, Number 6. Arlington, Va.: American Anthropological Association. Pp. 125-131.

Brunet, Michel, Alain Boauvilain, Yves Coppens, Emile Heintz, and Aladji H.E. Moutaye. 1995. The first Australopithecine 2,500 km west of the Rift Valley (Chad). *Nature* 378: 273-274.

Bryson, Reid A. 1988. What the climatic past tells us about the environmental future. In *Earth 88: Changing Geographic Perspectives*. Proceedings of the Centennial Symposium. Washington, D.C. : National Geographic Society. Pp. 230-247.

Burbank, D.W. and D.H. Reynolds. 1984. Sequential late Cenozoic disruption of the northern Himalayan foredeep. *Nature* 311:114-118.

Buth, G.M., R.N. Kaw. 1985. Plant husbandary in Neolithic Burzahom, Kashmir. In *Climate and Geology of Kashmir and Central Asia* (Eds.) D.P. Agrawal, S. Kusumgar, R.V. Krishnamurthy. Delhi: T.T. Printer and Publishers. Pp. 109-114.

Cammiade, L.A. 1924. Pygmy implements of the lower Godavery. *Man in India* 4: 83-105.

Cammiade, L.A., M.C. Burkitt. 1930. Fresh light on the Stone Age in Southeast India. *Antiquity* 4: 327-39.

Carllyle, A.C.L. 1883. Notes on lately discovered sepulchral mounds, cairns, caves, cave paintings and stone implements. *Proceedings of the Asiatic Society of Bengal* 52(2): 49-55.

Chakarbarti, D.K. 1979. The problem of tin in early India—a preliminary survey. *Man and Environment* 3: 61-74.

Chakrabarti, D.K. 1992. *The Early Use of Iron in India*. Madras : Oxford University Press.

Chakrabarti, Subrata. 1990. The Stone Age Prehistory of Khiching, Orissa. *Man and Environment* 15(2): 13-21.

Chamyal, L.S. and S.S. Merh. 1992. Sequence stratigraphy and surface Qnaternary deposits in the semi-arid basins of Gujarat. *Man and Environment* 17(1): 33-40.

Chandramouli, N. 1991. Rock paintings of Budagavi, Anantapur district, Andhra Pradesh. *Man and Environment* 16(2): 71-80.

Chang, K.C. 1970. The beginnings of agriculture in the Far East. *Antiquity* 44 (1):175-185.

Chattopadhyaya, Indrani. 2000a. Writing in space. In *Studies on Man: Issues & Challenges* (Ed.) M.K. Bhasin. Delhi: Kamla Raj Enterrprises. Pp. 33-48.

Chattopadhyaya, Indrani. 2000b. Meaningful action considered as text: hermeneutics and archaeology. In *Peeping Through the Past* (Eds) S.C. Bhattacharya, V.D. Misra, J.N. Pandey, and J.N. Pal. Allahabad: University of Allahabad. Pp. 131-139.

Chattopadhyaya U.C. 1990. *A Study of Subsistence and Settlement Patterns during the Late Prehistory of North-central India*. Unpublished Thesis. Cambridge: University of Cambridge.

Chattopadhyaya, U.C. 2000a. Complementary partitioned network system: A regional model of post-Pleistocene human adaptations in the Vindhya-Ganga complex. *Oriental Anthropologist* 1(1): 16-34.

Chattopadhyaya, U.C. 2000b. The post-modern denial of the past. In *Peeping Through the Past* (Eds) S.C. Bhattacharya, V.D. Misra, J.N. Pandey, and J.N. Pal. Allahabad: University of Allahabad. Pp. 169-182.

Chattopadhyaya, Indrani and U.C. Chattopadyaya 1990. The spatial organisation of mortuary practices in the Mesolithic Ganga Valley: implications for territoriality. In *Adaptation and other Essays* (Eds.) N.C. Ghosh and S. Chakrabarti. Shantiniketan: Vishwa Bharati. Pp. 103-121.

Chawla, S., R.P. Dhir and A.K. Singhvi. 1992. Thermoluminescence chronology of sand profiles in the Thar desert and their implications. *Quaternary Science Reviews* 11: 25-32

Chawla, S. and A.K. Singhvi. 1989. Thermoluminescence dating of archaeological sediments. *Naturwissenschaften* 76(9): 416.

Chawla, S., A.K. Singhvi, S.N. Rajaguru, V.N. Misra and R.P. Dhir. 1990. Significance of TL dating of fossil dunes in the study of Stone Age chronology and environment in the Thar desert. Paper presented in the *International Seminar on Rising Trends in Palaeonthropology, Environmental Change and Response* (the last two million years). Pune: Deccan College.

Childe, V.G. 1944. Archaeological ages as technological stages. *Journal of the Royal Anthropological Institute of Great Britain and Ireland* 74: 7-24.

Chippindale, C., Joane de Jongh, J. Flood and S. Rufolo. 2000. Stratigraphy, Harris matrices and relative dating of Australian rock art. *Antiquity* 74 (284):285-86.

Chowdhury, K.A. and S.S. Ghosh. 1947. Plant remains from Harappa 1946. *Ancient India* 7: 3-19.

Clark, J.D. and M.A.J. Williams. 1991. Prehistoric ecology, resources strategies and culture change in the Son Valley, Northern Madhya Pradesh, Central India. In *Man and Environment* 16(1): 13.

Cockburn J. 1883a. A short account of the petrographs in the caves and rock shelters of the Kaimur Range in the Mirzapur District. *Proceedings of the Asiatic Society of Bengal* 52(2): 125-126.

Cockburn, J. 1883b. On the recent existence of *Rhinoceros indicus* in the northwestern provinces, and a description of a tracing of an archaic rock painting from Mirzapore representing the hunting of this animal. *Journal of the Asiatic Society of Bengal* 52(2): 56-64.

Cockburn, J. 1888. On Palaeolithic implements from the drift-gravels of the Singrauli Basin, South Mirzapur. *Journal of Anthroplogical Institute* 17: 57-65.

Cockburn, J. 1899. Cave drawings in the Kaimur Range, northwest provinces. *Journal of the Asiatic Society* 18: 89-97.

Cohen, M.N. 1977. The *Food Crisis in Prehistory: Over Population and the Origins of Agriculture*. London: New Haven.

Cohmap. 1988. Climatic changes of the last 18,000 years: observations and model simulations. *Science* 241: 1043-1052.

Cooke, C.K. 1961. The copying and recording of rock painting. *The South African Archaeological Bulletin* 16: 61-65.

Cooper, Zarine, M. 1983. Adaptation patterns during the Late Stone Age in Bastar district, Madhya Pradesh. *Bulletin of the Indo-Pacific Prehistory Association* 3: 1-9.

Corvinus, G. 1983. *A Survey of the Pravara River System in Western Maharashtra, India, Vol. 2: The Excavations of the Acheulian Site of Chirki-on-Pravara, India*. Tubingen: Institute fur Urgeschichte.

Corvinus, G. 1990. A note on the first discovery of handaxe in Nepal. *Man and Environment* 15(2): 9-11.

Corvinus, G. 1994. Prehistoric sites in western Nepal. *Man and Environment* 19:73-89.

Costantini, L. 1979. Plant remians from Pirak. In *Foullies de Pirak*. 2 Vols (Eds.) Jean-Francois Jarrige and Marielle Santono. Paris: Publications de la commission des Foulles Archaeologique, Fouilles de Pakistan No 2: 326-33.

Costantini, L. 1981. Palaeoethnobotany at Pirak: a contribution to the second millennium BC agriculture of the Sibi-Kachi Plain, Pakistan. In *South Asian Archaeology* 1979 (Ed.) H. Hartel. Berlin: Dietrich Reimer Verlag. Pp. 271-77.

Costantini, L. 1984. The beginning of agriculture in the Kachi plain: the evidence of Mehrgarh. In *South Asian Archaeology* 1981 (Ed.) B. Allchin. Cambridge: Cambridge University Press. Pp. 29-33.

Cunningham, A. 1871. *Ancient Geography of India*. London: Tribune.

Dani, A.H. 1960. *Prehistory and Protohistory of Eastern India*. Calcutta: Firma K.L.Mukhopadyaya.

Dani, A.H. 1964. Sanghao Cave excavation. *Asian Perspectives* 1: 1-50.

Dani , A.H. 1967. Timargarh and Gandhara Grave Culture. *Ancient Pakistan* 3:1-407.

Daniel, G. 1962. *The Idea of Prehistory*. London: Watts & Co.

Davidson, Jeremy H.C.S. 1979. Archaeology in Northern Vietnam since 1954. In *Early South East Asia: Essays in Archaeology, History and Historical Geography* (Eds.) R.B. Smith and W. Watson. Oxford: Oxford University Press. Pp. 98-124.

Dawkins, Richard. 1995. *River Out of Eden*. London: Viking.

Dayton, Leigh and James Woodford. 1996. Australia's date with destiny. *New Scientist*, 7th December 1996: 28-31.

D'Errico, Francesco, C. Gaillard and V.N. Misra. 1989. Collection of non-utilitarian objects by *Homo erectus* in India. *Proceedings of the 2nd International Congress of Human Paleontology*. Pp. 237-239.

Deison, Eric. 1997. One skull does not a species make. *Nature* 389: 445-446.

De Lumley, Henry and A. Sonakia. 1985. Contexte Stratigrapbique et Archeologique de l'Homme de la Narmada, Hathnora, Madhya Pradesh, Inde. *L'Anthropologie* 89 (1): 3-12.

De Jesus, P.S. 1980. *The Development of Prehistoric Mining and Metallurgy in Anatolia* 2 parts. Oxford: British Archaeology Reports, International Series 74.

De, S. and P.K. Chattopadhyay. 1989. Iron objects from Pandurajar Dhibi: archaeometallurgical studies. *Steel India* 12 (1): 33-41.

Dennell, R.W. 1984. The importance of the Potwar Plateau of Pakistan to studies of early Man. In *South Asian Archaeology* 1981 (Ed.) B. Allchin. Cambridge: Cambridge University Press. Pp. 10-19.

Dennell, R.W. 1995. The Early Stone Age of Pakistan: a methodological review. *Man and Environment* 20 (1) : 21-28.

Dennell, R.W. and H.M. Rendell. 1991. De Terra and Paterson and the Soan flake industry: a new perspective from the Soan Valley north Pakistan. *Man and Environment* 15(2): 91-97.

Dennell, R.W., H.M. Rendell, and E. Hailwood. 1988a. Early tool making in Asia: two million year old artefacts in Pakistan. *Antiquity* 62: 98-106.

Dennell, R.W., H.M. Rendell, and E. Hailwood. 1988b.Late Pleistocene artifacts from northern Pakistan. *Current Anthropology* 29: 495-498.

De Terra, H. and T.T. Paterson. 1939. *Studies of the Ice Age of India and Associated Human Cultures*. Washington: Carnegie Institution of Washington.

Dhavalikar, M.K. 1970a. Kayatha: a new Chalcolithic culture. *Indica* 7(2): 85-93.

Dhavalikar, M.K. 1970b. Genesis of Jorwe Culture. In *Studies in Indian Archaeology* (Eds.) S.B. Deo and M.K. Dhavalikar (Prof. H.D. Sankalia Felicitation Volume) *Indian Antiquary* 4: 32-41.

Dhavalikar, M.K. 1979a. Early farming cultures of the Deccan. In *Essays in Indian Protohistory* (Eds.) D.P. Agrawal and D.K. Chakrabarti. Delhi: B.R. Publication. Pp. 247-265.

Dhavalikar M.K. 1979b. Early farming cultures of Central India. In *Essays in Indian Proto-history* (Eds.) D.P. Agrawal and D.K. Chakrabarti. New Delhi: B.R. Publication. Pp. 229-45.

Dhavalikar, M.K., H.D. Sankalia and Z.D. Ansari. 1988. *Excavataions at Inamgaon*. Vol.1. Pune: Deccan College.

Diamond, Jared. 1997. *Guns, Germs & Steel*. London: V. W Norton & Company.

Dodia, R. 1988. Mid-Pleistocene climate of Kashmir: the Baltal pollen profile. In *The Palaeoenvironment of East Asia from mid-Tertiary* Vol. II (Eds.) Pauline White *et al.* Hong-Kong: Hong-Kong University. Pp. 680-701.

Dodia, R., D.P. Agrawal, A.B. Vora. 1985. New pollen data from the Kashmir Bogs: a summary. In *Climate and Geology of Kashmir and Central Asia.* (Eds.) D.P. Agrawal, S. Kusumgar and R.V. Krishnamurthy. New Delhi: T. T. Printers and Publishers. Pp. 101-108.

Dowson, T.A. 1994. Reading art, writing history: rock art and social change in Southern Africa. *World Archaeology* 25 (3) : 332-345.

Dubey, Meenakshi. 1991. Scenes of head hunting in the rock art of the Pachmarhi hills. *Man and Environment* 16 (2): 81-85.

Dutta, Pratap C., Anadi Pal and Bimal Chandra Dutta. 1971. Sarai-Nahar-Rai: a Late Stone Age site in the plains of the Ganga. *Journal of Indian Anthropological Society* 6: 15-28.

Dyson, R.H. and W.C.S. Remsen. 1989. Observations on architecture and stratigraphy at Tappeh Hesar. In *Tappeh Hesar: Reports of the Restudy Project* 1976 (Eds.) R. Dyson and S. M. Howard. Firenze: Casa Editrice Le Lettre. Pp. 69-109.

Ehrhardt, S. and K.A.R. Kennedy. 1965. *The Excavations at Langhnaj: 1944-63. The Human Remains.* Poona: Deccan College.

Enault, Jean-Francois. 1979. *Fouilles de Pirak.* 2 Vols. Paris: Publications de la Commission de la Pakistan.

Fairservis, W.A. 1967. The origin, character and decline of an early civilization. *Novitates* (New York: American Museum of Natural History) No. 2302.

Fairservis, W.A. Jr. 1983. The script of the Indus Valley Civilization. *Scientific American* 248(3):58-66.

Fairservis, W.A. Jr. and F.C. Southworth. 1989. Linguistic archaeology and the Indus Valley Culture. In *Old Problems and New Perspectives in the Archaeology of South Asia* (Ed.) J.M. Kenoyer. Madison: Wisconsin Archaeological Reports 2: 133-41.

Farooqui, A. and G.G. Vaz. 2000. Holocene sea-level and climatic fluctuations: Pulicat lake — a case study. *Current Science* 79(10): 1184-1188.

Fatmi. A.N. 1974. Lithographic units of the Kohat-Potwar province, Indus Basin. *Memoirs of the Geological Survey of Pakistan* 10: 1-78.

Fawcett, F. 1901. Notes on the rock carvings in the Edakal cave, Wynaad. *The Indian Antiquary* 30: 409-21.

Flam, L. 1981. Towards the ecological analysis of prehistoric settlement patterns in Sind, Pakistan. *Man and Environment* 5: 52-58.

Flannery, Kent. 1972. The cultural evolution of civilisations. *Annual Review of Ecology and Systematics* 3: 399-426.

Fontugne, M.R., J.C. Duplessy. 1986. Variations in the Monsoon regime during the Upper Quaternary : evidence from Carbon Isotopic record of organic matter in North Indian sediment cores. *Palaeogeography, Palaeoclimatology, Palaeoecology* 56(1-2): 68-88.

Foote, R.B. 1866. On the occurrence of stone implements in the lateritic formations in various parts of Madras and North Arcot District. Reprinted 1966 In *Studies in Prehistory* (Eds.) D. Sen and A.K. Ghosh. Calcutta: Firma K. L. Mukhopadyaya. Pp. 1-22.

Foote, R.B. 1887. Notes on some recent Neolithic and Palaeolithic finds in South India. *Journal of the Asiatic Society of Bengal* 46(2): 259-282.

Foote, R.B. 1916. *The Foote Collection of Indian Prehistoric and Protohistoric Antiquities: Notes on their Ages and Distribution.* Madras: Madras Govt. Museum.

Francfort, H.-P. 1986. Preliminary report (1983-84): archaeological and environmental researches in the Ghaggar (Sarsawati plains). *Man and Environment* 10: 97-100.

Francfort, H.-P. 1989. *Fouilles de Shortugaï recherches sur l'Asie centrale protohistorique.* Paris: Diffusion de Boccard.

Gaillard, C. 1994. Processing sequences in Indian Lower Palaeolithic: examples from Acheulian and Soanian. Chiang Mai (Thailand): Paper presented at the *15th Indo-Pacific Prehistory Association (IPPA) Congress,* January 5-12.

Gaillard, C., D.R. Raju, V.N. Misra and S.N. Rajaguru. 1983. Acheulian occupation at Singi Talav in the Thar Desert: a preliminary report on 1982 excavation. *Man and Environment* 7: 112-130.

Gaillard, C., D.R. Raju, V.N. Misra and S.N. Rajaguru. 1986. Handaxe assemblages from the Didwana region, Thar desert, India: a metrical analysis. *Proceedings of the Prehistoric Society* 52: 189-214.

Gale, F. and J. Jacobs. 1987. Aboriginal art Australia's neglected inheritance. *World Archaeology* 19(2): 226-235.

Gamble, Clive. 1994. *Timewalkers: the Prehistory of Global Colonization.* Cambridge: Harvard University Press.

Garlake, P.S. 1994. Archetypes and attributes: rock paintings in Zimbabwe. *World Archaeology* 25 (3): 346-355.

Ghosh, M.N. 1932. Rock Paintings and other Antiquities of Prehistoric and later times. *Memoir of the Archaeological Survey of India.* No.24. Calcutta: Archaeological Survey of India.

Ghosh, A.K. 1970. The Palaeolithic cultures of Singbhum. *Transactions of American Philosophical Society* 60: (1): 1-68.

Gordon, Bryan C. 1999. *Preliminary Report on the Study of the Rise of Chinese Civilization Based on Paddy Rice Agriculture*. Hull, Quebec: Canadian Museum of Civilization.

Gordon, D.H. 1951. The Rock Engravings of Kupagallu Hill, Bellary, Madras. *Man* 51: 117-19.

Gordon, D.H. 1958. *The Prehistoric Background of Indian Culture*. Bombay: N. M. Tripathi.

Gore, Rick. 1996. The dawn of humans: Neandertals. *National Geographic* 18: 4-35.

Gore, Rick. 2000. The dawn of humans. *National Geographic* 198 (1): 90-117.

Gorman, Chester. 1970a. Excavation at Spirit Cave, north Thailand. *Asian Perspectives* 13: 97-107.

Gorman, Chester. 1970b. The Hoabinhian and after: subsistence pattern in Southeast Asia during the late Pleistocene and early recent periods. *World Archaeology* 2(3): 300-20.

Gorman, Chester and P. Charoenwongsa.1976. Ban Chiang: a mosaic of impressions from the first two years. *Expedition* 18(4): 14-26.

Goswami, M.C. and T.C. Sharma. 1963. Further report on the investigations into Prehistoric archaeology of north Cachar hills, Assam. *Journal of the University of Gauhati* 14(2):45-47.

Goudie, A.S., B. Allchin and K.T.M. Hegde. 1973. The former extension of of the great Indian desert. *Geographical Journal* 139(2):243-57.

Gardner, P. 1980. Lexicostatistics and Dravidian differentiation in situ. *Indian Linguistics* 41: 17-180.

Grant, P.M. 1967. *Prehistoric Art: Palaeolothic Paintings and Sculpture*. London: Studio Vasta.

Grierson, G.A. 1967-1968. *The Linguistic Survey Of India*, Vol. 1(1) and vol 9(4). Calcutta: Central Publication Branch. Govt. of India.

Gupta, H.P. 1976. Holocene palynology from Meander Lake in the Ganga Valley, district Pratapgarh, U.P. *The Palaeobotanist* 25: 109-119.

Gupta, J. 1967. *Pragaitihashik Bharatiya Chitrakala* (In Hindi). Delhi: National Publishing House.

Gupta, S.K. and B.S. Amin. 1974. Io/U Ages of corals from Saurashtra Coast. *Marine Geology* 16: M79-M83.

Gupta, S.K., P. Sharma, N. Juyal and D.P. Agrawal. 1991. Loess-palaeosol seqence in Kashmir: correlation of mineral magnetic stratigraphy with the marine palaeoclimatic records. *Journal of Quarternary Science* 6(1):3-12.

Gupta, S.P. 1967. The Mountainous Neolithic cultures of Central Asia and Northern India. *The Anthropologist* 14: 125-136.

Gupta, S.P. 1979. *Archaeology of Soviet Central Asia and the Indian Boderland*. 2 Vols. Delhi: B.R. Publishing Co.

Haquet, J. 1994. *Problematique de la Metallurgie Dans la Plaine De Kachi (Pakistan) Du Neolithique a La Fin De La Civilisation De l'Indus au IIIe Millenaire avant*. J.C. Memoire De D.E.A. University De Paris I: U.E.R. D'Art et D'Archaeologie, unpublished.

Harris, D.R. 1996. *The Origins and Spread of Agriculture and Pastoralism in Eurasia*. London: UCL Press.

Hegde. K.T.M., R.V. Karanth and S.P. Sychanthavong. 1982. On the composition and technology of Harappan microbeads. In *Harappan Civilization: A Contemporary Perspective* (Ed.)G.L. Possehl. Delhi: Oxford and IBH. Pp. 239-44.

Heizer, R.F. and M.A. Baumhoff. 1962. *Prehistoric Rock Art of Nevada and Eastern California*. California: University Press.

Hemphill, B.E., J.R. Lukacs and K.A.R. Kennedy. 1991. Biological adaptations and affinities of Bronze Age Harappans. In *Harappa Excavations* 1986-1990 (Ed.) R.H. Meadow. Madison: Prehistory Press. Pp. 137-182.

Herbert, T.H. 1909. Jewellery of Rajputana and Malwa of Central India. *The Journal of Indian Art* 12: 17-42.

Higham, C.F.W. 1983. The Ban Chiang culture in wider perspective. *Proceedings of the British Academy* 69:229-261.

Higham, C.F. W. 1989. *The Archaeology of Mainland Southeast Asia*. Cambridge: Cambridge University Press.

Higham, C.F.W. 1996. Archaeology and linguistics in Southeast Asia: implications of the Austric hypothesis. *Indo-Pacific Prehistory Association Bulletin* 14(1): 71-86.

Higham, C.F.W. and A Kijngam. 1984. *Prehistoric Investigations in Northeast Thailand*. Oxford: British Archaeolgical International Series Reports 231, part 3.

Higuchi, Takayasu. 1986. Relationship between Japan and Asia in ancient times. In *Windows on the Japanese Past: Studies in Archaeology and Prehistory*. (Ed.) R.J. Pearson. Michigan: The University of Michigan.

Holm, E. 1961. The Rock Art of South Africa. *ASA*: 153-204.

Horn, P.D. Muller-Sohnius, D. Storzer and L. Zoeller. 1993. K-Ar, fission track and thermoluminescence ages of Quaternary volcanic tuffs and their bearing on Acheulian artefacts from Bori, Kukdi valley, Pune district. *Zeitschrift dee Deutschen Geologischen Gesellschaft* 144: 326-329.

Huang, W.R., Ciochon, Y. Gu, R. Larick, F. Qiren, H. Schwartz, C. Younge, J. de Vos and W. Rink. 1995. Early Homo and associated artefacts from Asia. *Nature* 378: 275-278.

Hunter, R.G. 1935. Interim Report of the Excavation in the Dorothy Deep Shelter No. 1. *Nagpur University Journal* 1: 28-59.

Hutchinson, Sir Joseph. 1974 (Ed.). *Evolutionary Studies in World Crops: Diversity and Change in the Indian Subcontinent*. Cambridge: Cambridge University Press.

Hutchinson, Sir Joseph. 1976. India: local and introduced crops. In *The Early History of Agriculture* (Eds.) Sir Joseph Hutchinson, G. Clark and E.M. Jope and R. Riley. *Philosophical Transactions of the Royal Society of London* 275 (936):129-38.

Hutchinson, J. 1974. Crop plant evolution in the Indian subcontinent. In *Evolutionary Studies in World Crops* (Ed.) J. Hutchinson. Cambridge: Cambridge University Press. Pp. 151-60.

Hutchinson, J. 1977. India: local and introduced crops. In *Early History of Agriculture* (Eds.) J.G.D. Clark, E.M. Jope and R. Riley. Oxford: Oxford University Press. Pp. 129-138.

Hutton, J.H. 1928. Prehistory of Assam. *Man in India* 8:228-32.

IAR. *Indian Archaeology — A Review*. Annual Publication of the Archaeological Survey of India, New Delhi.

Imamura, Keiji. 1996. *Prehistoric Japan*. London: UCL Press.

Isaac, N. 1960. *The Stone Age Cultures of Kurnool*. Unpublished Thesis. Poona: Deccan College.

Jacobson, J. 1985. Acheulian surface sites in Central India. In *Indo-Pacific Prehistory* (Eds.) V.N. Misra and P. Bellwood. Delhi: Oxford and IBH. Pp. 49-57.

Jarrige, C., J.-F. Jarrige, R.H. Meadow and G. Quivron. 1995. *Mehrgarh Field Reports 1974-1985*. Karachi: Govt. of Sindh.

Jarrige, J.-F. 1981. Economy and society in the early chalcolithic/bronze age of Baluchistan: new perspectives from recent excavations at Mehrgarh. In *South Asian Archaeology 1979*. (Ed.) Herbert Hartel. Berlin:Dietrich Reimer. Pp. 93-114.

Jarrige, J.-F. 1982. Excavations at Mehergarh: their significance for understanding the background of the Harappa civilization. In *Harappan Civilization: A Contemporary Perspective*. (Ed.) G.L. Possehl. New Delhi: Oxford and IBH Publishung Co. Pp. 79-84.

Jarrige, J.-F. 1985a. A propos d'un foret a tige hélicoïdale en cuivre de Mundigak. In *De l'Indus aux Balkans, Recueil Jean Deshayes* (Eds.) J.-L. Huot, M.Yon, and Y. Calvet. Paris: Éditions Recherche sur les Civilisations. Pp. 281-292.

Jarrige, J.-F. 1985b. Continuity and change in the north Kachi plain (Baluchistan, Pakistan) at the beginning of the second millennium B.C. In *South Asian Archaeology 1983* (Eds.) J. Shotsmans and M. Taddei. Naples: Istituto Universitario Orientale. Pp. 35-68.

Jarrige, J.-F. and M. Lechevallier. 1979. Excavations at Mehrgarh, Baluchistan: their significance in the prehistoric context of the Indo-Pakistan borderlands. In *South Asian Archaeology 1977*. (Ed.) M. Taddei. Naples: Istituto Universitario Orientale. Pp. 463-536.

Jarrige, J.-F. and R.H. Meadow. 1980. The antecedents of civilization in the Indus valley. *Scientific American* 243(2): 122-133.

Jarrige, Catherine., Jean-Francois Jarrige, Richard H. Meadow and Gonzague Quivron. 1995. (Eds.) *Mehrgarh: Field Reports 1974-1985 from Neolithic Times to the Indus Civilization*. Karachi: Dept. of Culture & Tourism, Government of Sindh, Pakistan, in collaboration with the French Ministry of Foreign Affairs.

Jayaswal, Vidula. 1978. *Palaeo-history of India*. Delhi: Agam Kala Prakashan.

Jayaswal, Vidula. 1982. *Chopper Chopping Tool Component of the Palaeolithic in India*. Delhi: Agam Kala Prakashan.

Jettmar, Karl. 1987. *Between Gandhara and Silk Roads: Rock Carvings along the Karakorum Highway*. London: The Royal Geographic Society.

Joshi, J.P., Madhu Bala and Jassu Ram. 1984. The Indus civilization: a reconsideration on the basis of distribution maps. In *Frontiers of the Indus Civilization* (Eds.) B.B. Lal, S.P. Gupta and Shashi Asthana. New Delhi: Books and Books. Pp. 511-530.

Joshi, R.V. 1955. *Pleistocene Studies in the Malprabha Basin*. Poona: Deccan College.

Joshi, R.V. and M.D. Khare. 1966. Microlith bearing deposits of Adamgarh rock shelters. In *Brucefoote Memorial Volume* (Eds.) D. Sen and A.K. Ghosh. Calcutta: Firma K.L. Mukhopadhyaya. Pp. 90-95.

Kajale, M.D. 1974. Ancient grains from India. *Bulletin of Deccan College Postgraduate and Research Institute* 34 (1-4):55-74.

Kajale, M.D. 1988. Plant economy. In *Excavations at Inamgaon*, Vol. I, part ii (Eds.) M.K. Dhavalikar, H.D. Sankalia and Z.D. Ansari. Pune: Deccan College. Pp. 727-821.

Kajale, M.D., G.L. Badam and S.N. Rajaguru. 1976. Late Quaternary history of the Ghod Valley, Maharashtra. *Geophytology* 6(1): 122-132.

Kale, V.S., S.N. Rajaguru. 1985. Neogene and Quaternary transgressional and regressional history of the West Coast of India: an overview. *Bulletin of the Deccan College Research Institute* 44: 153-163.

Kaw, R.N. 1979. The Neolithic culture of Kashmir. In *Essays in Indian Protohistory* (Eds.) D.P. Agrawal and Dilip Chakrabarti. New Delhi: DK Publishers. Pp. 219-228.

Kennedy, K.A.R. 1992. The fossil hominid skull from the Narmada Valley: *Homo erectus or Homo sapiens*? In *South Asian Archaeology-1989* (Ed.) C. Jarrige. Madison: Prehistory Press. Pp. 145-152.

Kennedy, K.A.R. 1995. Southeast Asia: biological anthropology and concepts of ancient races. In *The Indo-Aryans of Ancient Southeast Asia: Language, Material Culture and Ethnicity* (Ed.) George Erdosy. Berlin: Walter De Gruyter. Pp. 32-66.

Kennedy, K.A.R. 2000. *God-apes and Fossil Men*. Ann Arbor: Michigan University.

Kennedy, K.A.R. and A.A. Elgart. 1998. *Hominid Remains — an Update: South Asia, India & Sri Lanka*. Brussels: Royal Belgian Institute of Natural Sciences.

Kennedy, K.A.R. and Joanne L. Zahorsky. 1997. Trends in prehistoric technology and biological adaptations: new evidence from pleistocene deposits at Fa Hien cave, Sri Lanka. In *South Asian Archaeology* (Ed.) B. Allchin. Delhi: Oxford & IBH Publishers. Pp. 839 & 853.

Khanduri, B.M., K.P. Nautiyal, Vinod Nautiyal, R.C. Bhatt, Pradeep Saklani and Y.S. Farswan. 1998-99. Excavation of burial complexes in Ramganga Valley, Kumaun Himalaya. *Puratattva* 29: 68-74.

Kharakwal, J.S. 1993. *Archaeological Explorations in Kumaun Himalayas*. Unpublished Ph.D. Dissertation. Poona University

Kharakwal, J.S., D. Bhatt and M. Pant. 1993. Madhya Himalaye kshetra Kumaon: puratattva and paramparain (in Hindi). *Sodh Patrika* 44:64-77.

Kharakwal, J.S. and Deep Harbola. 1996. Kumaon mai mahapasankalain savagar parampara. *Pragdhara* 6:169-76.

Kharakwal, J.S. and Anita Rane. 1997. Cup-marks and Gaychole game. In *Himkanti* (Eds.) B.M. Khanduri and V. Nautiyal. Delhi: Book India Publishing Co.

Kimbel, William H., Donald C. Johanson, and Yoel Rak 1994. The first skull and other new discoveries of *Australopithecus afarensis* at Hader, Ethiopia. *Nature* 368: 449-451.

King, C. 1940. Rock drawings on the Indus. *Man* XL: 65-68.

Kiyotari, Tsuboi. (Ed.) 1987. *Recent Archaeological Discoveries in Japan*. Tokyo: Centre for East Asian Studies.

Klein, R. 1989. Biological and behavioral perspectives on modern human origins in South Africa. In *The Human Revolution* (Eds.) P. Mellars and C. Stringer. Edinburgh: Edinburgh University Press. Pp. 529-546.

Korisettar, R., T.R. Venkatesan, S. Mishra, S.N. Rajaguru, B.L.K. Somyajulu, S.K. Tandon, V.D. Gogte, R.K. Ganjoo and V.S. Kale. 1989. Discovery of a tephra bed in the Quaternary alluvial sediments of Pune district, peninsular India. *Current Science* 58: 564-567.

Kosambi, D.D. 1962a. *Myth and Reality: Studies in the Formation of Indian Culture*. Bombay: Popular Prakashan.

Kosambi, D.D. 1962b. Pierced microliths from the Deccan plateau. *Man* 62: 10.

Kotlia, B.S., M.S. Bhalla, C. Sharma, G. Rajagopalan, R. Ramesh, M.S. Chauhan, P. D. Mathur, S. Bhandari and S.T. Chacko. 1997. Palaeoclimatic conditions in the Upper Pleistocene and Holocene: Bhimtal-Naukuchiatal lake basin in South-central Kumaun, North India. *Palaeogeography, Palaeoclimatology, Palaeoecology* 130:307-322.

Kravtchenko, K.N. 1964. Soan Formation – upper unit of Siwalik group in Potwar. *Science and Industry* 2(3): 230-233.

Krishnamurthi, R.V., S.K. Bhattacharya and S. Kusumgar. 1986. Palaeoclimatic changes deduced from $^{13}C/^{12}C$ and C/N ratios of Karewa lake sediments. India. *Nature* 269; 155-160.

Krishnamurthy, R.V., M.D. De Niro, and R.K. Pant. 1982. Isotope evidence for Pleistocene climatic changes in India. *Nature* 296: 640-641.

Krishnaswami, V.D. 1938. Changes of prehistoric man near Madras. *Journal of Madras Geographical Association* 13: 58-90.

Krishnaswami, V.D. 1947. Stone Age in India. *Ancient India* 3: 11-57.

Krishnaswami V.D. 1962. The Neolithic pattern of India. *Ancient India* 16:25-64.

Kshirsagar, A. 1996. Anthrosols from Balathal: a chemical study. *Man and Environment* 21 (1):111-116.

Kuhn, T. 1970. *The Structure of Scientific Revolutions.* Chicago: University of Chicago Press.

Kukla, G. 1989. Long continental records of climate–an introduction. *Palaeogeography, Palaeoclimatology and Palaeoecology* 72:1-9.

Kumar, Giriraj. 1996. Daraki-Chattan: a palaeolithic cupule site in India. *Rock Art Research* 13 (1): 38-46.

Kumar, Giriraj, Geeta Narvare and Ramesh Pancholi. 1988. Engraved ostrich eggshell objects: new evidence of Upper Palaeolithic art in India. *Rock Art Research* 5 (1): 43-53.

Kumar, Giriraj, Ashok Sahni, R.K. Pancholi and Geeta Narvare. 1991. Archaeological discoveries and a study of late Pleistocene ostrich egg shells and egg shell objects in India. *Man and Environment* 16(1): 29.

Kumar, Krishna. 1999. A Middle Palaeolithic assemblage from the Khudar Basin, Madhya Pradesh. *The Eastern Anthropologist* 52(3): 247-259.

Kumar, Sudhir, B. Prakash, M.L. Manchanda, A.K. Singhvi, and Pankaj Srivastava. 1996. Holocene landform and soil evolution of the western Gangertic plains: implications of neotectonics and climate. *Z. Geomorph. N.F. Suppl-Bd.* 103: 283-312.

Kumar, Tuk-Tuk. 1988. *History of Rice in India: Mythology, Culture and Agriculture.* Delhi: Gian Publishing House.

Kusumgar, S. 1980. *Geochronology of the Palaeoclimatic Events of the late Cenozoic period in the Kashmir Valley.* Mumbai University: Unpublished Ph.D dissertation.

Kusumgar, S., N. Bhandari and D.P. Agrawal. 1985. Fission track ages of the Romushi Lower Karewas, Kashmir, India. In *Climate and Geology of Kashmir and Central Asia* (Eds.) D.P. Agrawal, S.Kusumgar and R.V. Krishnamurthy. Delhi: T.T. Publishers. Pp. 245-247.

Kusumgar, S., B.S. Kotlia, D.P. Agrawal and A. Sahni. 1985. Magnetostratigraphy of the Karewa ossiferous horizons from the Kashmir Valley, India. In *Climate and Geology of Kashmir and Cental Asia.* (Eds.) D.P. Agrawal, S. Kusumgar, R.V. Krishnamurthy. Delhi: T.T. Printers and Publishers. Pp. 27-28.

Labbe, Armand J. 1985. *Ban Chiang: Art and Prehistory of Northeast Thailand.* Santa Ana: California Bowers Museum.

Lal, B.B. 1956. Palaeoliths from Beas and Banganga Valleys. *Ancient India* 12: 58-92.

Lal, B.B. 1958. Birbhanpur–a microlithic site in the Damodar valley, Bengal. *Ancient India* 14: 4-48.

Lamberg-Karlovsky, C.C. 1979a. Hunters, farmers and civilizations: Old World archaeology; Neolithic villagers and farmers. *Scientific American.* Pp. 85-89.

Lamberg-Karlovsky, C.C. 1979b. Trade mechanisms in Indus-Mesopotamian interrelations. In *Ancient Cities of the Indus* (Ed.) G.L. Possehl. New Delhi: Vikas. Pp. 130-137.

Lambrick, H.T. 1967. The Indus flood plain and the Indus Civilization. *The Geographical Journal* 133: 483-494.

Leakey, R. 1983. *One Life.* London: Michael Joseph.

Leakey, R. 1994. *The Origin of Humankind.* London: Weidenfeld and Nicolson.

Leakey Richard E. and Roger Lewin. 1977. *Origins.* New York: E.P.Dutton.

Lechevallier, M. 1984. Flint industry of Mehrgarh. In *South Asian Archaeology 1981* (Ed.) B. Allchin. Cambridge: Cambridge University Press. Pp. 41-51.

Lele, V.S. 1989. Quarternary Formations in the Bhadar Valley. *Bulletin of the Deccan College Post-graduate and Research Institute* 47-48: 165-206.

Leroi-Gourhan, A. 1965. *Prehistoric de l'art Occidentale.* Paris: Mazenod.

Lewin, Roger. 1998. *Principles of Human Evolution: A Core Textbook.* Oxford: Blackwell. Pp. 283-307.

Lewis-Williams, J.D. 1983. *Rock Art of South Africa.* Cambridge: University Press.

Lhote, H. 1961. The Rock art of Maghreb and Sahara. *ASA*:205-231.

Lorblanchet, M. (Ed.) 1991a. *Rock Art in the Old World.* New Delhi: Indira Gandhi National Centre for the Arts.

Lorblanchet, M. 1991b. From the cave art of the reindeer hunters to rock art of the kangaroo hunters. *Man and Environment* 16 (2): 1-38.

Lukacs, J.R. and V.D. Misra. 2000. The people of Lekhahia: a bioarchaeological analysis of late Mesolithic hunters-foragers of north India. In *Peeping Through the Past* (Eds.). Bhattacharya, S.C., V.D. Misra, J.N. Pandey, and J.N. Pal. Allahabad: University of Allahabad. Pp. 25-44.

Lukacs, J.R., V.N. Misra,. and K.A.R. Kennedy. 1982. *Bagor and Tilwara: Late Mesolithic Cultures of North-West India, the Human Skeletal Remains.* Pune: Deccan College.

Lyell, C. 1830-33. *Principles of Geology.* Vols. 3. London: John Murray.

Macdonell, A. 1995. *Vedic Mythology.* Delhi: Motilal Banarasidas.

Mair, V.H. 1995. Mummies of the Tarim basin. *Archaeology* 48(2):28-35.

Majoomdar, G.G. and S.N. Rajaguru. 1965. Comments on soils as environmental and chronological tool. In *Indian Prehistory* (Eds.) V.N. Misra and M.S. Mate. Poona: Decccan College. Pp. 248-53.

Majumdar, R.C. and A.D. Pusalkar. 1952. *The Vedic Age.* London: George Allen and Unwin. Pp. 565.

Makohonienko, Miroslaw. 2000. Palynological studies on vegetation history and human impact in north and north-eastern China. *YRCP Newsletter* 3(1): 4.

Malik, S.C. 1959. The *Stone Age Industries of Satara District.* Baroda: M.S. University.

Malik, S.C. 1966. The Late Stone Age industries from excavated sites in Gujarat, India. *Artibus Asiae* 28: 167-174.

Mallory, J.P. 1989. *In Search of the Indo-Europeans: Language, Archaeology and Myth.* New York: Thames and Hudson.

Mandal, D. 1972. *Radiocarbon Dates and Indian Archaeology.* Allahabad: Vaishali Publishing House.

Mathpal, Y. 1984. *Prehistoric Rock Paintings of Bhimbetka, Central India.* New Delhi: Abhinav Publication.

Mathpal, Y. 1987. Uttarakhand mai sanskriti ki pragaitihasik pristhbhjumi (in Hindi). *Uttarakhand* 1:1-8.

McAlpin, W. David. 1981. *Proto-Elamo-Dravidian: the Evidence and its Implications.* Philadelphia: *Transactions of the American Philosophical Society.* 71(3).

Meadow, R.H. 1984. Notes on the faunal remains from Mehrgarh with a focus on cattle(*Bos).* In *South Asian Archaeology 1981* (Ed.) Bridget Allchin. Cambridge : Cambridge University Press. Pp. 34-40.

Meadow, R.H. 1989. Continuity and change in the agriculture of the Greater Indus Valley: the palaeoethnobotanical and zooarchaeological evidence. *Wisconsin Archaeology Review*: 1-16.

Meadow, R.H. 1993. Animal domestication in the Middle East: a revised view from the eastern margin. In *Harappan Civilization: A Recent Perspective* (Ed.) G. L. Possehl. 2nd ed. Delhi: Oxford & IBH and the American Institute of Indian Studies. Pp. 295-320.

Meadow, R.H. 1996. The origins and spread of agriculture and pastoralism in northwestern South Asia. In *The Orgins and Spread of Agriculture and Pastoralism in Eurasia* (Ed.) David R., Harris. London: UCL Press. Pp. 390-412.

Miller, N.F. 1984. The use of dung as fuel: an ethnographic example and an archaeological application. *Palaeorient* 10 (2):71-79.

Mishra, Sheila. 1992. The age of the Acheulian in India: new evidence. *Current Anthropology* 33(3): 325-328.

Mishra, Sheila 1994. The South Asian Lower Palaeolithic. *Man and Environment* 19(1-2): 57-64.

Mishra, Sheila 1995. Chronology of the Indian Stone Age: the impact of recent absolute and relative dating attempts. *Man and Environment* 20(2):11-21.

Mihsra, Sheila, A. Kshirsagar and S.N. Rajaguru. 1988. Relative dating of Quaternary record from upland western Maharashtra. In *National Seminar on Recent Quaternary Studies in India* (Eds.) M.P. Patel and N. Desai. Baroda: M.S. University. Pp. 267-278.

Mishra, Sheila, T.R. Venkatesa, S.N. Rajaguru and B.L.K. Somyajulu. 1995. Earliest Acheulian industry from peninsular India. *Current Anthropology* 36(5):847-851.

Misra, V.D. 1977. *Some Aspects of Indian Archaeology.* Allahabad: Prabhat Prakashan.

Misra, V.D. 1999a. A brief note on Indian Stone Age archaeology. In *The Dawn of Indian Civilization Upto 600 BC* Vol.I, Part 1 (Ed.) G.C. Pande. New Delhi: Centre for Studies in Civilization. Pp. 129-138.

Misra, V.D. 1999b. Agriculture, domestication of animals, ceramics and other industries in prehistoric India: Mesolithic and Neolithic. In *The Dawn of Indian Civilization.* Vol. 1. Part I (Ed.) G.C. Pande. New Delhi: Centre for Studies in Civilisations. Pp. 233-252.

Misra, V.D., B.B. Misra, J.N. Pal and M.C. Gupta. 2000. Explorations at Tonkwa. In *Peeping Through the Past* (Eds.) Bhattacharya, S.C., V.D. Misra, J.N. Pandey, and J.N. Pal. Allahabad: University of Allahabad. Pp. 45-57.

Misra, V.N. 1961. *The Stone Age cultures of Rajputana.* Poona University: Unpublished Ph.D. dissertation.

Misra, V.N. 1962. Palaeolithic cultures of western Rajputana. *Bulletin of Deccan College Post-graduate and Research Institute* 21:85-156.

Misra, V.N. 1967. *Pre and Protohistory of the Berach Basin, South Rajasthan.* Pune: Deccan College.

Misra, V.N. 1969. Early village communities of the Banas Basin, Rajasthan. In *Anthropology and Archaeology: Essays in Commemoration of Verrier Elwin* (Eds.) M. C. Pradhan, R. D. Singh, P.K. Misra, and D. B. Sastry. Oxford: Oxford University Press. Pp. 296-310.

Misra, V.N. 1970a. Evidence for a new Chalcolithic culture in South Rajasthan. *Indian Antiquary* NS, (Festschrift Sankalia). Pp. 85-95.

Misra,V.N. 1970b. Cultural significance of three copper arrowheads from Rajasthan, India. *Journal of Near Eastern Studies* 29(4): 221-232.

Misra, V.N. 1971. Two microlithic sites in Rajasthan — a preliminary investigation. *The Eastern Anthropologist* 24(3): 237-288.

Misra, V.N. 1972. Burials from prehistoric Bagor, Rajasthan. In *Archaeological Congress and Seminar Papers* (Ed.) S.B. Deo. Nagpur: Nagpur University. Pp. 58-65.

Misra V.N. 1973. Bagor: a late Mesolithic settlement in north-west India. *World Archaeology* 5 (1):92-110.

Misra, V.N. 1974. Archaeological and ethnographic evidence for hafting and use of microliths. *Puratattva* 7:3-12.

Misra, V.N. 1976. Ecological adaptation during the terminal Stone Age in Western and Central India. In *Ecological Background of South Asian Prehistory* (Eds.) K.A.R. Kennedy and G.L.Possehl. Ithaca: Cornell university. No. 4:28-51.

Misra, V.N. 1985. Microlithic Industries in India. In *Recent Advances in Indo-Pacific Prehistory.* (Eds.) V.N. Misra, P. Bellwood. New Delhi: Oxford-IBH. Pp. 111-122.

Misra, V.N. 1987a. *Evolution of the Landscape and Human adaptation in the Thar desert.* Presidential address (Anthropology abd Archaeology Session) 74th Session of Indian Science Congress, Banglore.

Misra, V.N. 1987b. Middle Pleistocene adaptation in India. In *The Pleistocene Old World: Regional Perspective* (Ed.) Olga Soffer. New York: Plenum Press. Pp. 99-119.

Misra, V.N. 1989. Stone Age India: an ecological perspective. *Man and Environment* 14(1): 17-64.

Misra, V.N. 1994. Patterns of human adaptation in the semi-arid and arid zone of Rajasthan. In *Living Traditions: Studies in the Ethnoarchaeology of South Asia* (Ed.) Bridget Allchin. Bombay: Oxford & IBH publishing Co. Pvt. Ltd. Pp. 101-124.

Misra, V.N. and Y. Mathpal. 1979. Rock art of Bhimbetka region. *Man and Environment* 3:27-33.

Misra, V.N. and Malti Nagar. 1981. The Microlithic industry of Bagor, Rajasthan. In *Cultural Contours of India* (Ed.) Vijay Shankar Shrivasatava. Delhi: Abhinav Publication. Pp. 5-11.

Misra, V.N. and S.N. Rajaguru. 1986. Environmentet culture de l'hommeprehistorique dans le desert due Thar, Rajasthan Inde. *Anthropologie* 90:407-37.

Misra, V.N. and S.N. Rajaguru. 1989. Palaeoenvironment and prehsitory of the Thar desert, Rajasthan, India. In *South Asian Archaeology 1985* (Eds.) K. Frifelt and R. Sorensen. Copenhagen: Scandinavian Institute of Asian Studies, Occasional Papers no. 4: 296-320.

Misra, V.N., S.N. Rajaguru, D.R. Raju, H. Raghavan and C. Gaillard. 1982. Acheullian occupation and evolving landscape around Didwana in Thar desert, India. *Man and Environment* 6: 72.

Misra, V.N., S.N. Rajaguru and H. Raghavan. 1988. Late Middle Pleistocene environment and Acheulian Culture around Didwana, Rajasthan. *Proceedings of Indian National Science Academy* 54A(3): 425-438.

Misra, V.N., S.N. Rajaguru, G.L. Badam, R.K. Ganjoo and R. Korisettar 1990. Further Research in the Prehistory and Quaternary Geology of the Narmada Valley. In *Adaptation and other Essays* (Eds.) N.C. Ghosh and S. Chakrabarti. Shantiniketan: Visva-Bharari Research Publications. Pp. 53-60

Misra, V.N., S.N. Rajaguru, R.K. Ganjoo and R. Korisettar. 1989. Geoarchaeology of the Palaeolithic site at Samnapur, Central Narmada Valley. *Man and Environment* 15(1): 107-116.

Misra, V.N., V.S. Shinde, R.K. Mohanty, Kurush Dalal, Anup Mishra, Lalit Pandey and Jeewan S. Kharakwal.1995. Excavations at Balathal: their contribution to the Chalcolithic and Iron Age cultures of Mewar, Rajasthan. *Man and Environment* 20(1): 57-80.

Misra, V.N., S.N. Rajaguru, D.R. Raju, H. Raghvan, C. Gaillard. 1982. Acheulain Occupation and Evolving Landscape Around Didwana in the Thar Desert, India. *Man and Environment* 6: 72-86.

Mohapatra, G.C. 1962. The *Stone Age Culture of Orissa.* Poona: Deccan College.

Mohapatra, G.C. 1966. Preliminary report of the exploration and excavation in East Punjab. *Bulletin of Deccan College Post graduate and Research Institute* 25:221-237.

Mohapatra, G.C. 1976. Geotectonic developments, Sub-Himalayan lithic complex and Post-Siwalik sediments. In *Perspectives in Palaeoanthropology* (Ed.) AK. Ghosh. Calcutta: Firma K. L. Mukhopadhyay. Pp. 31-59.

Mohapatra, G.C. 1982. Acheulian distribution in the Siwalik of Punjab. In *Indian Archaeology : New Perspective* (Ed. R.K. Sharma). Delhi: Agam Kala Prakashan. Pp. 28-37.

Mohapatra, G.C. 1990. Soanian-Acheulian Relationship. *Bulletin of the Deccan College and Postgraduate and Research Institute* 49: 251-260.

Molleson, T. 1994. The eloquent bones of Abu Hureyra. *Scientific American* August: 60-65.

Moorey, P.R.S. 1994. *Ancient Mesopotamian Materials and Industries.* Oxford: Clarendon Press.

Mori, Fabrizio. 1992. Rock art and cultural evolution in the Pre-History of the Sahara. In *Rock Art in the Old World* (Ed.) Michel Lorblanchet. New Delhi: Indira Gandhi National Centre for the Arts. Pp. 3-8.

Movius, H.L. Jr. 1948. *Early Man and Pleistocene Stratigraphy in Southern and Eastern Asia.* Peabody Museum, Cambridge, Paper No. 19.

Mughal, M.R. 1982. Recent archaeological research in the Cholistan Desert. In *Harappan Civilization: A Contemporary Perspective.* (Ed.) G. L. Possehl. New Delhi: Oxford and IBH Publishing. Pp. 86-95.

Mughal, M.R. 1994. The Harappan nomads of Cholistan. In *Living Traditions: Studies in Ethnoarchaeology of South Asia* (Ed.) B. Allchin. Delhi: Oxford and IBH. Pp. 53-68.

Mughal, M.R. 1997. *Ancient Cholistan: Archaeology and Architecture.* Lahore: Ferozsons. Pp. 1-170.

Muhly, J.D. 1981. The origins of agriculture and technology— West or East Asia? *Technology and Culture* 22: 125-148.

Mujumdar, G.G. and S.N. Rajaguru. 1966. *Ashmound Excavations at Kupgal.* Poona: Deccan College.

Mulvaney, D.J. 1975. *The Prehistory of Australia.* Australia: Penguin Books.

Murty, M.L.K. 1966. *Stone Age Cultures of Chittoor District.* Pune : Ph.D. Dissertation, University of Poona (unpublished).

Murty, M.L.K. 1968. Blade and Burin Industries near Renigunta on the Southeast Coast of India. *Proceedings of the Prehistoric Society.* 34: 83-101.

Murty, M.L.K. 1969. Blade-and-Burin and Late Stone Age Industries around Renigunta, Chittoor Dist. *Indian Antiquary* 4: 106-28.

Murty, M.L.K. 1970. Blade and burin and Late Stone Age industries around Renigunta, Chittor district. In *Studies in Indian Archaeology: (Sankalia Felicitation Volume)* (Eds.) S.B. Deo and M.K. Dhavalikar. Bombay.

Murty, M.L.K. 1974. A Late Pleistocene cave site in southern India. *Proceedings of the American Philosophical Society* 118(2): 196-230.

Murty, M.L.K. 1975. Late Pleistocene fauna of Kurnool Caves, South India. In *Archaeolozoological Studies* (Ed.) A.T.Clason. Amsterdam: North Holland. Pp. 132-138.

Murty, M.L.K. 1979. Recent Research on the Upper Palaeolithic Phase in India. *Journal of Field Archaeology* 6(3): 301-320.

Murty, M.L.K. 1981. Hunter-gatherer ecosystems and archaeological patterns of subsistence behaviour on the south-east coast of India: an ethnographic model. *World Archaeology* 13(1): 47-58.

Murty M.L.K. and K. Thimma Reddy. 1976. The significance of lithic finds in the cave areas of Kurnool, India. *Asian Perspectives* 18 (2): 214-226.

Murty, M.L.K. 1985a. The uses of plant foods by some hunter gatherer communities in Andhra Padesh. In *Recent Advances in Indio-Pacific Prehistory.* (Eds.) V.N. Misra, P. Bellwood. New Delhi: Oxford —IBH. Pp. 329-336.

Murty, M.L.K. 1985b. Ethnoarchaeology of the Kurnool Cave Areas. *World Archaeology.* 17(2) : 192-205.

Mutua Museum, Imphal. Undated. *House Paintings and Rock Engravings of Khoupum Hills and Valley of Manipur.* A report submitted to Indira Gandhi National Centre for the Arts, New Delhi.

Nagar Malti. 1983. Ethnoarchaeology of the Bhimbetka Region. *Man And Environment.* VII: 61-69.

Nagaraja Rao. 1964. Recent Explorations in the Tungabhadra Basin: The Chalcolithc Phase. *Bulletin of the Deccan College Research Institute.* 23: 55-67.

Nagaraja Rao. 1966. *Chalcolithic culture of the Deccan with special reference to north Karnatka.* Ph.D. theis. Pune: Poona University.

Nagaraja Rao, M.S. and K.C. Malhotra. 1965. *The Stone Age Hill-Dwellers of Tekkalakota.* Poona: Deccan College.

Naik, S.N. 1978. Origin and domestication of Zebu cattle (*Bos indicus*). *Journal of Human Evolution* 7: 23-30.

Narain, L.A. 1979. The Neolithic cultures of Eastern India. In *Essays in Indian Protohistory* (Eds.) D.P. Agrawal and Dilip Chakrabarti. New Delhi: DK Publishers. Pp. 301-309.

Nautiyal, V., D.P. Agrawal and R.V. Krishnamurthy. 1981. Some new analysis on the protohistorical copper artefacts. *Man and Environment* 5: 48-51.

Nautiyal, K.P., B.M. Khanduri. 1978-79. Excavation at Mordhwaj — A Note. *Puratattva* 10: 86-87.

Nautiyal, K.P., B.M. Khanduri. 1986. New cultural dimension in the Central Himalayan region of Uttarakhand: an archaeological assessment. *Estratto da ANNALI dell, Instituto Universitario Orientale* 46: 77-100.

Neumayer, E. 1983. *Prehistoric Indian Rock Paintings.* New Delhi: Oxford University Press.

Neumayer, E. 1993. *Lines on Stone: The Prehistoric Rock Art of India.* Delhi: Manohar.

Neville, J. 1949. *The Prehistory of South Rhodesia: an Account of the Progress of Research from 1900-1946.* Museum Memoir 2. Cambridge: Cambridge University Press.

Oldham, C.F. 1893. The Saraswati and the lost river of the Indian desert. *Calcutta Review* 59:1-27.

Opdyke, N.D., E. Lindsay, G.D. Johnson, N. Johnson, K.A.R. Tahirkheli and M.A. Mirza. 1979. Magnetic polarity stratigraphy and vertebrate palaeontology of Upper Siwalik and subgroup of northern Pakistan. *Palaeogeography, Palaeoclimatology, Palaeoecology* 27:1-34.

Ota, S.B. 1992. Archaeological investigations in the submergence area of the Narmada Sagar Dam, M.P: a reconnaissance survey. *Man and Environment* 17(1): 97-103.

Paddayya, K. 1970. The blade tool industry of Shorapur Doab, peninsular India. *Indian Antiquary* 4: 165-190.

Paddayya, K. 1971. Radiocarbon dates and South Indian Neolithic Culture. *Antiquity* 45: 134-8.

Paddayya, K. 1973. *Investigations into the Neolithic Cultures of the Shorapur Doab, South India.* Leiden: E.J. Brill.

Paddayya, K. 1975. The faunal background of the South India Neolithic Culture. In *Archaeozoological Studies* (Ed.) A.T. Clason. Amsterdam: Elsevier Publishing Co. Pp. 329-334.

Paddayya, K. 1991. The Acheulian Culture of the Hunsgi-Baichbal Valleys, Peninsular India: a processual study. *QUARTÄR* 41-42: 111-138.

Paddayya, K. 1991-92. The Ashmounds of south India: fresh evidence and possible implications. *Bulletin of the Deccan College Research Institute* 51-52: 573-626.

Paddayya, K. 1993a. Ashmound investigations at Budihal, Gulbarga district, Karnataka. *Man and Environment* 18(1): 57-87.

Paddayya, K. 1993b. Further investigations at Budihal, Gulberga district, Karnataka. *Bulletin of the Deccan College Research Institute* (published 1995) 53: 277-322.

Paddayya, K., R. Jhaldiyal and M.D. Petraglia. 2000. Excavation of an Acheulian workshop at Isampur, Karnataka (India). *Antiquity* 74: 751-752.

Paddayya K. (in press). The problem of ashmounds in Southern Deccan in the light of recent research. In *Recent Advances in Indian Archaeology* (Ed.) K. Paddayya. Delhi: Munshiram Manoharlal.

Paddayya, K. and M.D. Petraglia 1993. Formation processes of Acheulian localities in the Hunsgi and Baichbal Valleys, peninsular India. In *Formation Processes in Archaeological Context* (Eds.) P. Goldberg, D.T. Nash and M.D. Petraglia. Monographs in World Archaeology no. 17. Madison: Prehistory Press. Pp. 61-82

Pal, J.N. 1986. *Archaeology of Southern Uttar Pradesh*. Allahabad: Swabha Prakashan.

Pande, B.M. 1970. The Neolithic in Kashmir: new discoveries. *The Anthroplogist* 27 (1&2) : 25-41.

Pande, B.M. 1971. Neolithic hunting scene on a stone slab from Burzahom, Kashmir. *Asian Perspectives*. 14: 194-198.

Pande, B.M. and B.D. Chattopadhyaya (Eds.) 1987. *Archaeology and History* Volumes I & II. New Delhi: Agam Kala Prakashan.

Pande, G.C. (Ed.) 1999. *The Dawn of Indian Civilization Upto 600 BC*. Volume I, Part 1. New Delhi: Centre for Studies in Civilization.

Pandey, S.K. 1969. Painted rock shelters of Madhya Pradesh with special reference to Mahakoshal. Saugar University: Unpublished PH.D. dissertation.

Pandey, S.K. 1984. Indian rock painting and its problems. In *Rock Art of India* (Ed.) K.K. Chakarvarti. New Delhi: Arnold-Heineman. Pp. 214-227.

Pandey, S.K. 1992. Central Indian rock art. In *Rock Art in the Old World* (Ed.) Michel Lorblanchet. New Delhi: Indira Gandhi National Centre for the Arts. Pp. 249-272.

Pant, R.K. 1979. Microwear studies on Burzahom Neolithic tools. *Man and Environment* 3:11-18.

Pant, Sushila. 1999. Cave paintings of Central India. In *The Dawn of Indian Civilization Upto 600 BC* (Ed.) G.C. Pande. Volume I, Part 1. New Delhi: Centre for Studies in Civilization. Pp. 205-231.

Pappu, Shanti. 1996. Reinvestigation of the prehistoric archaeological record in the Kortallayar Basin, Tamil Nadu. *Man and Environment* 21 (1): 1-23.

Pappu, Shanti. 1997. *Pleistocene Environments and Stone Age Adaptations in the Kortallayar Basin, Tamil Nadu*. Unpublished Ph.D. dissertation. Pune: University of Poona.

Pappu, Shanti. 1999 A study of natural site formation processes in the Kortallayar Basin, Tamil Nadu, South India. *Geoarchaeology* 14(2): 127-150.

Pappu, Shanti. 2001. Middle Palaeolithic stone tool technology in the Kortallayar Basin, South India, *Antiquity* 75:107-117

Parpola, A. 1984a. Interpreting the Indus script. In *Frontiers of the Indus Civilization* (Eds.) B.B. Lal and S.P. Gupta. Delhi: Books and Books. Pp. 179-91.

Parpola, A. 1984b. New correspondences between Harappa and Near Eastern glyptic art. In *South Asian Archaeology* 1981 (Ed.) B. Allchin. Cambridge: Cambridge University Press. Pp. 176-95.

Parpola, A. 1986. The Indus script: a challenging puzzle. *World Archaeology* 17(3):399-419.

Pascoe, E. 1931. Minerals and Metals. In *Mohenjo-daro and the Indus Civilization* (Ed.) J. Marshall. London: A. Probsthain.

Pastner, Stephen and Louis Flam. 1982. *Anthropology in Pakistan: Recent Socio-Cultural and Archaeological Perspectives*. Ithaca: Cornell University.

Peregrin, P. 1991. Some political aspects of craft specialization. *World Archaeology* 23 (1):1-11.

Piggott, S. 1944. Prehistoric Copper Hoards in the Ganga basin. *Antiquity* 173-182.

Piggott, S. 1961. *Prehistoric India*. Middlesex: Penguin.

Pilgrim, G.E. 1910. Notices of new mammalian genera and species from the Tertiaries of India. ***Records of** the Geological Survey of India* 40: 53-71.

Pitts, Michael and Mark Roberts. 1997. *Fairweather Eden: Life in Britain Half a Million Years **Ago as Revealed** by the Excavation as Boxgrove*. London: Century.

Porter, S.C. 1970. Quaternary glacial record in the Swat Kohistan, West Pakistan. *Geological Society of America Bulletin* 81: 1421-1446.

Possehl, G.L. 1986. African millets in South Aisan prehistory. In *Studies in the Archaeology of India and Pakistan* (Ed.) Jerome Jacobson. Delhi: Oxford and IBH. Pp. 237-56.

Possehl, G.L. 1993. (Ed.) *Harappan Civilisation*. Delhi: Oxford & IBH.

Possehl, G.L. 1994. *Radiometric Dates for South Asian Archaeology.* Philadelphia: University of Pennsylvania Museum.

Possehl, G.L. 1999a An Harappan outpost on the Amu Darya: Shortughai. Why was it there?. *Indologica Taurinensia* 23-24:57-70.

Possehl, G.L. 1999b Prehistoric population and settlement in Sindh. In *The Indus River: Biodiversity, Resources, Humankind* (Eds.) A. Meadows and P.S. Meadows. Karachi:Oxford University Press. Pp. 393-409.

Possehl, G.L. 1999c. *Indus Age: the Beginnings.* New Delhi & Calcutta: Oxford & IBH publishing Co. Pvt. Ltd.

Potts, D.T. 1990. *The Arabian Gulf in Antiquity: from Prehistory to the Fall of the Achaemenid Empire.* Oxford: Clarendon Press.

Prasad, Sushma, Sheela Kusumgar and S.K. Gupta. 1997. A mid to late Holocene record of palaeoclimatic changes from Nal Sarovar: a palaeodesert margin lake in western India. *Journal of Quaternary Science* 12(2): 153-159.

Raghavan, H., S.N. Rajaguru and V.N. Misra. 1989. Radiomatric dating of a Quaternary dune section. *Man and Environment* 13:19-22.

Rajaguru, S.N. and K.T.M. Hegde. 1972. The Pleistocene stratigraphy in India. In *Archaeology Congress and Seminar papers* (Ed.) S.B. Deo. Nagpur : Nagpur University.

Rajaguru, S.N., R.K. Ganjoo and V.N. Misra. 1994. A fresh look at the Quaternary lithostratigraphy of a part of the Central Narmada Valley, Narsinghpur district, M.P. in India. In *Geomorphological Diversity* (Eds.) K.R. Dikshit, V.S. Kale and M.N. Kaul. New Delhi and Jaipur: Rawat Publishers. Pp. 435-452.

Raju, D.R. 1988. *Stone Age Hunter-Gatherers: an Ethnoarchaeology of Caddapah Region, South-east India.* Pune: Ravish Publishers.

Rami Reddy, V. 1968. *Pre- and Protohistory of South-western Andhra Pradesh.* Unpublished Ph.D. thesis, University of Poona.

Rami Reddy, V. 1971. Rock Paintings and bruisings in Andhra Pradesh. *The Eastern Anthropologist* 24: 289-94.

Rami Reddy, V. 1976. *The Prehistoric and Protohistoric Cultures of Palavoy, South India with Special Reference to the Ashmound Problem.* Hyderabad: Dept of Archaeology & Museums (Archaeological series–43).

Rami Reddy, V. 1978. *A Study of Neolithic Culture of Southwestern Andhra Pradesh.* Hyderabad: Department of Archaeology & Museums (Archaeological series–51).

Rami Reddy, V. 1978. *The Study of Neolithic Culture of South-western Andhra Pradesh.* Archaeological Series 51. Hyderabad: Govt. of Andhra Pradesh.

Rami Reddy, V. 1990. Ashmounds in South India: a review. In *Archaeology in Karnataka-1985-99* (Ed.) A. Sundara. Mysore: Directorate of Archaeology and Museums.

Rao, S.N. 1977. Excavations at Sarutaru. *Man and Environment* 1: 39-43

Reid, L.A. 1988. Benedict's Austro-Tai hypothesis — an evaluation. *Asian Perspectives* 26(1): 19-34.

Rendell, H.M. and R.W. Dennell. 1985. Dated Lower Palaeolithic artifacts from northern Pakistan. *Current Anthropology* 26:393.

Rendell, H.M., R.W. Dennell and M.A. Halim. 1989. *Pleistocene and Palaeolithic Investigations in the Soan Valley, Northern Pakistan.* London: BAR International Series 544: 202-206.

Rendell, H.M., E.A. Hailwood and R.W. Dennell. 1987. Magnetic polarity stratigraphy of an upper Siwalik sub-group, Soan Valley, Pakistan: implications for early human occupance of Asia. *Earth and Planetary Science Letters* 85: 488-496.

Renfrew, C. 1973. Sitagroi and the independent invention of metallurgy in Europe. In *Actes du VIIIe Congress internationale des sciences prehistorique et protohistorique,* Beograd (1971) 2:473-481.

Renfrew, C. 1984. *Approaches to Social Archaeology.* Edinburgh: Edinburgh University Press

Renfrew, C. 1989. The origins of Indo-European Languages. *Scientific American* 261: 106-14.

Renfrew, C. 1997. *Archaeology and Language : the Puzzle of Indo-European Origins.* London: Pimlico.

Rightmire, G. Phillip. 1997. Deep roots for the Neanderthals. *Nature* 389: 917-918.

Rissman, Paul. 1986. Seasonal aspects of man/cattle interaction in Bronze Age Western India. *Journal of Ethnobiology* 6(2): 257-277.

Roberts, M.B. and S.A. Parfitt. 1999. Boxgrove, a Middle Pleistocene Hominid site at Eartham Quarry, Boxgrove, West Sussex. English Hetitage. *Archaeological Reports* 17.

Rosenfeld, A.D. Horton and J. Winter. 1981. Early man in North Queensland. *Terra Australis* 6.

Roychoudhury, S., S. Roy, B. Dey, M. Chakraborty, M. Roy, B. Roy, A. Ramesh, N. Prabhakaran, M.V.U. Rani, H. Vishwanathan, M. Mitra, S.K. Sil and P.P. Majumdar. 2000. Fundamental genomic unity of ethnic India is revealed by analysis of mitochondrial DNA. *Current Science* 79(9): 1182-1192.

Sai-Yok. 1967. *Archaeological Excavations in Thailand.* Vol. I, Stone-Age Settlements in the Kanchanaburi Province. Copenhagen (Denmark): Munksgaard.

Saklani, A. 1983. Gwarkhyaudyar ke Shailchitra, Gram Duntgri, Chamoli (in Hindi). *Pahar* 1: 217.

Sali, S.A. 1964. A new ceramic of the Chalcolithic from Dhule District, Maharashtra. *Journal of the Asiatic Society of Bombay* 38: 207-210.

Sali, S.A. 1973. Some aspects of the Quaternary stratigraphy of peninsular India. *Bulletin of the Deccan College Post-Graduate and Research Institute* 31-32: 70-80.

Salim, M. 1992. Early man in Lower Pleistocene, new evidence from Pinjor deposits in the Soan Valley. *Pakistan Journal of Central Asia* 15(2): 83-89.

Salim, M. 1997. *The Palaeolithic Cultures of Potwar with Special Reference to the Lower Palaeolithic.* Islamabad: Centre for the Study of the Civilisations of Central Asia, Quaid-i-Azam University. Pp. 35-152.

Samzun, Anaick. 1991. The early Chalcolithic: Mehrgarh Period III. In *Forgotten Cities on the Indus: Early Civilization in Pakistan from the 8th to the 2nd Millennium BC* (Eds.) Micheal Jansen, Maire Mulloy and Gunter Urban. Mainz: Verlag Philipp Von Zabern. Pp. 66-72.

Samzun, A. and P. Sellier. 1985. First anthropological and cultural evidences for the funerary practices of the Chalcolithic population of Mehrgarh, Pakistan. In *South Asian Archaeology 1983* (Eds.) J. Schotsmans and M. Taddei. Naples: Instituto Universitario Orientale, Dipartimento di Studi Asiatici, Series Minor 23: 91-120.

Sankalia, H.D. 1952. *The Godavari Palaeolithic Industry.* Poona: Deccan College.

Sankalia, H.D. 1963. New light on the Indo-Iranian or western Asiatic relations between 1970-1200BC. *Artibus Asiae* 26:312-32.

Sankalia, H.D. 1964. Middle Stone Age culture in India and Pakistan. *Science* 146:365-75.

Sankalia, H.D. 1965. *Excavations at Langhnaj: 1944-63.* Poona: Deccan College.

Sankalia, H.D. 1969. *Mesolithic and Pre-Mesolithic Industries from the excavations at Sangankallu, Bellary–1965.* Poona: Deccan College.

Sankalia, H.D. 1974. *The Pre and Protohistory of India and Pakistan.* Poona: Deccan College.

Sankalia, H.D. and S.B. Deo. 1958. *Excavation at Maheshwar and Navdatoli 1953-53.* Pune: Deccan College.

Sankalia, H.D., S.B. Deo and Z.D. Ansari. 1960. *From History to Pre-History at Nevasa:* 1954-56. Poona: Deccan College.

Sankalia, H.D., G.G. Mujumdar and K.T.M. Hegde. 1965. *Archaeology. Excavations at Langhnaj:* 1944-6. Part II Poona: Deccan College.

Sankrityayana, Rahul. 1958. *Kumaun* (in Hindi). Varanasi: Jnanmandal.

Santhanam, V., and J.B. Hutchinson. 1974. Cotton. In *Evolutionary Studies in World Crops: Diversity and Changes in the Indian Subcontinent.* Sir Joseph Hutchinson (Eds.). Cambridge: Cambridge Univesity Press. Pp. 89-100.

Santoni, M. 1984. Sibri and the south cemetry of Mehrgarh: 3rd millennium connections between the northern Kachi Plain (Pakistan) and Central Asia. In *South Asian Archaeology 1981* (Ed.) B. Allchin. Cambridge: Cambridge University Press. Pp. 52-60.

Saranthein, M. 1978. Sand deserts during glacial maximum and climatic optimum. *Nature* 272:43-46.

Sarkar, A., K. Ramesh, S.K. Bhattacharya and G. Rajagopalan. 1990. Oxygen isotope evidence for a stronger winter monsoon current during the last glaciation. *Nature* 243: 549-551.

Sarkar, S.S. 1960. Human skeletal remains from Brahmagiri. *Bulletin of Deptt. of Anthropology* 1: 5-25.

Sato, Yo-Ichiro. 1996. *Origin of Rice and Rice Cultivation based on DNA Analysis.* Tokyo: NHK Books.

Satsangi, P.P. and A.K. Dutta. 1967-68. Pleistocene alluvial deposits of Allahabad. Uttar Pradesh. *Progress Report of the Field Season.* G.S.I.

Semaw, S., P. Renne, J.W.K. Harris, C.S. Feibel, R.L. Bernor, N. Fesseha and K. Mowbray. 1997. 2.5 Million-year-old stone tools from Gona, Ethiopia. *Nature* 385:333-336.

Sen, D. and A.K. Ghosh. 1960. On the occurrence of Palaeoliths in Singhbum. *Man in India* 40(3): 178-191.

Seshadri, M. 1955. The Palaeolithic industry of Kibbanhalli, Mysore. *Artibus Asiae* 18: 271-287.

Seshadri, M. 1971. *Report on the Excavations at T. Narsipur.* Bangalore.

Shaffer Jim G. 1978. The later prehistoric periods. In *The Archaeology of Afghanistan: from Earliest Times to the Timurid Period* (Eds.) F.R. Allchin and Norman Hammond. London: Academic Press. Pp. 71-187.

Shaffer Jim G. 1981. The prehistoric periods in the eastern Punjab: a preliminary assesment. In (Ed.) *Indus Civilization New Perspective.* Islamabad: Quid-i-Azam University. Pp. 65-102.

Shaffer Jim G. 1986. Cultural development in the eastern Punjab. In (Ed.) J. Jacobson *Studies in the Archaeology of India and Pakistan.* Delhi: Oxford and IBH. Pp. 195-235.

Shane, P.J., Westgate, M. Williams and R. Korisettar. 1995. New geochemical evidence for the youngest Toba tuff in India. *Quaternary Research* 44: 200-204.

Sharma, A.K. 1982. Excavations at Gufkral-1981. *Puratattva* 11: 9-25.

Sharma, A.K. 1996. *Early Man in Eastern Himalayas.* New Delhi: Aryan Books International.

Sharma, A.K. 1998. *Prehistoric Burials of Kashmir.* Delhi: Agam Kala Prakashan.

Sharma, D.D. 1988. Kumauni language and dialects. In *Kumaun Land and People* (Ed.) K.S. Valdiya. Naini Tal: Gyanodaya. Pp. 120-136.

Sharma, G.R. 1965. Allahabad through the ages. *Paper presented in the 27th Seminar of Indian History Congress.* Allahabad in December.

Sharma, G.R. 1973a. Stone Age in the Vindhyas and the Ganga Valley. In *Radiocarbon and Indian Archaeology* (Eds.) D.P. Agrawal and A. Ghosh. Bombay: TIFR. Pp. 106.

Sharma, G.R. 1973b. Mesolithic lake cultures in the Ganga Valley. *Proceeding of the Prehistoric Society* 39: 129-146.

Sharma, G.R. 1975. Seasonal migrations and Mesolithic Lake Cultures of the Ganga Valley. *Presidential Address in the Annual Conference of Indian Prehistoric Society.* Pp. 1-20.

Sharma, G.R. and J.D. Clarke (Eds.). 1983. *Palaeoenvironment and Prehistory in the Middle Son Valley (Madhya Pradesh, North Central India).* Allahabad: Abinash Publication.

Sharma, G.R., V.D. Misra, D. Mandal, B.B. Misra, and J.N. Pal. 1980. *Beginnings of Agriculture.* Allahabad: Abinash Prakashan.

Sharma, M.L. 1996. The Sahibi River Valley: A new region of Rock Art in Rajasthan. In *Prehistoric Art in India* (Eds.) R.K. Sharma and K.K. Tripathi. Delhi: Aryan Books International. Pp. 153-159.

Sharma, M.L. 1997. Rock Art of northern Rajasthan. *Purakala* 8(1-2): 73-74.

Sharma, P., D.P. Agrawal, B.S. Kotlia and S.K. Gupta. 1988. Environmental magnetism of lake sedimentation in Kumaun Himalayas. In *Palaeoclimatic and Palaeoenvironmental Changes in Asia During the last 4 Million Years* (Eds.) D.P. Agrawal, P. Sharma, S.K. Gupta. Delhi: Indian National Science Academy. Pp. 257-266.

Sharma, T.C. 1966. *Prehistoric Archaeology of Assam.* Ph.D dissertation (unpublished), London University.

Sharma, T.C. 1974. Recent archaeological discoveries in north east India. *Puratattva* 7:17-19.

Sharma, T.C. 1985. Problems of the Upper Palaeolithic in Northeast India. In *Recent Advances in Indo-Pacific Prehistory* (Eds.) V.N. Misra and P. Bellwood. New Delhi: Oxford & IBH. Pp. 171-173.

Sharma, T.C. (In press). Place of Assam in the history and archaeology of India. *Presidential Address: Indian Archaeological Society: 33rd Annual Conference-1999.* Pune: Deccan collge.

Sharma, Y.D. 1964. Protohistoric remains. In *Archaeological Remains Monuments & Museums* Pt.1 (Ed.) A. Ghosh. New Delhi: Archaeological Survey of India. Pp. 1-42.

Shaw, Thurstan, Paul Sinclair, Bassey Andah & Alex Okpoko (Eds.) 1993. *The Archaeology of Africa: Food, Metals and Towns.* London: Routledge.

Shinde, V.S. 1987. Farming in the Chalcolithic Deccan. *Tools and Tillage 4(4):* 214-27.

Shinde, V.S. 1998. *Early Settlements in the Central Tapi Basin.* Delhi: Munshiram Manoharlal.

Shinde, Vasant. 2000. The origin and development of the Chalcolithic in Central India. *Indo-Pacific Prehistory Association Bulletin* 19-3: 125-135.

Silberrad, C.A. 1907. Rock Drawings in the Banda District. *Journal of the Asiatic Society of Bengal* 5: 567-70.

Singh, Gurdip. 1971. The Indus Valley Culture: seen in the context of post-glacial climate and ecological studies in North-west India. *Archaeology & Physical Anthropology in Oceania* 6(2): 177-189.

Singh Gurdip and D.P. Agrawal. 1976. Radiocarbon evidence for deglacation in North-Western Himalaya, India. *Nature* 260(5548): 232.

Singh, G., S.K. Chopra and A.B. Singh. 1973. Pollen-rain from vegetation of north-west India. *New Phytology* 72:191-206.

Singh, G., R.J. Wasson and D.P. Agrawal. 1990. Vegetational and seasonal climatic changes since last full glacial in the Thar desert. *Review of Palaeobotany and Palynology* 64: 351-358.

Singh, O.K. 1997. *The Stone Age Archaeology of Manipur.* Imphal: Amusana Institute of Antiquarian Studies, Manipur.

Singh, Purushottam. 1991. The *Neolithic Origins*. Delhi: Agam Kala Prakashan.

Singh, Purushottam. 1999. Rise of cultures in Eastern India. In *The Dawn of Indian Civilization Upto 600 BC* (Volume I, Part 1) (Ed.) G.C. Pande. New Delhi: Centre for Studies in Civilization. Pp. 509-529.

Singhvi, A.K., Günther A. Wagner and Ravi Korisettar. 1998. Techniques for the chronometry of the Palaeolithic: Evidence for global colonization. In *The Lower Paleolithic in the Old World* (Eds.) M. Petraglia and R. Korisettar. London: Routledge Press. Pp. 23-83.

Singhvi, A.K., Y. Sharma and D.P. Agrawal. 1982. Thermoluminescence dating of sand dunes in Rajasthan, India. *Nature* 295 (5847): 313-315.

Singhvi, A.K., Y. Sharma and D.P. Agrawal. 1983. Thermoluminescence dating of dune sands: some refinements. *PACT* 9: 385-390.

Smith, C.S. 1981. On art, invention and technology. In *A Search for Structure; Selected Essay on Science, Art and History* (Ed.) C.S. Smith. Cambridge: MIT. Pp. 325-331.

Smith, V.A. 1906. Pygmy flints. *The Indian Antiquary* 6: 185-195.

Sonakia, Arun. 1985. Skull cap of an early man from the Narmada Valley alluvium (Pleistocene) of Central India. *American Anthropologist* 87(3): 612-616.

Sonawane, V.H. 1997. Upper Palaeolithic art of India: a fresh look. *Purakala* 8 (1-2): 5-15.

Sonawane, V.H. 2000. Early Farming Communities of Gujarat, India. Indo-Pacific Prehistory: The Melaka Papers. *Bulletin of the Indo-Pacific Prehistroy Association* 19(3): 137-146.

Sorensen, P. 1988. *Archaeological Excavations in Thailand* (Surface finds and minor excavations). Scandinavian Institute of Asian Studies Occasional Papers No.1. London: Curzon Press Ltd.

Soundara Rajan, K.V. 1952. Stone Age industries in Giddalur District Kurnooj. *Ancient India* 8: 64-92.

Soundara Rajan, K.V. 1958. Studies in the Stone Age of Nagarjunakonda and its neighbourhood. *Ancient India* 14: 49-113.

Southworth 1979: Lexical evidence for early contacts between Indo-Aryan and Dravidian. In *Aryan and Non-Aryan in India* (Eds.) M. Deshpande and P. Hook. Ann Arbor: University of Michigan, Center for South and Southeast Asian Studies.

Spate, O.H.K., A.T.A. Learmonth and B.H. Farmer. 1967. *India, Pakistan and Ceylon: the Regions*. London: Metheun.

Stacul, G. 1975. The fractional burial customs in the Swat valley and some connected problems. *East and West* 25/3-4. Pp. 323-333.

Stacul, G. 1987. *Prehistoric and Protohistoric Swat, Pakistan*. Rome: IsMEO.

Stein, A. 1931. *An Archaeological Tour in Gedrosia* (Memoirs of Archaeological Survey of India 43). Delhi: Archaeological Survey of India.

Street, F.A. and A.T. Grove. 1979. Lake level fluctuations since 30,000 years B.P. *Quaternary Research* 12: 1-17.

Stringer, Chris and Robin McKie. 1996. *African Exodus*. London: Jonathan Cape.

Subbarao, B. 1948. *Stone Age Cultures of Bellary*. Poona: Deccan College.

Subbarao, B. 1949. *Prehistoric and Early Historic Cultures of Bellary*. Unpublished Ph.D. thesis. University of Bombay.

Subbarao, B. 1958. *The Personality of India*. Baroda: M.S. University of Baroda.

Sundara, A. 1968. Protohistoric sites in Bijapur District. *The Journal of the Karnatak University Social Sciences* 4:3-23.

Sundara, A. 1970. Neolithic cultural patterns and movements in North Mysore State. The *Journal of the Karnatak University Social Sciences* 6: 3-13.

Sundara, A. 1971. New discoveries of ashmound in North Karnatak: their implications. In *Prof. K.A. Nilakanta Sastri Felicitation Volume.* (Eds.) S. Ganeshan, S. Rajan and M.D. Sampath. Madras. Pp. 308-14.

Sundara, A. 1985. Cultural ecology of the Neolithic in India. In *Recent Advances in Indian Archaeology* (Eds.) S.B. Deo and K. Padayya. Pune: Deccan College. Pp. 39-57.

Sundara, A. 1987. Studies in Ashmounds. In *Archaeology and History* (Eds.) B.M. Pande and B.D. Chattopadhyaya. Delhi: Agam Kala Prakashan. Pp. 313-324.

Suwa, Gen., B. Asfaw, Y. Beyene, T.D. White, S. Katoh, S. Nagaoka, H. Nakaya, K. Uzawa, P. Renne and G. Wolde Gabriel. 1997. The first skull of Australopithecus boisei. *Nature* 389:489-492.

Swain, F.A., J.E. Kutzbach and Hastenrath. 1983. Estimates for Holocene precipitation in Rajasthan, India based on pollen and lake level data. *Quaternary Research* 19: 1-17.

Swisher, C.C., G.H. Curtis, T. Jacob, A.G. Getty, A. Susprijo and Widiasmoro. 1994. Age of the earliest known hominids in Java, Indonesia. *Science* 263: 1118-1121.

Szabo, B.J., C. McKinney, T.S. Delbey and K. Paddayya. 1990. On the age of the Acheulian Culture on the Hunsgi-Baichbal Valleys, Peninsular India. *Bulletin of the Deccan College Postgradudate and Research Institute* 50: 317-321.

Tewari, Rakesh. 1982a. *Thirakte Sail Chitra* (in Hindi)—Monograph on the dance scenes depicted in the rock paintings of Mirzapur. Lucknow: Yuva Paribhramana Evam Sanskratik Samiti.

Tewari, Rakesh. 1982b. Mirzapur ke sailasryon mein chitrit manvon mein Saaj-sajja ki pravratti (in Hindi). *Bulletin of Museums and Archaeology* 29-30:1-16.

Tewari, Rakesh. 1986. Rhino hunt scene of Ghora Mangar rock shelter, a reappraisal. *Bulletin of Museums and Archaeology* 39: 25-25.

Tewari, Rakesh. 1992. Rock Paintings of Mirzapur in Uttar Pradesh. In *Rock Art in the Old World* (Ed.) Michel Lorblanchet. New Delhi: Indira Gandhi National Centre for the Arts. Pp. 284-302.

Thapar, B.K. 1965. Neolithic problem in India. In *Indian Prehistory: 1964* (Eds.) V.N. Misra and M.S. Mate. Poona: Deccan College. Pp. 87-112.

Thieme, Hartmut. 1997. Lower Palaeolithic hunting spears from Germany. *Nature* 385: 807-810.

Thomas, P.K. 1975. Role of animals in the food economy of the Misolithic Cultures of Western and Central India. In *Arcaeozoological Stdies* (Ed.) A.T. Clason. Amsterdam: North Holland Publishing Co. Pp. 322-328.

Thomas, P.K. 1988. Faunal assemblage. In *Excavations at Inamgaon* Vol. I. (Eds.) M.K. Dhavalikar, H.D. Sankalia and Z.D. Ansari. Pune: Deccan College. Pp. 823-962.

Thomas, P.K. and P.P. Joglekar. 1994. Holocene faunal studies in India. *Man and Environment* 19 (1-2): 179-204.

Thomas, J.V., A. Kar, A.J. Kailath, N. Juyal, S.N. Rajaguru and A.K. Singhvi. 1999. Late Pleistocene-Holocene history of aeolian accumulation in the Thar Desert, India. *Z. Geomrph. N.F. Suppl. Band* 116: 181-194.

Thompson, R., and F. Oldfield. 1986. *Environental Magnetism.* London: Allen and Unwin.

Thorne, A.G. and Milford H. Wolpoff. 1992. The multi-regional evolution of humans. *Scientific American* 266: 76-83.

Tobias, Phillip V., M.A. Raath, J. Moggi-Cecchi and G.A. Doyle (Eds.). 2001. *Humanity from African Naissance to Coming Millennia.* Firenze: Firenze University Press.

Todd, K.R.U. 1939. Palaeolithic industries of Bombay. *Journal of Royal Anthropological Institute* 59(1) 257-272.

Tripathi, K.C. 1972. Lithic industries of southern western Orissa. Ph.D.diss., Utkal University.

Tripathi, Vibha. 2001. *The Age of Iron in South Asia.* New Delhi: Aryan Books International.

Trinkaus, Erik. 1983. *The Shanidar Neanderthals.* New York: Academic Press.

Tuross, Noreen and Ian Barnes.1996. Protein identification of blood residues on experimental stone tools. *Journal of Archaeological Science* 23: 289-296.

Tyagi, G.S. 1992. Decorative intricate patterns in Indian rock art. In *Rock Art in the Old World* (Ed.) Michel Lorblanchet. New Delhi: Indira Gandhi National Centre for the Arts. Pp. 303-317.

Ucko, P.J. and A. Rosenfeld. 1967. *Palaeolithic Cave Art*. London : Cambridge University Press.

Valdiya, K.S. 1980. *Geology of Kumaun Lesser Himalaya*. Dehradun: Wadiya Institute of Himalayan Geology.

Van Campo, E. 1986. Monsoon fluctuations in the last 20,000 years B.P. Oxygen isotope/ pollen records off South-west India. *Quaternary Researches* 26:376-588.

Van Campo, E., J.C. Duplessy and M. Rossignol-Strick. 1982. Climatic conditions deduced from a 150 kyr oxygen isotope pollen record from the Arabian Sea. *Nature* 296:56-59.

Varadan, V.K.S. 1976. *Geology and Mineral Resources of the States of India, Jammu and Kashmir State*. Calcutta: Miscellaneous Publication of Geological Survey of India No. 30.

Varma, R.K. 1964. *Stone Age Cultures of Mirzapur*. Allahabad University: Ph. D. dissertation.

Varma, R.K. 1987. *The Mesolithic Age in Mirzapur*. Allahabad: Paramjyoti Prakashan.

Varma R.K. 1997. Subsistence economy of the Mesolithic folk as reflected in rock-paintings of the Vindhyan region. In *Colloquia of the International Congress of Prehistoric and Prohistoric Sciences* 1996 (Eds.) G.E. Afanas'ev, S. Cleuziou, and J.R. Lukacs. Forli: ABACO Edizioni. Pp. 16 (23): 329-39

Varma, R.K. 1999. The emergence of culture in the Vindhyan Ganga region. In *The Dawn of Indian Civilization Upto 600 BC*. Volume I, Part 1 (Ed.) G.C. Pande. New Delhi: Centre for Studies in Civilization. Pp. 175-204.

Venkatasubbaiah. P.C. 1992. *Protohistoric Investigations in Central Pennar Basin, Cuddapah district, Andhra Pradesh*. Unpublished Ph.D dissertation. Pune: Deccan College (Poona University).

Vinnicombe, P. 1966. Recording Rock Paintings. *Man* 5(1): 559-60.

Vishnu-Mittre. 1974. The beginning of agriculture, palaeobotanical evidence in India. In *Evolutionary Studies in World Crops — diversity and Change in the Indian Subcontinent* (Ed.) J. Hutchinson. Cambridge: Cambridge University. Pp. 3-33.

Vishnu-Mittre. 1985. The uses of wild plants and the process of domestication in the subcontinent. In *Recent Advances in Indo-Pacific Prehistory* (Eds.) V.N. Misra and Peter Bellwood. Delhi: Oxford and IBH. Pp. 281-291.

Vishnu-Mittre and R. Savithri. 1973. Supposed remains of rice (*Oryza* sp.) in the terracotta cakes and pai at Kalibangan, Rajasthan. *The Palaeobotanist* 22(2):124-26.

Vishnu-Mittre and R. Savithri. 1982. Food economy of the Harappans. In *Harappan Civilization: A Contemporary Perspective* (Ed.) G.L. Possehl. Delhi: Oxford & IBH. Pp. 205-221.

Vishnu-Mittre, A. Sharma and Chanchala. 1986. Ancient plant economy at Daimabad. In *Daimabad 1976-79* (MASI 83) (Ed.) S.A. Sali. Delhi: Archaeological Survey of India. Pp. 588-623.

von Rad, Ulrich, M. Schaaf, K.H. Michels, H. Schultz, W.H. Berger and F. Sirocko. 1999. A 5000-yr record of climatic change in varved sediments from the oxygen minimum zone off Pakistan, Northeastern Arabian Sea. *Quaternary Research* 51: 39-53.

Wadia, D.N. 1928. *The Geology of Poonch state (Kashmir) and adjacent portions of the northern Punjab*. Memoirs of the Geological Survey of India 51: 185-370.

Wagneur, Christian and Janine Wagneur 1992. Fontainebleau rock art: an overview. In *Rock Art in the Old World*. (Ed.) Michel Lorblanchet. New Delhi: Indira Gandhi National Centre for the Arts. Pp. 519-535.

Wakankar, V.S. 1973. Bhimbetka Excavation. *Journal of Indian History* 51 (1): 7-29.

Wakankar, V.S. 1975. Bhimbetka: the prehistoric paradise. *Prachya Pratibha* 3(2): 7-29.

Wakankar, V.S. 1984. Technique of prehistoric paintings and engravings. In *Rock Art of India* (Ed.) K.K. Chakravarty. New Delhi: Arnold-Heinemann. Pp. 196-200.

Wakankar, V.S. 1987. Bhimbetka and dating of Indian rock paintings. Collected Works (Ujjain). Pp. 168-184.

Wakankar, V.S. and R.R. Brooks. 1976. *Stone Age Paintings in India*. Bombay: Taraporewala and Sons.

Ward, Ryk and Chris Stringer. 1997. A molecular handle on the Neanderthals. *Nature* 388: 225-226.

Wasson, R.J., S.N. Rajaguru, V.N. Misra, D.P. Agrawal, R.P. Dhir, A.K. Singhvi, and K.K. Rao. 1983. Geomorphology, late Quaternary stratigraphy and palaeoclimatology of the Thar Dunefield. *Zeitschrift Fur Geomorpholigie* (Supplement) 45: 117-151.

Wasson, R.J., G.I. Smith, and D.P. Agrawal. 1984. Late Quaternary sediments, minerals and inferred geochemical history of Didwana Lake, Thar Desert, India. *Palaeogeography, Palaeoclimatology, Palaeoecology* 46: 345-372.

Weber, Stephen A. 1998. Out of Africa: the initial impact of millets in South Asia. *Current Anthropology* 39(2): 267-274.

Wellmaan, K.F. 1979. *A Survey of North American Rock Art*. Graz: Akademische Druk. Verlagsanstatt.

Wendorf, Fred and Angela E. Close. 1982. *Advances in World Archaeology*. Volume I. London: Academic Press.

Wheeler, R.E.M. 1948. Brahmagiri and Chandravalli 1947: Megalithic and other Cultures in Mysore state. *Ancient India* 4: 180-310.

White, Joyce. 1997. A brief note on new dates for the Ban Chiang cultural tradition. *Bulletin of the Indo-Pacific Prehistory Association* 16:103-106.

White, Time. 1975. Geomorphology to palaeoecology: *Gigantopithecus* reappraised. *Journal of Human Evolution* 4:219-33.

Whitley, D.S. 1994. By the hunter, for the gatherer: art, social relations, subsistence change in the prehistoric great basin. *World Archaeology* 25 (3) : 15-164.

Whitley, D.S. and R.I. Dorn. 1987. Rock art chronology in eastern Califorina. *World Archaeology* 19(2): 150-164.

Wilhelmy, H. 1969. Urstromtal am ostrand der indusebene und der Sarasvati-problem. *Glazialmorphologie. Zeitschrift Fur Geomorphologie, Supplementband* 8: 76-93.

Willcox, G.H. 1992. Some differences between crops of Near Eastern origin and those from the tropics. In *South Asian Archaeology 1989*(Ed.) C. Jarriage. Madison: Prehistory press, Monographs in World Archaeology 14:291-99.

Williams, M.A.J. and M.F. Clarke. 1995. Quaternary geology and prehistoric environments in the Son and Belan Valleys, North Central India. In *Quaternary Environments and Geoarchaeology of India* (Eds.) S. Wadia, R. Korrisettar, V.S. Kale. Bangalore: Geographical Society of India Memoir 32: 282-308.

Wood, Bernard. 1997. The oldest whodunnit in the world. *Nature* 385: 292-293.

Worman, E.C. 1949. The Neolithic problem in the Prehistory of India. *Journal of the Washington Academy of Sciences* 39(6): 181-201.

Worms, E. A. 1955. Contemporary and Palaeolithic rock paintings in central and north Kimberley. *Anthropos* 50: 546-566.

Yasuda, Y. 1999a. The forest dwellers started rice cultivation in China. *YRCP Newsletter* 1 (1) :1-4.

Yasuda,Y. 1999b. Recent archaeological discoveries in the Middle Yangtze basin, China. *YRCP Newsletter* 2 (1): 1-2.

Yasuda, Y. 2000. The oldest remains of a Chinese circular walled fortification with a ritual earth mound related to rice cultivation. *YRCP Newsletter* 3(1): 1-4.

Yellen, John, E. Alison, S. Brooks, E. Cornelissen, M.J. Mehlman and K. Stewart. 1995. A Middle Stone Age worked bone industry from Katanda, Upper Semliki Valley, Zaire. *Science* 268: 553-556.

Yosida, M. and P. Gautam. 1988. Magentostratigraphy of Plio-Pleistocene lacustrine deposits in the Kathmandu Valley, Central Nepal. In *Palaeoclimatic and Paleoenvironmemntal changes in Asia During the Last 4 Million Years* (Eds.) D.P. Agrawal, P.Sharma, and S.K. Gupta. Delhi: Indian National Science Academy. Pp. 78-85.

Zeuner, F.E. 1950. *Stone Age and Pleistocene Chronology in Gujarat*. Pune: Deccan College.

Zeuner, F.E. 1959. On the origin of the cinder mounds of the Bellary district, India. *Bulletin of the Institute of Archaeology* (London) 2:37-44.

Zeuner, F.E. 1963. A *History of Domesticated Animals*. London: Hutchinson.

Zeuner, F.E. and B. Allchin. 1956. Microlithic sites of Tinnevelley district. Madras *Ancient India* 12: 4-20.

Zohary Daniel and Maria Hopf. 1993. *Domestication of Plants in the Old World*. Oxford: Clarendon Press. Pp. 202-211 and 228-239.

INDEX